STANDARD GRAPHICAL SYMBOLS

To my wife Helene
for her patience...
To Susan and Peter
for their future...

PREFACE

To an engineer, the compact symbols of graphics represent the language of communication. This book is a dictionary of that language for all forms of engineering and science. It is useful for cross-reference study and presents an expeditious method for selection of the proper symbol. All the symbols reproduced herein are taken directly from standards published by a specific technical or engineering society; this procedure preserves the original concept of the symbol and in no way introduces artistic interpretation.

Eighteen years of using graphic symbols in such art forms as trademarks, advertising technical literature, and graphic representation of products, with the constant necessity to consult hundreds of sources in order to locate specific symbols, generated the idea for this book. Its purpose is to present, rather than select, the proper form of symbol for the engineer, draftsman, or student.

The first problem is that each industry, or more specifically companies within each industry, has its own drafting standards. In working with these companies and in analyzing their standards, one finds a close parallel to established standards, but modified by draftsmen's minute deviations and artistic interpretation. In some cases the variation is sufficient to make identification of a specific symbol difficult. An engineer transferring from one company to another may find that a practice in use at the former does not exist at the latter.

The second problem in achieving uniformity of this most important language is the difficulty and cost involved in obtaining such standards from the various technical societies.

The purpose of this book is to provide the draftsman with a quick and economical symbols' reference guide and to assist the standards organizations in eliminating styleographic representation.

The 9,000 or more illustrations contained herein form the nucleus of common symbolic language. As the technology of the sciences continues to advance more symbolic forms will be developed, just as new words are added to the English language. Symbols are often presented more than once to show the established practices of two or more organizations serving a specific science or technology.

The goal of any author is that his book be used. I hope use of this book will result in the ultimate establishment of a more uniform symbolic representative language.

Alvin Arnell

v

ACKNOWLEDGMENTS

It is impossible to list the hundreds of publications, the numerous organizations, societies, associations, and companies and the many individuals who have assisted in making this book possible. I therefore wish to express my indebtedness to the scores of people for their many courtesies in connection with this book.

In addition to the credits appearing at the head of each standard, to those individuals and organizations who took a personal interest in this project and who have contributed many hours and extensive use of published material, I wish to take this opportunity to acknowledge their assistance and express my gratitude.

GEORGE A. MCNAMARA, *Secretary of Defense, Department of Defense, Washington, D.C.*

EDWARD A. FENTON, *Technical Director, American Welding Society*

THE OFFICERS AND STAFF, *National Electrical Manufacturers Association*

VIRGINIA MORGAN, *Standards Publications Editor, National Electrical Manufacturers Association*

H. KEITH OWENS, *Staff Engineer, Instrument Society of America*

GEORGE E. EARLEY, *Cannon Electric Company*

R. CARLSON, *American Petroleum Institute*

EDITH MIDGETTE, *Chief, Magazine-Book Section, Office of the Secretary of Defense, Washington, D.C.*

C. E. HILTON, *Secretary, Graphics Standards Board, American Standards Association*

THE EDITORS AND STAFF, *American Society of Mechanical Engineers*

JOHN C. SEARS, *Executive Director, American Gear Manufacturers Association*

NORMAN ERDOS, *Electronic Tube Division, Radio Corporation of America*

F. M. MULLEN, *Supervisor, Standards Distribution, General Motors Corporation*

THE DIRECTORS AND STAFF, *U.S. Department of Commerce, U.S. Department of Interior*

E. A. BRADY, *Data Processing Division, International Business Machines Corporation*

The standards referred to in this book may be purchased from the specific organization listed.

All MIL-STDS and government publications are available from the Superintendent of Documents, Government Printing Office, Washington, D.C.

CONTENTS

ELECTRICAL-ELECTRONIC SYMBOLS

MIL-STD 15-1
ELECTRICAL

Extracted from MIL-STD-15-1, Graphical Symbols for Electrical and Electronic Diagrams; 15-2, Electrical Wiring Equipment for Ships Plans; 15-3, Electrical Wiring Symbols for Architectural and Electrical Layout Drawings, with the permission of the Office of the Secretary of Defense, Public Affairs Department, Washington. MIL-STD-15-1 is exactly the same as ASA Y32.2-1962, Graphical Symbols for Electrical and Electronic Diagrams.

1. SCOPE

1.1 Purpose and scope. This Standard provides a list of graphical symbols for use on electrical and electronic schematic diagrams.

1.2 Use of symbols. Graphical symbols for electrical engineering are a shorthand used to show graphically the functioning or interconnections of a circuit. *A graphical symbol represents the function of a part in the circuit.* Graphical symbols are used on single-line (one-line) diagrams, on schematic or elementary diagrams or as applicable on connection or wiring diagrams. Graphical symbols are correlated with parts lists, descriptions, or instructions by means of reference designations.

1.3 Arrangement. All terms appear in the index. In the index, "item" refers to the number assigned a symbol in the list of symbols. Items are arranged alphabetically in order of family-group names. Terms in preferred usage and current alternates are listed. The symbol Ⓕ indicates standard item names from the Federal Item Identification Guide, Handbook H6-1, and are included wherever applicable.

1.4 In the list, graphical symbols appear directly under their respective family names. Single-line (one-line) symbols appear at the left in each column. Complete symbols appear at the right of the column. Symbols suitable for both purposes are centered in each column.

1.5 Symbols that have been recommended by the International Electrotechnical Commission are indicated by IEC.

1.6 Where alternative symbols are shown, the relative position of the symbols does not necessarily imply a preference.

1.7 Application. An application is an example of a combination of symbols in the list. No attempt has been made to list all possible applications. Additional applications may be devised provided they are a reasonable and intelligible use of the symbols in the list.

1.7.1 For application of these symbols in electrical diagrams see American Drafting Standard Manual ASA-Y14.15-1960.

2. APPLICABLE DOCUMENTS

2.1 The following documents, of the issue in effect on date of invitation for bids, form a part of this standard to the extent specified herein.

STANDARDS

MILITARY

MIL-STD-12—Abbreviations for Use on Drawings and in Technical-Type Publications.

MIL-STD-15-2—Electrical Wiring Equipment Symbols for Ships' Plans.

MIL-STD-15-3—Electrical Wiring Symbols for Architectural and Electrical Layout Drawings.

MIL-STD-16—Electrical and Electronic Reference Designations.

2.2 Other publications. The following document forms a part of this standard to the extent specified herein. Unless otherwise indicated, the issue in effect on date of invitation for bids shall apply.

AMERICAN STANDARDS ASSOCIATION

C37.2—Automatic Station Control, Supervisory, and Associated Telemetering Equipments.

(Application for copies should be addressed to the American Standards Association Incorporated, 10 East 40th Street, New York 16, N. Y.)

3. DEFINITIONS AND APPLICABLE DRAFTING PRACTICES

3.1 Single-line (one-line diagrams). A diagram which shows, by means of single lines and graphical symbols, the course of an electric circuit or system of circuits and the component devices or parts used therein.

3.2 Schematic or elementary diagrams. A diagram which shows, by means of graphical symbols, the electrical connections and functions of a specific circuit arrangement. The schematic diagram facilitates tracing the circuit and its functions without regard to the actual physical size, shape, or location of the component device or parts.

3.3 A symbol shall be considered as the aggregate of all its parts.

3.4 The orientation of a symbol on a drawing, including a mirror image presentation, does not alter the meaning of the symbol.

3.5 The width of a line does not affect the meaning of the symbol. In specific cases, a wider line may be used for emphasis.

3.6 The symbols shown in this standard are in their correct relative size. This relationship shall be maintained as nearly as possible on any particular drawing, regardless of the size of the symbol used.

3.7 A symbol may be drawn to any proportional size that suits a particular drawing, depending on reduction or enlargement anticipated. If essential for purposes of contrast, some symbols may be drawn relatively smaller than the other symbols on a diagram. It is recommended that only two sizes be used on any one diagram.

3.8 The arrowhead of a symbol may be closed → or open → unless otherwise noted in this standard.

3.9 The standard symbol for a TERMINAL (∘) may be added to each point of attachment to the connecting lines to any one of the graphical symbols. Such added terminal symbols should not be considered as part of the individual graphical symbol, unless the terminal symbol is included in the symbol shown in this standard.

3.10 For simplification of a diagram, parts of a symbol for a device, such as a relay or contactor, may be separated. If this is done, provide suitable designations to show proper correlation of the parts.

3.11 In general, the angle at which a connecting line is brought to a graphical symbol has no particular significance unless otherwise noted in this standard.

3.12 Associated or future paths and equipment shall be shown by lines composed of short dashes: - - - .

3.13 Details of type, impedance, rating and so forth may be added when required, adjacent to any symbol. If used, abbreviations shall be in accordance with Standard MIL-STD-12. Letter combinations used as parts of graphical symbols are not abbreviations.

3.14 Reference designations shall be assigned and used in accordance with Standard MIL-STD-16.

3.15 Symbols for ships' plans shall be in accordance with Standard MIL-STD-15-2.

3.16 Symbols for architectural and layout drawings shall be in accordance with Standard MIL-STD-15-3, supplemented by symbols herein for items not contained in Part 3.

4. GENERAL REQUIREMENTS

4.1 Not applicable.

5. LIST OF SYMBOLS AND DETAILS

5.1 The graphic symbols (items) in this list are arranged by item number indicating a generic class. The item number is not significant other than to distinguish between classes. The initial decimal portion of the complete item number indicates a further breakdown of symbols by type or functional designation, usually in alphabetical sequence. Further decimal subordinations indicate a symbol designed for a specific single function arranged alphabetically in order of the name modifiers. Thus the use of this decimal, item-numbering system for each symbol permits changes and revisions, or insertions, to be made conveniently, and without regard for paragraph and· section numbering.

5.2 To locate the symbol for a specific part. find the item number under the colloquial or functional name in the index.

3

Description	Single-line	Both / Note	Complete
1 ADJUSTABLE **CONTINUOUSLY ADJUSTABLE** (Variable) The shaft of the arrow is drawn at about 45 degrees across the body of the symbol.		IEC	
2 AMPLIFIER F See also MACHINE, ROTATING (items 46.8.20 to 46.8.23). 2.1 General The triangle is pointed in the direction of transmission. The symbol represents any method of amplification (electron tube, solid state device, magnetic device, etc.). Note 2.1A—If identification, electrical values, location data and similar information must be noted within a symbol the size or aspect ratio of the original symbol may be altered providing its distinctive shape is retained. Amplifier use may be indicated in the triangle by words, standard abbreviations, or a letter combination from the following list. BDG Bridging MON Monitoring BST Booster PGM Program CMP Compression PRE Preliminary DC Direct Current PWR Power EXP Expansion TRQ Torque LIM Limiting	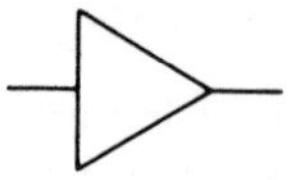	See note 2.1A	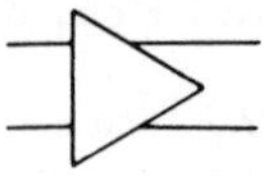
2.2 Applications 2.2.1 Amplifier with two inputs	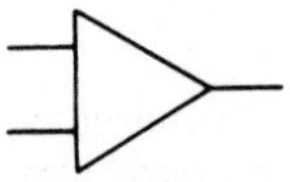	See note 2.1A	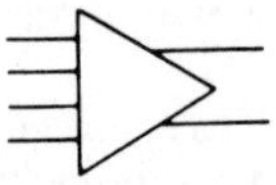
2.2.2 Amplifier with two outputs	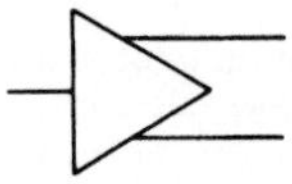	See note 2.1A	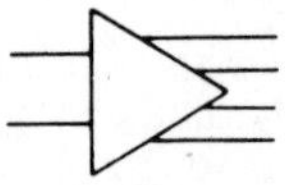
2.2.3 Amplifier with adjustable gain	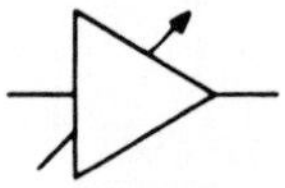	See note 2.1A	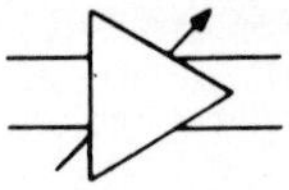
2.2.4 Amplifier with associated attenuator	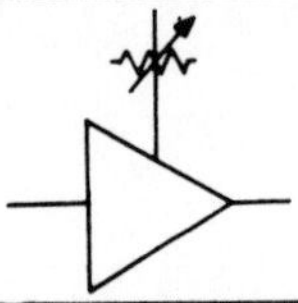	See note 2.1A	
2.2.5 Amplifier with associated power supply	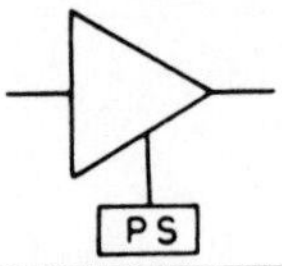 P S	See note 2.1A	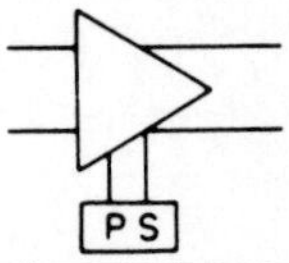 P S
2.2.6 Amplifier with external feedback path	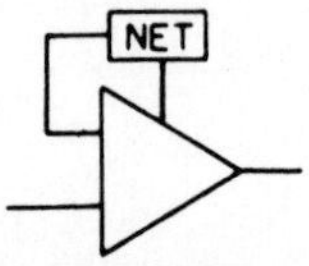 NET	See note 2.1A	

Note—Single-line (one-line) symbols appear at the left, complete symbols at the right, and symbols suitable for both purposes are centered in each column.

3 ANTENNA F			
3.1 General Types or functions may be indicated by words or abbreviations adjacent to the symbol for clarity.			
3.1.1 Dipole			
3.1.2 Loop			
3.2 Counterpoise, antenna F			
4 ARRESTER, LIGHTNING F **ARRESTER** (Electric surge, etc.) **GAP** 4.1 General			

4.2 Carbon block
    Block, telephone protector F
        The sides of the rectangle are to be approximately in the ratio of 1 to 2 and the space between rectangles shall be approximately equal to the width of a rectangle.			

4.3 Electrolytic or aluminum cell This symbol is not composed of arrowheads.			
4.4 Horn gap			
4.5 Protective gap These triangles shall not be filled.			
4.6 Sphere gap			
4.7 Valve or film element			
4.8 Multigap, general			
4.9 Application : gap plus valve plus ground, 2 pole			
5 ATTENUATOR (ATTENUATOR, VARIABLE F) See also PAD (item 57). 5.1 General			
5.2 Balanced, general			
5.3 Unbalanced, general			

6 AUDIBLE SIGNALING DEVICE			
6.1 Bell, electrical Ⓕ; ringer, telephone Ⓕ Note 6.1A—If specific identification is required, the abbreviation AC or DC may be added within the square.		See note 6.1A	 $\overline{\text{IEC}}$
6.2 Buzzer Ⓕ		See note 6.1A	 $\overline{\text{IEC}}$
6.3 Horn, electrical Ⓕ; loudspeaker Ⓕ; siren Ⓕ; underwater sound projector or transceiver 6.3.1 General			
6.3.2 If specific identification of loudspeaker parts is required, the following letter combinations may be added in the symbol at the locations indicated by the * and the ‡ *HN Horn, electrical Ⓕ *HW Howler *LS Loudspeaker Ⓕ *SN Siren Ⓕ ‡EM Electromagnetic with moving coil (moving coil leads should be identified) ‡EMN Electromagnetic with moving coil and neutralizing winding (moving coil leads should be identified) ‡MG Magnetic armature ‡PM Permanent magnet with moving coil		*‡ *The * and ‡ are not part of the symbol.*	 OR
6.4 Sounder, telegraph Ⓕ			
7 BATTERY Ⓕ The long line is always positive, but polarity may be indicated in addition. <div align="right">Example:</div>		$\overline{\text{IEC}}$	
7.1 Generalized direct-current source			
7.2 One cell		$\overline{\text{IEC}}$	
7.3 Multicell		$\overline{\text{IEC}}$	
7.3.1 Multicell battery with 3 taps			
7.3.2 Multicell battery with adjustable tap			

8 CAPACITOR [F] See also TERMINATION (item 82.4). 8.1 General If it is necessary to identify the capacitor electrodes, the curved element shall represent the outside electrode in fixed paper-dielectric and ceramic-dielectric capacitors, the moving element in adjustable and variable capacitors, and the low-potential element in feed-through capacitors.		IEC	
8.1.1 Polarized capacitor		(symbol)	
8.1.2 Application: shielded capacitor		(symbol)	
8.1.3 Application: adjustable or variable capacitor If it is necessary to identify trimmer capacitors, the letter T should appear adjacent to the symbol.		IEC	
8.1.4 Application: adjustable or variable capacitors with mechanical linkage of units			(symbol)
8.2 Continuously adjustable or variable differential capacitor The capacitance of one part increases as the capacitance of the other part decreases.			(symbol)
8.2.1 Phase-shifter capacitor			(symbol)
8.3 Split-stator capacitor The capacitances of both parts increase simultaneously.			(symbol)
8.4 Shunt capacitor		(symbol)	

8.4.1 Coupling capacitor (for power line carrier)
    Note 8.4.1A—The asterisk is not part of the symbol. If specific identification is desired, the asterisk is to be replaced by one of the following letter combinations.
    COM   Carrier communication
    LC   Carrier load control
    REL   Carrier relaying
    SUP   Carrier supervisory
    TLM   Carrier telemetering
    TT   Carrier transferred trip
	(symbol) * See note 8.4.1A		

8.5 Feed-through capacitor (with terminals shown on feed-through element for clarity) Commonly used for bypassing high-frequency currents to chassis.			(symbol)

8.5.1 Application: feed-through capacitor between 2 inductors with third lead connected to chassis			
8.6 Capacitance bushing for circuit breaker or transformer			
8.6.1 Application: capacitance-bushing potential device			
8.7 Application: Carrier coupling capacitor potential device (used to provide a power-system-frequency voltage and also coupling for carrier signals) Note 8.7A—The dagger is not a part of the symbol. If specific indication is desired, the dagger is to be replaced by a letter combination from item 48, note 48A.		* See note 8.4.1A † See note 8.7A	
8.7.1 Application: Coupling capacitor potential device (used only to provide a power-system frequency voltage)		† See note 8.7A	
9 CELL, PHOTOSENSITIVE (Semiconductor) See also PHOTOTUBE (item 34.11.6). indicates that the primary characteristic of the element within the circle is designed to vary under the influence of light. 9.1 Asymmetrical photoconductive transducer The equilateral triangle within the circle shall be filled.			
9.2 Symmetrical photoconductive transducer (resistive)			
9.3 Photovoltaic transducer; barrier photocell; blocking-layer cell; solar cell			
10 CHASSIS CONNECTION **FRAME CONNECTION** See CIRCUIT RETURN (item 13.2).			
11 CIRCUIT BREAKER If it is desired to show the condition causing the breaker to trip, the relay-protective-function symbols in item 66.6 may be used alongside the breaker symbol. 11.1 General		IEC	
11.2 Air circuit breaker, if distinction is needed; for alternating-current circuit breakers rated at 1,500 volts or less and for all direct-current circuit breakers		IEC	
11.2.1 Network protector			

11.3 Circuit breaker, other than covered by item 11.2 The symbol in the right column is for a 3-pole breaker. Note 11.3A—On a power diagram, the symbol may be used without other identification. On a composite drawing where confusion with the general circuit element symbol (item 12) may result, add the identifying letters CB inside or adjacent to the square.	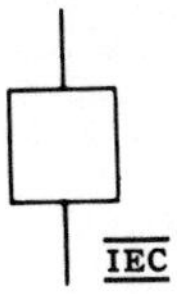 IEC	See note 11.3A	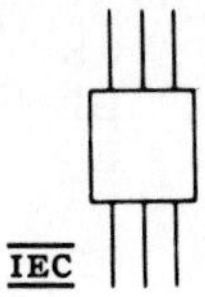 IEC
11.3.1 On a connection or wiring diagram, a 3-pole single-throw circuit breaker (with terminals shown) may be drawn as shown below		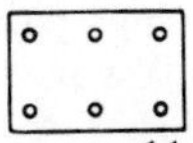 See note 11.3A FOR CONNECTION OR WIRING DIAGRAM	
11.4 Applications 11.4.1 3-pole circuit breaker with thermal overload device in all 3 poles	 OR 		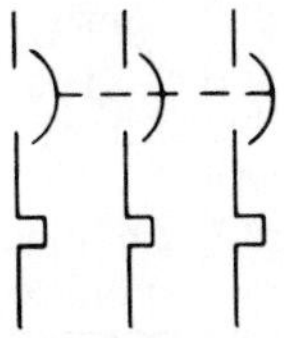 OR 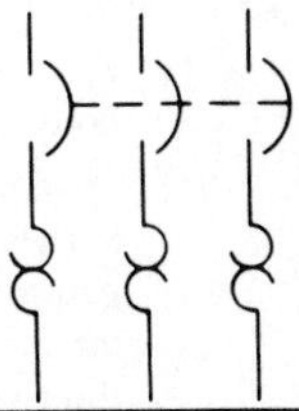
11.4.2 3-pole circuit breaker with magnetic overload device in all 3 poles 11.4.3 3-pole circuit breaker, drawout type			
12 CIRCUIT ELEMENT (General) Note 12A—The asterisk is not a part of the symbol. Always indicate the type of apparatus by appropriate words or letters in the rectangle. Note 12B—If identification, electrical values, location data and similar information must be noted within a symbol the size or the proportion of the original symbol may be altered providing its distinctive shape is retained.		 * *See note 12A	
12.1 Accepted abbreviations in the latest edition of Standard MIL-STD-12 may be used in the rectangle.			

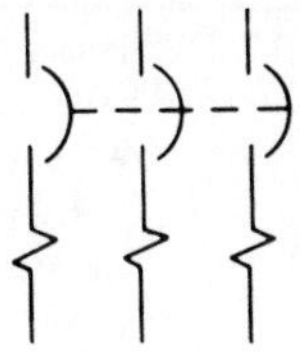

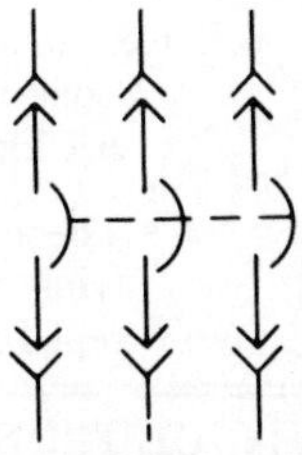

12.2 The following letter combinations may be used in the rectangle.

CB	Circuit breaker 🄵
DIAL	Telephone dial
EQ	Equalizer
FAX	Facsimile set 🄵
FL	Filter
FL-BE	Filter, band elimination
FL-BP	Filter, band pass 🄵
FL-HP	Filter, high pass 🄵
FL-LP	Filter, low pass 🄵
NET	Network
PS	Power supply 🄵
RU	Reproducing unit
RG	Recording unit
TEL	Telephone station
TPR	Teleprinter 🄵
TTY	Teletypewriter 🄵

12.3 Additional letter combinations as follows may be employed, but the use of specific graphical symbols included elsewhere in this standard is preferred.

AR	Amplifier 🄵
AT	Attenuator
C	Capacitor 🄵
HS	Handset 🄵
I	Indicating or switchboard lamp
L	Inductor
LS	Loudspeaker 🄵
J	Jack
MIC	Microphone 🄵
OSC	Oscillator
PAD	Pad
P	Plug
HT	Receiver, headset
K	Relay 🄵
R	Resistor 🄵
S	Switch 🄵 or key switch
T	Transformer 🄵
WR	Wall receptacle

13 CIRCUIT RETURN

13.1 Ground

(*A*) A direct conducting connection to the earth or body of water that is a part thereof.

(*B*) A conducting connection to a structure that serves a function similar to that of an earth ground (that is, a structure such as a frame of an air, space, or land vehicle that is not conductively connected to earth).

13.2 Chassis or frame connection

A conducting connection to a chassis or frame of a unit. The chassis or frame may be at a substantial potential with respect to the earth or structure in which this chassis or frame is mounted.

13.3 Common connections

Conducting connections made to one another. All like-designated points are connected.

* The asterisk is not a part of the symbol. Identifying values, letters, numbers, or marks shall replace the asterisk.

14 CLUTCH BRAKE

14.1 Clutch disengaged when operating means (not shown) is de-energized or non-operated

14.2 Clutch engaged when operating means (not shown) is de-energized or non-operated

14.3 Brake applied when operating means (not shown) is energized

14.4 Brake released when operating means (not shown) is energized		OR	
15 ‡ COIL, MAGNETIC BLOWOUT 🄵		N OR	

16 COIL, OPERATING
COIL, RELAY 🄵
    See also item 42; INDUCTOR; WINDING (Machine or transformer); REACTOR.
    Note 16A—The asterisk is not a part of the symbol. Always replace the asterisk by a device designation.
		OR
		OR ⌇ OR ⊛
		* See note 16A	

16.1 Semicircular dot indicates inner end of winding		OR	
16.2 Application: multiwinding coil (2 windings shown) Note 16.2A—The ends of a given winding shall be shown directly opposite each other on opposite sides of the core, or adjacent to each other on the same side of the core.		See note 16.2A	
17 CONNECTION, MECHANICAL INTERLOCK, MECHANICAL The preferred location of the mechanical connection is as shown in the various applications, but other locations may be equally acceptable. 17.1 Mechanical connection (*short dashes*)		— — — — — IEC	
17.2 Mechanical connection or interlock with fulcrum (*short dashes*)		— — ⋏ — —	
17.3 Mechanical interlock, other	INDICATE BY A NOTE		
18 CONNECTOR DISCONNECTING DEVICE The connector symbol is not an arrowhead. It is larger and the lines are drawn at a 90-degree angle. 18.1 Female contact			IEC —<
18.2 Male contact			IEC —→
18.3 Connector assembly, movable or stationary portion; jack, plug, or receptacle Note 18.3A—Use appropriate number of contact symbols. IEC	→ IEC OR —< IEC See note 18.3A		
18.3.1 Commonly used for a jack or receptacle (usually stationary)	—< IEC	See note 18.3A OR ▯	

‡ *The broken line - —— indicates where line connection to a symbol is made and is not a part of the symbol.*

11

18.3.2 Commonly used for a plug (usually movable)	→ IEC	See note 18.3A OR	
18.4 Separable connectors (engaged)	→→— IEC	See note 18.3A OR	
18.4.1 Application: engaged 4-conductor connectors; the plug has 1 male and 3 female contacts	→→— IEC		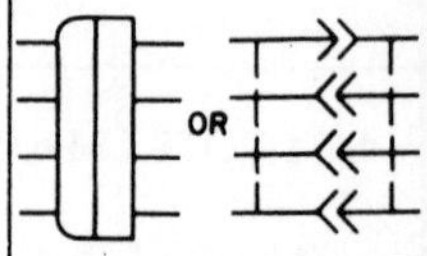 OR
18.4.2 Application: engaged 4-conductor connectors, the plug has 1 male and 3 female contacts with individual contact designations shown in the complete-symbol column	→→— IEC		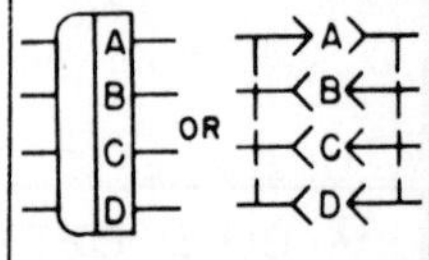 OR
18.5 Coaxial connectors 18.5.1 Engaged coaxial and waveguide connectors Coaxial recognition sign may be added if necessary. See PATH, TRANSMISSION (item 58.8.2)		→→— IEC	
18.5.1.1 Coaxial with the outside conductor shown carried through			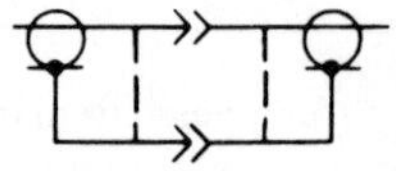
18.5.1.2 Coaxial with outside conductor shown carried through; with outside conductor terminated on chassis			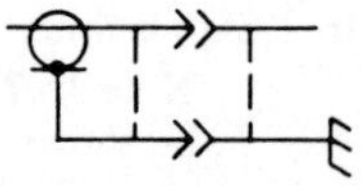
18.5.1.3 Coaxial with center conductor shown carried through; outside conductor not carried through			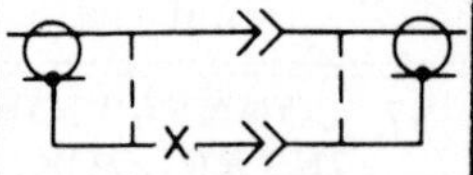
18.6 Communication switchboard-type connector 18.6.1 2-conductor (jack)			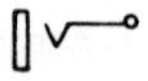
18.6.2 2-conductor (plug)			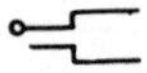
18.6.3 3-conductor (jack) with 2 break contacts (normals) and 1 auxiliary make contact			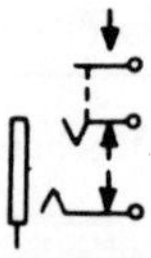
18.6.4 3-conductor (plug)			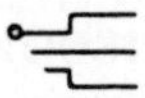
18.7 Communication switchboard-type connector with circuit normalled through "Normalled" indicates that a through circuit may be interrupted by an inserted connector. As shown here, the inserted connector opens the through circuit and connects to the circuit towards the left. Items 18.7.1 through 18.7.4 show 2-conductor jacks. The "normal" symbol is applicable to other types of connectors.	←—		
18.7.1 Jacks with circuit normalled through one way	←—		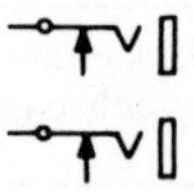

18.7.2 Jacks with circuit normalled through both ways			
18.7.3 Jacks in multiple, one set with circuit normalled through both ways			
18.7.4 Jacks with auxiliary contacts, with circuit normalled through both ways			
18.8 Connectors of the type commonly used for power-supply purposes (convenience outlets and mating connectors) 18.8.1 Female contact			
18.8.2 Male contact			
18.8.3 2-conductor nonpolarized connector with female contacts			
18.8.4 2-conductor nonpolarized connector with male contacts			
18.8.5 2-conductor polarized connector with female contacts			
18.8.6 2-conductor polarized connector with male contacts			
18.8.7 3-conductor polarized connector with female contacts			
18.8.8 3-conductor polarized connector with male contacts			
18.8.9 4-conductor polarized connector with female contacts			
18.8.10 4-conductor polarized connector with male contacts			
18.9 Test blocks 18.9.1 Female portion with short-circuiting bar (with terminals shown)			
18.9.2 Male portion (with terminals shown)			

18.10 WAVEGUIDE FLANGES Note 18.10A—If necessary to indicate flange type (plain or choke), place waveguide recognition symbol immediately adjacent to the connector symbol. If the recognition symbol is omitted or is spaced from the connector symbol, the nature of the flange is not to be implied from the symbol.			
18.10.1 Mated (General)		$\longrightarrow\!\!\!\gg\!\!\!-$ See note 18.10A	
18.10.2 Plain (Rectangular waveguide)		$-\!\!\Box\!\!\gg$ See note 18.10A	
18.10.3 Choke (Rectangular waveguide)		$-\!\!\Box\!\!\!<$	
18.10.3.1. Application: Mated choke flanges in rectangular waveguide line		$-\!\!\Box\!\!\!<\;>\!\!\Box\!\!-$	
18.10.4 Application: Rectangular waveguide with mated plain and choke flanges with DC isolation (insulation) between sections of waveguide.			
19 RESERVED 20 RESERVED		21 RESERVED 22 RESERVED	
23 CONTACT, ELECTRICAL For build-ups or forms using electrical contacts, see applications under CONNECTOR (item 18), RELAY (item 66), SWITCH (item 76), and SWITCHING FUNCTION (item 77). See DRAFTING PRACTICES (par. 3.8). 23.1 Fixed contact 23.1.1. Fixed contact for jack, key, relay, etc.		$\longrightarrow$ OR $\overset{}{\underset{}{\dashv}}$ OR $\longrightarrow\!\!\!\blacktriangledown$	
23.1.2 Fixed contact for switch		○ OR $\longrightarrow$	
23.1.3 Fixed contact for momentary switch See SWITCH (items 76.8 and 76.10).		$\longrightarrow\!\!\!\blacktriangledown$	
23.1.4 Sleeve		$\parallel$ OR $\parallel$ OR L	
23.2 Moving contact 23.2.1 Adjustable or sliding contact for resistor, inductor, etc.		$\longrightarrow$ OR $\overset{}{\underset{}{\dashv}}$	
23.2.2 Locking		$\circ\!\!\!-\!\!\!\vee$	
23.2.3 Nonlocking		$\circ\!\!\!-\!\!\!-$	
23.2.4 Segment; bridging contact See SWITCH (items 76.12.3 and 76.12.4).		$\frown$ OR $\sqsubset\!\!\sqsupset$	
23.2.5 Vibrator reed		$\circ\!\!\!-\!\!\!-\!\!\!\square\!\!\!-$	
23.2.6 Vibrator split reed		$\circ\!\!\!-\!-\!\!\square\!\!\!-$	
23.2.7 Rotating contact (slip ring) and brush		$\longrightarrow\!\!\!\bullet\!\!\!\bigcirc\!\!\!-$	

23.3 Basic contact assemblies

The standard method of showing a contact is by a symbol indicating the circuit condition it produces when the actuating device is in the de-energized or nonoperated position. The actuating device may be of a mechanical, electrical, or other nature, and a clarifying note may be necessary with the symbol to explain the proper point at which the contact functions, for example, the point where a contact closes or opens as a function of changing pressure, level, flow, voltage, current, etc. In cases where it is desirable to show contacts in the energized or operated condition and where confusion may result, a clarifying note shall be added to the drawing.

Auxiliary switches or contacts for circuit breakers, etc., may be designated as follows:

(a) Closed when device is in energized or operated position,

(b) Closed when device is in de-energized or nonoperated position,

(aa) Closed when operating mechanism of main device is in energized or operated position,

(bb) Closed when operating mechanism of main device is in de-energized or nonoperated position.

See American Standard C37.2 for further details.

In the parallel-line contact symbols shown below, the length of the parallel lines shall be approximately 1¼ times the width of the gap (except for item 23.6)

23.3.1 Closed contact (break) See also SWITCHING FUNCTION (item 77).		
23.3.2 Open contact (make) See also SWITCHING FUNCTION (item 77).		
23.3.3 Transfer See also SWITCHING FUNCTION (item 77).		
23.3.4 Make-before-break		
23.4 Application: open contact with time closing (TC) or time delay closing (TDC) feature		
23.5 Application: closed contact with time opening (TO) or time delay opening (TDO) feature		
23.6 Time sequential closing		

24 CONTACTOR

See also RELAY (item 66).

Fundamental symbols for contacts, coils, mechanical connections, etc., are the basis of contactor symbols and should be used to represent contactors on complete diagrams. Complete diagrams of contactors consist of combinations of fundamental symbols for control coils, mechanical connections, etc., in such configurations as to represent the actual device.

Mechanical interlocking should be indicated by notes.

24.1 Manually operated 3-pole contactor

24.2 Electrically operated 1-pole contactor with series blowout coil Note 24.2A—The asterisk is not a part of the symbol. Always replace the asterisk by a device designation.		* See note 24.2A	
24.3 Electrically operated 3-pole contactor with series blowout coils; 2 open and 1 closed auxiliary contacts (shown smaller than the main contacts)		* See note 24.2A	
24.4 Electrically operated 1-pole contactor with shunt blowout coil		* See note 24.2A	
25 CORE 25.1 General or air core If it is necessary to identify an air core, a note should appear adjacent to the symbol of the inductor or transformer.		NO SYMBOL	
25.2 Magnetic core of inductor or transformer Not to be used unless it is necessary to identify a magnetic core. See INDUCTOR (item 42.2) and TRANSFORMER (item 86.2).			
25.3 Core of magnet For use if representation of the core is necessary. See MAGNET, PERMANENT (item 47).			
26 COUNTER, ELECTROMAGNETICALLY OPERATED MESSAGE REGISTER 26.1 General			
26.2 With a make contact			
27 COUPLER, DIRECTIONAL E Commonly used in coaxial and waveguide diagrams. The arrows indicate the direction of power flow. Number of coupling paths, type of coupling, and transmission loss may be indicated. 27.1 General			
27.2 Applications 27.2.1 E-plane aperture coupling, 30-decibel transmission loss			

27.2.2 Loop coupling, 30-decibel transmission loss		⨯ ⌇ 30DB	
27.2.3 Probe coupling, 30-decibel transmission loss		⨯ ❘ 30DB	
27.2.4 Resistance coupling, 30-decibel transmission loss		⨯ ⧨ 30DB	

28 COUPLING

Commonly used in coaxial and waveguide diagrams.

28.1 Coupling by aperture with an opening of less than full waveguide size

Transmission loss may be indicated.

Note 28.1A—The asterisk is not a part of the symbol. Always replace the asterisk by E, H, or HE, depending on the type of coupling.

E indicates that the physical plane of the aperture is perpendicular to the transverse component of the major E lines.

H indicates that the physical plane of the aperture is parallel to the transverse component of the major E lines.

HE indicates coupling by all other kinds of apertures.

⊛

* See note 28.1A

28.1.1 Application: E-plane coupling by aperture to space		—(E)	
28.1.2 Application: E-plane coupling by aperture; 2 ends of transmission path available		—(E)—	
28.1.3 Application: E-plane coupling by aperture; 3 ends of transmission path available		(E)	
28.1.4 Application: E-plane coupling by aperture; 4 ends of transmission path available		(E)	
28.2 Coupling by loop to space		⌐	
28.2.1 Coupling by loop to guided transmission path		↳	
28.2.2 Application: coupling by loop from coaxial to circular waveguide with direct-current grounds connected			
28.3 Coupling by probe to space See OPEN CIRCUIT (item 82.2).		—•	
28.3.1 Application: coupling by probe to a guided transmission path		❘•	
28.3.2 Application: coupling by probe from coaxial to rectangular waveguide with direct-current grounds connected			
29 RESERVED			
30 RESERVED			

31 DELAY FUNCTION **DELAY LINE** 🇫 31.1 General Note 31.1A—Length of delay may be indicated. Asterisk is not part of symbol. See also note 12B.		* See note 31.1A	
31.2 Tapped delay function		* See note 31.1A	
32 DIRECTION OF FLOW OF POWER, SIGNAL, OR INFORMATION 32.1 One-way Note 32.1A—The lower symbol is used if it is necessary to conserve space. The arrowhead in the lower symbol shall be filled.		OR See note 32.1A	
32.2 Both ways		OR See note 32.1A	
32.3 Application: one-way circuit element, general Note 32.3A—In all cases indicate the type of apparatus by appropriate words or letters in the rectangle.		OR See note 32.3A	

33 DISCONTINUITY
 	
    A component that exhibits throughout the frequency range of interest the properties of the type of circuit element indicated by the symbol within the triangle.
 	
    Commonly used for coaxial and waveguide transmission.
 	
33.1 Equivalent series element, general
		Z	

33.1.1 Capacitive reactance			
33.1.2 Inductive reactance			
33.1.3 Inductance-capacitance circuit with infinite reactance at resonance			
33.1.4 Inductance-capacitance circuit with zero reactance at resonance			
33.1.5 Resistance			
33.2 Equivalent shunt element, general		Y	

33.2.1 Capacitive susceptance			
33.2.2 Conductance			
33.2.3 Inductive susceptance			
33.2.4 Inductance-capacitance circuit with infinite susceptance at resonance			
33.2.5 Inductance-capacitance circuit with zero susceptance at resonance			

34 ELECTRON TUBE [E]

Tube-component symbols are shown first. These are followed by typical applications showing the use of these specific symbols in the various classes of devices such as thermionic, cold-cathode, and photoemissive tubes of varying structures and combinations of elements (triodes, pentodes, cathode-ray tubes, magnetrons, etc.).

Lines outside of the envelope are not part of the symbol but are electrical connections thereto.

Connections between the external circuit and electron tube symbols within the envelope may be located as required to simplify the diagram.

34.1 Emitting electrode			
34.1.1 Directly heated (filamentary) cathode Note 34.1.1A—Leads may be connected in any convenient manner to ends of the ∧ provided the identity of the ∧ is retained.		∧ IEC See note 34.1.1A	
34.1.1.1 With tap See item 34.10.3.			
34.1.2 Indirectly heated cathode Lead may be connected to either extreme end of the ⌐ or, if required, to both ends, in any convenient manner.		IEC	
34.1.3 Cold cathode (including ionically heated cathode)		—o IEC	
34.1.4 Photocathode		—C IEC	
34.1.5 Pool cathode		IEC	
34.1.6 Ionically heated cathode with provision for supplementary heating See note 34.1.1A.		☿ IEC	
34.2 Controlling electrode			
34.2.1 Grid (including beam-confining or beam-forming electrodes)		—---- IEC	
34.2.2 Deflecting electrodes (used in pairs); reflecting or repelling electrode (used in velocity-modulated tube)		—< IEC	
34.2.3 Ignitor (in pool tubes) (should extend into pool); Starter (in gas tubes)		—\ IEC	
34.2.4 Excitor (contactor type)		—	

34.3 Collecting electrode			
34.3.1 Anode or plate (including collector electrode and fluorescent target)		⊥ IEC	
34.3.2 Target or X-ray anode Drawn at about a 45-degree angle.		⊬ IEC	
34.4 Collecting and emitting electrode 34.4.1 Dynode		⊥ IEC	
34.4.2 Alternately collecting and emitting electrode 34.4.2.1 Composite anode-photocathode		⊥	
34.4.2.2 Composite anode-cold cathode		⊥ IEC	
34.4.2.3 Composite anode-ionically heated cathode with provision for supplementary heating See note 34.1.1A.		⅄ IEC	
34.5 Heater See note 34.1.1A.		⌒	
34.5.1 With tap See item 34.10.3.			
34.6 Envelope See item 35.			
34.7 Shield See item 34.10.10. This is understood to shield against electric fields unless otherwise noted.			
34.7.1 Any shield against electric fields that is within the envelope and that is connected to an independent terminal		◯	
34.7.2 Outside envelope of X-ray tube		◎	
34.8 Coupling See COUPLING (item 28) and PATH, TRANSMISSION (items 58.8.2 and 58.11). 34.8.1 Coupling by loop (electromagnetic type) Coupling loop may be shown inside or outside envelope as desired.		⌐	
34.9 Resonators (cavity type) 34.9.1 Single-cavity envelope and grid-type associated electrodes		◯	
34.9.2 Double-cavity envelope and grid-type associated electrodes		◯	
34.9.3 Multicavity magnetron anode and envelope		◯	

34.10 General notes

34.10.1 If new symbols are necessary, they should be formed where possible from component symbols. For example, see DYNODE (item 34.4.1), which combines the anode and photocathode convention.

34.10.2 A connection to anode, dynode, pool cathode, photocathode, deflecting electrode, composite anode-photocathode, and composite anode-cold cathode shall be to the center of that symbol. Connection to any other electrode may be shown at either end or both ends of the electrode symbol.

34.10.3 A diagram for a tube having more than one heater or filament shall show only one heater or filament symbol ⋀ unless they have entirely separate connections. If a heater or filament tap is made, either brought out to a terminal or internally connected to another element, it shall be connected at the vertex of the symbol, regardless of the actual division of voltage across the heater or filament.

34.10.4 Standard symbols, such as the inclined arrow for tunability and connecting dotted lines for ganged components, may be added to a tube symbol to extend the meaning of the tube symbol, provided such added feature or component is integral with the tube.

34.10.5 Electric components, such as resistors, capacitors, or inductors, which are integral parts of the tube and are important to its functional operation, shall be shown in the standard manner.

34.10.6 Multiple equipotential cathodes that are directly connected inside the tube shall be shown as a single cathode.

34.10.7 A tube having two or more grids tied internally shall be shown with symbols for each grid, except when the grids are adjacent in the tube structure. Thus, the diagram for a twin pentode having a common screen-grid connection for each section and for a converter tube having the No. 3 and No. 5 grids connected internally will show separate symbols for each grid. However, a triode where the control grid is physically in the form of two grid windings would show only one grid.

34.10.8 A tube having a grid adjacent to a plate but internally connected to the plate to form a portion of it shall be shown as having a plate only.

34.10.9 Associated parts of a circuit, such as focusing coils, deflecting coils, field coils, etc., are not a part of the tube symbol but may be added to the circuit in the form of standard symbols. For example, resonant-type magnetron with permanent magnet may be shown:

34.10.10 External and internal shields, whether integral parts of tubes or not, shall be omitted from the circuit diagram unless the circuit diagram requires their inclusion.

34.10.11 In line with standard drafting practice, straight-line crossovers are recommended.

34.11 Typical applications 34.11.1 Triode with directly heated filamentary cathode and envelope connection to base terminal	
34.11.2 Equipotential-cathode pentode showing use of elongated envelope	
34.11.3 Equipotential-cathode twin triode illustrating elongated envelope and rule of item 34.10.3.	
34.11.4 Typical wiring figure This figure illustrates how tube symbols may be placed in any convenient position in a circuit.	

34.11.5 Cold-cathode gas-filled tube 34.11.5.1 Rectifier; voltage regulator for direct-current operation 　　　See also LAMP, GLOW (item 44.3).			
34.11.6 Phototube 34.11.6.1 Single-unit, vacuum type			
34.11.6.2 Multiplier type			
34.11.7 Cathode-ray tube 34.11.7.1 With electric-field deflection			
34.11.7.2 For magnetic deflection			
34.11.8 Mercury-pool tube 　　　See also RECTIFIER (item 65.4).			
34.11.8.1 With ignitor and control grid			
34.11.8.2 With excitor, control grid, and holding anode			
34.11.8.3 Single-anode pool-type vapor rectifier with ignitor			
34.11.8.4 6-anode metallic-tank pool-type vapor rectifier with excitor, showing rigid-terminal symbol for control connection to tank (pool cathode is insulated from tank) 　　　Anode symbols are located as convenient.			
34.11.9 Magnetron 34.11.9.1 Resonant type with coaxial output			
34.11.9.2 Transit-time split-plate type with stabilizing deflecting electrodes and internal circuit			
34.11.9.3 Tunable, aperture coupled			

34.11.10 Velocity-modulation (velocity-variation) tube 34.11.10.1 Reflex klystron, integral cavity, aperture coupled			
34.11.10.2 Double-cavity klystron, integral cavity, permanent external-ganged tuning, loop coupled (coupling loop may be shown inside if desired) See item 34.8.1.			
34.11.11 Transmit-receive (TR) tube Gas filled, tunable integral cavity, aperture coupled, with starter.			
34.11.12 X-ray tube 34.11.12.1 With filamentary cathode and focusing grid (cup). The anode may be cooled by fluid or radiation.			
34.11.12.2 With control grid, filamentary cathode, and focusing cup			
34.11.12.3 With grounded electrostatic shield			
34.11.12.4 Double focus with rotating anode (see item 34.10.9)			
34.11.12.5 With multiple accelerating electrode, electrostatically and electromagnetically focused See item 34.10.9.			
35 ENVELOPE ENCLOSURE The general envelope symbol identifies the envelope or enclosure regardless of evacuation or pressure. When used with electron-tube component symbols, the general envelope symbol indicates a vacuum enclosure unless otherwise specified. A gas-filled device may be indicated by a dot within the envelope symbol. 35.1 General		IEC OR IEC	
35.1.1 Split envelope If necessary, envelope may be split.		IEC	
35.2 Gas-filled envelope The dot may be located as convenient.		IEC	

36 FUSE		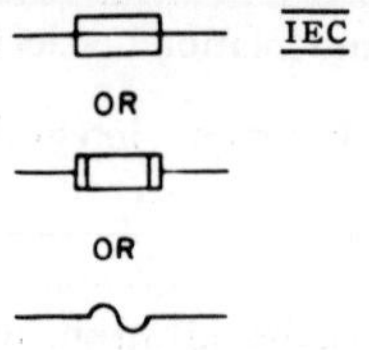 IEC OR OR	
36.1 High-voltage primary fuse cutout, dry		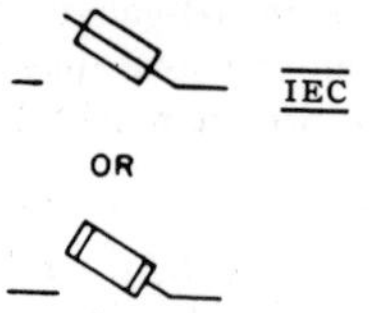 IEC OR	
36.2 High-voltage primary fuse cutout, oil		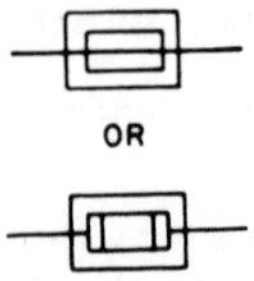 OR	
36.3 With alarm contact When fuse blows, alarm bus A is connected to power bus B. Letters are for explanation and are not part of the symbol.		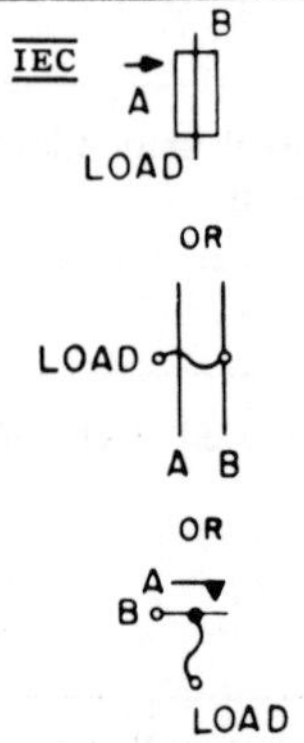 IEC B A LOAD OR LOAD A B OR A B LOAD	
37 GOVERNOR 🇫 (Contact-making) **SPEED REGULATOR** Contacts open or closed as required (shown here as closed).			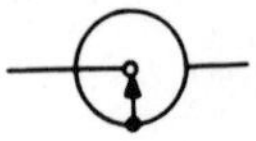
38 GROUND See CIRCUIT RETURN (item 13.1).			
39 HALL GENERATOR			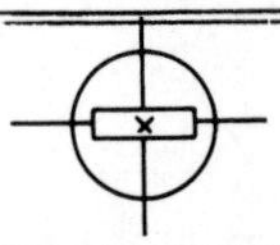
40 HANDSET 🇫 **OPERATOR'S SET** 40.1 General			
40.2 With push-to-talk switch			
40.3 3-conductor handset			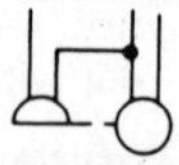
40.4 4-conductor handset			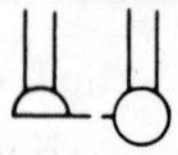

40.5 4-conductor handset with push-to-talk switch			
40.6 Operator's set			

41 HYBRID

41.1 Hybrid, general			
41.2 Hybrid, junction Commonly used in coaxial and waveguide transmission.			
41.3 Application: rectangular waveguide and coaxial coupling			
41.4 Hybrid, circular (basic) Note 41.4A—The asterisk is not a part of the symbol. Always replace the asterisk by E, H, or HE. E indicates that there is a principal E transverse field in the plane of the ring. H indicates that there is a principal H transverse field in the plane of the ring. HE shall be used for all other cases. An arm that has coupling of a different type from that designated above shall be marked according to COUPLING (item 28.1). Critical distances should be labeled in terms of guide wavelengths.		 * See note 41.4A.	
41.4.1 Application: 5-arm circular hybrid with principal coupling in the *E* plane and with 1-arm *H* coupling using rectangular waveguide			

42 INDUCTOR
WINDING Ⓕ (Machine or transformer)
REACTOR Ⓕ
See also COIL, OPERATING (item 16) and TERMINATION (item 82).

42.1 General Either symbol may be used in the following items.		$\underline{\text{IEC}}$ OR	
42.2 If it is desired especially to distinguish magnetic-core inductors			
42.3 Tapped			
42.4 Application: adjustable inductor			
42.5 Application: adjustable or continuously adjustable inductor		$\underline{\text{IEC}}$	
42.6 Shunt inductor			

			DC WINDING
42.7 Saturable-core inductor (reactor) Polarity marks may be added to direct-current winding. Explanatory words and arrow are not part of the symbol shown.			

42.8 Application: carrier line trap
Note 42.8A—Asterisk is not part of the symbol. The symbol represents a general trap or single-frequency trap unless one of the following letter combinations is used.
      2f   Two-frequency
      WB Wide band
		* See note 42.8A	

43 KEY, TELEGRAPH Ⓕ 43.1 Simple			
43.2 Simple with shorting switch			
43.3 Open circuit or pole changing			
44 LAMP 44.1 Ballast lamp; ballast tube The primary characteristic of the element within the circle is designed to vary nonlinearly with the temperature of the element.			
44.2 Lamp, fluorescent Ⓕ 44.2.1 2-terminal			
44.2.2 4-terminal			
44.3 Lamp, glow Ⓕ, cold-cathode lamp; neon lamp 44.3.1 Alternating-current type			
44.3.2 Direct-current type See also ELECTRON TUBE (item 34.11.5.1).			
44.4 Lamp, incandescent Ⓕ (Incandescent-filament illuminating lamp)			
44.5 Indicating lamp; switchboard lamp See VISUAL SIGNALING DEVICE (item 88).			
45 LIMITER, CURRENT Ⓕ (For power cable) The arrowheads in this case are filled. Note 45A—Use appropriate number of single-line diagram symbols.			See note 45A
46 MACHINE, ROTATING 46.1 Basic			
46.2 Generator Ⓕ (general)			
46.3 Motor Ⓕ (general)			

46.4 Motor, multispeed	USE BASIC MOTOR SYMBOL AND NOTE SPEEDS		
46.5 ‡ Rotating armature with commutator and brushes			
46.6 Field, generator or motor Either symbol of item **42.1** may be used in the following items.			
46.6.1 Compensating or commutating		$\overline{\text{IEC}}$	
46.6.2 Series		$\overline{\text{IEC}}$	
46.6.3 Shunt, or separately excited		$\overline{\text{IEC}}$	
46.6.4 Magnet, permanent See item **47**.			
46.7 Winding symbols Motor and generator winding symbols may be shown in the basic circle using the following representations.			
46.7.1 1-phase			
46.7.2 2-phase			
46.7.3 3-phase wye (ungrounded)			
46.7.4 3-phase wye (grounded)			
46.7.5 3-phase delta			
46.7.6 6-phase diametrical			
46.7.7 6-phase double-delta			
46.8 Direct-current machines; applications 46.8.1. ‡ Separately excited direct-current generator or motor			
46.8.2 ‡ Separately excited direct-current generator or motor; with commutating or compensating field winding or both			
46.8.3 ‡ Compositely excited direct-current generator or motor; with commutating or compensating field winding or both			
46.8.4 ‡ Direct-current series motor or 2-wire generator			
‡ *The broken line -—- indicates where line connection to a symbol is made and is not a part of the symbol.*			

46.8.5 ‡ Direct-current series motor or 2-wire generator; with commutating or compensating field winding or both			
46.8.6 ‡ Direct-current shunt motor or 2-wire generator			
46.8.7 ‡ Direct-current shunt motor or 2-wire generator; with commutating or compensating field winding or both			
46.8.8 ‡ Direct-current permanent-magnet-field generator or motor			
46.8.9 ‡ Direct-current compound motor or 2-wire generator or stabilized shunt motor			
46.8.10 ‡ Direct-current compound motor or 2-wire generator or stabilized shunt motor; with commutating or compensating field winding or both			
46.8.11 ‡ Direct-current 3-wire shunt generator			
46.8.12 ‡ Direct-current 3-wire shunt generator; with commutating or compensating field winding or both			
46.8.13 ‡ Direct-current 3-wire compound generator			
46.8.14 ‡ Direct-current 3-wire compound generator; with commutating or compensating field winding or both			

‡ *The broken line - - — - indicates where line connection to a symbol is made and is not a part of the symbol.*

46.8 15 ‡ Direct-current balancer, shunt wound			
46.8.16 ‡ Direct-current balancer, compound wound			
46.8.17 ‡ Dynamotor			
46.8.18 ‡ Double-current generator			
46.8.19 ‡ Acyclic generator, separately excited			
46.8.20 ‡ Regulating generator (rotary amplifier) shunt wound with short-circuited brushes			
46.8.21 ‡ Regulating generator (rotary amplifier) shunt wound without short-circuited brushes			
46.8.22 ‡ Regulating generator (rotary amplifier) shunt wound with compensating field winding and short-circuited brushes			
46.8.23 ‡ Regulating generator (rotary amplifier) shunt wound with compensating field winding but without short-circuited brushes			
46.9 Alternating-current machines; applications 46.9.1 ‡ Squirrel-cage induction motor or generator, split-phase induction motor or generator, rotary phase converter, or repulsion motor			
‡ *The broken line - — - indicates where line connection to a symbol is made and is not a part of the symbol.*			

46.9.2 ‡ Wound-rotor induction motor, synchronous induction motor, induction generator, or induction frequency converter			
46.9.3 ‡ Alternating-current series motor			
46.9.4 ‡ Alternating-current series motor; with commutating or compensating field winding or both			
46.9.5 ‡ 1-phase shaded-pole motor			
46.9.6 ‡ 1-phase repulsion-start induction motor			
46.9.7 ‡ 1-phase hysteresis motor			
46.9.8 ‡ Reluctance motor			
46.9.9 ‡ 1-phase subsynchronous reluctance motor			
46.9.10 ‡ Magnetoelectric generator, 1 phase			
46.9.11 ‡ Shunt-characteristic brush-shifting motor			
46.9.12 ‡ Series-characteristic brush-shifting motor with 3-phase rotor			
46.9.13 Series-characteristic brush-shifting motor with 6- or 8-phase rotor			
46.9.14 Ohmic-drop exciter with 3- or 6-phase input			
46.9.15 Ohmic-drop exciter with 3- or 6-phase input, with output leads			
46.9.16 3-phase regulating machine			

‡ *The broken line - -—- indicates where line connection to a symbol is made and is not a part of the symbol.*

46.9.17 Phase shifter with 1-phase output See PHASE SHIFTER (item 60). See TRANSFORMER (item 86).			
46.9.18 Phase shifter with 3-phase output See PHASE SHIFTER (item 60). See TRANSFORMER (item 86).			
46.10.1 ‡ Synchronous motor, generator, or condenser			
46.10.2 ‡ Synchronous motor, generator, or condenser with neutral brought out			
46.10.3 ‡ Synchronous motor, generator, or condenser with both ends of each phase brought out			
46.10.4 ‡ Double-winding synchronous generator, motor, or condenser			
46.10.5 ‡ Synchronous-synchronous frequency changer			
46.10.6 ‡ Synchronous induction frequency changer			
46.11 Alternating- and direct-current composite machines; applications 46.11.1 ‡ Synchronous or regulating-pole converter			
46.11.2 ‡ Synchronous booster or regulating-pole converter; with commutating or compensating field windings or both			
46.11.3 ‡ Synchronous shunt-wound converter; with commutating or compensating windings or both			
46.11.4 ‡ Synchronous converter compound wound; with commutating or compensating field windings or both			

‡ *The broken line -—- indicates where line connection to a symbol is made and is not a part of the symbol.*

46.11.5 ‡ Motor converter			

47 **MAGNET, PERMANENT** Ⓕ — PM

48 **METER**
INSTRUMENT

Note 48A—The asterisk is not a part of the symbol. Always replace the asterisk by one of the following letter combinations, depending on the function of the meter or instrument, unless some other identification is provided in the circle and explained on the diagram.

* See note 48A

A	Ammeter Ⓕ IEC	OSCG	Oscillograph, string
AH	Ampere-hour	PH	Phasemeter Ⓕ
CMA	Contact-making (or breaking) ammeter	PI	Position indicator
CMC	Contact-making (or breaking) clock	PF	Power Factor
CMV	Contact-making (or breaking) voltmeter	RD	Recording demand meter
CRO	Oscilloscope or cathode-ray oscillograph	REC	Recording
DB	DB (decibel) meter	RF	Reactive factor
DBM	DBM (decibels referred to 1 milliwatt) meter	SY	Synchroscope
DM	Demand meter	TLM	Telemeter
DTR	Demand-totalizing relay	T	Temperature meter
F	Frequency meter Ⓕ	THC	Thermal converter
G	Galvanometer Ⓕ	TT	Total time
GD	Ground detector	V	Voltmeter Ⓕ IEC
I	Indicating	VA	Volt-ammeter
INT	Integrating	VAR	Varmeter Ⓕ
μA or		VARH	Varhour meter
UA	Microammeter	VI	Volume indicator ; Meter, audio level Ⓕ
MA	Milliammeter	VU	Standard volume indicator ; Meter, audio level Ⓕ
NM	Noise meter		
OHM	Ohmmeter Ⓕ	W	Wattmeter Ⓕ IEC
OP	Oil pressure	WH	Watthour meter

49 **RESERVED**

50 **RESERVED**

51 **MICROPHONE** Ⓕ

52 **MODE SUPPRESSION** Ⓕ
Commonly used in coaxial and waveguide transmission.

53 **MODE TRANSDUCER** Ⓕ
Commonly used in coaxial and waveguide diagrams.

53.1 General

53.2 Application : transducer from rectangular to circular waveguide

53.3 Application : transducer from rectangular waveguide to coaxial with mode suppression and direct-current grounds connected

54 MOTION, MECHANICAL			
54.1 Translation, one direction		$\longmapsto$	
54.2 Translation, both directions		$\longleftrightarrow$	
54.3 Rotation, one direction		↻ IEC	
54.4 Rotation, both directions		↻ IEC	
54.5 Rotation designation (applied to a resistor) CW indicates position of adjustable contact at the limit of clockwise travel viewed from knob or actuator end unless otherwise indicated. Note 54.5A—The asterisk is not a part of the symbol. Always add identification within or adjacent to the rectangle.		CW OR CW * * See note 54.5A	
55 NETWORK 55.1. General		NET	
55.2 Network, low-voltage power	⬧		
56 OSCILLATOR GENERALIZED ALTERNATING- CURRENT SOURCE		◯∿	
57 PAD (ATTENUATOR, FIXED ⒡) See also ATTENUATOR (item 5).			
57.1 General	⌇		
57.2 Balanced, general	⌇		⌇
57.3 Unbalanced, general	⌇		⌇
57.4 Unidirectional (Isolator) Power flowing in direction of arrow is not intentionally attenuated.	◯↻		
58 PATH, TRANSMISSION CONDUCTOR CABLE WIRING 58.1 Guided path, general A single line represents the entire group of conductors or the transmission path needed to guide the power or the signal. For coaxial and	waveguide work, the recognition symbol is used at the beginning and end of each kind of transmission path and at intermediate points as needed for clarity. In waveguide work, mode may be indicated.		
	———— IEC		
58.2 Conductive path or conductor; wire	———— IEC		
58.2.1 Two conductors or conductive paths of wires	—//— IEC		IEC ═══
58.2.2 Three conductors or conductive paths of wires	—///— IEC		IEC ≡
58.2.3 "n" conductors or conductive paths of wires	—n/—		"n" conductors
58.3 Air or space path		$\sim\!\!\sim\!\!\sim$	

58.4 Dielectric path other than air Commonly used for coaxial and waveguide transmission.		DIEL	
58.5 Crossing of paths or conductors not connected The crossing is not necessarily at a 90-degree angle.		IEC	
58.6 Junction of paths or conductors 58.6.1 Junction (if desired)		• IEC	
58.6.1.1 Application: junction of paths, conductor, or cable. If desired indicate path type, or size		IEC	
58.6.1.2 Application: splice (if desired) of same size cables. Junction of conductors of same size or different size cables. If desired indicate sizes of conductors		SPLICE IEC	
58.6.2 Junction of connected paths, conductors, or wires		IEC OR IEC OR ONLY IF REQUIRED BY SPACE LIMITATION IEC	
58.7 Associated conductors 58.7.1 Pair (twisted unless otherwise specified)			P OR P
58.7.2 Triple (twisted unless otherwise specified)			T
58.7.3 Quad			Q
58.8 Assembled conductors; cable Commonly used in communication diagrams. 58.8.1 Shielded single conductor			
58.8.2 Coaxial cable, recognition symbol Coaxial transmission path Cable, radio frequency F, (Coaxial) See item 58.1.			
58.8.3 2-conductor cable			
58.8.4 Shielded 2-conductor cable with shield grounded			

58.8.5 5-conductor cable			
58.8.6 Shielded 5-conductor cable			
58.8.6.1 Shielded 5-conductor cable with conductors separated on the diagram for convenience			
58.8.7 Cable underground or in conduit (*long dashes*)		— — — — —	
58.8.8 Grouping of leads Normally, bend of line indicates direction of conductor joining cable.			

58.9 Alternate or conditional wiring
    Not commonly used on power diagrams.
    The arrowheads in this case shall be solid.
    Note 58.9A—A note shall explain the connections.
			
			See note 58.9A

58.9.1 Application: 3 alternate paths			 See note 58.9A
58.10 Associated or future (*short dashes*) 58.10.1 Application: associated or future equipment (amplifier shown)		— — — — —	
58.11 Waveguide 🄵 See item 58.1. If necessary, indicate special characteristics by a note. 58.11.1 Circular, recognition symbol			
58.11.2 Rectangular, recognition symbol			
59 RESERVED			

**60 PHASE SHIFTER
    NETWORK, PHASE CHANGING** 🄵
    For power circuits see MACHINE, ROTATING (items 46.9.17 and 46.9.18).
 	
60.1 General			

60.2 3-wire or 3-phase			
60.2.1 Application: adjustable			
60.3 Differential phase shifter Phase shift φ in direction of arrowhead; magnitudes shall be indicated.			
60.3.1 Application: adjustable			
61 PICKUP HEAD 61.1 ‡ General			
61.2 ‡ Writing; Recording; Head, sound recorder Ⓕ			
61.3 ‡ Reading; Playback; Head, sound reproducer Ⓕ			
61.4 ‡ Erasing; Eraser, magnetic Ⓕ			
61.5 ‡ Application: writing, reading, and erasing			
61.6 ‡ Stereo			
62 PIEZOELECTRIC CRYSTAL UNIT (including CRYSTAL UNIT, QUARTZ Ⓕ)			
63 POLARITY SYMBOL 63.1 Positive		+ IEC	
63.2 Negative		— IEC	
64 RECEIVER, TELEPHONE EARPHONE Ⓕ HEARING AID RECEIVER See also HANDSET (item 40). 64.1 General			
64.2 Headset, double			
64.3 Headset, single			
65 RECTIFIER See ELECTRON TUBE (item 34), SEMICONDUCTOR DIODE (item 73.9.1) and SEMICONDUCTOR DEVICE (item 73).			

‡ *The broken line -—- indicates where line connection to a symbol is made and is not a part of the symbol.*

65.1 General Note 65.1A—Triangle points in direction of forward (easy) current as indicated by a direct current ammeter, unless otherwise noted adjacent to the symbol. Electron flow is in the opposite direction. Note 65.1B — This symbol represents any method of rectification (electron tube, solid state device, electrochemical device, etc.).	⊳⊢ IEC		See note 65.1A and B
65.1.1 Controlled	⊳⊢		See note 65.1A and B
65.2 Semiconductor diode; metallic rectifier; electrolytic rectifier; asymmetrical varistor The triangle in this case shall be filled.		▸⊢ See note 65.1A	
65.2.1 Application: fullwave bridge-type rectifier			+ ◇ −
65.3 On connection or wiring diagrams, rectifier may be shown with terminals and polarity marking. Heavy line may be used to indicate nameplate or positive polarity end.		FOR CONNECTION OR WIRING DIAGRAM	
65.4 Pool-type-cathode power rectifier		⊗ IEC	

66 RELAY ꔐ See also CONTACTOR (item 24). Fundamental symbols for contacts, mechanical connections, coils, etc., are the basis of relay symbols and should be used to represent relays on complete diagrams. The following letter combinations or symbols may be used with any relay symbols. The requisite number of these letters or symbols may be used to show what special features a relay possesses. Terms "slow" and "fast" are relative and the degree is not to be noted by multiplicity of same symbol on a relay. Relays that are DC operated are not marked. ⊡ AC Alternating-current or ringing relay D Differential DB Double biased (biased in both directions) DP Dashpot EP Electrically polarized	⊡ †FO Fast operate ◳ †FR Fast release MG Marginal NB No bias NR Nonreactive ⊞ P Magnetically polarized using biasing spring, or having magnet bias SA Slow operate and slow release ⊠ SO Slow operate ▥ SR Slow release SW Sandwich wound to improve balance to longitudinal currents The proper poling for a polarized relay shall be shown by the use of + and − designations applied to the winding leads. The interpretation of this shall be that current in the direction indicated shall move or tend to move the armature toward the contact shown nearest the coil on the diagram. If the relay is equipped with numbered terminals, the proper terminal numbers shall also be shown. † Used where unusually fast operation or fast releasing is essential to the circuit operation.	
66.1 Basic		ⓡ
66.2 Relay coil See item 16: COIL, OPERATING; COIL, RELAY. **66.3 Application: relay with transfer contacts**	* See note 16A	

66.4 Application: polarized relay with transfer contacts			
66.5 Application: polarized (no bias) marginal relay with transfer contacts			
66.6 Relay protective functions The following symbols may be used to indicate protective functions, or device-function numbers may be placed in the circle or adjacent to the basic symbol (see American Standard C37.2).			
66.6.1 Over, general			
66.6.2 Under, general			
66.6.3 Direction, general; directional over			
66.6.4 Balance, general			
66.6.5 Differential, general			
66.6.6 Pilot wire, general		PW	
66.6.7 Carrier current, general		CC	

66.6.8 Operating quantity

The operating quantity is indicated by the following letters or symbols placed either on or above the center of the relay protective-function symbols shown above.

C	*Current	W	Power
Z	Distance	S	Synchronism
F	Frequency	T	Temperature
GP	Gas pressure	V	Voltage
φ	Phase		

* The use of the letter may be omitted in the case of current and the absence of such letter presupposes that the relay operates on current.

66.6.9 Ground relays

Relays operative on residual current only are so designated by attaching the ground symbol ⊣⊢ to the relay protective-function symbol. Note that the zero phase-sequence designation given below may be used instead when desirable.

66.6.10 Phase sequence quantities

Operation on phase-sequence quantities may be indicated by the use of the conventional subscripts 0, 1, and 2 after the letter indicating the operating quantity.

66.6.11 Applications			
66.6.11.1 Overcurrent			
66.6.11.2 Directional overcurrent			
66.6.11.3 Directional residual overcurrent			
66.6.11.4 Undervoltage			
66.6.11.5 Power directional			
66.6.11.6 Balanced current			
66.6.11.7 Differential current			
66.6.11.8 Distance			
66.6.11.9 Directional distance			

66.6.11.10 Overfrequency			
66.6.11.11 Overtemperature			
66.6.11.12 Phase balance			
66.6.11.13 Phase sequence			
66.6.11.14 Pilot wire, differential current			
66.6.11.15 Pilot wire, directional comparison			
66.6.11.16 Carrier pilot			
66.6.11.17 Positive phase sequence undervoltage			
66.6.11.18 Negative phase sequence overcurrent			
66.6.11.19 Gas-pressure (Bucholz)			
66.6.11.20 Out-of-step			
67 REPEATER (includes REPEATER, TELEPHONE[E]) 67.1 1-way repeater Triangle points in the direction of transmission.			
67.2 2-wire 2-way repeater			
67.2.1 2-wire 2-way repeater with low-frequency by-pass			
67.3 4-wire 2-way repeater			
68 RESISTOR[E] See also TERMINATION (item 82). For resistors with nonlinear characteristics, see BALLAST LAMP (item 44.1), THERMISTOR (item 84). Note 68A—The asterisk is not a part of the symbol. Always add identification within or adjacent to the rectangle. 68.1 General	 * See note 68A		
68.2 Tapped resistor	 * See note 68A		
68.3 Application : with adjustable contact		 * See note 68A	

68.4 Application: adjustable or continuously adjustable (variable) resistor		IEC OR IEC * See note 68A	
68.5 Heating resistor		OR * See note 68A	
68.6 Instrument or relay shunt Connect instrument or relay to terminals in the rectangle.			
68.7 Shunt resistor		OR * See note 68A	
68.8 Nonlinear resistor		OR * See note 68A	
68.8.1 Symmetrical varistor Resistor, voltage sensitive ⨍ (silicon carbide, etc.)		OR OR * See note 68A	
69 RESERVED			
70 RESERVED			
71 RESONATOR **CAVITY, TUNED** ⨍ Excluding piezoelectric and magnetostriction devices. 71.1 General Commonly used for coaxial and waveguide transmission.			
71.2 Applications			
71.2.1 Resonator with mode suppression coupled by an E-plane aperture to a guided transmission path and by a loop to a coaxial path			
71.2.2 Tunable resonator having adjustable Q coupled by a probe to a coaxial system			
71.2.3 Tunable resonator with direct-current ground connected to an electron device and adjustably coupled by an E-plane aperture to a rectangular waveguide			

72 ROTARY JOINT (COUPLER, ROTARY, RADIO FREQUENCY 🄴) **72.1** General: with rectangular waveguide system Note 72.1A—If necessary a transmission path recognition symbol may be added. See item 58. The asterisk is not part of the symbol.		 * See note 72.1A	
72.2 Coaxial type in rectangular waveguide system			
72.3 Circular waveguide type in rectangular waveguide system			

73 SEMICONDUCTOR DEVICE 🄴 TRANSISTOR 🄴
    Note 73A—The equilateral triangle shall be filled and shall touch the semiconductor base region symbol.
    Note 73B—Arrowheads on both the N and P emitter symbols shall be half the length of the arrow away from the semiconductor base region.
		Note 73C—Emitter, collector and transition line symbols shall be drawn at approximately 60° to the semiconductor base region symbol.
		Note 73D—The short lines used in transition symbols shall be appreciably shorter than collector or emitter symbols.	

73.1 Semiconductor region with one ohmic connection As shown, the horizontal line is the semiconductor region and the vertical line is an ohmic connection.			
73.1.1 Semiconductor region with a plurality of ohmic connections (Examples show 2 ohmic connections.)			
73.2 Rectifying junction or junction which influences a depletion layer			
73.2.1 P region on N region			
73.2.2 N region on P region			
73.3 Emitter on region of dissimilar conductivity type As shown, the slant line with arrow represents the emitter. **73.3.1** P emitter on N region			
73.3.1.1 Plurality of P emitters on N region		See note 73B	
73.3.2 N emitter on P region			
73.3.2.1 Plurality of N emitters on P region		See note 73B	
73.4 Collector on region of dissimilar conductivity type As shown, the slant line represents the collector.			
73.4.1 Plurality of collectors on region of dissimilar conductivity type			
73.5 Transition between regions of dissimilar conductivity types either P to N, or N to P The short slant line indicates point of change along the horizontal line from P to N or N to P. No connection shall be made to the short slant line.			

73.6 Intrinsic region between 2 regions The intrinsic region lies *between* the linked slant lines.			
73.6.1 Between regions of dissimilar conductivity type, either PIN or NIP			
73.6.2 Between regions of similar conductivity type, either PIP or NIN			
73.6.3 Between a collector and a region of dissimilar conductivity type, either PIN or NIP The connection to the collector is made to the long slant line.			
73.6.4 Between a collector and a region of similar conductivity type, either PIP or NIN The connection to the collector is made to the long slant line.			

73.7 Special properties Note 73.7A—If necessary, a special function or property, essential for circuit operation may be indicated by a supplementary symbol placed within envelope, or adjacent to the symbol.	**73.7.1** Light dependence	
	73.7.2 t° Temperature dependence	
	73.7.3 —)⊢— Capacitive device	
	73.7.4] Tunneling device	
	73.7.5 J Breakdown device	

73.8 Rules for drawing semiconductor device symbols
Note 73.8A—To draw a device symbol, start at an electrode whose polarity is known (usually an emitter) and proceed along the device, showing all of its regions individually. Finally, indicate ohmic connections where required.

73.8.1 PNP Transistor (example of a 3 element device)

ACTUAL DEVICE

Construction of symbol by successively using items 73.3.1, 73.4, and 73.1.

SYMBOL
(LETTERS AND NUMBERS ARE NOT A PART OF THE SYMBOL)

73.8.2 PNINIP (example of a multi-element device

ACTUAL DEVICE

Construction of symbol by successively using items 73.3.1.1, 73.6.2, 73.6.3, and 73.1.1.

SYMBOL
(LETTERS AND NUMBERS ARE NOT A PART OF THE SYMBOL)

73.9 Typical applications; two terminal devices (See notes in item 73.10.) 73.9.1 Semiconductor diode 　　　Semiconductor rectifier diode			OR OR
73.9.2 Capacitive diode (Varactor)			OR
73.9.3 Breakdown diode, unidirectional (also Back-ward diode)			OR
73.9.4 Breakdown diode, bidirectional			OR
73.9.5 Tunnel diode			OR
73.9.6 Temperature dependent diode			OR
73.9.7 Photodiode			OR
73.9.8 Semiconductor diode, PNPN-type switch			OR

73.10 Typical applications; three or more terminal devices	confusion would arise or if none of the elements is connected to the envelope.		
	73.10C Orientation, including a mirror-image presentation, does not change the meaning of a symbol.		
73.10A In general, the angle at which a lead is brought to a symbol element has no significance.	**73.10D** The elements of the symbol must be drawn in such an order as to show clearly the operating function of the device.		
73.10B The envelope symbol may be omitted if no			

73.10.1 PNP transistor (also PNIP transistor, if omitting the intrinsic region will not result in ambiguity)			
73.10.1.1 Application: PNP transistor with one electrode connected to envelope (in this case the collector electrode) See note 73.10B			
73.10.2 NPN transistor (also NPIN transistor, if omitting the intrinsic region will not result in ambiguity)			
73.10.3 Unijunction transistor with N-type base			
73.10.4 Unijunction transistor with P-type base			
73.10.5 Field-effect transistor with N-type base			OR
73.10.6 Field-effect transistor with P-type base			OR
73.10.7 Semiconductor triode, PNPN-type switch			
73.10.8 Semiconductor triode, NPNP-type switch			
73.10.9 NPN transistor with transverse-biased base			OR

73.10.10 PNIP transistor with ohmic connection to the intrinsic region			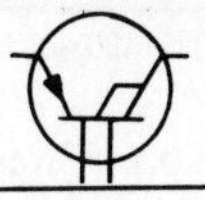
73.10.11 NPIN transistor with ohmic connection to the intrinsic region			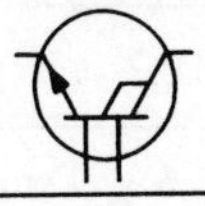
73.10.12 PNIN transistor with ohmic connection to the intrinsic region			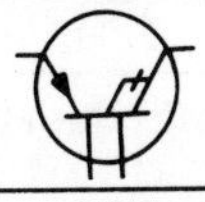
73.10.13 NPIP transistor with ohmic connection to the intrinsic region			
74 SHIELD **SHIELDING** (*short dashes*) Normally used for electric or magnetic shielding. When used for other shielding, a note should so indicate. For typical applications see:	CAPACITOR (item 8.1.2). PATH, TRANSMISSION (items 58.8.1, 58.8.4, and 58.8.6). TRANSFORMER (items 86.2.1 and 86.2.2). — — — — —		
75 SQUIB 75.1 Explosive			
75.2 Igniter		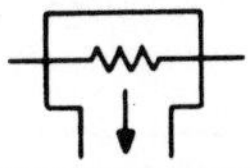	
75.3 Sensing link; Fusible link, ambient temperature operated			
76 SWITCH F See also FUSE (item 36); CONTACT, ELECTRIC (item 23); and DRAFTING PRACTICES (paragraphs 3.7 and 3.9). Fundamental symbols for contacts, mechanical connections, etc., may be used for switch symbols. The standard method of showing switches is in a position with no operating force applied. For	switches that may be in any one of two or more positions with no operating force applied and for switches actuated by some mechanical device (as in air-pressure, liquid-level, rate-of-flow, etc., switches), a clarifying note may be necessary to explain the point at which the switch functions. When the basic switch symbols in items 76.1 through 76.4 are shown on a diagram in the closed position, terminals must be added for clarity.		
76.1 Single throw, general		 IEC	
76.2 Double throw, general		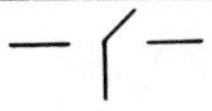	
76.2.1 Application: 2-pole double-throw switch with terminals shown			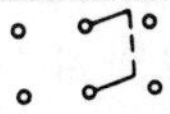
76.3 Knife switch, general		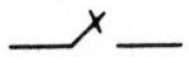	
76.3.1 Application: 3-pole double-throw knife switch with auxiliary contacts and terminals			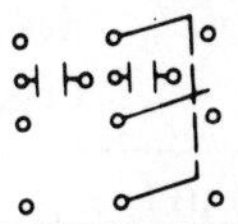
76.3.2 Application: 2-pole field-discharge knife switch with terminals and discharge resistor Note 76.3.2A—The asterisk is not a part of the symbol. Always add identification within or adjacent to the rectangle.			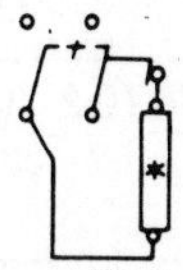 * See note 76.3.2A
76.4 Switch with horn gap		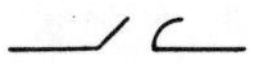	
76.5 Sector switch		 IEC	

76.6 Push button, momentary or spring return 76.6.1 Circuit closing (make)			
76.6.2 Circuit opening (break)			
76.6.3 Two-circuit			
76.7 Push button, maintained or not spring return 76.7.1 Two circuit			
76.8 Switch, nonlocking; momentary or spring return The symbols to the left are commonly used for spring buildups in key switches, relays, and	jacks. The symbols to the right are commonly used for toggle switches.		
76.8.1 Circuit closing (make)		OR	
76.8.2 Circuit opening (break)		OR	
76.8.3 Two-circuit		OR	
76.8.4 Transfer		OR	
76.8.5 Make-before-break		IEC	
76.9 Switch, locking The symbols to the left are commonly used for spring buildups in key switches, relays, and	jacks. The symbols to the right are commonly used for toggle switches.		
76.9.1 Circuit closing (make)		OR IEC	
76.9.2 Circuit opening (break)		OR IEC	
76.9.3 Transfer, 2-position		OR IEC	
76.9.4 Transfer, 3-position		OFF	
76.9.5 Make-before-break			

76.10 Switch, combination locking and nonlocking
   See also item 76.11.
   Commonly used for toggle-switches.			

76.10.1 3-position 1-pole: circuit closing (make), off, momentary circuit closing (make)		OFF	
76.10.2 3-position 2-pole: circuit closing (make), off, momentary circuit closing (make)		OFF	
76.11 Switch, key-type, applications 76.11.1 2-position with locking transfer and break contacts			
76.11.2 3-position with nonlocking transfer and locking break contacts		OR	

76.11.3 3-position, multicontact combination	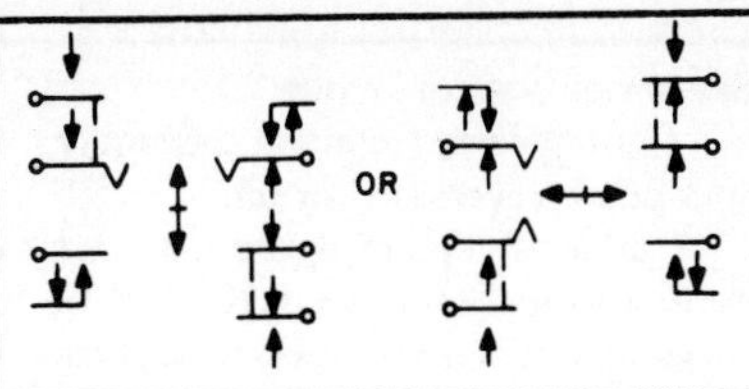
76.11.4 2-position, half of key switch normally operated, multicontact combination	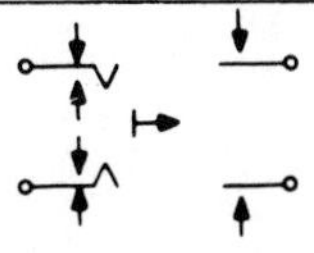
76.12 Selector or multiposition switch The position in which the switch is shown may	be indicated by a note or designation of switch position.
76.12.1 General (for power and control diagrams) Any number of transmission paths may be shown.	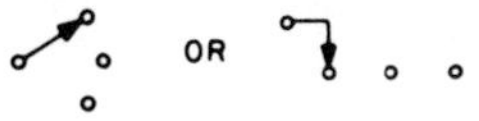
76.12.2 Break-before-make, nonshorting (nonbridging) during contact transfer	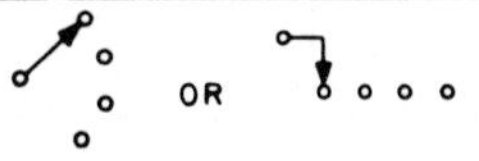
76.12.3 Make-before-break, shorting (bridging) during contact transfer	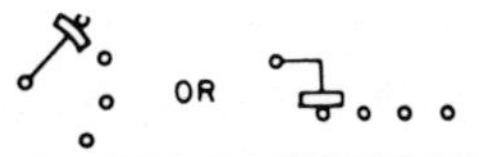
76.12.4 Segmental contact	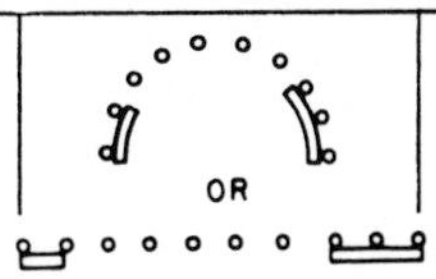
76.12.5 22-point selector switch	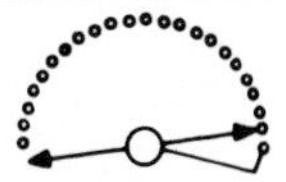
76.12.6 10-point selector switch with fixed segment	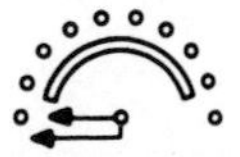

76.12.7 Wafer, 3-pole 3-circuit with 2 nonshorting and 1 shorting moving contacts
    Viewed from end opposite control knob or actuator unless otherwise indicated.
    For more than one section, section No. 1 is nearest control knob.
    When contacts are on both sides, front contacts are nearest control knob.
	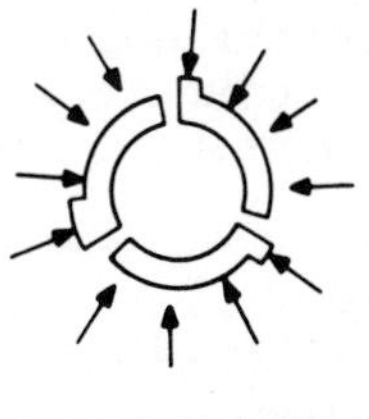

76.12.8 Slide switch, typical ladder-type interlock In the example, one slide is shown operated. Slides are shown in released position unless otherwise noted.	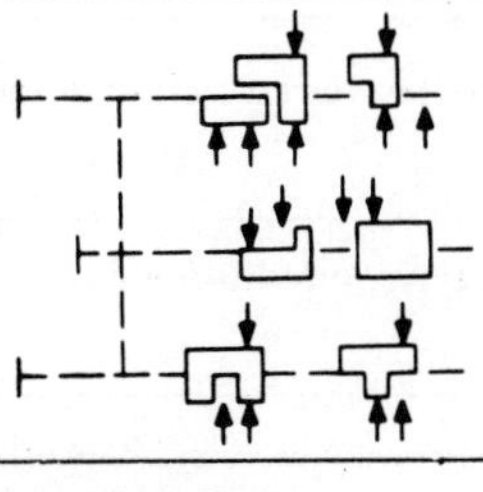
76.12.9 Master or control switch A table of contact operation must be shown on the diagram. A typical table is shown below.	DETACHED CONTACTS SHOWN ELSEWHERE ON DIAGRAM HANDLE END

DETACHED CONTACTS
SHOWN ELSEWHERE
ON DIAGRAM

CONTACT	POSITION		
	A	B	C
1-2			X
3-4	X		
5-6			X
7-8	X		

X INDICATES CONTACT CLOSED

HANDLE END

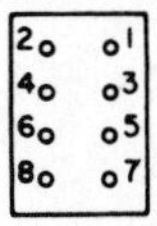

2o o1
4o o3
6o o5
8o o7

FOR CONNECTION
OR WIRING DIAGRAM

			DETACHED CONTACTS SHOWN ELSEWHERE ON DIAGRAM
76.12.10 Master or control switch (Cam-operated contact assembly) 6-circuit 3-point reversing switch. A table of contact operation must be shown on the diagram. A typical table is shown below. Tabulate special features in note.			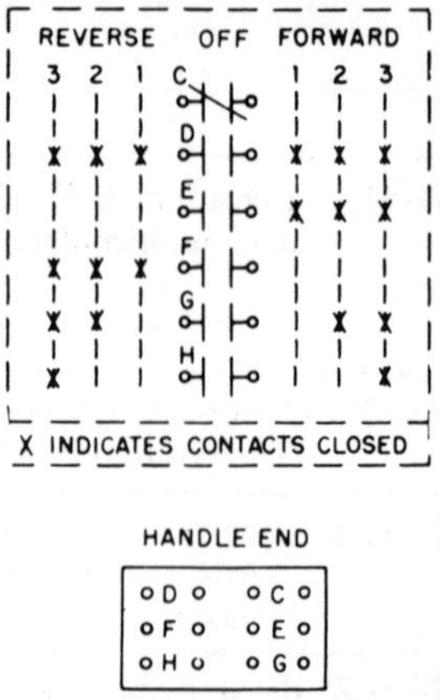 REVERSE OFF FORWARD X INDICATES CONTACTS CLOSED HANDLE END FOR CONNECTION OR WIRING DIAGRAM
76.12.11 Drum switch, sliding-contact type, typical example	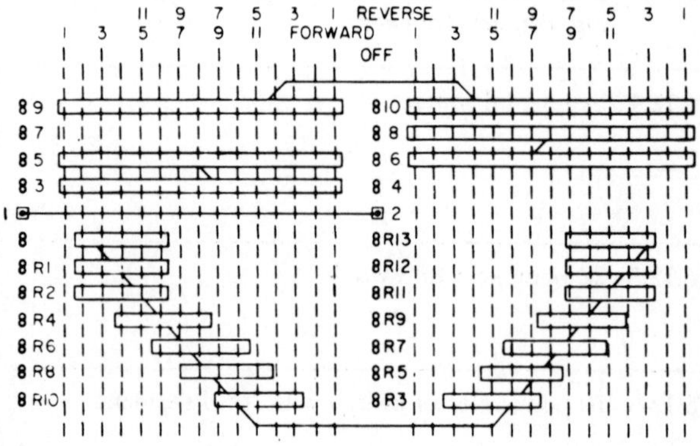		
76.13 Switches with specific features **76.13.1** Key-operated lock switch Use appropriate standard symbol and add key designation or other information in note.			
76.13.2 Limit switch Note 76.13.2A—Identify by LS or other suitable note.			
76.13.2.1 Track-type, circuit-closing contact	See note 76.13.2A		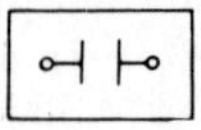
76.13.2.2 Track-type, circuit-opening contact	See note 76.13.2A		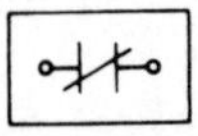
76.13.2.3 Lead-screw type, circuit-opening contacts			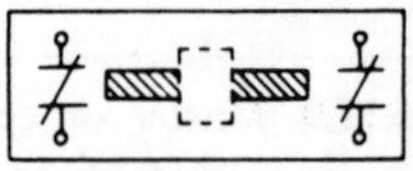 See note 76.13.2A
76.13.2.4 Rotary type			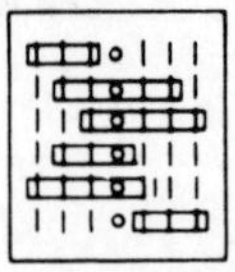 See note 76.13.2A

76.13.3 Mushroom-head safety feature Application to 2-circuit push-button switch.			
76.13.4 Safety interlock 76.13.4.1 General If specific type identification is not re- quired, use applicable standard symbol.			
76.13.4.2 If specific type identification is required; cir- cuit opening			
76.13.4.3 If specific type identification is required; cir- cuit closing			
76.13.5 Switch, hook ⁊			
76.13.6 Telephone dial ⁊, (switch)	DIAL		TYPICAL
76.13.7 Switch in evacuated envelope, 1-pole double- throw		OR	
76.13.8 Switches with time delay feature (see also items 23.4 and 23.5) Note 76.13.8A—The point of the arrow in- dicates the direction of switch operation in which contact action is delayed.			
76.13.8.1 Open switch with time delay closing (TDC) feature		TDC OR	See note 76.13.8A
76.13.8.2 Closed switch with time delay opening (TDO) feature		TDO OR	See note 76.13.8A
76.13.8.3 Open switch with time delay opening (TDO) feature		TDO OR	See note 76.13.8A
76.13.8.4 Closed switch with time delay closing (TDC) feature		TDC OR	See note 76.13.8A
76.13.9 Flow actuated switch 76.13.9.1 Closing on increase in flow			
76.13.9.2 Opening on increase in flow			
76.13.10 Liquid level actuated switch 76.13.10.1 Closing on rising level			
76.13.10.2 Opening on rising level			
76.13.11 Pressure or Vacuum actuated switch 76.13.11.1 Closing on rising pressure			
76.13.11.2 Opening on rising pressure			
76.13.12 Temperature actuated switch 76.13.12.1 Closing on rising temperature		IEC OR	

76.13.12.2 Opening on rising temperature		IEC OR	
76.13.13 Foot operated switch 76.13.13.1 Opened by foot pressure			
76.13.13.2 Closed by foot pressure			
76.13.14 Switch operated by shaft rotation and responsive to speed or direction (see also item 37) 76.13.14.1 Speed			
76.13.14.2 Plugging: to stop drive after it has practically come to rest			
76.13.14.3 Anti-plugging: to prevent plugging of drive			
76.13.15 Limit switch, direct actuated, spring returned 76.13.15.1 Normally open			
76.13.15.2 Normally open-held closed			
76.13.15.3 Normally closed			
76.13.15.4 Normally closed-held open			
77 SWITCHING FUNCTION 77.1 Conducting, closed contact (break)			
77.2 Nonconducting, open contact (make)			
77.3 Application: transfer		OR	
78 SYNCHRO ℱ If identification is required, a letter combination from the following list shall be placed adjacent to the symbol to indicate the type of synchro. CDX Control-differential transmitter CT Control transformer CX Control transmitter TDR Torque-differential receiver TDX Torque-differential transmitter	TR Torque receiver TX Torque transmitter RS Resolver If the outer winding is rotatable in bearings, the suffix B shall be added to the above letter combinations.		
78.1 Synchro, control transformer ℱ Synchro, receiver ℱ Synchro, transmitter ℱ			
78.2 Synchro, differential receiver ℱ Synchro, differential transmitter ℱ			

78.3 Synchro, resolver Ⓕ Type shown, 2 phase rotor and 2 phase stator.			
79 RESERVED			
80 TERMINAL, CIRCUIT Ⓕ See also TUBE TERMINALS (item 81.2).	∘ IEC		
80.1 Terminal board Ⓕ or terminal strip, with 4 terminals shown; group of 4 terminals Number and arrangement as convenient.			
81 TERMINAL AND BASING CONNECTIONS FOR CONNECTION (WIRING) DIAGRAMS Not normally used for schematic diagrams. 81.1 Basing orientation symbols			
81.1.1 For tubes with keyed bases Explanatory word and arrow are not a part of the symbol shown.			
81.1.2 For tubes with bayonets, bosses, and other reference points			
81.2 Tube terminals The usage of the rigid-envelope-terminal symbol of item 81.2.2 includes the indication of any external metallic envelope or conducting coating or casing that has a contact area (as in cathode-ray tubes, metallic "pencil" tubes, etc.). However, where contact to such external me-	tallic elements is made through a base terminal, a dot junction is employed as in item 81.3.1 to indicate that voltage applied to this base terminal may make the envelope alive. Terminal symbols may be added to the composite device symbols where desired without changing the meaning or becoming a part of the symbol.		
81.2.1 Base terminals Explanatory words and arrows are not a part of the symbol.			
81.2.2 Envelope terminals Explanatory words and arrows are not a part of the symbol.			
81.3 Applications 81.3.1 Triode with indirectly heated cathode and envelope connected to base terminal			
81.3.2 Triode-heptode with rigid envelope connection			

81.3.3 Ultra-high-frequency triode (disk-seal-tube type) with internal capacitor			
81.3.4 Rectifier with heater tap and envelope connected to base terminal			
81.3.5 Equipotential-cathode twin triode with tapped heater			

82 TERMINATION

82.1 Cable termination Line on left of symbol shown indicates cable.	IEC		
82.2 Open circuit (open) Not a fault. Commonly used in coaxial and waveguide diagrams.			
82.3 Short circuit (short) Not a fault. Commonly used in coaxial and waveguide diagrams.			
82.3.1 Application: movable short			
82.4 Terminating capacitor Commonly used in coaxial and waveguide diagrams.			
82.4.1 Application: series capacitor and path open			
82.4.2 Application: series capacitor and path shorted			
82.5 Terminating inductor Commonly used in coaxial and waveguide diagrams.			
82.5.1 Application: series inductor and path open			
82.5.2 Application: series inductor and path shorted			
82.6 Terminating resistor Commonly used in coaxial and waveguide diagrams.			
82.6.1 Application: series resistor and path open			
82.6.2 Application: series resistor and path shorted			

83 THERMAL ELEMENT (Thermomechanical transducer)			

83.1 Actuating device
  May be either self or externally heated.
  Note 83.1A—Use appropriate number of single-line diagram symbols.
	OR		See note 83.1A

83.2 Thermal cutout; flasher	OR		See note 83.1A
83.3 Thermal relay		OR ... OR ... OR ... OR ... OR	

83.4 Thermostat
  Ambient-temperature-operated device.
  Operates on rising temperature.
 	
83.4.1 With break contact
  See also item 76.13.12.2
			OR

83.4.2 With make contact See also item 76.13.12.1			OR
83.4.3 With integral heater and transfer contacts		OR	
84 THERMISTOR **RESISTOR, THERMAL** 🄵 "T" indicates that the primary characteristic of the element within the circle is a function of temperature. 84.1 General			T
84.2 With independent integral heater			
85 THERMOCOUPLE 🄵 85.1 Dissimilar-metals device 85.1.1 Temperature-measuring thermocouple			IEC
85.1.2 Current-measuring thermocouple Explanatory words and arrows are not a part of the symbols shown. 85.1.2.1 Thermocouple with integral heater internally connected			HEATER

85.1.2.2 Thermocouple with integral insulated heater			HEATER
85.2 Semiconductor device 85.2.1 Temperature-measuring semiconductor thermo-couple			
85.2.2 Current-measuring semiconductor thermocouple			

86 TRANSFORMER [F]
 	
86.1 General
    Either winding symbol may be used. In the following items, the left symbol is used.
    Additional windings may be shown or indicated by a note.
    For polarity markings on current and potential transformers, see items 86.16.1 and 86.17.1.
    In coaxial and waveguide circuits, this symbol will represent a taper or step transformer without mode change.
		IEC
		
		OR	

86.1.1 Application: transformer with direct-current connections and mode suppression between two rectangular waveguides			
86.2 If it is desired especially to distinguish a magnetic-core transformer			
86.2.1 Application: shielded transformer with magnetic core shown			
86.2.2 Application: transformer with magnetic core shown and with a shield between windings. The shield is shown connected to the frame			
86.3 One winding with adjustable inductance			
86.4 Each winding with separately adjustable inductance			
86.5 Adjustable mutual inductor, constant-current transformer			
86.6 With taps, 1-phase			
86.7 Autotransformer, 1-phase			
86.7.1 Adjustable			

86.8 Step-voltage regulator or load-ratio control auto-transformer			
86.9 Load-ratio control transformer with taps			
86.10 1-phase induction voltage regulator(s) Number of regulators may be written adjacent to the symbol.	OR		OR
86.11 Triplex induction voltage regulator			
86.12 3-phase induction voltage regulator			OR
86.13 1-phase 2-winding transformer	IEC		IEC
86.13.1 3-phase bank of 1-phase 2-winding transformers	IEC		IEC
86.14 Polyphase transformer	OR IEC		IEC
86.15 1-phase 3-winding transformer	OR IEC		OR IEC
86.16 Current transformer(s)	IEC OR IEC₂ OR IEC₃		IEC IEC IEC

86.16.1 Current transformer with polarity marking. Instantaneous direction of current into one polarity mark corresponds to current out of the other polarity mark. Symbol used shall not conflict with item 77 when used on same drawing.			OR
86.16.2 ‡ Bushing-type current transformer			

86.17 Potential transformer(s)			

86.17.1 Potential transformer with polarity mark. Instantaneous direction of current into one polarity mark corresponds to current out of the other polarity mark.	Symbol used shall not conflict with item 77 when used on same drawing.	OR

86.18 Outdoor metering device		SHOW ACTUAL CONNECTION INSIDE BORDER

86.19 Transformer winding connection symbols
For use adjacent to the symbols for the transformer windings.

86.19.1 2-phase 3-wire, ungrounded

86.19.1.1 2-phase 3-wire, grounded

86.19.2 2-phase 4-wire

86.19.2.1 2-phase 5-wire, grounded

86.19.3 3-phase 3-wire, delta or mesh

86.19.3.1 3-phase 3-wire, delta, grounded

86.19.4 3-phase 4-wire, delta, ungrounded

86.19.4.1 3-phase 4-wire, delta, grounded

86.19.5 3-phase, open-delta

86.19.5.1 3-phase, open-delta, grounded at common point

86.19.5.2 3-phase, open-delta, grounded at middle point of one transformer

86.19.6 3-phase, broken-delta

86.19.7 3-phase, wye or star, ungrounded

‡ *The broken line -·—·- indicates where line connection to a symbol is made and is not a part of the symbol.*

86.19.7.1 3-phase, wye, grounded neutral The direction of the stroke representing the neutral can be arbitrarily chosen. $\perp$ IEC **86.19.8** 3-phase 4-wire, ungrounded $\curlywedge$ IEC **86.19.9** 3-phase, zigzag, ungrounded IEC **86.19.9.1** 3-phase, zigzag, grounded IEC **86.19.10** 3-phase, Scott or T $\perp$ IEC	**86.19.11** 6-phase, double-delta ✡ IEC **86.19.12** 6-phase, hexagonal (or chordal) ⬡ IEC **86.19.13** 6-phase, star (or diametrical) ✳ IEC **86.19.13.1** 6-phase, star, with grounded neutral IEC **86.19.14** 6-phase, double zigzag with neutral brought out and grounded IEC		

87 VIBRATOR, INTERRUPTER Ⓕ			
87.1 Typical shunt drive (with terminals shown) Show contacts as required.			
87.2 Typical separate drive (with terminals shown) Show contacts as required.			

88 VISUAL SIGNALING DEVICE			
88.1 Annunciator Ⓕ (general)			OR
88.1.1 Annunciator drop or signal, shutter or grid type			
88.1.2 Annunciator drop or signal, ball type			
88.1.3 Manually restored drop			
88.1.4 Electrically restored drop			
88.2 Communication switchboard-type lamp			
88.3 Indicating, pilot, signaling, or switchboard light Light, indicator Ⓕ Light, signal Ⓕ See also LAMP (item 44). If confusion with other circular symbols may occur, the D-shaped symbol should be used. Note 88.3A—To indicate the following characteristics, the specified letter or letters may be inserted within or placed adjacent to the symbol.	A Amber OP Opalescent B Blue P Purple C Clear R Red G Green W White NE Neon Y Yellow O Orange		

Note 88.3B—The asterisk is not part of the circular symbol. Always add the letter or letters specified in Note 88.3A within or adjacent to the circle. To avoid confusion with meter or basic relay symbols, add suffix L or IL to the above letter or letters; for example, RL or RIL placed within or adjacent to the circle.	See note 88.3A	⊐ OR ⊐⊐ OR (＊)	* See note 88.3B
88.3.1 Application: green signal light		⊏G⊐ OR (GL)	
88.4 Jeweled signal light		⊕ See note 88.3A	

ELECTRICAL WIRING EQUIPMENT SYMBOLS FOR SHIPS' PLANS

1. SCOPE

1.1 Purpose. The purpose of this standard is to establish a uniform system of graphic symbols for use on drawings and plans of shipboard (marine) electrical installations. Standard electrical symbol designations shown in the Standard Electrical Symbol List NAV-SHIPS 250-560-3 provide a means of correlating graphical symbols, when shown on drawings, with parts lists and descriptions of and instructions concerning the wiring.

1.2 Scope. This standard establishes the principles governing the formation and application of symbols for electrical wiring equipment to be used on ships' plans and provides a general list of such symbols. It does not cover electronic equipments aboard ship, which will be found in Standard MIL-STD-15-1, although it does cover wiring appliances used in their power supply systems.

1.3 Abbreviations shall be in accordance with Standard MIL-STD-12. Letter combinations used as parts of the graphical symbols are not abbreviations.

1.4 Items are identified by colloquial names to facilitate identification of parts. For standard item names see Part I of the Federal Item Identification Guides for Supply Cataloguing, H6-1.

1.5 A buildup (composite) symbol can be contrived from basic symbols.

2. REFERENCED DOCUMENTS

2.1 Not applicable.

3. DEFINITIONS

3.1 Not applicable.

4. LIST OF SYMBOLS FOR MARINE EQUIPMENT

4.1 The graphic symbols (items) in this list are arranged by item number indicating a generic class. The item number is not significant other than to distinguish between classes. The initial decimal portion of the complete item number indicates a further breakdown of symbols by type or functional designation, usually in alphabetical sequence. Further decimal subordinations indicate a symbol designed for a specific single function arranged alphabetically in order of the name modifiers. Thus the use of this decimal, item-numbering system for each symbol permits changes and revisions, or insertions, to be made conveniently, and without regard for paragraph and section numbering.

4.2 To locate the symbol for a specific part, find the item number under the colloquial or functional name in the index.

---

1 APPLIANCES; MISCELLANEOUS WIRING (GENERAL)

2 BOXES, GENERAL

2.1 Buildup examples

2.1.1 Branch

2.1.2 Connection

2.1.3 Distribution

2.1.4 Junction

3 BUS TRANSFER EQUIPMENT

3.1 Automatic:

3.1.1 AC without phase failure

3.1.2 AC with phase failure

3.1.3 DC

3.2 Nonautomatic or push button control

3.2.1 AC

3.2.2 DC

4 CASUALTY POWER SUPPLY EQUIPMENT

5 COMMUNICATION EQUIPMENT

5.1 Annunciator for torpedo panel

5.2 Box, plug and receptacle, gyrocompass repeater

5.3 Box, switch, telephone

5.4 Dimmer for torpedo firing panel

5.5 Fire alarm system mercurial thermostat

5.6 Indicators

5.7 Jacks

5.8 Panel, sector control for air defense

5.9 Panel, torpedo firing

5.10 Plugs, telephone

6 CONTROLLER, MOTOR (GENERAL)

6.1 Buildup examples

6.1.1 Controller with low voltage release, recloses upon return of power

6.1.2 Controller with low voltage protection, remains open upon return of power

7 COUNTER, SHAFT REVOLUTION

8 FANS

8.1 Fan, portable bracket

8.2 Fan, overhead

9 HEATERS

9.1 Heater, general

9.2 Heater, portable radiant

10 LIGHTING UNITS

10.1 Bulkhead

10.2 Bulkhead, berth

10.3 Hand lantern

10.4 Navigational

10.5 Night flight

10.6 Overhead

10.7 Overhead, magazine

10.8 Portable

10.9 Special

10.10 Overhead, fluorescent

Arrows show direction of tubes

10.11 Overhead fluorescent with separately controlled red and white sections

10.12 Overhead fluorescent

Short arrow shows direction of maximum intensity when sidewise light distribution is asymmetrical

10.13 Overhead, fluorescent with separately controlled red and white sections

Short arrow shows direction of maximum intensity

11 PLUG

12 RECEPTACLE OR OUTLET

13 SWITCH

13.1 Push button

13.2 On-off

13.3 Selector

13.4 Snap

13.5 Transfer

13.6 Water switch

14 SWITCH AND RECEPTACLE

15 SWITCH (CONTACT MAKER) (GENERAL)

15.1 Buildup examples

15.2 Sensitive switch type

15.3 Motor operated

15.4 Pressure operated

15.5 Temperature operated

16 SOUND MOTION PICTURE EQUIPMENT

16.1 Amplifier, motion picture

16.2 Monitor, loudspeaker

16.3 Panel, control

16.4 Phonograph unit

16.5 Projector

16.6 Rectifier, arc

17 TELEPHONE EQUIPMENT

17.1 Box, jack, with volume control

17.2 Box, telephone ringer

17.3   Hand set, sound powered telephone

18.5   Special indicators

18.5.1   Salinity indicator

17.4   Telephone, wall type

18.5.2   Shaft revolution indicators, frequency-control unit

"A" represents type letter

17.5   Telephone desk type

"A" represents type letter

18   TRANSMITTERS, INDICATORS, RECORDERS

For the following and any other similar applications:
Anemometer
Engine control
Wind direction and intensity
Engine order and revolution telegraph
Steering telegraph and rudder angle indicator
Shaft revolution
Oil burner telegraph
Underwater log system
Shaft torsion

18.1   Indicators

The number of lines used in the symbol signify that the indicator is double, triple, etc.
See items 5.6 and 18.5 for special indicators.

18.2   Transmitter and indicator combination

18.3   Recorders

18.4   Transmitters

18.4.1   Master transmitter

ELECTRICAL WIRING SYMBOLS FOR ARCHITECTURAL AND ELECTRICAL LAYOUT DRAWINGS

1. SCOPE

1.1 This Standard provides a basis of:

(a) Showing the general physical location and arrangement of the sections of the required wiring system.

(b) Identifying the physical requirements for various types of materials needed to provide the electrical installation in buildings.

1.2 In some instances, the symbols may indicate the function or electrical characteristics of the system; however, that is not their primary purpose. Such functions or characteristics are shown by the use of the graphical symbols for electrical diagrams, as specified in Standard MIL-STD-15-1.

1.3 The required installation is shown on the drawing by the use of the various applicable outlet and equipment symbols, together with interconnecting circuit or feeder run lines, supplemented with necessary notations.

1.4 In general, basic symbols have been included in the symbol schedule. In some instances, the use of numbers or letters of the alphabet drawn in, or at the side of, the basic symbol to identify a specific application of the symbol for a particular type or use of outlet may be required. In some instances, the physical or electrical size of the item identified by the symbol will be noted to one side of it.

2. REFERENCED DOCUMENTS

2.1 Not applicable.

3. DEFINITIONS AND GENERAL REQUIREMENTS

3.1 Drafting Practices applicable to graphical electrical wiring symbols.

3.1.1 Electrical layouts shall be drawn to an appropriate scale or figure dimensions noted. They shall be made on drawing sheets separate from the architectural or structural drawings or the drawing sheets for mechanical or other facilities.

3.1.2 Clearness of drawings is often impaired when all different electrical systems to be installed in the same building area are laid out on the same drawing sheet. Clearness is further impaired when an extremely small drawing scale is used. Under these circumstances, each or certain of the different systems will be laid out on separate drawing sheets. For example, it may be better to show signal system outlets and circuits on drawings separate from the lighting and power branch circuit wiring.

3.1.3 Outlet and equipment locations with respect to the building should be shown as accurately as possible on the electrical drawing sheets to reduce reference to architectural drawings. Where extremely accurate final locations of outlets and equipment are required, figure dimensions shall be noted on the drawings. Circuit and feeder run lines should be drawn so as to show their installed location in relation to the building insofar as it is practical to do so. The number and size of conductors in the runs shall be identified by notation when the circuit run symbol does not identify them.

3.1.4 All branch circuits, control circuits, and signal system circuits shall be laid out in complete detail on the electrical drawings, including identification of the number, size, and type of all conductors.

3.1.5 Electrical wiring required in conjunction with such mechanical facilities as heating, ventilating, and air-conditioning equipment, machinery, and processing equipment shall be included in detail in the electrical layout insofar as possible when its installation will be required under the electrical contract. This is desirable to make reference to mechanical drawings unnecessary and to avoid confusion as to responsibility for the installation of the work.

3.1.6 A complete electrical layout shall include at least the following on one or more drawings:

3.1.6.1 Floor plan layout, to scale, of all outlet and equipment locations and wiring runs.

3.1.6.2 A complete schedule of all of the symbols used, with appropriate description of the requirements.

3.1.6.3 Riser diagram showing the physical relationship of the service, feeder and major power runs, unit substations, isolated power transformers, switchboards, panel boards, pull boxes, terminal cabinets, and other systems and equipment.

3.1.6.4 Where necessary for clearness, a single line diagram showing the electrical relationship of the component items and sections of the wiring system.

3.1.6.5 Where necessary to provide adequate information, elevations, sections and details of equipment and special installations, and details of special lighting fixtures and devices.

3.1.6.6 Sections of the building or elevation of the structure showing floor-to-floor, outlet, and equipment heights, relation to the established grade, general type of building construction, etc. Where practicable, suspended ceiling heights indicated either by figure dimensions on the electrical floor plan layout drawings or on the electrical building section or elevation drawings.

3.1.6.7 Where necessary to provide adequate information, plot plan to scale, showing the relation of the building or structure to other buildings or structures, service poles, service manholes, exterior area lighting, exterior wiring runs, etc.

3.1.6.8 In the case of exterior wiring systems for street and highway lighting, area drawings showing the complete system.

3.1.6.9 Any changes to the electrical layout should be clearly indicated on the drawings, when such changes are made after the original drawings have been completed, and should be identified on the drawing by a revision symbol.

3.2 Explanation supplementing the schedule of symbols.

3.2.1 General.

3.2.1.1 *Type of wiring method or material requirements.* When the general wiring method and material requirements for the entire installation are described in the specifications or specification notations on drawings, no special notation need be made in relation to symbols on the drawing layout; e.g., if an entire installation is required by the specifications and general reference on the drawings to be explosion proof, the outlet symbols do not need to have special identification.

3.2.1.2 When certain different wiring methods or special materials will be required in different areas of the building or for certain sections of the wiring system or certain outlets, such requirements should be clearly identified on the drawing layout by special identification of outlet symbols rather than only by reference in the specifications.

3.2.1.3 *Special identification of outlets.* Weatherproof, vaportight, watertight, raintight, dust-tight, explosion-proof, grounded, or recessed outlets or other outlets requiring special identification may be indicated by the use of upper case letter abbreviations at the standard outlet symbol, e.g.:

Weatherproof	WP	Dust-tight	DT
Vaportight	VT	Explosion-proof	EP
Watertight	WT	Grounded	G
Raintight	RT	Recessed	R

3.2.1.4 The grade, rating, and function of wiring devices used at special outlets should be indicated by abbreviated notation at the outlet location.

3.2.1.5 When the standard special purpose outlet symbol is used to denote the location of special equipment or outlets or points of connection for such equipment, the specific usage will be identified by the use of a subscript numeral or letter alongside the symbol. The usage indicated by different subscripts will be noted on the drawing schedule of symbols.

3.2.2 Lighting outlets.

3.2.2.1 *Indication of type of installation.* A major variation in the type of outlet box, outlet supporting means, wiring system arrangement, and outlet connection and need of special items, such as plaster rings or roughing-in cans, often depend upon whether a lighting fixture is to be recessed or surface mounted. A means of readily differentiating between such situations on drawings is deemed necessary. In the case of a recessed fixture installation, the standard adopted consists of a capital letter "R" drawn within the outlet symbol.

3.2.2.2 *Fixture identification.* Lighting fixtures are identified as to type and size by the use of an upper case letter, placed alongside each outlet symbol, together with a notation of the lamp size and number of lamps per fixture unit when two or more lamps per unit are required. A description of the fixture identified by the letter will be given in the drawing schedule of symbols, in the separate fixture schedule on the drawing, or in the electrical specifications. When the use of lamp and fixture identifications causes drawing congestion, a schedule shall be used to clearly identify the lamps and fixtures required for each location.

3.2.2.3 *Switching of outlets.* When different lighting outlets within a given local area are to be controlled by separately located wall switches, the related switching will be indicated by the use of lower case letters at the lighting and switch outlet locations.

3.2.3 Signalling systems.

3.2.3.1 *Basic symbols.* Each different basic category of signalling system shall be represented by a distinguishing basic symbol. Every item of equipment or outlet comprising that category of system shall be identified by that basic symbol.

3.2.3.2 *Identification of individual items.* Different types of individual items of equipment or outlets indicated by a basic symbol shall be further identified by a numeral placed within the open basic symbol. All such individual symbols used on the drawings shall be included on the drawing schedule of symbols.

3.2.3.3 *Use of symbols.* Only the basic signalling system outlet symbols are included in this Standard. The system or schedule of numbers referred to in paragraph 3.2.3.2 above will be developed by the designer.

3.2.3.4 *Residential symbols.* Signalling system symbols for use in identifying certain specific standardized residential type signal system items on residential drawings are included in this Standard. The reason for this specific group of symbols is that a descriptive symbol list such as is necessary for the above group of basic system symbols is often not included on residential drawings.

3.2.4 Power equipment.

3.2.4.1 *Rotating equipment.* At motor and generator locations, note on the drawing adjacent to the symbol the horsepower of each motor or the capacity of each generator. When motors and generators of more than one type or system characteristic (i.e., voltage and phase) are required on a given installation, the specific types and system characteristics should be noted at the outlet symbol.

3.2.4.2 *Switchboards, power control centers, unit substations and transformer vaults.* The exact location of such equipment on the electrical layout floor plan drawing should be shown.

3.2.4.3 A detailed layout including plan, elevation, and sectional views should be shown when needed for clearness in showing the relationship of such equipment to the building structure or other sections of the electrical system.

3.2.4.4 A single line diagram, using standard graphical symbols for electrical diagrams (as specified in Standard MIL-STD-15-1), should be included to show the electrical relationship of the components of the equipment to each other and to the other sections of the electrical system.

3.2.5 Symbols not included in this Standard.

3.2.5.1 Certain electrical symbols which are commonly used in making electrical system layouts on drawings are not included in this Standard because they are included in Standard MIL-STD-15-1, Graphical Symbols for Electrical and Electronic Diagrams.

3.2.5.2 Standardization requires that the same symbol not be included in two or more Standards. This requirement is necessary because if a symbol is revised in one Standard, the same symbol in another Standard might not be so revised, thus leading to confusion concerning the proper symbol to use.

3.2.5.3 Some examples of items for which symbols are not given in this Standard are listed below:

Electric Motor	Circuit Breaker
Electric Generator	Fusible Element
Power Transformer	Single-Throw Knife
Pothead (Cable Termi-	Switch
nation)	Double-Throw Knife
Electric Watthour Meter	Switch
Circuit Element, e.g.,	Ground
Circuit Breaker	Battery

3.2.5.4 Because of the omission of certain symbols in this Standard, as described above, it is incumbent upon the designer to use and refer to both this Standard and Standard MIL-STD-15-1 for a complete listing of applicable symbols.

4. LIST OF ELECTRICAL WIRING SYMBOLS

4.1 The graphic symbols (items) in this list are arranged by item number indicating a generic class. The item number is not significant other than to distinguish between classes. The initial decimal portion of the complete item number indicates a further breakdown of symbols by type or functional designation, usually in alphabetical sequence. Further decimal subordinations indicate a symbol designed for a specific single function arranged alphabetically in order of the special name modifiers. Thus the use of this decimal, item-numbering system for each symbol permits changes and revisions, or insertions, to be made conveniently, and without regard for paragraph and section numbering.

4.2 To locate the symbol for a specific part, find the item number under the colloquial or functional name in the index.

1 LIGHTING OUTLETS

Ceiling   *Wall*

1.1 Surface or Pendant Incandescent Fixture

1.2 Recessed Incandescent Fixture

1.3 Surface or Pendant Individual Fluorescent Fixture

1.4 Recessed Individual Fluorescent Fixture

1.5 .Surface or Pendant Continuous Row Fluorescent Fixture

1.6 * Recessed Continuous Row Fluorescent Fixture

1.7 ** Bare Lamp Fluorescent Strip

1.8 Surface or Pendant Exit Light

1.9 Recessed Exit Light

1.10 Blanked Outlet

1.11 Junction Box

1.12 Outlet Controlled by Low-Voltage Switching When Relay Is Installed in Outlet Box

* In the case of combination continuous-row fluorescent and incandescent spot lights, use combinations of the above standard symbols.

** In the case of a continuous-row bare lamp fluorescent strip with diffusing means, show each fixture run, using the standard symbol; indicate the area and type of the diffusing means by light shading and drawing notation.

2 RECEPTACLE OUTLETS

Where all or a majority of the receptacles in an installation are to be of the grounding type, the upper case letter abbreviated notation may be omitted and the types of receptacles required noted in the drawing list of symbols and in the specifications. When this is done, any nongrounding receptacles may be so identified by notation at the outlet location. Where weatherproof, explosion-proof, or other specific types of devices are to be required, use the type of upper case subscript letters referred to in paragraph 3.2.1.3 of this Standard. For example, weatherproof single or duplex receptacles would have the upper case subscript letters noted alongside the symbol (WP,GWP).

Ungrounded	*Grounding*

2.1 Single Receptacle Outlet

2.2 Duplex Receptacle Outlet

2.3 Triplex Receptacle Outlet

2.4 Quadruplex Receptacle Outlet

2.5 Duplex Receptacle Outlet—Split Wired

2.6 Triplex Receptacle Outlet—Split Wired

2.7 Single Special Purpose Receptacle Outlet
Asterisk is not part of the symbol; see footnote ‡‡.

2.8 Duplex Special Purpose Receptacle Outlet
Asterisk is not part of the symbol; see footnote ‡‡.

2.9 Range Outlet

2.10. Special Purpose Connection or Provision for Connection
Use subscript letters to indicate function (DW —Dishwasher; CD—Clothes Dryer, etc).

Ungrounded	*Grounding*

2.11 Multioutlet Assembly
Extend arrows to limit of installation. Use appropriate symbol to indicate type of outlet. Also indicate spacing of outlets in inches.

2.12 Clock Hanger Receptacle

2.13 Fan Hanger Receptacle

2.14 Floor Single Receptacle Outlet

2.15 Floor Duplex Receptacle Outlet

2.16 Floor Special Purpose Outlet
Asterisk is not part of the symbol; see footnote ‡‡.

2.17 Floor Telephone Outlet—Public

2.18 Floor Telephone Outlet—Private

2.18.1 Application: example of the use of several floor outlet symbols to identify 2, 3 or more ganged floor outlets.

2.19 Underfloor Duct and Junction Box
Triple, Double, or Single Duct System is indicated by the number of parallel lines.

‡‡ *Use numeral or letter as a subscript alongside the symbol keyed to explanation in the drawing list of symbols to indicate type of receptacle or usage.*

2.19.1 Application: example of the use of various symbols to identify location of different types of outlets or connections for underfloor duct or cellular floor systems.

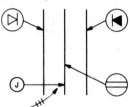

2.20 Cellular Floor Header Duct

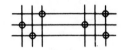

3 SWITCH OUTLETS

3.1 Single Pole Switch

S

3.2 Double Pole Switch

S2

3.3 Three-Way Switch

S3

3.4 Four-Way Switch

S4

3.5 Key-Operated Switch

SK

3.6 Switch and Pilot Lamp

SP

3.7 Switch for Low-Voltage Switching System

SL

3.8 Master Switch for Low-Voltage Switching System

SLM

3.9 Switch and Single Receptacle

—⊖**S**

3.10 Switch and Double Receptacle

=⊖**S**

3.11 Door Switch

SD

3.12 Time Switch

ST

3.13 Circuit Breaker Switch

SCB

3.14 Momentary Contact Switch or Push Button for Other than Signalling System

SMC

3.15 Ceiling Pull Switch

4 SIGNALLING SYSTEM OUTLETS (INSTITUTIONAL COMMERCIAL AND INDUSTRIAL OCCUPANCIES)

4.1 Nurses Call System Devices (any type)

4.1.1 ‡ Nurses' Annunciator
Number may be added after symbol to indicate number of lamps, e.g.:   24.

4.1.2 ‡ Call Station, Single Cord, Pilot Light

4.1.3 ‡ Call Station, Double Cord, Microphone-Speaker

4.1.4 ‡ Corridor Dome Light, 1 lamp

4.1.5 ‡ Transformer

4.1.6 ‡ Any other item on same system (Use numbers as required.)

4.2 Paging System Devices (any type)

4.2.1 ‡ Keyboard

4.2.2 ‡ Flush Annunciator

‡ *Example of Individual Item Identification, not a part of the standard symbol.*

4.2.3 ‡ 2-Face Annunciator

4.2.4 ‡ Any other item on same system (Use numbers as required.)

4.3　Fire Alarm System Devices (any type)
Including smoke and sprinkler alarm devices.

4.3.1 ‡ Control Panel

4.3.2 ‡ Station

4.3.3 ‡ 10-inch Gong

4.3.4 ‡ Pre-signal Chime

4.3.5 ‡ Any other item on same system (Use numbers as required.)

4.4　Staff Register System Devices (any type)

4.4.1 ‡ Phone Operators' Register

4.4.2 ‡ Entrance Register—Flush

4.4.3 ‡ Staff Room Register

4.4.4 ‡ Transformer

4.4.5 ‡ Any other item on same system (Use numbers as required.)

4.5　Electric Clock System Devices (any type)

4.5.1 ‡ Master Clock

4.5.2 ‡ 12-inch Secondary—Flush

4.5.3 ‡ 12-inch Double Dial—Wall Mounted

4.5.4 ‡ 18-inch Skeleton Dial

4.5.5 ‡ Any other item on same system (Use numbers as required.)

4.6　Public Telephone System Devices (any type)

4.6.1 ‡ Switchboard

4.6.2 ‡ Desk Phone

4.6.3 ‡ Any other item on same system (Use numbers as required.)

4.7　Private Telephone System Devices (any type)

4.7.1 ‡ Switchboard

4.7.2 ‡ Wall Phone

4.7.3 ‡ Any other item on same system (Use numbers as required.)

4.8　Watchman System Devices (any type)

4.8.1 ‡ Central Station

4.8.2 ‡ Key Station

‡ *Example of Individual Item Identification, not a part of the standard symbol.*

4.8.3 ‡ Any other item on same system (Use numbers as required.)

4.9 Sound System (any type)

4.9.1 ‡ Amplifier

4.9.2 ‡ Microphone

4.9.3 ‡ Interior Speaker

4.9.4 ‡ Exterior Speaker

4.9.5 ‡ Any other item on same system (Use numbers as required.)

4.10 Other Signal System Devices

4.10.1 ‡ Buzzer

4.10.2 ‡ Bell

4.10.3 ‡ Push Button

4.10.4 ‡ Annunciator

4.10.5 ‡ Any other item on same system (Use numbers as required.)

on residential drawings where a descriptive symbol list is not included on the drawing. When other signal system items are to be identified, use the above basic symbols for such items, together with a descriptive symbol list.

5.1 Push Button

5.2 Buzzer

5.3 Bell

5.4 Combination Bell-Buzzer

5.5 Chime

5.6 Annunciator

5.7 Electric Door Opener

5.8 Maid's Signal Plug

5.9 Interconnection Box

5.10 Bell-Ringing Transformer

5.11 Outside Telephone

5.12 Interconnecting Telephone

5.13 Radio Outlet

5.14 Television Outlet

5 RESIDENTIAL OCCUPANCIES

Signalling system symbols for use in identifying standardized residential type signal system items

‡ *Example of Individual Item Identification, not a part of the standard symbol.*

* *Identify by notation or schedule.*

6 PANELBOARDS, SWITCHBOARDS, AND RELATED EQUIPMENT

6.1 * Flush-Mounted Panel Board and Cabinet

6.2 * Surface-Mounted Panel Board and Cabinet

6.3 * Switchboard, Power Control Center, Unit Sub-stations (should be drawn to scale)

6.4 * Flush-Mounted Terminal Cabinet

6.5 * Surface-Mounted Terminal Cabinet

6.6 Pull Box
Identify in relation to wiring system section and size.

6.7 *Motor or Other Power Controller

6.8 * Externally Operated Disconnection Switch

6.9 * Combination Controller and Disconnection Means

7 BUS-DUCTS AND WIREWAYS

7.1 * Trolley Duct

7.2 * Bus-Ducts (Service, Feeder, or Plug-in)

7.3 * Cable Trough Ladder or Channel

7.4 * Wireway

8 REMOTE CONTROL STATIONS FOR MOTORS OR OTHER EQUIPMENT

8.1 Push Button Stations in General

8.2 Float Switch—Mechanical

8.3 Limit Switch—Mechanical

8.4 Pneumatic Switch—Mechanical

8.5 Electric Eye—Beam Source

8.6 Electric Eye—Relay

8.7 Thermostat

9 CIRCUITING

Wiring method identified by notation on drawing or in Specifications.

9.1 ** Wiring Concealed in Ceiling or Wall

9.2 ** Wiring Concealed in Floor

9.3 ** Branch Circuit Exposed

9.4 Branch Circuit Home Run to Panel Board
Number of arrows indicates number of circuits. (A numeral at each arrow may be used to identify circuit number.)

NOTE: Any circuit without further identification indicates a 2-wire circuit. For a greater number of wires, indicate with cross lines (see Applications).

9.4.1 Applications:

3 wires;

4 wires, etc.

Unless indicated otherwise, the wire size of the circuit is the minimum size required by the specification.

* *Identify by notation or schedule.*

** *Use heavy weight line to identify service and feed runs.*

9.5 Empty Raceway

Indicate size in inches and identify different functions of wiring system, such as signalling, by notation or other means.

$$\underline{\quad\quad\quad\quad\quad\overset{\text{X in.}}{\underset{\text{CO}}{\quad}}\quad\quad\quad\quad\quad}$$

9.6 Wiring Turned Up

9.7 Wiring Turned Down

10 UNDERGROUND ELECTRICAL DISTRIBUTION OR LIGHTING SYSTEMS

10.1 * Manhole

10.2 * Handhole

10.3 * Transformer Manhole or Vault

10.4 * Transformer Pad

10.5 Underground Direct Burial Cable

Indicate type, size, and number of conductors by notation or schedule.

10.6 Underground Duct Line

Indicate type, size, and number of ducts by cross section identification of each run by notation or schedule. Indicate type, size, and number of conductors by notation or schedule.

10.7 * Street Light Standard Fed from Underground Circuit

11 AERIAL ELECTRICAL DISTRIBUTION OR LIGHTING SYSTEMS

11.1 * Pole

11.2 * Pole, with Street Light

11.3 * Pole, with Down Guy and Anchor

11.4 * Transformer

11.5 * Transformer, Constant Current

11.6 * Switch, Manual

11.7 * Circuit Recloser, Automatic

11.8 * Line Sectionalizer, Automatic

11.9 * Circuit, Primary

11.10 * Circuit, Secondary

11.11 * Circuit, Series Street Lighting

* *Identify by notation or schedule.*

NEMA BU-1 BUSWAYS	*Extracted from NEMA BU-1-1955, Busways, with the permission of the National Electrical Manufacturers Association, 155 East 44 Street, New York 17, N.Y.*		
P Plug-in busway section	**F** Feeder busway section	**F** Feeder weatherproof busway section	End flange
End closure	Elbow	Tee	Cross
Center cable tap box	End cable tap box	Single-phase transformer tap **1∅**	Three-phase transformer tap **3∅**
Expansion joint	**Rd.** Reducer	**FSW** Fusible switch adapter cubicle	**C/B** Circuit breaker adapter cubicle
Bus bar extension	Cover-operated switch device	Handle-operated switch device	Circuit breaker device
Potentializer device	Ebony end with bus bar extension	**PBA** Panelboard adapter	Wall flange

Roof flange	End tap switch box	End tap circuit breaker box	Plug-in cable tap box
Fusible plug-in branch run adapter	Plug-in branch run adapter	Capacitor plug	Temperature-indicating plug
Transformer plug	Transposition		

CONSTRUCTION (ELECTRICAL WIRING SYSTEMS)

Extracted from TM5-760; TO 00-105A-10, Electrical Wiring, Department of the Army, Department of the Air Force, with the permission of the Office of the Secretary of Defense, Public Affairs Department, Washington.

① General Outlets

Ceiling   Wall

Ceiling	Wall	
○	─○	Outlet
Ⓑ	─Ⓑ	Blanked outlet
Ⓒ	─Ⓒ	Clock outlet
Ⓓ		Drop cord
Ⓕ	─Ⓕ	Fan outlet
Ⓗ	─Ⓗ	Unit heater or cooler
Ⓙ	─Ⓙ	Junction box
Ⓛ	─Ⓛ	Lamp holder

ⓁPS	─ⓁPS	Lamp holder with pull switch
Ⓢ	─Ⓢ	Pull Switch
	─Ⓣ	Thermostat
▢○	─▢○	Outlet for fluorescent fixture
Ⓧ	─Ⓧ	Exit-light outlet
◍	─◍	Night light
Ⓖ		Generator
Ⓜ		Motor

② Convenience Outlets

R	Range outlet
	20-amp 250-v receptacle and plug, polarized
	30-amp 250-v receptacle and plug, polarized
▲	Special-purpose outlet
◉	Floor outlet

	Duplex convenience outlet
⊖1,3	Convenience outlet other than duplex. 1 single, 3 triplex
⊖WP	Weatherproof convenience outlet
⊖S	Switch and convenience outlet
⊖ R	Radio and convenience outlet

③ Switch Outlets

S	Single-pole switch	S_E	Electrolier switch
S_2	Double-pole switch	S_K	Key-operated switch
S_3	Three-way switch	S_P	Switch and pilot lamp
S_4	Four-way switch	S_MC	Momentary-contact switch
S_D	Automatic door switch	S_RC	Remote-control switch
		S_WP	Weatherproof switch

④ Panels, Circuits, and Miscellaneous

Note: Any circuit without further designation indicates a two-wire circuit. A greater number of wires is indicated as follows: ─╫─ (3 wires) ─╫─╫─ (4 wires)

▬ Lighting panel

▭ Power panel

⊠ Motor controller

⊐ Disconnect switch

▬ Service switch or circuit breaker

──── Branch circuit concealed in ceiling or wall

─ ─ ─ Branch circuit concealed in floor

------ Branch circuit exposed

→ Home run to panel board. Number of arrows indicates number of circuits

── Feeders. Use heavy lines

⊒□ Underfloor duct and junction box, triple system. Single and double systems are indicated by one and two lines, respectively

Heights to center of wall outlets unless otherwise specified or noted:

Bracket light	5'–8''
Bracket light over mirror	6'–3''
Switch	4'–0''
Thermostat	5'–0''
Receptacles	1'–0''

⑤ Auxiliary Systems

● Push button

Buzzer

Bell

F Fire-alarm bell

F Fire-alarm station

FA Fire-alarm central station

FS Automatic fire-alarm device

W Watchman's station

W Watchman's central station

H Horn

R Radio outlet

N Nurses' calling station

T Transformer, signal

◇ Annunciator

◀ Telephone outlet

◁ Intercommunication outlet

◁L Loud-speaker outlet

Telephone or signal cabinet

Ⓝ Single nurses' call dome light

Ⓝ₂ Nurses' call dome light. Number indicates number of lights.

⊖ Single-combination nurses' call station and radio outlet

⊖_D Double-combination nurses' call station and radio outlet

C/P Control-station doctors' paging system

P Doctors' paging station, ceiling

P Doctors' paging station, wall

Ⓒ_M Master clock

Ⓒ Single-face clock, ceiling

Ⓒ Single-face clock, wall

Ⓒ_DF Double-face clock, ceiling

Ⓒ_DF Double-face clock, wall

Heights to center of wall outlets unless otherwise specified or noted:

Radio	1'–0''
Telephone	1'–0''
Nurses' calling station	4'–6''
Combination nurses' call and radio	4'–6''
Watchman's station	4'–6''

⑥ Special Outlets

Any standard symbol as given above with the addition of a lower-case subscript letter may be used to designate some special variation of standard

Ⓞa,b,c

⊖a,b,c

Sa,b,c

▢a,b,c

equipment of particular interest in a specific set of architectural plans. They must be listed in the key of symbols on each drawing and if necessary further described in the specifications

Extracted from AHLMA Standard Wiring Diagram Symbols, for use in Field Service of Home Laundry Equipment, with the permission of the American Home Laundry Manufacturers' Association, 20 North Wacker Drive, Chicago, Ill.

1. Conductor
(wire or other electrical path)

2. Ground

3. Connection

a. Permanent

b. Terminal

4. Crossover
Recommended

Alternate

5. Inductors

a. Coil

b. Solenoid

6. Insulated-core transformer

7. Resistance

8. Heating element
(as in heat source for dryers, etc.)

9. Ballast

10. Lamp

a. Incandescent

b. Germicidal

Recommended

c. Fluorescent 4-terminal

Alternate

Recommended

Alternate

d. Fluorescent 2-terminal

11. Starter
(for fluorescent lamp)

12. Fusible element
Fuse
Fuse link

13. Circuit breaker
(overload device)

14. Capacitor
(or condenser)

15. Switches
a. Single-pole, single-throw

b. Single-pole, double-throw
(2-position)

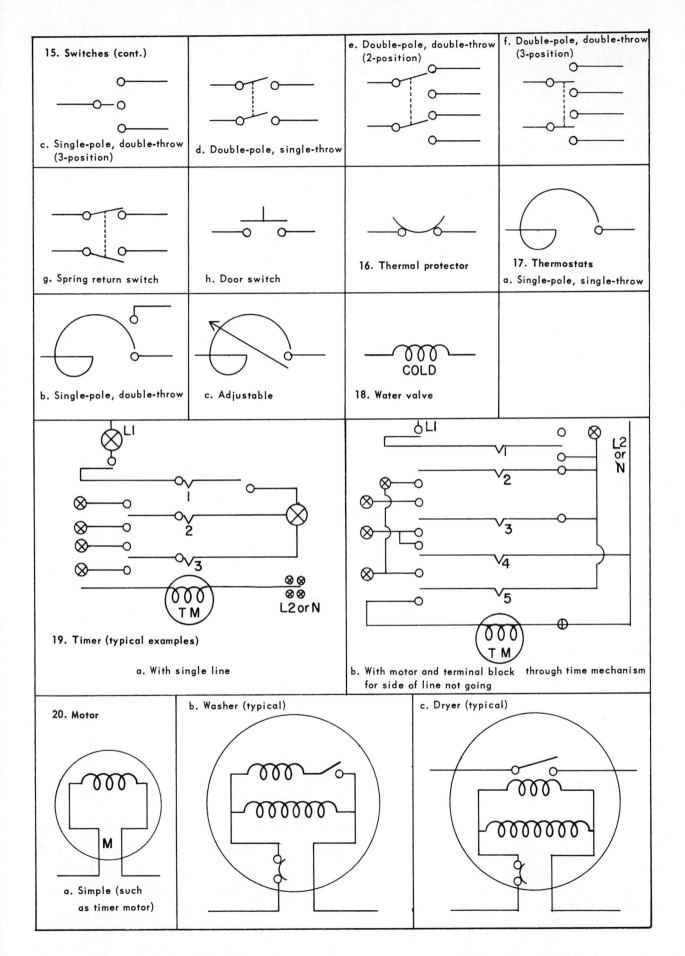

15. Switches (cont.)

c. Single-pole, double-throw (3-position)

d. Double-pole, single-throw

e. Double-pole, double-throw (2-position)

f. Double-pole, double-throw (3-position)

g. Spring return switch

h. Door switch

16. Thermal protector

17. Thermostats
a. Single-pole, single-throw

b. Single-pole, double-throw

c. Adjustable

18. Water valve

COLD

19. Timer (typical examples)

a. With single line

b. With motor and terminal block for side of line not going through time mechanism

20. Motor

a. Simple (such as timer motor)

b. Washer (typical)

c. Dryer (typical)

IC 1-25♦

Extracted from NEMA IC-1-1959, Control, Industrial, Section IC1-25, Controllers, A-C Motor Contactors, with the permission of the National Electrical Manufacturers Association, 155 East 44 Street, New York, N.Y.

Typical Methods of Connecting A-c Windings for Synchronous Motor Starting

Typical methods of starting alternating-current synchronous motors are shown in Fig. 25-1.

Determination of Synchronous Motor Starting Current

The starting current values for the various methods of motor starting as shown in Fig. 25-1 may be determined as follows:

1. With full voltage starting (Sketch A in Fig. 25-1), the starting current is equal to the locked-rotor current at full voltage.

2. With reactor or resistor starting (Sketches B, C and D in Fig. 25-1), the starting current is determined from the sum of the impedances of the starting reactor or resistor and of the motor under locked rotor conditions.

3. With autotransformer reduced voltage starting (Sketches H, I, J, K, L and M in Fig. 25-1) where:

   I = locked rotor amperes at full voltage

   p = transformer tap used (fraction of full voltage)

   I_m = rated full load current of motor

   a. The starting current drawn from line $= I \times p^2 + 0.25 I_m$

   b. The starting current taken by the motor $= I \times p$

   c. The autotransformer neutral current $= I \times p - I \times p^2 + 0.25 I_m$

   NOTE—$0.25 I_m$ is a term introduced to allow for transformer magnetizing current.

4. With part winding starting (Sketch G in Fig. 25-1), the starting current is the locked rotor current of the motor connected for starting.

5. With wye-delta starting (Sketches E and F in Fig. 25-1), the starting current on the wye connection is equal to 0.33 of the locked rotor current on the delta connection.

Horsepower and Current Ratings of Low-voltage Controllers for Synchronous Motors (Nonplugging or Nonjogging Duty)

Size of Controller	Horsepower Ratings				Continuous Current Rating, Amperes
	220 Volts		440-550 Volts		
	Power Factor		Power Factor		
	1.0	0.8	1.0	0.8	
2	20	15	30	25	45
3	40	30	60	50	90
4	60	50	125	100	135
5	125	100	250	200	270
6	250	200	500	400	540
7	350	300	700	600	810
8	500	450	1000	900	1215
9	1000	800	2000	1600	2250

These controllers shall not be used with synchronous motors whose full load currents or horsepower ratings exceed the values given in the above table.

The accelerating contactor of single-step primary-resistor, autotransformer and reactor-type controllers shall have the same rating as the line contactor when the controller has a continuous rating of 135 amperes or less. When a controller has a rating of 270 amperes or more, an accelerating contactor having the next lower rating than the line contactor may be used. The ratings of accelerating contactors of multiple-step starters shall be in accordance with IC 1-11.26.

♦ Part 25 completely revised.

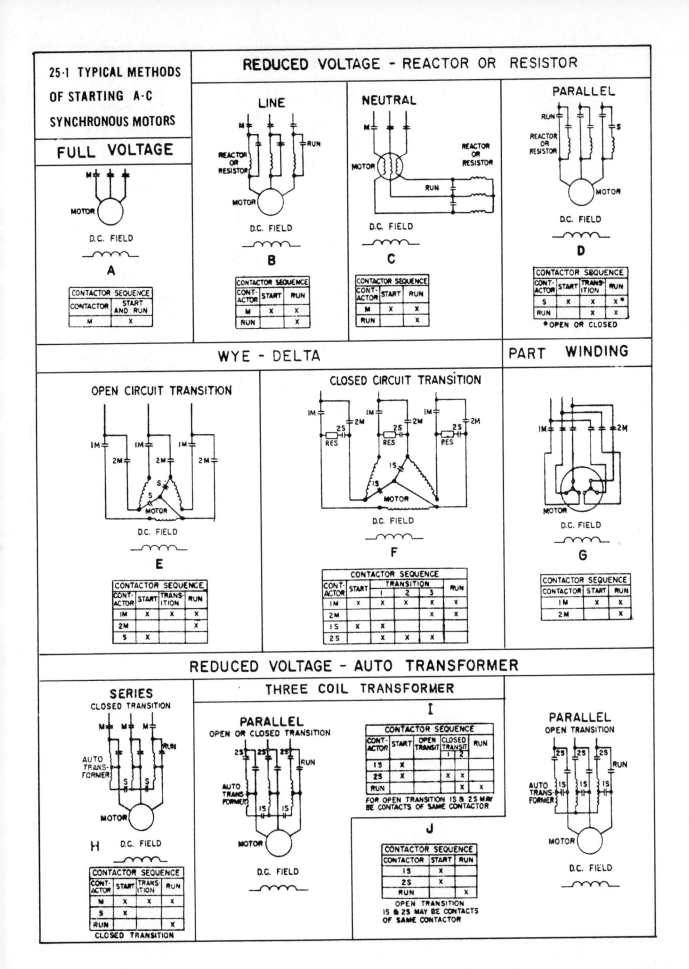

SERIES
CLOSED TRANSITION

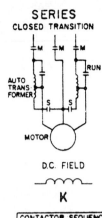

AUTO TRANS- FORMER

M M M

RUN

S S

MOTOR

D.C. FIELD

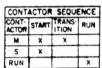

K

CONTACTOR SEQUENCE			
CONT- ACTOR	START	TRANS- ITION	RUN
M	X	X	
S	X		
RUN			X

PARALLEL
OPEN OR CLOSED TRANSITION

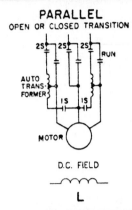

AUTO TRANS- FORMER

2S 2S 2S

RUN

1S 1S

MOTOR

D.C. FIELD

L

CONTACTOR SEQUENCE					
CONT- ACTOR	START	OPEN TRANSIT	CLOSED TRANSIT		RUN
			1	2	
1S	X				
2S	X		X	X	
RUN				X	X

FOR OPEN TRANSITION 1S & 2S MAY BE CONTACTS OF SAME CONTACTOR

PARALLEL
OPEN TRANSITION

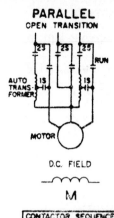

AUTO TRANS- FORMER

2S 2S 2S

RUN

1S 1S

MOTOR

D.C. FIELD

M

CONTACTOR SEQUENCE		
CONTACTOR	START	RUN
1S	X	
2S	X	
RUN		X

OPEN TRANSITION 1S & 2S MAY BE CONTACTS OF SAME CONTACTOR

NEMA MG1-3
ELECTRICAL
(MOTOR MOUNTING)

Extracted from NEMA MG1-1963, Motors and Generators, Section MG1-11.04, Motor Mounting, with the permission of the National Electrical Manufacturers Association, 155 East 44 Street, New York, N.Y.

Assembly symbols for floor-, wall- and
ceiling-mounted motors shall be as follows:

FLOOR MOUNTINGS

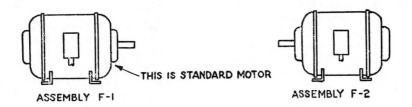

ASSEMBLY F-1   THIS IS STANDARD MOTOR   ASSEMBLY F-2

WALL MOUNTINGS

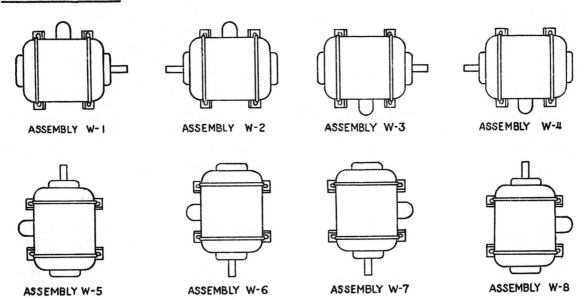

ASSEMBLY W-1   ASSEMBLY W-2   ASSEMBLY W-3   ASSEMBLY W-4

ASSEMBLY W-5   ASSEMBLY W-6   ASSEMBLY W-7   ASSEMBLY W-8

CEILING MOUNTINGS

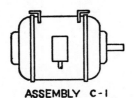 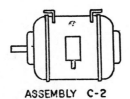

ASSEMBLY C-1   ASSEMBLY C-2

Standard lead location—F-1, W-2, W-3, W-6, W-8, C-2.
Lead location opposite standard—F-2, W-1, W-4, W-5, W-7, C-1.

Extracted from NEMA SG4-1954, Standards for Power Circuit Breakers, with the permission of the National Electrical Manufacturers Association, 155 East 44 Street, New York, N.Y.

Starting Current

The maximum amount of starting current in rms symmetrical amperes that each electrically operated breaker should be required to make at any time during the motor starting cycle should not exceed 30 per cent of the ampere interrupting rating of the breaker at circuit voltage. The breaker should not be required to carry this value of starting current for longer than one minute.

The above percentages should apply to breakers with electrical operation or "quick make and break" manual operating mechanisms but, for breakers with other types of manual operating mechanisms, the percentages should be reduced to $7\frac{1}{2}$ per cent.

The starting current values for the various methods of motor starting as shown in Fig. 9 should be determined as follows:

1. With full voltage starting (Fig. 9.a) the starting current is equal to the locked rotor current at full voltage.

2. With wye-delta starting (Fig. 9.m) the starting current is equal to 0.33 of the locked rotor current on the running (delta) connection.

3. With reactor starting (Fig. 9.b, 9.c and 9.d) the starting current is determined from the sum of the reactances of the starting reactor and of the motor under locked rotor conditions.

4. With part winding starting (Fig. 9.i, 9.j and 9.k) the starting current is determined from the reactance of the motor starting winding under locked rotor conditions.

5. With autotransformer reduced voltage starting (Fig. 9.e, 9.f and 9.g) where:
   I = Locked rotor amperes at full voltage
   p = Transformer tap used (fraction of full voltage)
   Im = Rated full load current of motor
   a. The starting current drawn from the line $= I \times p^2 + 0.25\ Im$.
   b. The starting current taken by the motor $= I \times p$.
   c. The autotransformer neutral current $= I \times p - I \times p^2 + 0.25\ Im$.

6. With power transformer tap starting (Fig. 9.h), the starting current equals $I \times p$ as covered in par. D.5.b for autotransformer reduced voltage starting.

Methods of Alternating-current Motor Starting

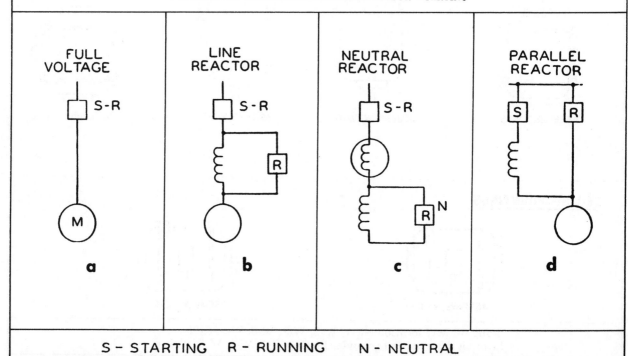

FULL VOLTAGE

LINE REACTOR

NEUTRAL REACTOR

PARALLEL REACTOR

a   b   c   d

S – STARTING   R – RUNNING   N – NEUTRAL

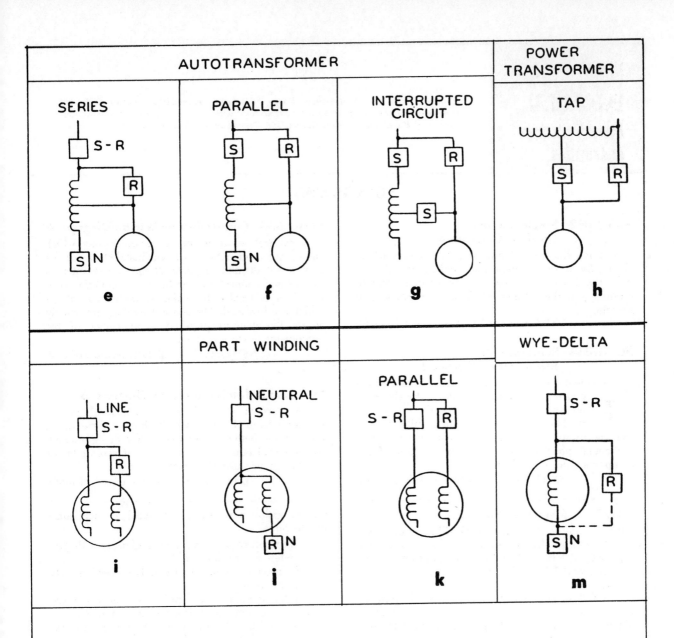

AUTOTRANSFORMER			POWER TRANSFORMER
SERIES	PARALLEL	INTERRUPTED CIRCUIT	TAP
e	f	g	h

	PART WINDING		WYE-DELTA
LINE	NEUTRAL	PARALLEL	
i	j	k	m

S – STARTING
R – RUNNING
N – NEUTRAL

Extracted from NEMA SG5-1959, Power Switchgear Assemblies, Section SG5-1.052, Diagrams for Power Switchgear Assemblies, with the permission of the National Electrical Manufacturers Association, 155 East 44 Street, New York, N.Y.

DIAGRAMS

SG5-1.052 Single-line or One-line Diagram ♦

A single-line or one-line diagram is one which shows, by means of single lines and graphical symbols, the course of an electric circuit or system of circuits and the component devices or parts used therein.

NEMA Standard 3-17-1949, revised 11-9-1961.

SG5-1.053 Schematic or Elementary Diagram ♦

A schematic or elementary diagram is one which shows, by means of graphical symbols, the electrical connections and functions of a specific circuit arrangement. The schematic diagram facilitates tracing the circuit and its functions without regard to the actual physical size, shape or location of the component device or parts.

NEMA Standard 3-17-1949, revised 11-9-1961.

SG5-1.054 Connection or Wiring Diagram ♦

A connection or wiring diagram is one which shows the connections of an installation or its component devices or parts. It may cover internal or external connections, or both, and contains such detail as is needed to make or trace connections which are involved. The connection diagram usually shows the general physical arrangement of the component devices or parts.

NEMA Standard 3-17-1949, revised 11-9-1961.

SG5-1.055 Interconnection Diagram ♦

An interconnection diagram is a form of connection or wiring diagram which shows only external connections between unit assemblies or equipment. The internal connections of the unit assemblies or equipment are usually omitted.

NEMA Standard 3-17-1949, revised 11-9-1961.

SG5-7.03 Metal-clad Switchgear

(Indoor and outdoor types, with oilless or oil power breakers rated 4.16 to 13.8 kilovolts, 600 to 2000 amperes, 25000 to 500000 kva interrupting capacity of the standard NEMA ratings.)

The following specification covers standard metal-clad units and the devices associated with them. When the metal-clad switchgear is intended for outdoor use, each of the following items shall be located within a weatherproof housing, each housing to have:

1. Weatherproof doors, front and rear, with provision for padlocking.
2. Necessary screened protective openings for ventilation.
3. Interior lighting and utility outlets with fuses.
4. Strip heaters with fuses where required.
5. An additional compartment to house the accessories when so specified.

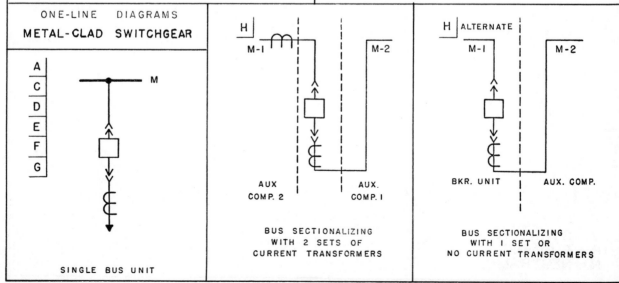

ONE-LINE DIAGRAMS
METAL-CLAD SWITCHGEAR

SINGLE BUS UNIT

BUS SECTIONALIZING
WITH 2 SETS OF
CURRENT TRANSFORMERS

BUS SECTIONALIZING
WITH I SET OR
NO CURRENT TRANSFORMERS

LETTERS IN UPPER LEFT CORNERS REFER TO SECTION NUMBERS IN TEXT OF STANDARD   ♦ Revised.

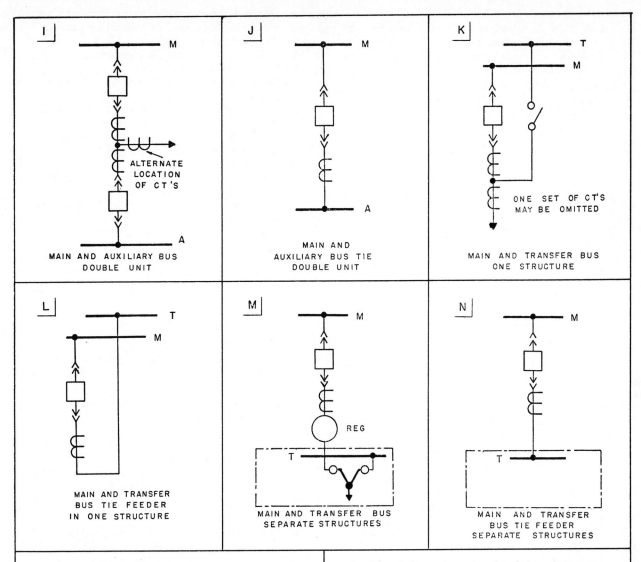

I	J	K
MAIN AND AUXILIARY BUS DOUBLE UNIT (ALTERNATE LOCATION OF CT'S)	**MAIN AND AUXILIARY BUS TIE DOUBLE UNIT**	**MAIN AND TRANSFER BUS ONE STRUCTURE** (ONE SET OF CT'S MAY BE OMITTED)
MAIN AND TRANSFER BUS TIE FEEDER IN ONE STRUCTURE	**MAIN AND TRANSFER BUS SEPARATE STRUCTURES** (REG)	**MAIN AND TRANSFER BUS TIE FEEDER SEPARATE STRUCTURES**

Single-bus Arrangement

A. BASIC BREAKER UNIT

A basic breaker unit shall consist of:

1—Metal-clad unit, complete, including

1—Hinged front panel.

1—Power circuit breaker, three pole, single throw, electrically-operated with closing relays.

1—Circuit breaker position-changing mechanism (for vertical lift units with oil breakers rated 250000-kva, 2000 amperes and all 500000-kva ratings and all vertical lift units with 7200-volt and 13800-volt air breakers, this to include built-in electric position-changing mechanism).

1—Set of primary disconnecting devices.

1—Set of secondary disconnecting contact devices.

1—Control switch with indicating lamps.

1—Control circuit cutout device.

1—Set of three-phase insulated buses rated 1200 amperes minimum. Structures which include 2000-ampere power breakers will have buses rated not less than 2000 amperes throughout.

1—Set of three-phase insulated connections, current-carrying capacity equal to that of power circuit breaker.

1—Set of terminal blocks, small wiring, ground bus and control buses, where required.

1—Set of automatic shutters provided on all units rated 50000 kva and above.

Provision for terminating cables (potheads not included).

B. BASIC LOAD INTERRUPTER SWITCH AND FUSE UNIT

A basic load interrupter switch and fuse unit shall consist of:

1—Metal-clad unit complete, including

1—Hinged front panel.

1—Load interrupter switch, three pole, single throw, with three power fuses.

1—Mechanical interlock between the switch and access door to the fuses.

1—Set of three-phase insulated buses rated 1200 amperes minimum.

1—Set of three-phase insulated connections, current-carrying capacity equal to the fuses but not less than 400 amperes.

1—Set of terminal blocks, small wiring and ground bus, where required.

Provision for terminating cables (potheads not included).

C. Auxiliary Compartments

Auxiliary compartments shall consist of:

1—Metal enclosure of the same height and depth as the metal-clad structure of which it is a part.

1—Hinged front panel.

1—Set of three-phase insulated buses rated 1200 amperes minimum, if required.

NOTE—Auxiliary compartments are provided to supply space for potential transformers, surge protective equipment, control power transformers, extra current transformers, trip batteries and other auxiliary equipment. These compartments are also used to provide for transition of buses or the formation of bus-tie connections.

D. Feeder, Incoming-Line or Transformer Equipment

Feeder, incoming-line or transformer equipment shall consist of:

1—Metal-clad basic unit as covered by par. A.

1—Ammeter and three-phase transfer switch.

3—Single-phase overcurrent relays, direct-current trip, complete with test facilities.

3—Current transformers, single secondary.

NOTE—Differential protection is recommended for transformers rated 1000 kva and above. Equipment shall include:
   3—Single-phase differential relays, direct-current trip, complete with test facilities.
   1—Multicontact lockout tripping relay.
   3—Current transformers (or transformer secondaries) located in the metal-clad structure. (The three current transformers for the other side of the power transformer are not included.)

E. Generator Equipment

Generator equipment shall consist of:

1—Metal-clad basic unit as covered by par. A.

1—Ammeter and three-phase transfer switch.

1—Three-phase indicating wattmeter.

1—Indicating power factor meter or varmeter.

1—Field ammeter with shunt.

3—Relays, time-overcurrent voltage restraint.

1—Three-phase potential switch.

1—Synchronizing switch.

1—Governor motor control switch.

Rheostat operating mechanisms or control switches as required.

1—Low-voltage-power-circuit-breaker-type field switch.

2—Potential transformers with disconnecting features and current-limiting fuses.

3—Current transformers, single secondary. (Space for switchboard-type generator voltage regulator, instrument transformers and regulator accessories is provided.)

1—Auxiliary compartment as covered by par. C.

NOTE—Differential protection is recommended for generators rated:
   2200 to 5000 volts—above 500 kva.
   Above 5000 volts—all ratings.
Equipment shall include:
   3—Single-phase differential relays, direct-current trip, complete with test facilities.
   1—Multicontact lockout tripping relay.
   3—Current transformers or transformer secondaries located within the structure.
   3—Current transformers at machine neutral.
For generators below 500 kva, the field ammeter and the low-voltage-power-circuit-breaker-type field switch shall be omitted.

F. Synchronous Motor Equipment

Synchronous motor equipment for full-voltage starting or the main unit in other starting methods shall consist of:

1—Metal-clad basic unit as covered by par. A.

1—Ammeter, single phase.

1—Indicating wattmeter or varmeter.

1—Field ammeter with shunt.

1—Rheostat operating mechanism or control switch.

1—Field application and field protective equipment in a suitable compartment.

1—Single-phase time-delay undervoltage protective equipment (potential transformer not included).

3—Single-phase overcurrent relays, direct-current trip, complete with test facilities.

Necessary thermal relays as required for overload protection.

3—Current transformers, single secondary.

Damper winding protection as required.

NOTE—Differential protection is recommended for motors rated:
   2200 to 5000 volts—1500 horsepower and above.
   Above 5000 volts—above 500 horsepower.
Equipment shall include:
   3—Single-phase differential relays, direct-current trip, complete with test facilities.
   3—Current transformers or transformer secondaries located within the structure.
   3—Current transformers at machine neutral.

G. Induction Motor Equipment

Induction motor equipment for full-voltage starting or the main unit of other starting methods shall consist of:

1—Metal-clad basic unit as covered by par. A.

1—Ammeter, single phase.

1—Single-phase time-delay undervoltage protective equipment as required (potential transformer not included).

3—Single-phase overcurrent relays, direct-current trip, complete with test facilities.

Necessary thermal relays as required for overload protection.

3—Current transformers, single secondary.

Damper winding protection as required.

NOTE I—Differential protection is recommended for motors rated:
   2200 to 5000 volts—1500 horsepower and above.
   Above 5000 volts—above 500 horsepower.
Equipment shall include:
   3—Single-phase differential relays, direct-current trip, complete with test facilities.
   3—Current transformers or transformer secondaries located within the structure.
   3—Current transformers at machine neutral.
NOTE II—For power auxiliaries, undervoltage protective equipment, thermo relays and surge capacitors are not required.

H. Starting Methods Other Than Full Voltage

For starting methods other than full-voltage starting, the equipment shall consist of:

Neutral or line-reactor starting consisting of:

   1—Motor-control unit as covered by par. F or G.

   1—Auxiliary starting unit as covered by par. A.

   Necessary time-delay or auxiliary relays as determined by the starting method.

   1—Reactor compartment. (Reactor not included.)

Autotransformer starting consisting of:

   1—Motor-control unit as covered by par. F or G.

   2—Starting units as covered by par. A.

   Necessary time-delay or auxiliary relays as determined by the starting method.

1—Autotransformer compartment. (Autotransformer not included.)

NOTE—Other methods of starting may be obtained by a proper selection of a main motor-control unit and the necessary auxiliary starting units.

I. Bus-sectionalizing Unit

A bus-sectionalizing unit shall consist of:

1—Metal-clad basic unit as covered by par. A.

Necessary auxiliary compartments as covered by par. C to provide for bus transition connections and current transformers, when required.

Multiple-bus Arrangements

J. Double-bus Back-to-back Breakers

Double-bus back-to-back breakers (each side) shall consist of:

1—Metal-clad unit as covered by par. D, E, F or G.

1—Metal-clad unit as covered by par. A.

K. Main and Auxiliary Bus Tie Unit

Main and auxiliary bus tie unit shall consist of:

1—Metal-clad unit as covered by par. D.

1—Auxiliary compartment as covered by par. C.

L. Main and Transfer Bus

The main and transfer bus (one structure) shall consist of:

1—Metal-clad unit as covered by par. D, E, F or G.

1—Superstructure with insulated three-phase transfer bus and interconnections, as required.

1—Group-operated three-pole single-throw disconnect switch with interlock.

M. Main and Transfer Bus Tie Feeder

Main and transfer bus tie feeder (one structure) shall consist of:

1—Metal-clad unit as covered by par. D.

1—Superstructure with insulated three-phase transfer bus and interconnections as required.

N. Main and Transfer Bus with Regulator By-pass

Main and transfer bus with regulator by-pass (separate structure) shall consist of:

1—Metal-clad unit as covered by par. D.

1—Auxiliary compartment as covered by par. C.

1—Group-operated three-pole transfer switch with electrical interlock between switch and regulator. (Regulator enclosure not included.)

Provision for terminating cables (potheads not included).

O. Main and Transfer Bus-Tie with Regulator By-pass

Main and transfer bus tie with regulator by-pass (separate structure) shall consist of:

1—Metal-clad unit as covered by par. D.

1—Auxiliary compartment as covered by par. C.

Provision for terminating cables (potheads not included).

P. General Requirements

Accessories such as inspection rack (or cabinet), transfer trucks, maintenance closing lever for electrically-operated circuit breakers, crank for elevating mechanism and control jumpers shall be included as required for each installation.

The equipments listed do not include potential transformers (except for generators). Additional potential transformers and compartments shall be added as required.

The equipments listed in par. A to O are typical factory-built and shipped-assembled units having the standard control, meter and protective equipment integral with the structure units. It may be desired under various conditions to provide additional devices for other functions or to mount and wire the control, meter and protective devices on separate structures or vertical panels.

NOTE I—Operating conditions may require the addition of wattmeter, varmeter, watthour meter, voltmeters or synchronizing equipment, etc.

NOTE II—Other forms of relay protection such as directional-distance-pilot wire and temperature may be provided.

SG5-7.04 Station-type Cubicle Switchgear

(Indoor and outdoor with oilless or oil power circuit breakers rated 14.4 to 34.5 kv, 1200 to 5000 amperes, 1,000,000 to 2,500,000 kva interrupting ratings of standard NEMA ratings.)

The following specifications cover standard station-type cubicle switchgear. When the equipment is intended for outdoor use, each of the following items shall be located within a weatherproof housing, each housing to have:

1. Weatherproofed doors on the front, with provision for locking.

2. Weatherproofed doors on the rear, with provision for locking or bolting.

3. Necessary screened protective openings for ventilation.

4. Interior lighting and utility outlets with fuses.

5. Strip heaters with fuses, where required.

6. An additional compartment to house air compressor equipment for oilless-type power circuit breakers when so specified.

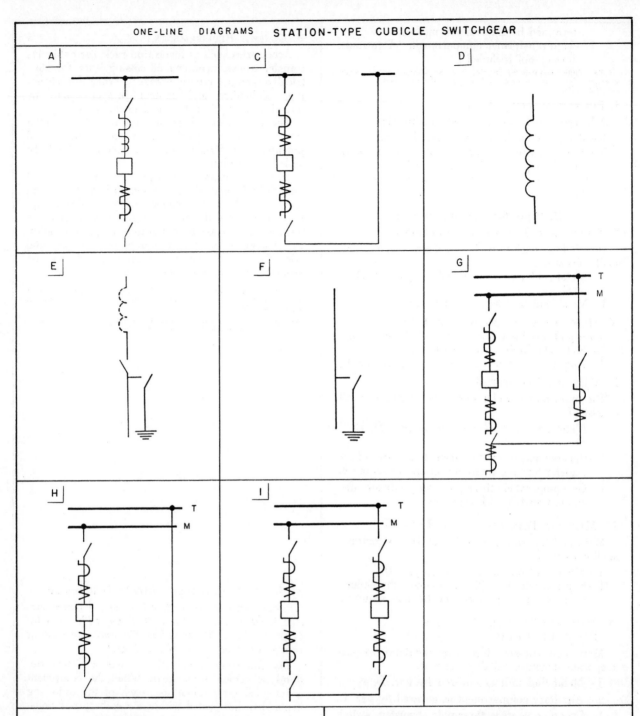

Single-bus Arrangement

A. Basic Unit

A basic unit shall consist of:

1—Metal-enclosed cubicle with hinged front doors giving access to the power circuit breaker and with bolted-on rear cover plates.

1—Power circuit breaker, three pole, single throw, power operated, with closing relay.

1—Control circuit cut-out device.

2—Sets of group-operated disconnecting switches, three pole, single throw.

Interlocks between power circuit breaker, disconnecting switches and front doors giving access to primary compartments.

1—Set of three-phase bare buses rated 2000 amperes minimum. Structures which include 3000-, 4000- and 5000-ampere power circuit breakers will have buses rated throughout not less than the ampere rating of the highest rating of power circuit breaker in the line-up.

1—Set of three-phase bare connections, current-carrying capacity equal to that of power circuit breaker.

1—Set of terminal blocks, small wiring, ground bus and control buses, as required.

6—Bushing-type current transformers.

LETTERS IN UPPER LEFT CORNERS REFER TO SECTION NUMBERS IN TEXT OF STANDARD

B. Auxiliary Compartment

Auxiliary compartments shall consist of:

1—Metal enclosure with bolted-on cover plates. Doors are provided on enclosures for draw-out potential transformers.

1—Set of three-phase bare buses, if required, rated not less than the buses in adjacent cubicles.

NOTE—Auxiliary compartments are provided for potential transformers and fuses, transition of buses, or for the formation of bus tap connections, disconnecting switches and current transformers, where required.

C. Bus-sectionalizing Unit

A bus-sectionalizing unit shall consist of:

1—Basic unit as covered by par. A.

1—Auxiliary compartment as covered by par. B.

1—Underfloor metal-enclosed bus, three phase, current-carrying capacity equal to that of the basic unit for connecting it to the auxiliary compartment.

D. Reactor Unit

A reactor unit shall consist of:

1—Metal enclosure with bolted-on cover plates.

3—Air core reactors, single phase, supported on porcelain insulators and separated by interphase barriers.

1—Metal-enclosed bus, three phase, of proper current-carrying capacity, for connecting the basic unit to the reactor unit.

E. Cable Disconnecting and Grounding Unit

The cable disconnecting and grounding unit for the reactor shall consist of:

1—Metal enclosure with bolted-on front cover plates.

1—Set of group-operated disconnecting switches, three pole with interlock between these switches and the disconnecting switches of the associated basic unit for disconnecting outgoing cable.

3—Grounding switches, single pole, with individual operating mechanisms and with mechanical interlocks to the cable disconnecting switch mechanism.

1—Set of three-phase bare connections, current-carrying capacity equal to that of the cable disconnecting switch.

1—Metal-enclosed bus, three phase, current-carrying capacity equal to that of the cable disconnecting switch for connecting cable disconnecting and grounding unit to reactor unit.

F. Cable Grounding Unit

A cable grounding unit shall consist of:

1—Metal enclosure with bolted-on front cover plates.

3—Grounding switches, single pole with individual operating mechanisms and with interlocks to the disconnecting switch mechanism in the basic unit.

1—Metal-enclosed bus, three phase, current-carrying capacity equal to the associated basic unit for connecting the grounding unit to the basic unit.

Multiple-bus Arrangement

G. Main and Transfer Bus Unit

The main and transfer bus unit shall consist of:

1—Basic unit as covered by par. A.

1—Auxiliary compartment as covered by par. B.

1—Set of group-operated disconnecting switches of the same rating as the basic unit with interlock between these switches and the main bus disconnecting switches or the power circuit breaker.

1—Underfloor metal-enclosed bus, three phase, current-carrying capacity equal to that of the basic unit, with provision for three current transformers in line tap.

H. Bus Tie Unit

The bus tie unit shall consist of:

1—Basic unit as covered by par. A.

1—Auxiliary compartment as covered by par. B.

1—Underfloor metal-enclosed bus, three phase, current-carrying capacity equal to that of the basic unit.

I. Double-bus Double-breaker Equipment

The double-bus double-breaker equipment shall consist of:

2—Basic units, each as covered by par. A.

1—Underfloor metal-enclosed bus, three phase, current-carrying capacity equal to that of the basic unit.

J. General Requirements

Accessories such as tank lifter, manual maintenance device for power circuit breakers, end covers for bus compartments, and disconnecting switch crank handles to be included where necessary for each installation. The equipments listed do not include potential transformers or potential transformer compartments. These must be added as required.

The equipments listed in par. A to I are typical factory-built and shipped-assembled units.

Extracted from NEMA SG6-1960, Power Switching Equipment, Section SG6-1.037, Diagrams and Classification by Construction, Mounting, and Operation, with the permission of the National Electrical Manufacturers Association, 155 East 44 Street, New York, N.Y.

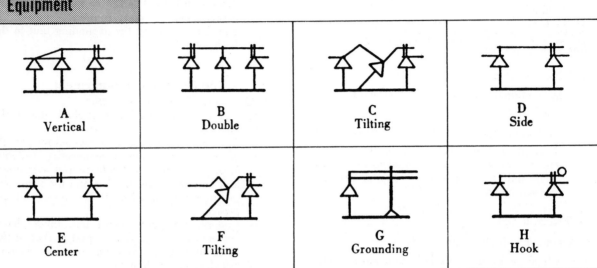

A Vertical	**B** Double	**C** Tilting	**D** Side
E Center	**F** Tilting	**G** Grounding	**H** Hook

CLASSIFICATION BY CONSTRUCTION, MOUNTING AND OPERATION

SG6-1.037 Switch

A switch is a device for making, breaking or changing the connections in an electric circuit.

NEMA Standard 1-15-1925.

SG6-1.038 Air Switch

An air switch is a switch in which air is the insulating medium between contacts in the open position.

NEMA Standard 3-17-1932, revised 10-29-1943.

SG6-1.039 Oil Switch

An oil switch is a switch in which oil is the insulating medium between contacts in the open position.

NEMA Standard 7-21-1954.

SG6-1.040 Single-break Switch

A single-break switch is a switch which breaks the circuit at one point only.

NEMA Standard 3-6-1929.

SG6-1.041 Double-break Switch

A double-break switch is a switch which opens the circuit at two points.

NEMA Standard 3-6-1929, revised 10-29-1943.

SG6-1.042 Single-throw Switch

A single-throw switch is a switch by means of which the circuit can be closed or opened by moving the switch blade into or out of one set of contacts only.

NEMA Standard 3-6-1929.

SG6-1.043 Double-throw Switch

A double-throw switch is a switch by means of which a change in circuit connections can be obtained by closing the switch blade into either of two sets of contacts.

NEMA Standard 3-6-1929, revised 3-13-1933.

SG6-1.044 Rotating-insulator Switch

A rotating-insulator switch is a switch in which the opening and closing travel of the blade is accomplished by the rotation of one or more of the insulators supporting the conducting parts of the switch. NEMA Standard 3-6-1929.

SG6-1.045 Tilting-insulator Switch

A tilting-insulator switch is a switch in which the opening and closing travel of the blade is accomplished by a tilting movement of one or more of the insulators supporting the conducting parts of the switch.

NEMA Standard 3-6-1929.

SG6-1.046 Vertical-break Switch

A vertical-break switch is a switch in which the travel of the blade is in a plane perpendicular to the plane of the base mounting.

NEMA Standard 3-6-1929.

SG6-1.047 Side-break Switch (Horizontal-break Switch)

A side-break switch is a switch in which the travel of the blade is in a plane parallel to the base of the switch. NEMA Standard 10-29-1943.

SG6-1.048 Center-break Switch

A center-break switch is a two-rotating-insulator switch in which both the blade and contact clip are moved to engage at a point substantially midway between the insulators.

NEMA Standard 3-7-1947.

SG6-1.049 Front-connected Switch

A front-connected switch is a switch in which the current-carrying conductors are connected to the fixed terminal pads in front of the mounting base.

NEMA Standard 3-6-1929.

SG6-1.050 Back-connected Switch

A back-connected switch is a switch in which the current-carrying conductors are connected to the studs back of the mounting base.

NEMA Standard 3-6-1929, revised 10-29-1943.

SG6-1.051 Front- and Back-connected Switch

A front- and back-connected switch is a switch in which one or more current-carrying conductors are connected directly to fixed terminal pads located at the front of the mounting base, the remaining conductors being connected to studs back of the mounting base.

NEMA Standard 3-6-1929, revised 10-29-1943.

SG6-1.052 Quick-break Switch

A quick-break switch is a switch which has a high contact opening speed independent of the operator.　NEMA Standard 3-6-1929.

SG6-1.053 Quick-make Switch

A quick-make switch is a switch which has a high contact closing speed independent of the operator.　NEMA Standard 3-6-1929.

SG6-1.054 Horn-gap Switch

A horn-gap switch is an air switch which is provided with arcing horns.

NEMA Standard 3-6-1929, revised 1-11-1932.

SG6-1.055 Disconnecting Switch

A disconnecting switch is an air switch which is used for changing the connections in a circuit or system, or for isolating purposes. It has no interrupting rating and is intended to be operated only after the circuit has been opened by some other means.

NEMA Standard 3-6-1929, revised 1-11-1932; 10-29-1943.

SG6-1.056 Transfer Switch

A transfer switch is an air switch which is arranged so that a conductor connection can be transferred from one circuit to another without interrupting the current.

1. A tandem transfer switch is a switch with two blades, each of which can be moved into or out of only one contact.
2. A double-blade double-throw transfer switch is a switch with two blades, each of which can be moved into or out of either of two contacts.

NEMA Standard 3-6-1929, revised 3-13-1933; 10-29-1943.

SG6-1.057 Selector Switch

A selector switch is an air switch which is arranged so that a conductor may be connected to any one of three or more conductors.

NEMA Standard 3-6-1929, revised 3-13-1933; 10-29-1943.

SG6-1.058 Grounding Switch

A grounding switch is an air switch by means of which a circuit or a piece of apparatus may be connected to ground.

NEMA Standard 3-6-1929, revised 3-13-1933.

SG6-1.059 High-speed Grounding Switch

A high-speed grounding switch is a form of grounding switch incorporating a stored energy mechanism capable of closing the switch automatically within a specified rated closing time at its rated making current. The switch is opened either manually or by a power-operated mechanism.

NEMA Standard 6-9-1947, revised 8-13-1959.

SG6-1.060 Open-type Switch

An open-type switch is a switch in which the current-carrying parts are exposed.

NEMA Standard 3-17-1932.

SG6-1.061 Interrupter Switch

An interrupter switch is a switch which combines the functions of an air disconnecting switch and a circuit interrupter and which has a current interrupting rating at rated voltage and under specified conditions equal to or less than the continuous current rating of the switch.

NEMA Standard 4-22-1943, revised 7-21-1954.

SG6-1.062 Full-load Interrupter Switch

A full-load interrupter switch is an interrupter switch having a current interrupting rating at rated voltage and under specified conditions equal to the continuous current rating of the switch.

NEMA Standard 7-21-1954.

SG6-1.063 Limited-current Interrupter Switch

A limited-current interrupter switch is an interrupter switch having applications limited to certain types or magnitudes of current such as magnetizing currents, capacitor currents and load currents less than the continuous current rating of the switch. A limited-current interrupter switch may be identified by a suitable prefix to the words "interrupter switch" to describe the limitation: for example, magnetizing current interrupter switch.

NEMA Standard 7-21-1954.

SG6-1.064 Clamp and Release Switch

A clamp and release switch is a switch which is provided with means for applying contact pressure after the blade has reached the end of its travel in the closing direction and means for releasing contact pressure before the blade starts its travel in the opening direction.　NEMA Standard 7-22-1943.

SG6-1.065 Automatic Throw-over Switch

An automatic throw-over switch is an air switch and automatic means responsive to changes in circuit conditions to change a conductor connection from one circuit to another. NEMA Standard 3-7-1947.

SG6-1.066 Air Circuit Breaker

An air circuit breaker is a circuit breaker in which the interruption occurs in air.

NEMA Standard 9-17-1926.

SG6-1.067 Mounting Position of an Air Switch

The mounting position of an air switch is determined by and corresponds to the position of the base of the switch and may be designated as:
1. Horizontal upright.
2. Horizontal underhung.
3. Vertical.
4. Angular.

NEMA Standard 3-6-1929, revised 10-29-1943.

SG6-1.068 Operation

Operation of a switch is the act of opening or closing the switch.

NEMA Standard 3-6-1929, revised 1-11-1932; 10-29-1943; 7-21-1954.

SG6-1.110 Bearing Support

A shaft bearing support is a support for the bearing of a shaft.

NEMA Standard 3-6-1929, revised 3-13-1933.

SG6-1.111 Interlock

An interlock is a device actuated or governed by the operation of some other device with which it is directly associated to govern succeeding operations of the same or allied devices.

NEMA Standard 6-13-1925.

SG6-1.112 Switch Hook

A switch hook is a hook provided with an insulating handle for opening and closing hook-operated switches.

NEMA Standard 1-11-1932.

SG6-1.113 Opening Eye

An opening eye of a hook-operated air switch is an eye provided at the contact end of the blade of the switch for receiving a switch hook.

NEMA Standard 1-26-1934.

SG6-1.114 Shunt

A shunt is a flexible electrical conductor comprised of braid, cable or flat laminations designed to conduct current around the mechanical joint between two conductors.

NEMA Standard 8-13-1959.

MISCELLANEOUS

SG6-1.115 Break Distance

The break distance of a switch is the minimum open gap distance between the stationary and movable contacts, or live parts connected thereto, when the blade is in the open position.

NEMA Standard 3-6-1929.

SG6-1.116 Clearance

Clearance is the minimum distance between two conductors, between conductors and supports or other objects, or between conductors and ground.

NEMA Standard 7-22-1938.

SG6-1.117 Minimum Clearance to Ground

The minimum clearance to ground is the shortest distance between any live part and adjacent grounded parts.

NEMA Standard 3-6-1929, revised 1-11-1932.

SG6-1.118 Minimum Clearance between Poles

The minimum clearance between poles is the shortest distance between any live parts of adjacent poles.

NEMA Standard 3-6-1929, revised 1-11-1932.

SG6-1.119 Pole Spacing (Phase Spacing)

The pole spacing of air switches is the distance between centerlines of the current-carrying parts of the adjacent poles of the switch.

NEMA Standard 7-22-1938.

SG6-1.120 Voltage to Ground

The voltage to ground is the voltage between any live conductor of a circuit and earth. Where safety considerations are involved, the voltage to ground for ungrounded circuits shall be taken as the highest voltage between the conductors of the circuit.

NEMA Standard 7-12-1928, revised 10-29-1943.

Extracted from NEMA 1C-1-1959, Control, Industrial, Section 1C1-16, Pushbuttons and Pushbutton Stations Used in the Pilot Control Circuit of Industrial Control Apparatus, with the permission of the National Electrical Manufacturers Association, 155 East 44 Street, New York, N.Y.

Arrangement of Elements in Pushbutton Stations

On all single-row pushbutton stations, the stop button shall be located below or to the right of all other associated buttons, indicating pilot lights and selector switches.

Color Coding of Pushbuttons

The color of those pushbuttons which function to stop a motor shall be red.

Marking of Pushbutton Station Nameplates

Standard-duty Pushbutton Stations

One Button	Two Button	Three Button
Start Stop	Start-Stop Forward-Reverse Open-Close Up-Down Raise-Lower†	Forward-Reverse-Stop Open-Close-Stop Up-Down-Stop Raise-Lower†-Stop Fast-Slow-Stop

Heavy-duty Pushbutton Stations

One Button	Two Button	Three Button
Start Stop Jog Reset Inch*	Start-Stop Run-Stop Forward-Reverse Fast-Slow Open-Close Up-Down Raise-Lower†	Start-Jog-Stop Run-Jog-Stop Forward-Reverse-Stop Open-Close-Stop Fast-Slow-Stop Up-Down-Stop Raise-Lower†-Stop Start-Inch*-Stop Run-Inch*-Stop

*Jog is preferred.
†Up-Down is preferred.

Direction of Rotation of Selector Switches having Levers with Straightline Motion

When a selector switch having a lever with straight-line motion is mounted in a pushbotton station or in the cover of an alternating-current magnetic nonreversing controller, the direction of motion shall be such that the "hand" function is obtained when the lever is moved to the left or moved downward and the "automatic" function is obtained when the lever is moved to the right or moved upward.

Arrangement of Pushbutton Stations for Multispeed Motor Controllers

Pushbutton stations used with multispeed motors shall be arranged as follows:
1. When mounted vertically, the lowest button shall be the stop button. The lowest-speed button shall be above the stop button followed by those for consecutively higher speeds.
2. When mounted horizontally, the right-hand button shall be the stop button. The lowest-speed button shall be to the left of the stop button followed by those for consecutively higher speeds.

Direction of Operation of Rotary Selector Switches

When a rotary selector switch is mounted in a pushbutton station or in the cover of an alternating-current magnetic nonreversing controller, the direction of rotation shall be such that the "hand" function is obtained in the counterclockwise direction of motion and the "automatic" function is obtained in the clockwise direction of motion.

EXAMPLES:

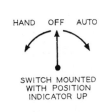

SWITCH MOUNTED WITH POSITION INDICATOR UP

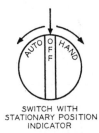

SWITCH WITH STATIONARY POSITION INDICATOR

EXAMPLES:

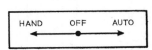

Extracted from NEMA SG-6-1960, Power Switching Equipment, Pictorial Classification of Indoor Disconnecting Switch Forms, with the permission of the National Electrical Manufacturers Association, 155 East 44 Street, New York, N.Y.

	FRONT CONNECTED	CENTER UNIT BACK CONNECTED	TWO OUTSIDE UNITS BACK CONNECTED	ALL BACK CONNECTED
SINGLE-THROW HOOK **S**	S-A	X X	S-C	X X
SINGLE-THROW GROUP **S-G**	SG-A	X X	SG-C	X X
DOUBLE-THROW HOOK **D**	D-A	D-B	D-C	D-D
DOUBLE-THROW GROUP **DG**	DG-A	DG-B	DG-C	DG-D
90-DEGREE TANDEM TRANSFER HOOK **TT**	TT-A	TT-B	TT-C	TT-D
180-DEGREE DOUBLE-BLADE TRANSFER HOOK **TF** (FULL CAPACITY) **TH** (HALF CAPACITY)	TF-A / TH-A	TF-B / TH-B	TF-C / TH-C	TF-D / TH-D

	ONE UPPER UNIT BACK CONNECTED	TWO UPPER UNITS BACK CONNECTED	TWO LOWER UNITS BACK CONNECTED	ONE LOWER UNIT BACK CONNECTED
SINGLE-THROW HOOK S	S-E	✕ ✕	✕ ✕	S-H
SINGLE-THROW GROUP S-G	SG-E	✕ ✕	✕ ✕	SG-H
DOUBLE-THROW HOOK D	D-E	D-F	D-G	D-H
DOUBLE-THROW GROUP DG	DG-E	DG-F	DG-G	DG-H
90-DEGREE TANDEM TRANSFER HOOK TT	TT-E	TT-F	TT-G	TT-H
180-DEGREE DOUBLE-BLADE TRANSFER HOOK TF (FULL CAPACITY) TH (HALF CAPACITY)	TF-E TH-E	TD-F TH-F	TF-G TH-G	TF-H TH-H

MAGNETICS

Reproduced through the courtesy of the Ferroxcube Corporation of America, Saugerties, N.Y., Publication EB-135.

DEFINITION	MAGNETIZATION	SYMBOL
1. AXIAL	N [ ] S	[ ]
1a. 4-POLE AXIAL	N S N S [ ] S N S N	[ ]
2. LATERAL	N S [ ]	[ ]
2a. 2-POLE BI-LATERAL	N S [ ] N S	[ ]
3. AXIAL	N [ ] S	[ ]
4. DIAMETRICAL	N ( ) S	( )
5. 4-POLE LATERAL	N S / S N	( )

DEFINITION	MAGNETIZATION	SYMBOL
6. CONCENTRIC-LATERAL		
6a. 3-POLE CONCENTRIC-LATERAL		
7. 6-POLE LATERO—RADIAL		
8. RADIAL		
8a. 4-POLE RADIAL		
9. 8-POLE LATERAL		
10. DIAMETRICAL		
10a. 2-POLE MEDIO-RADIAL		

DEFINITION	MAGNETIZATION	SYMBOL
11. 8-POLE LATERO-RADIAL		
12. 8-POLE MEDIO-RADIAL		
13. 2-POLE PARTIAL– LATERO-RADIAL		

N.A.R.M.

RELAYS COILS[1]

These relay symbols are taken from "Definitions of Relay Terms," as published by the National Association of Relay Manufacturers. They are the same, except for those cases in which there is direct disagreement with long-established independent telephone practice, or where omissions existed. (Quoted from "Definitions of Relay Terms," published by Automatic Electric Sales Company, Division of General Telephone.)

A Make SPSTNO	B Break SPSTNC	C Break, make (transfer) SPDT	D Make, break (continuity transfer)
E Break, make, break	F Make, make	G Break, break	H Break, break, make
I Make, break, make	J Make, make, break	K Single pole, double throw, center off. SPDTNO	L Break, make, make
U Double make, contact on arm	V Double break, contact on arm	W Double make, double break, contact on arm	X Double make SPSTNODB
Y Double break SPSTNCDB	Z Double make, double break SPDTDB	**COILS** Quick-Acting / Slow-Acting	
Slow-Operating	Slow-Releasing	Multi-Wound Coils / [1] Automatic Electric Company	

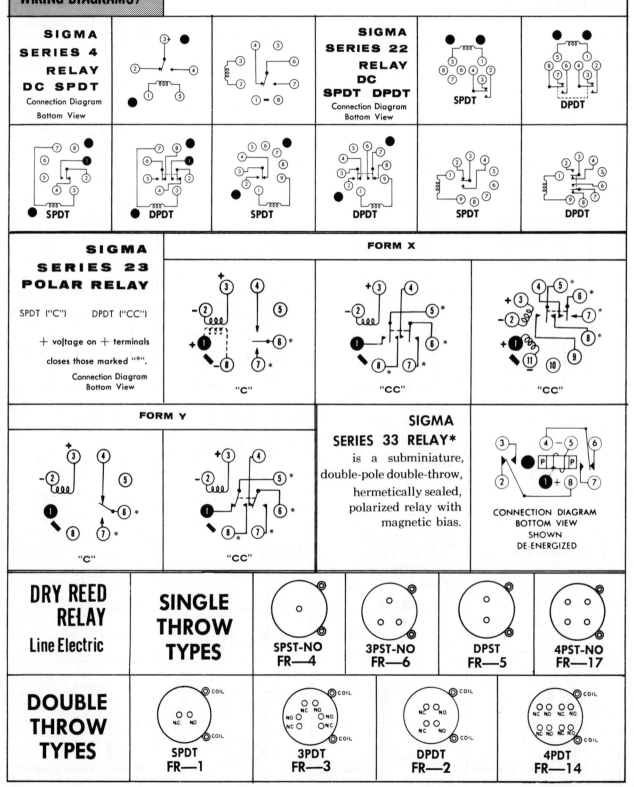

SIGMA - LINE
RELAY (SEALED)
(TYPICAL BASE WIRING DIAGRAMS)

Reproduced through the courtesy of Sigma Instruments, Inc., from their master catalog to present representative sealed relay basing diagrams. Dry reed relay diagrams reproduced through the courtesy of Line Electric Company, Orange, N.J.

(Note: On sigma diagrams, black dots indicate mounting screws.)

SIGMA SERIES 4 RELAY DC SPDT
Connection Diagram
Bottom View

SIGMA SERIES 22 RELAY DC SPDT DPDT
Connection Diagram
Bottom View

SPDT

DPDT

SPDT

DPDT

SPDT

DPDT

SPDT

DPDT

SIGMA SERIES 23 POLAR RELAY

SPDT ("C")   DPDT ("CC")

+ voltage on + terminals closes those marked "*".

Connection Diagram
Bottom View

FORM X

"C"

"CC"

"CC"

FORM Y

"C"

"CC"

SIGMA SERIES 33 RELAY*
is a subminiature, double-pole double-throw, hermetically sealed, polarized relay with magnetic bias.

CONNECTION DIAGRAM
BOTTOM VIEW
SHOWN
DE-ENERGIZED

DRY REED RELAY
Line Electric

SINGLE THROW TYPES

SPST-NO
FR—4

3PST-NO
FR—6

DPST
FR—5

4PST-NO
FR—17

DOUBLE THROW TYPES

SPDT
FR—1

3PDT
FR—3

DPDT
FR—2

4PDT
FR—14

MIL-STD 221A

RESISTORS
(COLOR CODE)

Extracted from MIL-STD-221A, Resistors, with the permission of the Office of the Secretary of Defense, Public Affairs Department, Washington.

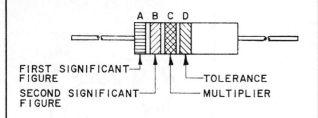

FIRST SIGNIFICANT FIGURE

SECOND SIGNIFICANT FIGURE

TOLERANCE

MULTIPLIER

Color-code marking for composition-type resistors.

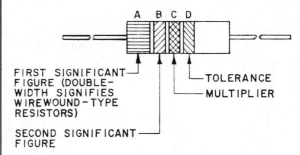

FIRST SIGNIFICANT FIGURE (DOUBLE-WIDTH SIGNIFIES WIREWOUND-TYPE RESISTORS)

SECOND SIGNIFICANT FIGURE

TOLERANCE

MULTIPLIER

Color-code marking for wirewound-type resistors.

Band A

The first significant figure of the resistance value. (For composition-type resistors, all bands shall be of equal width. For wirewound-type resistors, band A shall be double width.)

Band B

The second significant figure of the resistance value.

Band C

The multiplier. (The multiplier is the factor by which the two significant figures are multiplied to yield the nominal resistance value.)

Band D

The resistance tolerance.

Color code for composition-type and wirewound-type resistors.

Band A		Band B		Band C		Band D	
Color	First significant figure	Color	Second significant figure	Color	Multiplier	Color	Resistance tolerance (percent)
Black	0	Black	0	Black	1		
Brown	1	Brown	1	Brown	10		
Red	2	Red	2	Red	100		
Orange	3	Orange	3	Orange ...	1,000		
Yellow	4	Yellow	4	Yellow	10,000	Silver	±10
Green	5	Green	5	Green	100,000	Gold	±5
Blue	6	Blue	6	Blue	1,000,000		
Purple (violet)	7	Purple (violet) ..	7	...	...		
Gray	8	Gray	8	Silver	0.01		
White	9	White	9	Gold	0.1		

Examples of color coding

3,900 ohms ±10 percent — Band A, orange; band B, white; band C, red; band D, silver.

43,000 ohms ±5 percent — Band A, yellow; band B, orange; band C, orange; band D, gold.

Reproduced through the courtesy of the Heathkit Company and the Resistor Manufacturers Association.

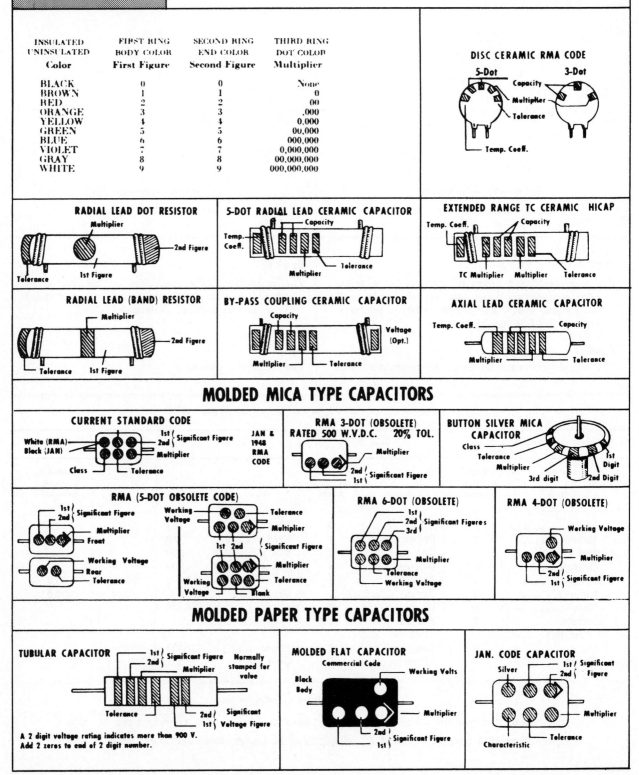

Extracted from 57 IRE (IEEE) 21.S3, Standards on Graphical Symbols for Semiconductor Devices, with the permission of the IRE (now Institute of Electrical and Electronic Engineers).

Semiconductor region with one ohmic connection. (In the illustration, the horizontal line indicates the base region and the vertical line indicates the ohmic connection.)	
Semiconductor region with a plurality of ohmic connections. (In the illustrations, the horizontal lines indicate base regions and the vertical lines indicate ohmic connections.)	
Transition between P and N regions (either P to N or N to P). (Slant lines indicating transitions shall be appreciably shorter than collector and emitter lines. Note that the transition is along the horizontal line and that no ohmic connection is made to the slant line.	SEE PNPN without base as example
Intrinsic (I) region between regions of dissimilar conductivity type. (Slant lines indicating transitions shall be appreciably shorter than collector and emitter lines. Note that the transition is along the horizontal line and that no ohmic connection is made to the slant line.	SEE PNIP Ohmic NPIN Ohmic as examples
Intrinsic (I) region between regions of similar conductivity type. (Slant lines indicating transitions shall be appreciably shorter than collector and emitter lines. Note that the transition is along the horizontal line and that no ohmic connection is made to the slant line.	See PNIN, NPIP as example
P region on N region (rectifying junction).	or (a) (b)
P emitter on N region. (The slant line with arrowhead represents the emitter and the horizontal line represents the N region.)	
Plurality of P emitters on N region. (When possible, the electrodes on the symbol drawing should have the same relative order as the electrodes on the device.)	

N region on P region (rectifying junction).	(a) or (b)
N emitter on P region. (The slant line with arrowhead represents the emitter and the horizontal line represents the P region.)	
Plurality of N emitters on P region. (When possible, the electrodes on the symbol drawing should have the same relative order as the electrodes on the device.)	
Collector on semiconductor region of dissimilar-conductivity type. (The slant line represents the collector, and the horizontal line does *not* undergo a transition at the point where the slant line meets it.)	
Plurality of collectors on semiconductor region. (When possible, the electrodes on the symbol drawing should have the same relative order as the electrodes on the device.)	
Collector separated from a region of opposite-conductivity type by an intrinsic region. The intrinsic region is the region between the slant lines, and the collector connection is made to the long solid slant line.	
Collector separated from a region of the same conductivity type by an intrinsic region. The intrinsic region is the region between the slant lines.	

The line enclosing the device symbol is for recognition purposes and its use is recommended.

Arrowheads on both N- and P-emitter symbols shall be of 45° included angle. They shall be filled and approximately half their length away from the semiconductor-region symbol. The emitter and collector symbols as well as the transition lines shall be drawn at approximately 60° to the semiconductor-region symbol.

The following device properties may be indicated with the aid of identifying letters placed within the enclosure or adjacent to the symbol.

B = breakdown device
τ = storage device
T = thermally actuated device
λ = light-actuated device.

It is recognized that all semiconductor devices are light and temperature sensitive and exhibit breakdown and storage characteristics. The letters listed are to be used only if these properties are essential to the operation of the circuit.

GLOSSARY OF DEVICE SYMBOLS

In this section, a listing is made of some semiconductor devices, together with their graphical symbols. It is recognized that in many cases it is possible to develop other device symbols using the standard symbol elements. In general, the angle at which a connecting lead is brought to a graphical symbol has no particular significance. Orientation, including a mirror-image presentation, does not change the meaning of a symbol.

P-N-P transistor (also *P-N-I-P* transistor, if omitting the intrinsic region will not result in ambiguity).	
N-P-N transistor (also *N-P-I-N* transistor, if omitting the intrinsic region will not result in ambiguity).	
P-type unijunction transistor (sometimes called double-base diode or filamentary transistor).	
N-type unijunction transistor (sometimes called double-base diode or filamentary transistor).	
P-type field-effects transistor.	
N-type field-effects transistor.	
P-N-P-N transistor (hook or conjugate- emitter connection).	

N-P-N-P transistor (hook or conjugate- emitter connection).	
P-N-P-N transistor (remote base connection).	
N-P-N-P transistor (remote base connection).	
P-N-P-N transistor without base connection.	
P-N-P tetrode.	or
N-P-N tetrode.	M or
P-N-I-P transistor with ohmic connection to the intrinsic region.	
N-P-I-N transistor with ohmic connection to the intrinsic region.	
P-N-I-N transistor with ohmic connection to the intrinsic region.	

N-P-I-P transistor with ohmic connection to the intrinsic region.	
P-N diode. (The arrowhead shall be of 60° included angle; the point of the arrowhead shall touch the adjacent element symbol.)	
Breakdown P-N diode. (The arrowhead shall be of 60° included angle; the point of the arrowhead shall touch the adjacent element symbol.)	
Bipolar voltage limiter. (The arrowhead shall be of 60° included angle; the point of the arrowhead shall touch the adjacent element symbol.)	
P-I-N triode.[1]	
P-I-N diode.[1]	
[1] It will be noted that these symbols do not exactly conform to the rules They are, in effect, the transition between the diode and the multielement-device symbols. Arrowheads shall be of 60° included angle; the point of the arrowhead shall touch the adjacent element symbol.	

SWITCHES
(Snap-Acting, Limit, Level, Pressure, etc.)

Extracted from NEMA 1C-3-1963, Precision Snap-acting Switches, Section 1C3-3.01, Symbols to Illustrate Contact Arrangements, and J1C—Electrical Standards for Industrial Equipment, with the permission of the National Electrical Manufacturers Association (NEMA Standard only), 155 East 44 Street, New York, N.Y.

SNAP - ACTING		2	
	SPST, maintained open, maintained closed (SPST= single-pole, single-throw)		SPST, normally open, momentarily closed
3	SPST, normally closed, momentarily open	**4**	SPST, double-break, maintained open, maintained closed
5	SPST, double-break, normally open, momentarily closed	**6**	SPST, double-break, normally closed, momentarily open
7	SPDT, maintained closed, maintained closed (SPDT=single-pole, double-throw)	**8**	SPDT, normally closed, momentarily closed
9	Two-circuit, double-throw, double-break, maintained closed, maintained closed	**10**	Two-circuit, double-throw, double-break, normally closed, momentarily closed

NOTE 1 Character appearing in symbol denotes snap-acting mechanism.

NOTE 2

Arrow used in symbols 2, 3, 5, 6, 8, and 10 denotes direction of spring return force.

The standard symbol for a terminal (o) may be added to the extremity of the stem of the symbol which denotes a double-break snap-acting mechanism if the switch is to be used with a common terminal.

Symbols may be shown in other orientations when used on schematic diagrams. NEMA Standard 11-17-1960

NOTE 5

Snap switches of the two-circuit type (represented by symbols 7, 8, 9, and 10) are generally useable only if both circuits are of the same polarity. For sufficiently low voltages and very low (dry-circuit) currents, opposite polarity may be acceptable if substantiated by proper tests for the particular application involved.

Authorized Engineering Information 1-25-1961.

NEMA ··· JIC SWITCHES	DISCONNECT	CIRCUIT INTERRUPTER	CIRCUIT BREAKER

LIMIT

SPRING RETURN		NEUTRAL POSITION	MAINTAINED POSITION
NORMALLY OPEN	NORMALLY CLOSED		
HELD CLOSED	HELD OPEN		

	NORMALLY OPEN	NORMALLY CLOSED	SPEED (PLUGGING)		ANTI-PLUG
LIQUID LEVEL					

SELECTOR

VACUUM & PRESSURE			PREFERRED PUSH BUTTON TYPE	ALTERNATE DRUM TYPE
TEMPERATURE ACTUATED				

FOOT

FLOW(AIR,WATER,ETC)			NORMALLY CLOSED	NORMALLY OPEN

PUSH BUTTONS		TIMER CONTACTS. CONTACT ACTION RETARDED WHEN COIL IS:		
SINGLE CiRCUIT			NORMALLY OPEN	NORMALLY CLOSED
NORMALLY OPEN	NORMALLY CLOSED	ENERGIZED		
DOUBLE CIRCUIT	MUSHROOM HEAD	DE-ENERGIZED		
MAINTAINED CONTACT		GENERAL CONTACTS. STARTERS , RELAYS , ETC		
		OVERLOAD THERMAL	NORMALLY OPEN	NORMALLY CLOSED

Reproduced through the courtesy of Centralab, Electronics Division, Globe-Union, Inc., 900 East Keefe Avenue, Milwaukee, Wis., and the Electro Switch Corporation, Weymouth (Boston 88), Mass.

SERIES 001 & 002 Slide Switch

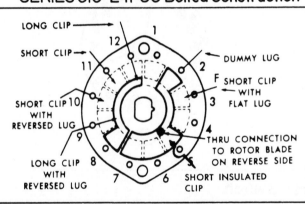

NON-SHORTING CONTACT

SHORTING CONTACT

DUMMY LUG

SHORT CLIP

LONG CLIP

Outline slide Contacts (Shorting or Non Shorting), draw short, long or dummy clips as required.

SERIES 20 Printed Circuit Switch

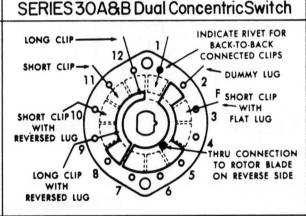

LONG CLIP

SHORT CLIP

INDICATE RIVET FOR BACK-TO-BACK CONNECTED CLIPS

DUMMY LUG

SHORT CLIP WITH FLAT LUG

THRU CONNECTION TO ROTOR BLADE ON REVERSE SIDE

STATOR CLIPS NUMBERED CCW WITH MATCHING PATH TERMINATIONS NUMBERED "L" TO "R"

SERIES 010-241-50 Bolted Construction

LONG CLIP

SHORT CLIP

DUMMY LUG

F SHORT CLIP WITH FLAT LUG

SHORT CLIP WITH REVERSED LUG

THRU CONNECTION TO ROTOR BLADE ON REVERSE SIDE

LONG CLIP WITH REVERSED LUG

SHORT INSULATED CLIP

SERIES 30A&B Dual Concentric Switch

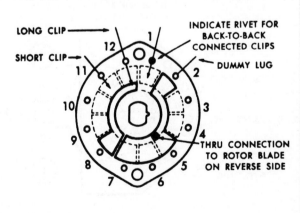

LONG CLIP

SHORT CLIP

INDICATE RIVET FOR BACK-TO-BACK CONNECTED CLIPS

DUMMY LUG

F SHORT CLIP WITH FLAT LUG

SHORT CLIP WITH REVERSED LUG

THRU CONNECTION TO ROTOR BLADE ON REVERSE SIDE

LONG CLIP WITH REVERSED LUG

SERIES 20-30C-70 Switches

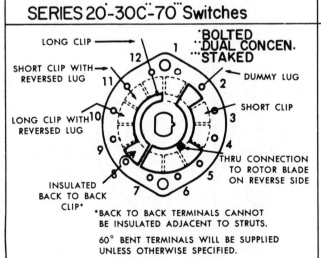

LONG CLIP

SHORT CLIP WITH REVERSED LUG

LONG CLIP WITH REVERSED LUG

INSULATED BACK TO BACK CLIP*

*BOLTED
**DUAL CONCEN.
***STAKED

DUMMY LUG

SHORT CLIP

THRU CONNECTION TO ROTOR BLADE ON REVERSE SIDE

*BACK TO BACK TERMINALS CANNOT BE INSULATED ADJACENT TO STRUTS.

60° BENT TERMINALS WILL BE SUPPLIED UNLESS OTHERWISE SPECIFIED.

SERIES 100 Sub Miniature Switches

LONG CLIP

SHORT CLIP

INDICATE RIVET FOR BACK-TO-BACK CONNECTED CLIPS

DUMMY LUG

THRU CONNECTION TO ROTOR BLADE ON REVERSE SIDE

SERIES 600 Bolted Construction Sw.

LONG CLIP

SHORT CLIP

SHORT CLIP 10 WITH REVERSED LUG

LONG CLIP 8 WITH REVERSED LUG

INDICATE RIVET FOR BACK-TO-BACK CONNECTED CLIPS

DUMMY LUG

F SHORT CLIP WITH FLAT LUG

THRU CONNECTION TO ROTOR BLADE ON REVERSE SIDE

SHORT INSULATED CLIP (CANNOT INSULATE CLIP AT POSITIONS 1, 6, 7 AND 12)

12 1 2 3 4 5 6 7 8 9 10 11

SERIES 650-654 (2-18 Pos)...670-672 (2-24)

BOLTED CONSTRUCTION

LONG CLIP

SHORT CLIP

LONG CLIP

DUMMY LUG

SHORT CLIP

THRU CONNECTION TO ROTOR BLADE ON REVERSE SIDE

INSULATED BACK TO BACK CLIP

60° BENT TERMINALS WILL BE SUPPLIED UNLESS OTHERWISE SPECIFIED.

18 1 2 3 4 5 6 7 8 9 10 11 12 13 14 15 16 17

SERIES 200 Tone Switch

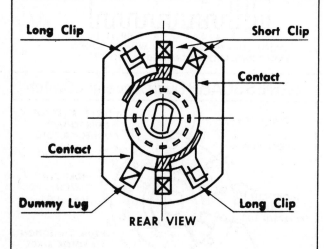

Long Clip

Short Clip

Contact

Contact

Dummy Lug

Long Clip

REAR VIEW

SERIES 230 Heavy Duty Power Switch

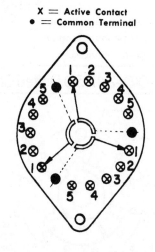

X = Active Contact
● = Common Terminal

SERIES 220 Lever Switch

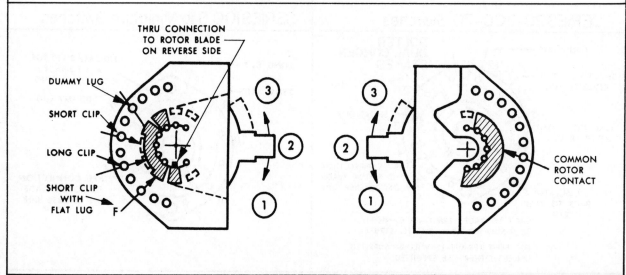

THRU CONNECTION TO ROTOR BLADE ON REVERSE SIDE

DUMMY LUG

SHORT CLIP

LONG CLIP

SHORT CLIP WITH FLAT LUG

F

COMMON ROTOR CONTACT

Typical Assemblages
of Type JM Rotary Switches
Viewed from handle-end of switch with handle in zero-degrees position.

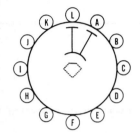

ASSEMBLAGE 1

For single-pole, double-make, double-break, break-before-make switching.

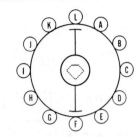

ASSEMBLAGE 9

One rotor provides double-break, break-before-make switching.

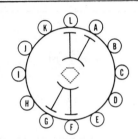

ASSEMBLAGE 2

For double-pole, double-break, break-before-make switching.

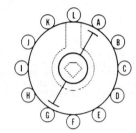

ASSEMBLAGE 8

Allows pairs of circuits to be fed from a common source; break-before-make switching.

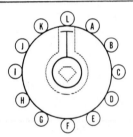

ASSEMBLAGE 3

Tap switch section using slip-ring and feeder terminal for 11 tap positions, break-before-make, with one OFF position.

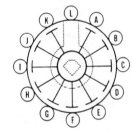

ASSEMBLAGE 12

Provides break-before-make switching for special circuit design. Any combination of fingers may be utilized.

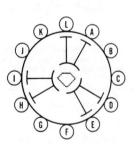

ASSEMBLAGE 5

Provides triple-pole, double-break, break-before-make switching.

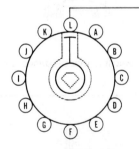

ASSEMBLAGE 3, ASSEMBLAGE 3A

Tandem arrangement to provide 12 "ON" positions, break-before-make.

Dept of the Army

TELEPHONY
(CIRCUIT SYMBOLS, TM 11-678)

Extracted from Department of the Army TM11-678, Fundamentals of Telephony, with the permission of the Office of the Secretary of Defense, Public Affairs Department, Washington. Elementary circuit symbols (telephony) reproduced through the courtesy of Automatic Electric Sales Company, Division of General Telephone.

BATTERY CELL, POLARITY AS INDICATED	BELL	CAPACITOR, FIXED	CARBON-BLOCK PROTECTOR
BATTERY, MULTICELL POLARITY AS INDICATED	BUZZER / DROP SHUTTER	CAPACITOR, FIXED, SHIELDED	

NOTE:
WHERE IT IS NECESSARY TO IDENTIFY THE CAPACITOR ELECTRODES, THE CURVED ELEMENT SHOULD REPRESENT THE OUTSIDE ELECTRODE IN FIXED PAPER-DIELECTRIC AND CERAMIC-DIELECTRIC CAPACITORS, THE NEGATIVE ELECTRODE IN ELECTROLYTIC CAPACITORS, AND THE MOVING ELEMENT IN VARIABLE AND ADJUSTABLE CAPACITORS.

DIAL

FUSE	D-C GENERATOR / SOURCE OF ALTERNATING VOLTAGE	GENERATOR, HAND	GROUND

DOUBLE SINGLE / HEADSET	HANDSET, THREE-CONDUCTOR	HANDSET, FOUR-CONDUCTOR	HANDSET, FOUR-CONDUCTOR, WITH TRANSMITTER CUT-OUT SWITCH (HANDSET SWITCH)

INDUCTOR OR COIL, FIXED, AIR-CORE	INDUCTOR OR COIL, FIXED, MAGNETIC-CORE	INDUCTOR OR COIL, FIXED, TAPPED, AIR-CORE	JACK, TWO-CONDUCTOR / JACK, TWO-CONDUCTOR

JACK, THREE-CONDUCTOR	JACK, TWO-CONDUCTOR, CUT-OFF	JACK, THREE-CONDUCTOR, CUT-OFF	JACK, TWO-CONDUCTOR, BREAK OR SINGLE CUT-OFF

JACK, THREE-CONDUCTOR, BREAK-ONE OR SINGLE CUT-OFF, AND MAKE-ONE	JACK, TWO-CONDUCTOR BREAK-ONE	JACK, TWO-CONDUCTOR MAKE-ONE	JACK, THREE-CONDUCTOR CUT-OFF AND MAKE-ONE
JACK, DOUBLE, FOUR-CONDUCTOR	TELEGRAPH KEY, MANUAL	LAMP, ILLUMINATING	LAMP, SWITCHBOARD
MAGNET, BAR	MAGNET, HORSESHOE	AMMETER	VOLTMETER
MOTOR * A-C MOT OR D-C MOT	PLUG, TWO-CONDUCTOR	PLUG, THREE-CONDUCTOR	RECEIVER
ELECTRON CURRENT RECTIFIER, DRY-DISK, HALF-WAVE	RECTIFIER, DRY-DISK FULL-WAVE ELECTRON CURRENT	RELAY, WITH MAKE CONTACT	RELAY, WITH BREAK CONTACT
RESISTOR, FIXED	RESISTOR, VARIABLE, (RHEOSTAT)	RESISTOR, VARIABLE, (POTENTIOMETER)	RESISTOR, TAPPED
SWITCH, SINGLE-POLE, SINGLE-THROW	SWITCH, SINGLE-POLE, DOUBLE-THROW	SWITCH, DOUBLE-POLE, SINGLE-THROW	SWITCH, DOUBLE-POLE, DOUBLE-THROW

SWITCH, SELECTOR TYPE	SWITCH, LOCKING	SWITCH, NONLOCKING	SWITCH HOOK
SWITCH, POWER	○ FEMALE ● MALE TERMINALS	INDUCTION COIL	TRANSFORMER, MAGNETIC CORE
TRANSFORMER, MULTIWINDING, MAGNETIC-CORE	AUTO TRANSFORMER, MAGNETIC-CORE	AUTO TRANSFORMER, MAGNETIC-CORE. TERMINALS AND DESIGNATIONS ARE SHOWN ONLY WHEN TERMINALS REQUIRE IDENTIFICATION	TRANSMITTER VARISTOR
VIBRATOR REED	VIBRATOR, SPLIT-REED	VIBRATOR, TYPICAL	WIRE OR CONDUCTOR CROSSED WIRES: TOP, CONNECTION BOTTOM, NO CONNECTION
WIRE, TWISTED PAIR	**Automatic Electric** # TELEPHONY (ELEMENTARY CIRCUIT SYMBOLS)	WIRES OR CONDUCTORS WIRES CROSSING NOT IN ELECTRICAL CONTACT WIRES CONNECTED ELECTRICALLY	
+ − CELL + − BATTERY	GROUND	− + BATTERY WITH GROUND CONNECTION	G OR G DIRECT CURRENT GENERATOR

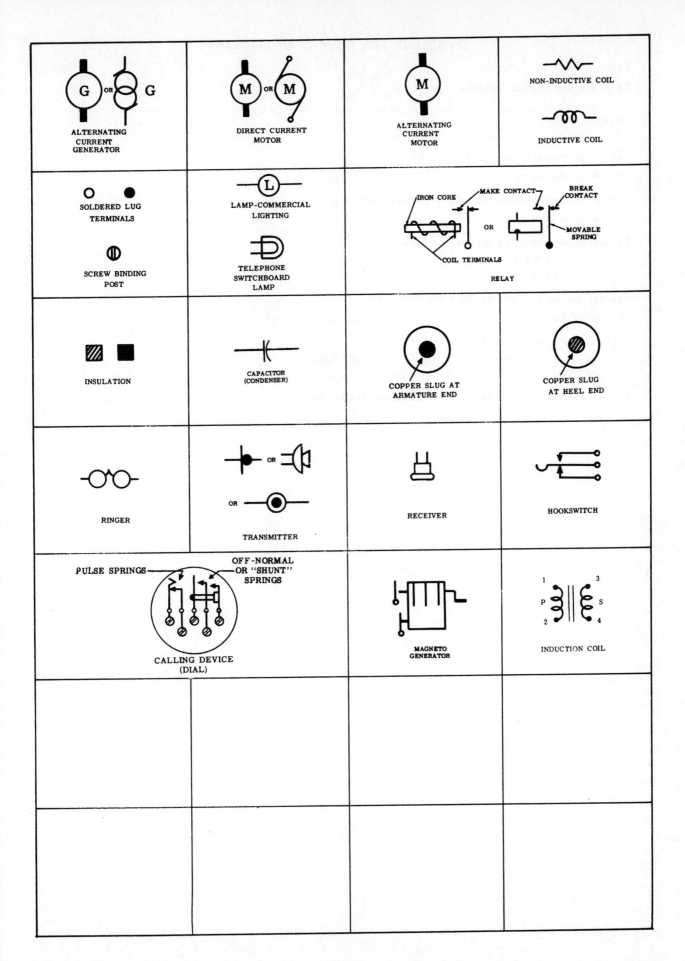

ALTERNATING CURRENT GENERATOR

DIRECT CURRENT MOTOR

ALTERNATING CURRENT MOTOR

NON-INDUCTIVE COIL

INDUCTIVE COIL

SOLDERED LUG TERMINALS

SCREW BINDING POST

LAMP-COMMERCIAL LIGHTING

TELEPHONE SWITCHBOARD LAMP

IRON CORE   MAKE CONTACT   BREAK CONTACT

OR

MOVABLE SPRING

COIL TERMINALS

RELAY

INSULATION

CAPACITOR (CONDENSER)

COPPER SLUG AT ARMATURE END

COPPER SLUG AT HEEL END

RINGER

OR

OR

TRANSMITTER

RECEIVER

HOOKSWITCH

PULSE SPRINGS

OFF-NORMAL OR "SHUNT" SPRINGS

CALLING DEVICE (DIAL)

MAGNETO GENERATOR

1   3

P   S

2   4

INDUCTION COIL

SYMBOLOGY FOR FLOW PLAN DIAGRAMS

ISA RP5.1
Instrumentation Flow Plan

Extracted from ISA-RP5.1, Instrumentation Flow Plan Symbols, with the permission of the Instrument Society of America, 313 Sixth Avenue, Pittsburgh, Pa.

INSTRUMENT PROCESS PIPING (Pressure, Differential, Etc., Connecting Lead Lines; Also Hydraulic Actuating Medium Lines)	————————————	All lines to be fine in relation to process piping
INSTRUMENT AIR LINES	—//——//——//——//—	
INSTRUMENT ELECTRICAL LEADS	— — — — — — —	
INSTRUMENT CAPILLARY TUBING	—✕——✕——✕——✕—	

Locally Mounted   Board Mounted

BASIC SYMBOLS FOR INSTRUMENT WITH SINGLE SERVICE AND FUNCTION

Locally Mounted   Board Mounted

BASIC SYMBOLS FOR COMBINATION INSTRUMENT OR DEVICE WITH TWO SERVICES OR FUNCTIONS

Locally Mounted   Board Mounted

BASIC SYMBOLS FOR TRANSMITTER

BASIC SYMBOL FOR DIAPHRAGM MOTOR VALVE

BASIC SYMBOL FOR ELECTRICALLY OPERATED VALVE (SOLENOID OR MOTOR)

BASIC SYMBOL FOR PISTON-OPERATED VALVE (HYDRAULIC OR PNEUMATIC)

3-WAY BODY FOR ANY VALVE

BASIC SYMBOL FOR SAFETY (RELIEF) VALVE

BASIC SYMBOL FOR SELF-ACTUATED (INTEGRAL) REGULATING VALVE

BASIC SYMBOL FOR MANUALLY OPERATED CONTROL VALVE

BASIC SYMBOL SHOWING PNEUMATIC TRANSMISSION INSTRUMENT (ELECTRIC TRANSMISSION SAME EXCEPT FOR TYPE OF CONNECTION)

BASIC SYMBOL SHOWING PNEUMATIC CONNECTION FROM INSTRUMENT TO DIAPHRAGM MOTOR VALVE

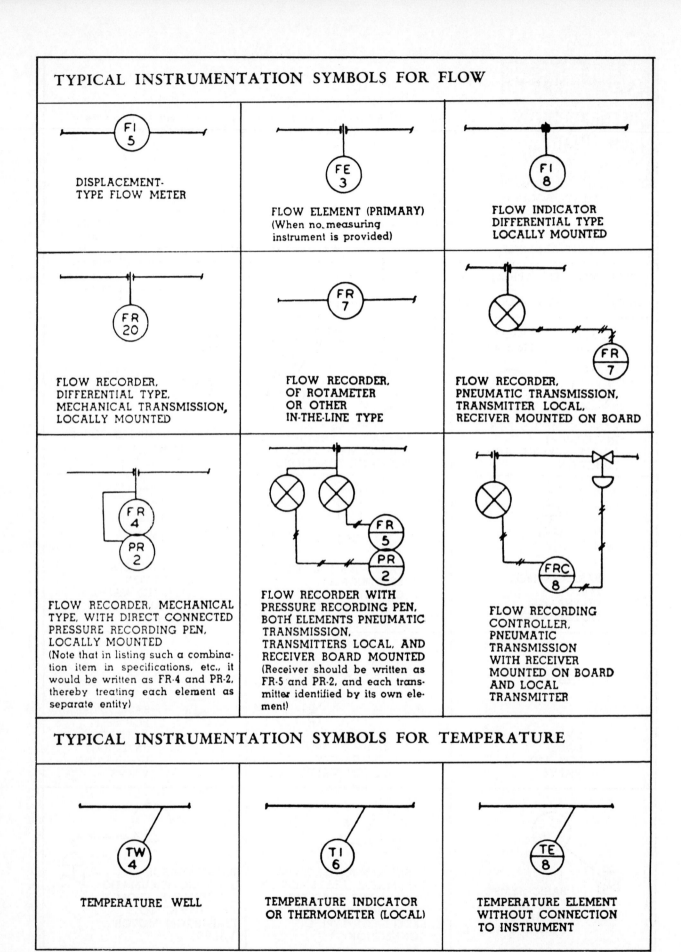

TYPICAL INSTRUMENTATION SYMBOLS FOR FLOW

FI 5

DISPLACEMENT-TYPE FLOW METER

FE 3

FLOW ELEMENT (PRIMARY)
(When no. measuring instrument is provided)

FI 8

FLOW INDICATOR DIFFERENTIAL TYPE LOCALLY MOUNTED

FR 20

FLOW RECORDER, DIFFERENTIAL TYPE, MECHANICAL TRANSMISSION, LOCALLY MOUNTED

FR 7

FLOW RECORDER, OF ROTAMETER OR OTHER IN-THE-LINE TYPE

FR 7

FLOW RECORDER, PNEUMATIC TRANSMISSION, TRANSMITTER LOCAL, RECEIVER MOUNTED ON BOARD

FR 4 / PR 2

FLOW RECORDER, MECHANICAL TYPE, WITH DIRECT CONNECTED PRESSURE RECORDING PEN, LOCALLY MOUNTED
(Note that in listing such a combination item in specifications, etc., it would be written as FR-4 and PR-2, thereby treating each element as separate entity)

FR 5 / PR 2

FLOW RECORDER WITH PRESSURE RECORDING PEN, BOTH ELEMENTS PNEUMATIC TRANSMISSION, TRANSMITTERS LOCAL, AND RECEIVER BOARD MOUNTED
(Receiver should be written as FR-5 and PR-2, and each transmitter identified by its own element)

FRC 8

FLOW RECORDING CONTROLLER, PNEUMATIC TRANSMISSION WITH RECEIVER MOUNTED ON BOARD AND LOCAL TRANSMITTER

TYPICAL INSTRUMENTATION SYMBOLS FOR TEMPERATURE

TW 4

TEMPERATURE WELL

TI 6

TEMPERATURE INDICATOR OR THERMOMETER (LOCAL)

TE 8

TEMPERATURE ELEMENT WITHOUT CONNECTION TO INSTRUMENT

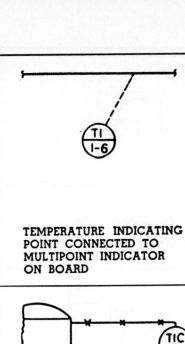

TEMPERATURE INDICATING
POINT CONNECTED TO
MULTIPOINT INDICATOR
ON BOARD

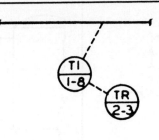

TEMPERATURE INDICATING
AND RECORDING POINT
CONNECTED TO MULTIPOINT
INSTRUMENTS ON BOARD

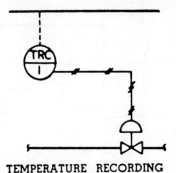

TEMPERATURE RECORDING
CONTROLLER, BOARD
MOUNTED (ELECTRIC
MEASUREMENT)

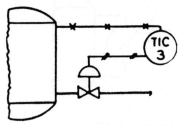

TEMPERATURE INDICATING
CONTROLLER, FILLED
SYSTEM TYPE,
LOCALLY MOUNTED

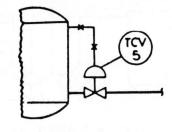

TEMPERATURE CONTROLLER
OF SELF-ACTUATED TYPE

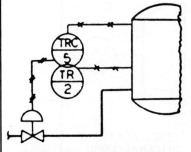

TEMPERATURE RECORDING
CONTROLLER AND TEMPERATURE
RECORDER, COMBINED
INSTRUMENT BOARD MOUNTED

TYPICAL INSTRUMENTATION SYMBOLS FOR LEVEL

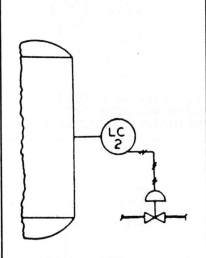

BLIND LEVEL CONTROLLER,
INTERNAL TYPE

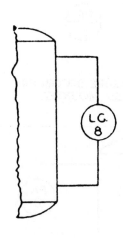

GAGE GLASS

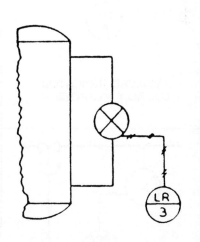

LEVEL RECORDER, PNEUMATIC
TRANSMISSION, WITH BOARD
MOUNTED RECEIVER,
EXTERNAL TYPE TRANSMITTER

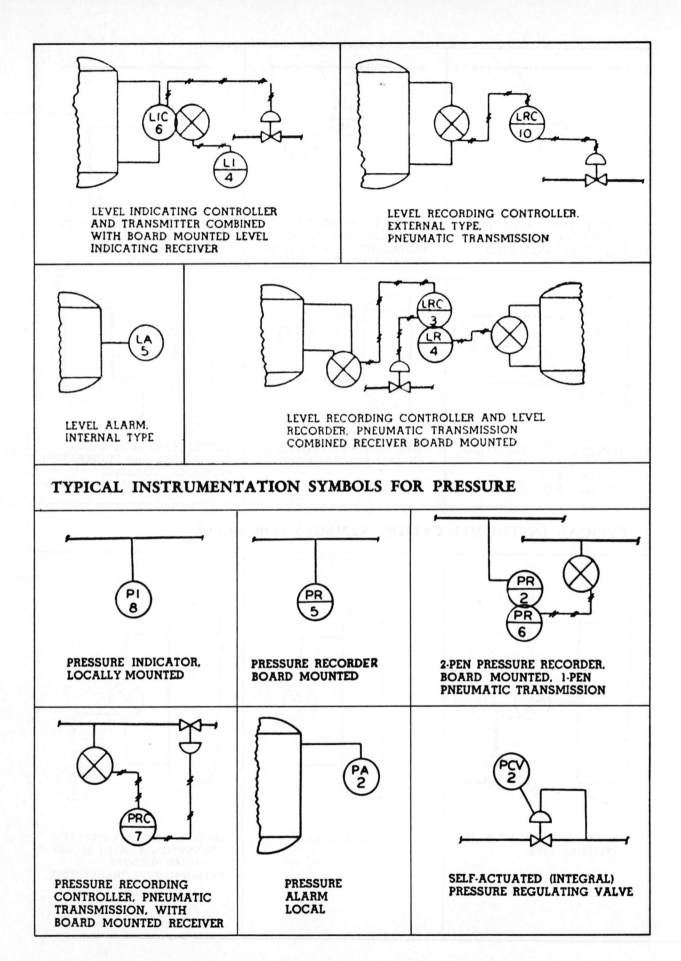

LEVEL INDICATING CONTROLLER
AND TRANSMITTER COMBINED
WITH BOARD MOUNTED LEVEL
INDICATING RECEIVER

LEVEL RECORDING CONTROLLER.
EXTERNAL TYPE.
PNEUMATIC TRANSMISSION

LEVEL ALARM.
INTERNAL TYPE

LEVEL RECORDING CONTROLLER AND LEVEL
RECORDER, PNEUMATIC TRANSMISSION
COMBINED RECEIVER BOARD MOUNTED

TYPICAL INSTRUMENTATION SYMBOLS FOR PRESSURE

PRESSURE INDICATOR,
LOCALLY MOUNTED

PRESSURE RECORDER
BOARD MOUNTED

2-PEN PRESSURE RECORDER,
BOARD MOUNTED, 1-PEN
PNEUMATIC TRANSMISSION

PRESSURE RECORDING
CONTROLLER, PNEUMATIC
TRANSMISSION, WITH
BOARD MOUNTED RECEIVER

PRESSURE
ALARM
LOCAL

SELF-ACTUATED (INTEGRAL)
PRESSURE REGULATING VALVE

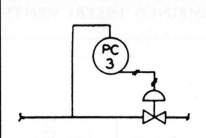

**PRESSURE CONTROLLER,
BLIND TYPE**
(Show controller
directly above diaphragm
if so mounted)

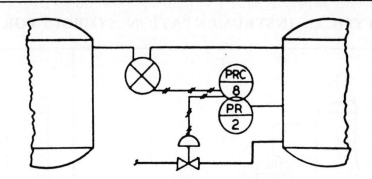

**PRESSURE RECORDING CONTROLLER (DIFFERENTIAL),
PNEUMATIC TRANSMISSION; WITH PRESSURE RECORDER,
COMBINED INSTRUMENT BOARD MOUNTED**

TYPICAL INSTRUMENTATION SYMBOLS (MISCELLANEOUS)

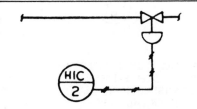

**HAND ACTUATED PNEUMATIC
CONTROLLER, BOARD MOUNTED,
WITH INDICATION**

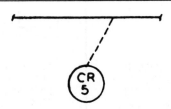

**CONDUCTIVITY RECORDER,
LOCALLY MOUNTED**

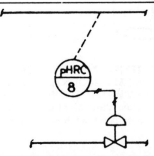

**pH RECORDING CONTROLLER,
BOARD MOUNTED**

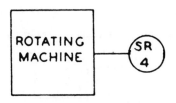

**SPEED RECORDER,
LOCALLY MOUNTED**

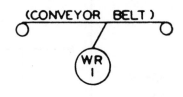

**WEIGHT RECORDER,
LOCALLY MOUNTED**

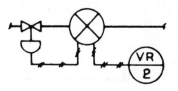

**VISCOSITY RECORDER,
PNEUMATIC TRANSMISSION,
BOARD MOUNTED**
(Element in sample flow line)

**DENSITY CONTROLLER
BLIND, INTERNAL
ELEMENT TYPE**

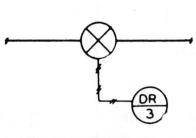

**DENSITY RECORDER,
PNEUMATIC TRANSMISSION
BOARD MOUNTED**
(Element in sample flow line)

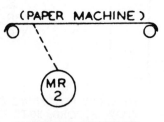

**MOISTURE RECORDER,
LOCALLY MOUNTED**

123

TYPICAL INSTRUMENTATION SYMBOLS FOR COMBINED INSTRUMENTS

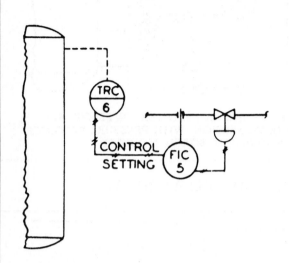

TEMPERATURE RECORDING CONTROLLER,
BOARD MOUNTED, RESETTING LOCALLY
MOUNTED FLOW INDICATING CONTROLLER
(Note that "Control Setting" should be shown
alongside air line to indicate cascade control)

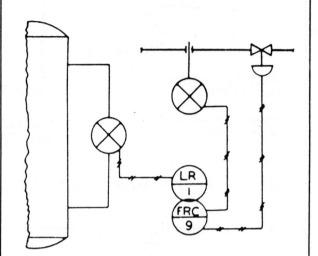

FLOW RECORDING CONTROLLER WITH
LEVEL RECORD. BOTH ELEMENTS
PNEUMATIC TRANSMISSION. LEVEL
TRANSMITTER EXTERNAL TYPE.
COMBINED RECEIVER BOARD MOUNTED

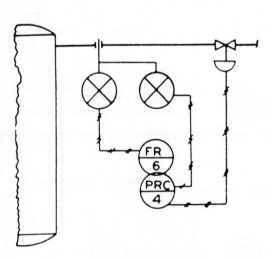

PRESSURE RECORDING CONTROLLER WITH
FLOW RECORD. BOTH ELEMENTS
PNEUMATIC TRANSMISSION, COMBINED
RECEIVER BOARD MOUNTED

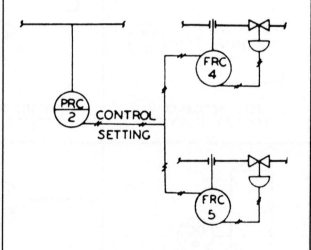

PRESSURE RECORDING CONTROLLER,
BOARD MOUNTED, RESETTING
LOCALLY MOUNTED FLOW
RECORDING CONTROLLERS

SYMBOLOGY FOR LOGIC-DATA PROCESSING

Reproduced through the courtesy of Radio Corporation of America (RCA), Government Service Department, Camden, N.J., from the Language and Symbology of Digital Computer Systems, originally prepared for the United States Air Force.

	Preferred	Burroughs	IBM	RCA	Remington Rand
Adder					
Adder, Half					
Adder, Quarter (Exclusive OR) (AND-NOT)					
Amplifier (No inversion)					
Amplifier, With inverted output					
Amplifier, With multiple outputs					
Cathode Follower					
AND Gate					

CROSS-REFERENCE CHART

	Preferred	Burroughs	IBM	RCA	Remington Rand
AND Gate, With inhibiting input			AG		G436
AND Gate, With inverted output			AI		VACUUM TUBE GATE — G436 — INPUT AND OUTPUT ALWAYS ON OPPOSITE SIDES
AND Thyratron	(EXTINGUISHING INPUT) (DOT INDICATES GAS-FILLED)		ATH		(EXTINGUISHING INPUT) TG
Binary (Flip-Flop) (Toggle)	S FF R	S R	T	S FF R	R FF S
Counter, Binary	S T R	S C R		S T CTR R	SET TO 1 STEP — BC SET TO 0
Counter, Binary Multistage	RESET STEP — R T OUTPUTS			N CTR	(CLEAR TO SPECIFIC NUMBER) STEP MOST SIGNIFICANT DIGIT LEAST SIGNIFICANT DIGIT
Counter, Multiposition	ODD RESET TO 0 0123456789 EVEN				
Delay Line	5 USEC	DL	D	5D 5 USEC DELAY	D7 SEVEN-PULSE DELAY 1/2 PULSE DELAY LESS THAN 1/2 PULSE DELAY
Delay, Flip-Flop	S R 5 USEC	DMV OR DMV	SS	OS N R	DF 4MS

CROSS-REFERENCE CHART

	Preferred	Burroughs	IBM	RCA	Remington Rand
Delay, Logical			\nDELAY IN USEC		
Inverter					
Magnetic Amplifier					
Magnetic Core, Binary					
Magnetic Drum					
Magnetic Head					
Matrix, Decoder					
Matrix, Encoder					
OR Circuit					

CROSS-REFERENCE CHART

	Preferred	Burroughs	IBM	RCA	Remington Rand
OR Circuit, With inverted output			OI		
Oscillator	OR		OSC	OSC	OSC
Pulse Transformer (Without inversion)	PX		PX	OR / P	PT
Pulse Transformer (With inversion)	PX			OR / P	PT
Shift Register	SR-			SR- / A ... B	SHIFT REGISTER OR / A B A B
Signal Identifiers					
		PULSE		TIME PULSE WITHOUT OR DIODE	
		LEVEL	GATING	LEVEL WITHOUT OR DIODE	
		PULSE OVERRIDE		TIME PULSE WITH OR DIODE	
		LEVEL OVERRIDE		LEVEL WITH OR DIODE	
		INHIBIT (A INHIBITS B) A B	INHIBITING INPUT	INHIBITING INPUT	INHIBITING INPUT
					FUNCTION SIGNAL 230

Extracted from AIEE No. 91 (now IEEE) ASA Y32.14-1962, Graphic Symbols for Logic Diagrams, through the courtesy of the American Institute of Electrical Engineers (now the Institute of Electrical and Electronic Engineers), 345 East 47 Street, New York, N.Y.

DEFINITIONS FOR THIS STANDARD

1. **Logic Function**—a combinational, storage, delay, or sequential function expressing a relationship between signal input(s) to a system or device and the resultant output(s).

2. **Logic Symbol**—the graphical representation in diagrammatic form of a logic function.

3. **Logic Diagram**—a diagram that depicts by logic symbols and supplementary notations the details of signal flow and control, but not necessarily the point-to-point wiring, existing in a system of two-state devices.

3. 1 **Basic Logic Diagram**—a logic diagram that depicts logic functions with no reference to physical implementations. It consists primarily of logic symbols and is used to depict all logic relationships as simply as possible.

3. 2 **Detailed Logic Diagram**—a logic diagram that depicts all logic functions and also shows non-logic functions, socket locations, pin numbers, test points, and other physical elements necessary to describe the physical and electrical aspects of the logic.

3. 3 **Distinctive Shape Logic Diagram**—a basic or detailed logic diagram in which commonly used logic and non-logic functions are represented by enclosures with distinctive shapes. Functions less commonly used are represented by rectangles, within which an internal label denotes the function. It is the intention to develop new distinctive shapes and internal labels, as required.

3. 4 **Uniform Shape Logic Diagram**—a basic or detailed logic diagram in which both logic and non-logic functions are represented by rectangles, within which an internal label denotes the function. It is the intention to develop new internal labels, as required.

4. **States in Binary Logic**—The two physical states on each terminal of each signal line shall be referred to as the 0-state and the 1-state. The 0-state may be called the reference (inactive, anti-fiducial) state, and the 1-state the significant (active, fiducial) state.

   The above must not be construed as implying that the 1-state requires more power, contains more energy, or is at a higher potential than the 0-state. The state designations are purely arbitrary as far as the physical interpretation is concerned.

5. **Kinds of Logic.** If all signal line terminals in a logic diagram of a system, or device, have the same pair of physical states, and if both are electric potentials (currents), and if the more positive potential (current) is consistently selected as the 1-state, the resultant system, or device, is said to have positive logic.
   If the less positive potential (current) is consistently selected as the 1-state, the resultant system, or device, is said to have negative logic.

ASSIGNMENT OF LOGIC LEVELS TO BINARY LOGIC ELEMENTS

Consider a circuit whose output (F) is a function of two variables (A, B), and whose output and input levels are capable of assuming only +2 volts and −3 volts. Assume that the circuit behaves according to the following table of combinations:

INPUTS		OUTPUT
A	B	F
−3v	−3v	−3v
−3v	+2v	−3v
+2v	−3v	−3v
+2v	+2v	+2v

4.1.1 In positive logic the —3v level is the 0-state and +2v is the 1-state (see paragraph 5). Substitution of the logic values for the voltage levels results in the following table:

This is the truth table for the AND function. Therefore, the circuit is said to perform the AND operation.

INPUTS		OUTPUT
A	B	F
0	0	0
0	1	0
1	0	0
1	1	1

4.1.2 In negative logic the —3v level is the 1-state and +2v is the 0-state (see paragraph 5). Substitution of the logic values for the voltage levels results in the following table:

This is the truth table for the OR function. Therefore, the circuit is said to perform the OR operation.

INPUTS		OUTPUT
A	B	F
1	1	1
1	0	1
0	1	1
0	0	0

Paragraphs 4.1.1 and 4.1.2 illustrate that a single circuit can perform either the AND operation or the OR operation. This duality has been employed in numerous single-device as well as multi-device systems.

Given a physical device characterized by a table of combinations, the logic function performed by the device is determined by the specified choices of the 1-states at its inputs and outputs.

Each choice of the 1-states at each input and each output of a logic circuit shall be specified on the detailed logic diagram in a manner that correctly represents the logic function designated by the logical designer.

In a diagram where positive logic, negative logic, or both is used, the state choices on the signal lines shall be identified as follows.

1 A small, open, right triangle at the point where a signal line joins a logic symbol indicates that the line's 1-state (activating) with respect to that logic symbol is the less positive potential (current).

2 A small, filled, right triangle at the point where a signal line joins a logic symbol indicates that the line's 1-state (activating) with respect to that logic symbol is the more positive potential (current).

3 The right triangle shall be so oriented as to point in the direction of signal flow.

4 Either of the two kinds of right triangles, open or filled, may be omitted providing the convention is suitably noted on the diagram. In diagrams in which both kinds of right triangles would appear, only one kind may be omitted.

If lines are labeled with logic or English titles, they may apply to the 1-state indicated by either the nearest level indicator, the previous level indicator, or the following level indicator. Any such convention used must be noted on the diagram.

PRESENTATION TECHNIQUES

Symbol Orientation—does not affect the meaning of the symbol.

Symbol Line Thickness—does not affect the meaning of the symbol.

Symbol Size—does not affect the meaning of the symbol. An effort shall be made to keep like symbols of like size.

Internal Functional Identification—the internal functional identification of a rectangular block is part of the symbol.

Internal Information—(if included) shall follow the functional identification and will be referred to as tagging lines. (The internal functional identification is not considered to be a tagging line.)

   1 If a means of uniquely identifying a logic symbol is required, this information shall be contained in the first tagging line(s).

   2 The last tagging line(s) within the symbol, when used, shall provide a means of locating the logic hardware within the equipment system.

   3 **Additional Information**—may be included on intermediate tagging lines when required for clarity. This additional information may include such items as stylized waveforms, time delays, hardware information, etc.

Peripheral Information—Some of the additional information can best be presented outside of and adjacent to the symbol. For example, pin numbers, wave forms, test points.

Signal Flow Direction—While logic diagrams may completely indicate direction of signal flow by the symbols themselves, arrowheads superimposed on lines, an extended border on the input side of a rectangle, or a convention of unidirectional flow suitably noted on the diagram, may be used where required for clarity. No input shall enter a symbol in the vicinity of an output, or on the output side of a symbol e.g., the arc of a distinctive shaped symbol. Inputs may be drawn on any side of the symbol (except the output side), although the side opposite the output is preferred.

GENERAL LIST OF GRAPHICAL SYMBOLS

Use of Symbols—In the following listing of graphical symbols the Uniform Shape symbols are shown on the left and the Distinctive Shape symbols on the right. Logic diagrams must use symbols from one list or the other, not a mixture of the two. Symbols to be used on either list are shown in the center. The lines indicating input and output connections are not part of the symbol.

6.2 Symbol for AND

6.2.1 The output of an AND assumes the 1-state if and only if all of the inputs assume the 1-state. An example of the truth table for an AND with three inputs is:

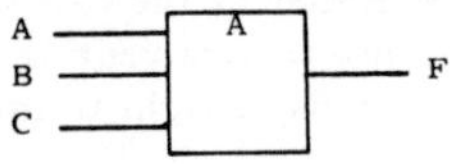

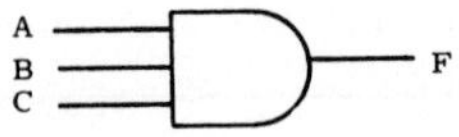

INPUT			OUTPUT
A	B	C	F
0	0	0	0
0	0	1	0
0	1	0	0
0	1	1	0
1	0	0	0
1	0	1	0
1	1	0	0
1	1	1	1

INPUT			OUTPUT
A	B	C	F
L	L	L	L
L	L	H	L
L	H	L	L
L	H	H	L
H	L	L	L
H	L	H	L
H	H	L	L
H	H	H	H

6.2.2 In a device operated with positive logic, the truth table of 6.2.1 corresponds to the following table of combinations, where H stands for more positive (high) and L for less positive (low):

6.3 Symbol for OR

6.3.1 The output of an OR assumes the 1-state if one or more of the inputs assume the 1-state. An example of the truth table for an OR with three inputs is:

INPUT			OUTPUT
A	B	C	F
0	0	0	0
0	0	1	1
0	1	0	1
0	1	1	1
1	0	0	1
1	0	1	1
1	1	0	1
1	1	1	1

6.3.2 In a device operated with positive logic, the truth table of paragraph 6.3.1 corresponds to the following table of combinations, where H stands for more positive (high), and L for less positive (low):

INPUT			OUTPUT
A	B	C	F
L	L	L	L
L	L	H	H
L	H	L	H
L	H	H	H
H	L	L	H
H	L	H	H
H	H	L	H
H	H	H	H

6.4 Symbol for EXCLUSIVE OR

6.4.1 The output of an EXCLUSIVE OR with two inputs assumes the 1-state if one and only one input assumes the 1-state.

INPUT		OUTPUT
A	B	F
0	0	0
0	1	1
1	0	1
1	1	0

INPUT		OUTPUT
A	B	F
L	L	L
L	H	H
H	L	H
H	H	L

6.4.2 In a device operated with positive logic, the truth table of paragraph 6.4.1 corresponds to the following table of combinations, where H stands for more positive (high) and L for less positive (low):

6.5 LOGIC NEGATION AND ELECTRIC INVERTER

6.5.1 Symbol for LOGIC NEGATION

The output of a LOGIC NEGATION operation takes on the 1-state if and only if the input does not take on the 1-state. A small circle drawn at the point where a signal line joins a logic symbol indicates a LOGIC NEGATION.

6.5.2 It should be noted that logic negation, in a detailed logic diagram, can be indicated by the relationship between types of level indicators (see paragraph 6.13) on opposite ends of a line.

6.5.3 Symbol for ELECTRIC INVERTER

6.5.3.1 The output of an ELECTRIC INVERTER assumes the 1-state if and only if the input assumes the 1-state. An example of the truth table for an ELECTRIC INVERTER is:

The output of an ELECTRIC INVERTER is relatively more positive if and only if the input is relatively less positive. (For illustration of correct usage and implementation of negation and inverter symbols on detailed logic diagrams, see Appendix D.)

INPUT	OUTPUT
A	B
0	0
1	1

Flip-Flop—a logic device that stores a single bit of information. It normally has two inputs, set (S), and clear (reset) (C), and two possible outputs, 0 and 1.

A 1 is stored in a FLIP-FLOP when a 1-state signal is first applied to the set input.

The 1 output assumes the 1-state, and the 0 output assumes the 0-state. A 0 is stored in the FLIP-FLOP when a 1-state signal is first applied to the clear input. The outputs then are in the opposite states from what they were when the FLIP-FLOP stored a 1.

There are several possible versions of the FLIP-FLOP, depending upon the response of the circuit when 1-state signals are applied to more than one input simultaneously.

Flip-Flop Complementary—has outputs which are always of opposite states.

This flip-flop has a third input, toggle (trigger) (T) The application of a 1-state signal to the toggle (T) input, or of simultaneous 1-state signals to the set and clear inputs, reverses the state of this flip-flop.

(The inputs are not required to be identified with S, T, and C, as shown.)

The internal numbers, 1 and 0, are part of the symbol, and shall be in close proximity to their respective outputs. The set input shall be in proximity to the 1 output; the clear input shall be in proximity to the 0 output.

Flip-Flop Latch—has outputs which are not necessarily of opposite states. The application of simultaneous 1-state signals to the set and clear inputs cause both outputs to assume the same state for the duration of the inputs (both assume the 1-state or both assume the 0-state, depending upon the design of the circuit).

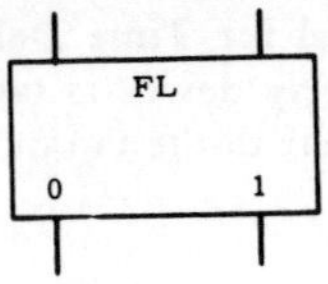

Single Shot—is activated by the indicated significant transition of the input signal. Output signal shape, amplitude, duration and polarity are determined by the circuit characteristics of the SINGLE SHOT, not by the input signal.

The normal (inactive) state of the SINGLE SHOT output is the 0-state. When activated, it changes to the indicated 1-state, remains there for the characteristic time of the device, and returns to the 0-state.

The duration of the on time of the SINGLE SHOT will normally need to be included on a tagging line inside the symbol. When required, stylized waveforms indicating duration, amplitude, and rise and fall time may be used.

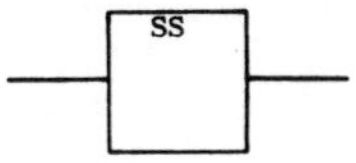

Schmitt Trigger—is activated when the input signal crosses a specified turn-on threshold toward the indicated 1-state and remains active until the input signal crosses a specified turn-off threshold toward the 0-state. Output signal shape, amplitude and polarity are determined by the circuit characteristics of the SCHMITT TRIGGER, not by the input signal.

The normal (inactive) state of the SCHMITT TRIGGER output is the 0-state. When activated, it changes to the indicated 1-state and remains there as long as the input exceeds the threshold value.

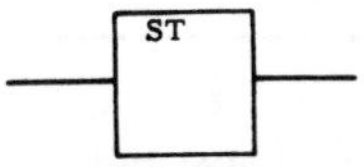

Symbol for AMPLIFIER

This symbol represents a linear or nonlinear current or voltage amplifier. This amplifier may have one or more stages.

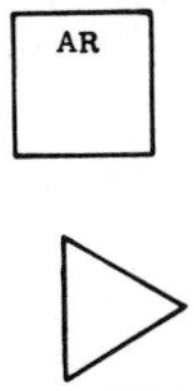

Refer to ASA Y32.2-1962

The output of an AMPLIFIER assumes the 1-state if and only if the input assumes the 1-state. An example of the truth table for an AMPLIFIER is:

The output of a non-inverting AMPLIFIER is relatively more positive if and only if the input is relatively more positive. The output of an inverting AMPLIFIER is relatively more positive if and only if the input is relatively less positive. (See Appendix D for correct usage and implementation of AMPLIFIER symbols on detailed logic diagrams.)

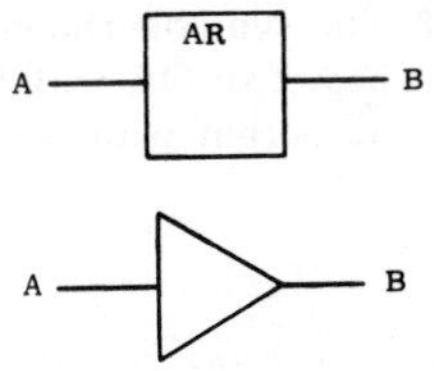

INPUT	OUTPUT
A	B
1	1
0	0

Symbol for OSCILLATOR

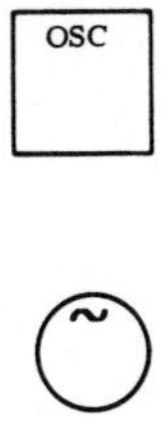

Refer to ASA Y32.2-1962

Symbol for Time Delay—the duration of the delay is included with the symbol. If the delay device is tapped, the delay time with respect to the input shall be included adjacent to the tap output.

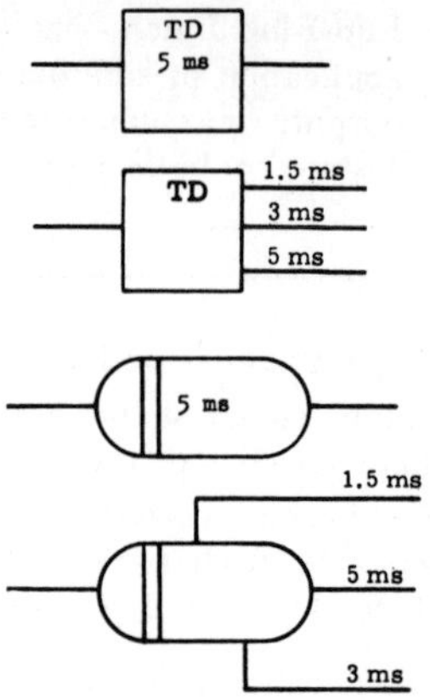

Symbol for functions not elsewhere specified. The symbol shall be adequately labeled to identify the function performed. It is not intended that this symbol be used for functions which can be logically expressed by a single symbol established in this Standard.

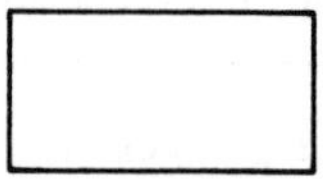

6.13

Relative Level Indicators—indicate the state choices described in paragraphs 4.4.1 and 4.4.2. The examples below illustrate the use of the right triangle as relative level indicators. (See also Appendix D.)

6.13.1 The symbols shown below represent an AND with input 1-states at the more positive potential (current) level and an output with the 1-state at the less positive potential (current) level.

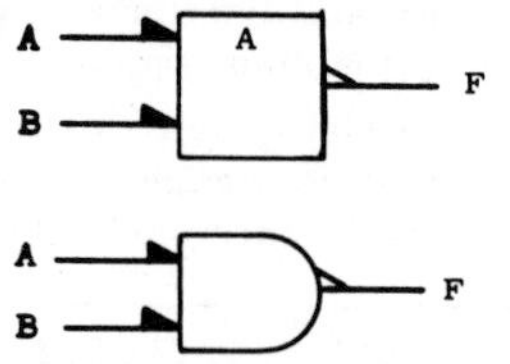

INPUT		OUTPUT
A	B	F
L	L	H
L	H	H
H	L	H
H	H	L

6.13.2 The symbols shown below represent the same device as paragraph 6.13.1. They depict an OR with input 1-states at the less positive potential (current) level and an output with the 1-state at the more positive potential (current) level.

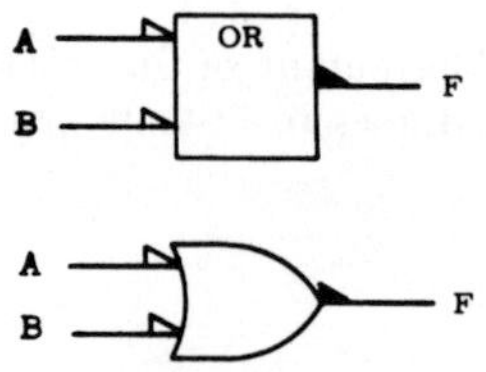

6.13.3 For additional examples of the above as shown in paragraphs 6.13.1 and 6.13.2, see Appendix C.

6.13.4 The symbols shown below represent an AND with mixed inputs.

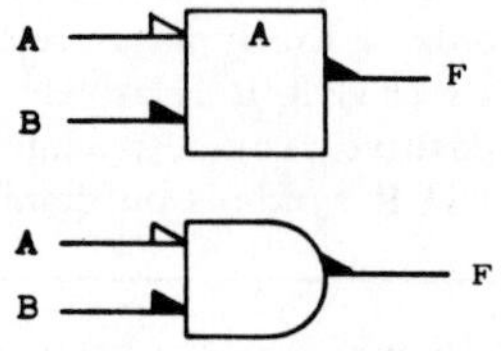

INPUT		OUTPUT
A	B	F
L	L	L
L	H	H
H	L	L
H	H	L

PRACTICE	
Multiple Inputs—To accommodate more than three inputs, the input side of the Distinctive Shape symbol shall be extended.	
Six inputs to an AND	
Nine inputs to an OR	
Use of Separate Circuits—Where circuits have the capability of being combined according to the AND (or OR) function, simply by having the outputs connected, that capability shall be shown by having an additional A (or OR) inside the Uniform Shape symbol. If needed for clarity, an additional A (or OR) shall be added as a note adjacent to the connection (for the uniform shape). The Distinctive Shape symbol representation shall show this capability by enveloping the branched connection with a smaller sized AND or OR symbol.	
Extension of Inputs—In the case where a circuit is used to add inputs to another AND or OR circuit, and the connection from this second circuit to the first is made at other than a normal input or output of the first circuit, the connection will be shown without polarity and will be labeled E (for extender). The relative position of the symbols and of the interconnecting extender line in the below example is not intended to be significant, and it may be drawn as any other input.	

Suggested Symbols for Buildups—The need for a symbol and the specific symbol to be used for repetitive logic depends essentially on the complexity of the equipment to be diagrammed. A buildup symbol may be used in a basic logic diagram or in a detail logic diagram, as needed.

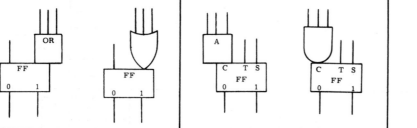

Shown is an example which may be used with either the Distinctive Shape symbols or the Uniform Shape symbols. The first section is shown in detail. The clear input is common for all the stages.

Applications—Multiple inputs to a FLIP-FLOP, (Examples 1 and 2) are drawn with the logic symbol tangent to the FLIP-FLOP symbol to indicate that they are part of the FLIP-FLOP hardware.

Inputs to the FLIP-FLOP symbol from other hardware are illustrated in Example 3.

Example 1.

Example 2.

Example 3.

APPENDIX A

EXAMPLES OF MIXED, POSITIVE AND NEGATIVE LOGIC

In the Table of Combinations, H refers to more positive (high), and L refers to less positive (low).

UNIFORM SHAPES		TABLE OF COMBINATIONS			DISTINCTIVE SHAPES	
AND	OR	A	B	X	AND	OR
		H	H	H		
		H	L	L		
		L	H	L		
		L	L	L		
		H	H	L		
		H	L	L		
		L	H	H		
		L	L	L		
		H	H	L		
		H	L	H		
		L	H	L		
		L	L	L		
		H	H	L		
		H	L	L		
		L	H	L		
		L	L	H		
		H	H	H		
		H	L	H		
		L	H	H		
		L	L	L		
		H	H	H		
		H	L	L		
		L	H	H		
		L	L	H		
		H	H	H		
		H	L	H		
		L	H	L		
		L	L	H		
		H	H	L		
		H	L	H		
		L	H	H		
		L	L	H		

138

EXAMPLES OF BASIC LOGIC DIAGRAMS

The following drawings illustrate the use of this Standard in the preparation of basic logic diagrams with either Uniform Shapes or Distinctive Shapes.

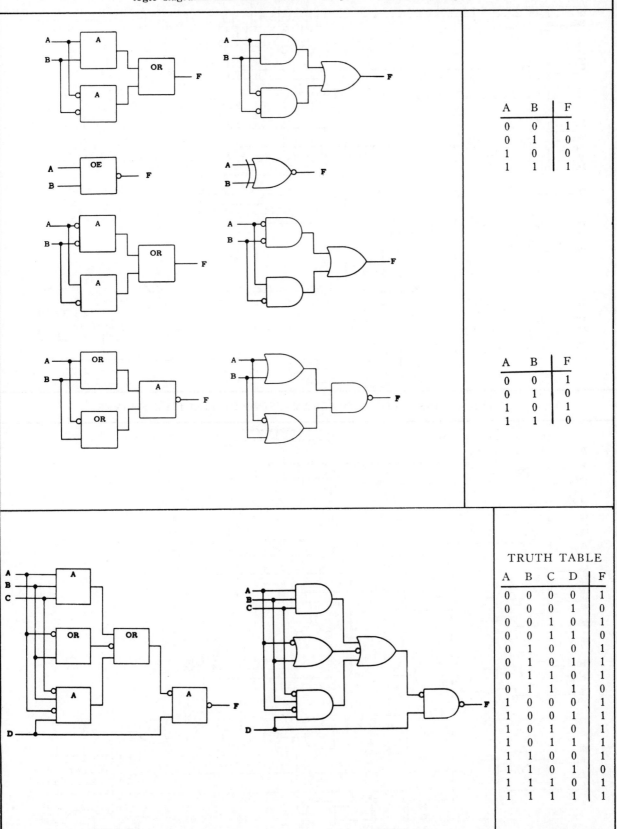

A	B	F
0	0	1
0	1	0
1	0	0
1	1	1

A	B	F
0	0	1
0	1	0
1	0	1
1	1	0

TRUTH TABLE

A	B	C	D	F
0	0	0	0	1
0	0	0	1	0
0	0	1	0	1
0	0	1	1	0
0	1	0	0	1
0	1	0	1	1
0	1	1	0	1
0	1	1	1	0
1	0	0	0	1
1	0	0	1	1
1	0	1	0	1
1	0	1	1	1
1	1	0	0	1
1	1	0	1	0
1	1	1	0	1
1	1	1	1	1

TYPICAL BASIC LOGIC DIAGRAM USING UNIFORM SHAPES

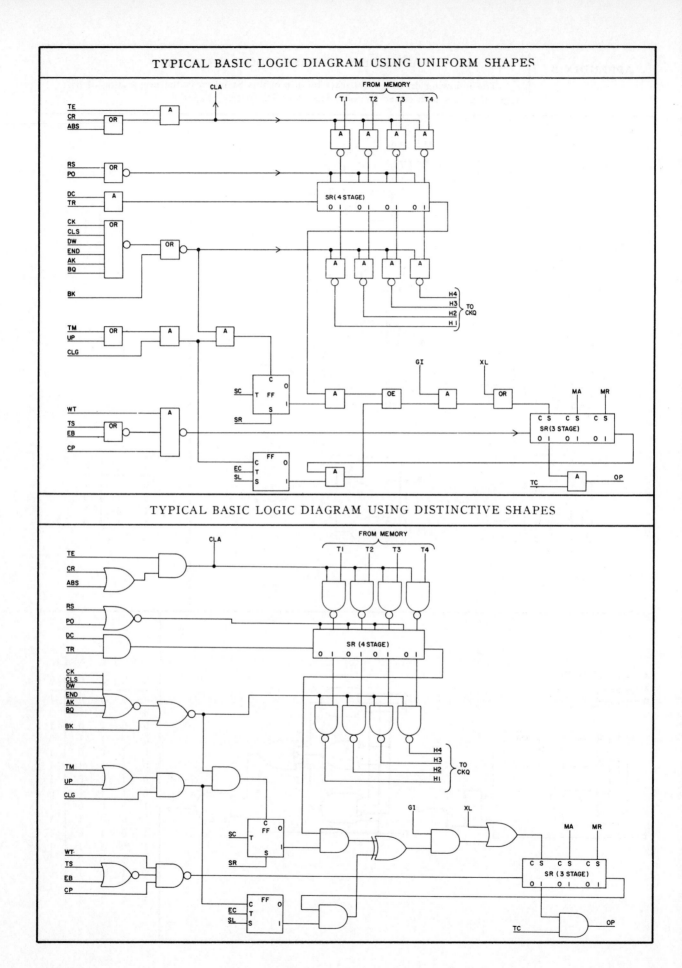

TYPICAL BASIC LOGIC DIAGRAM USING DISTINCTIVE SHAPES

EXAMPLES OF DETAILED LOGIC DIAGRAMS

APPENDIX C

The following drawings illustrate the use of this Standard in the preparation of detailed logic diagrams with either Uniform Shapes or Distinctive Shapes.

TYPICAL DETAILED LOGIC DIAGRAM IN MIXED LOGIC
USING UNIFORM SHAPES

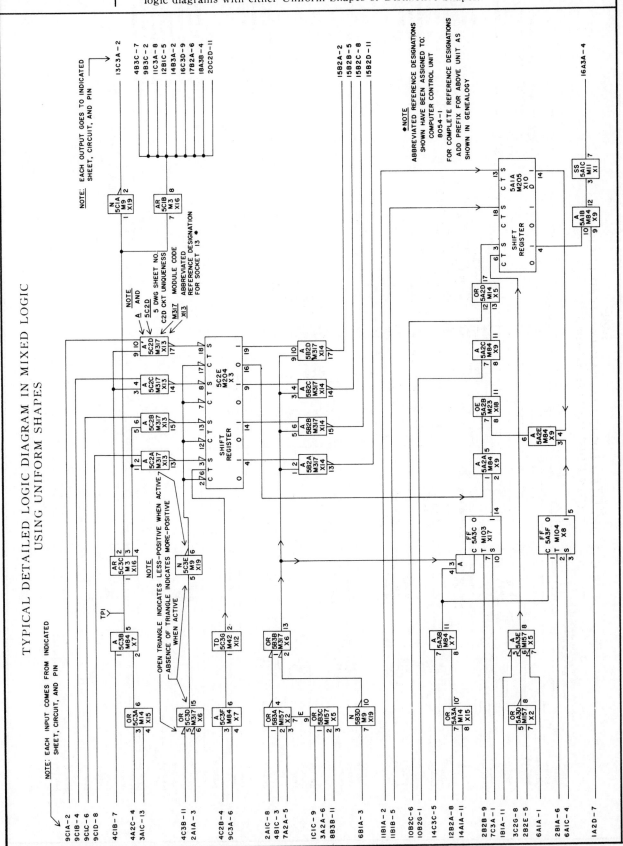

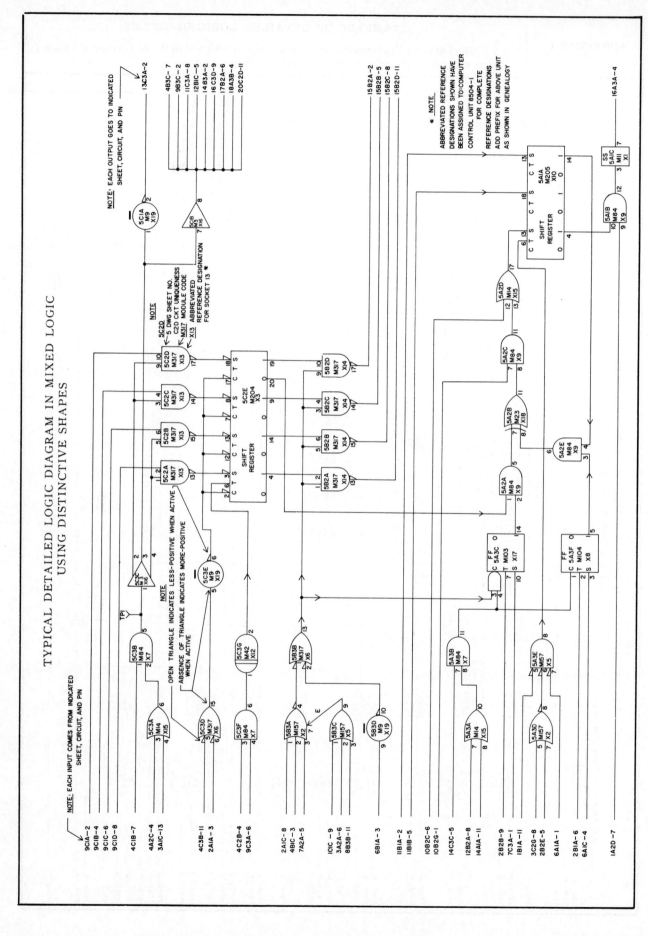

TYPICAL DETAILED LOGIC DIAGRAM IN MIXED LOGIC
USING DISTINCTIVE SHAPES

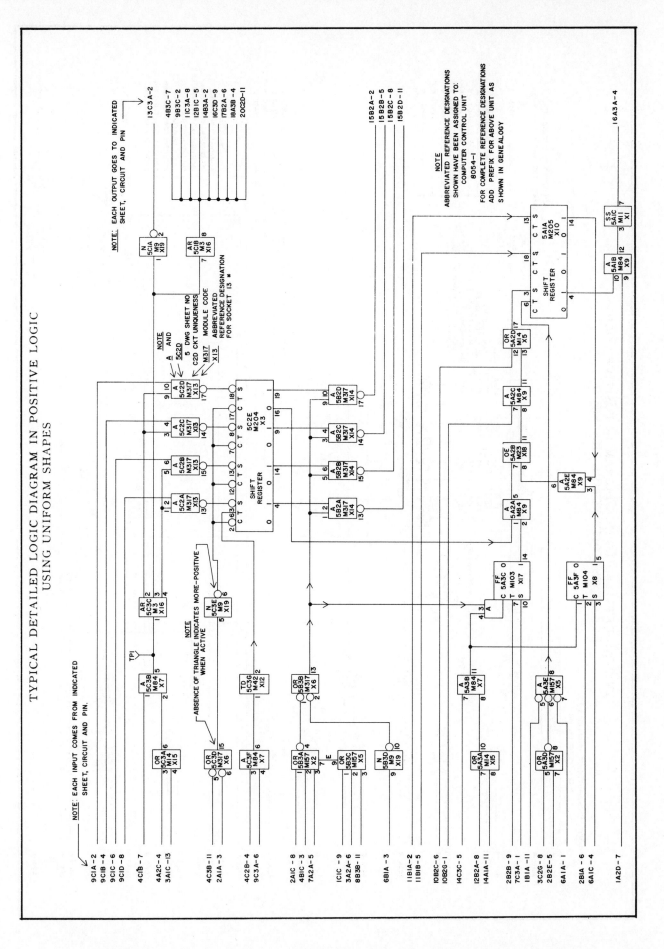

TYPICAL DETAILED LOGIC DIAGRAM IN POSITIVE LOGIC
USING UNIFORM SHAPES

143

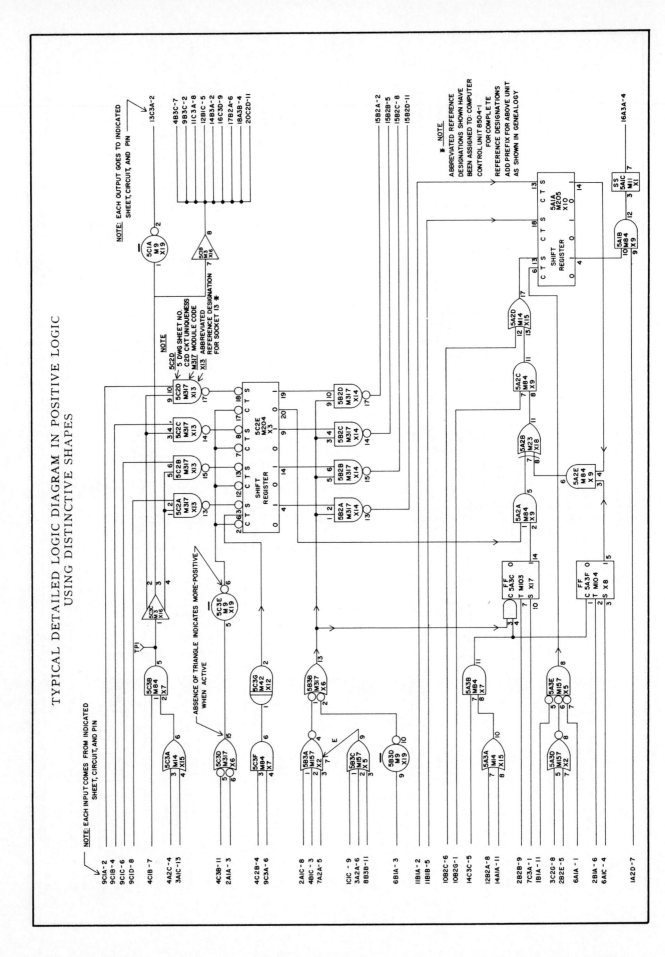

TYPICAL DETAILED LOGIC DIAGRAM IN POSITIVE LOGIC
USING DISTINCTIVE SHAPES

144

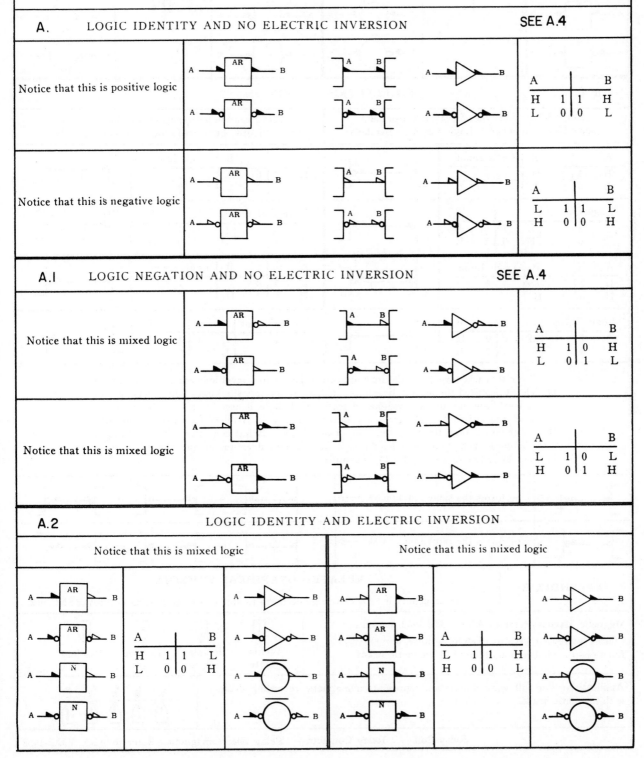

EXAMPLES OF USAGE OF
NEGATION, INVERTER AND AMPLIFIER SYMBOLS

APPENDIX D

The following examples illustrate the correct logic and electrical interpretation of the relative level indicators as applied to amplifiers and inverters, and the correct representation of logic negation on detailed logic diagrams, as specified in paragraphs 4.4.1 and 4.4.2, 6.5 and 6.9. The table associated with each group of diagrams shows both a truth table and a table of combinations where H and L stand for more positive (high) and less positive (low), respectively. The labels (A or B) on the lines refer to the nearest relative level indicator.

A. LOGIC IDENTITY AND NO ELECTRIC INVERSION   SEE A.4

Notice that this is positive logic

A			B
H	1	1	H
L	0	0	L

Notice that this is negative logic

A			B
L	1	1	L
H	0	0	H

A.1 LOGIC NEGATION AND NO ELECTRIC INVERSION   SEE A.4

Notice that this is mixed logic

A			B
H	1	0	H
L	0	1	L

Notice that this is mixed logic

A			B
L	1	0	L
H	0	1	H

A.2 LOGIC IDENTITY AND ELECTRIC INVERSION

Notice that this is mixed logic

Notice that this is mixed logic

A			B
H	1	1	L
L	0	0	H

A			B
L	1	1	H
H	0	0	L

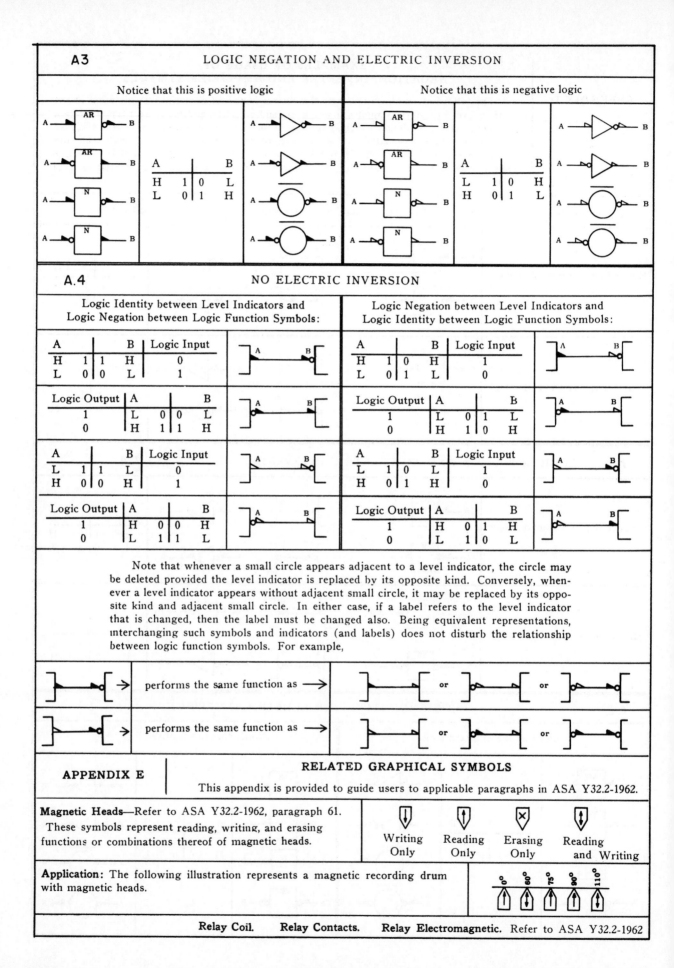

A3 — LOGIC NEGATION AND ELECTRIC INVERSION

Notice that this is positive logic

A		B
H	1 0	L
L	0 1	H

Notice that this is negative logic

A		B
L	1 0	H
H	0 1	L

A.4 — NO ELECTRIC INVERSION

Logic Identity between Level Indicators and Logic Negation between Logic Function Symbols:

A		B	Logic Input
H	1 1	H	0
L	0 0	L	1

Logic Output	A		B
1	L	0 0	L
0	H	1 1	H

A		B	Logic Input
L	1 1	L	0
H	0 0	H	1

Logic Output	A		B
1	H	0 0	H
0	L	1 1	L

Logic Negation between Level Indicators and Logic Identity between Logic Function Symbols:

A		B	Logic Input
H	1 0	H	1
L	0 1	L	0

Logic Output	A		B
1	L	0 1	L
0	H	1 0	H

A		B	Logic Input
L	1 0	L	1
H	0 1	H	0

Logic Output	A		B
1	H	0 1	H
0	L	1 0	L

Note that whenever a small circle appears adjacent to a level indicator, the circle may be deleted provided the level indicator is replaced by its opposite kind. Conversely, whenever a level indicator appears without adjacent small circle, it may be replaced by its opposite kind and adjacent small circle. In either case, if a label refers to the level indicator that is changed, then the label must be changed also. Being equivalent representations, interchanging such symbols and indicators (and labels) does not disturb the relationship between logic function symbols. For example,

performs the same function as — or — or

performs the same function as — or — or

APPENDIX E — RELATED GRAPHICAL SYMBOLS

This appendix is provided to guide users to applicable paragraphs in ASA Y32.2-1962.

Magnetic Heads—Refer to ASA Y32.2-1962, paragraph 61. These symbols represent reading, writing, and erasing functions or combinations thereof of magnetic heads.

Writing Only Reading Only Erasing Only Reading and Writing

Application: The following illustration represents a magnetic recording drum with magnetic heads.

0° 60° 75° 90° 110°

Relay Coil.   **Relay Contacts.**   **Relay Electromagnetic.** Refer to ASA Y32.2-1962

Extracted from MIL-STD-806B, Graphic Symbols for Logic Diagrams, with the permission of the Office of the Secretary of Defense, Public Affairs Department, Washington.

LOGIC FUNCTION	SYMBOL	EXPLANATION
AND.	* INPUT SIDE * OUTPUT SIDE A ─── B ─── F	The symbol shown represents the AND function. The AND output is high if and only if all the inputs are high. Input | Output A B | F L L | L L H | L H L | L H H | H
OR.	* INPUT SIDE * OUTPUT SIDE A ─── B ─── F	The symbol shown represents the INCLUSIVE OR function. The OR output is high (H) if and only if any one or more of the inputs are high (H). Input | Output A B | F L L | L L H | H H L | H H H | H
STATE INDICATOR (Active).	↗○ * Not part of symbol	The presence of the small circle symbol at the input(s) or output(s) of a function indicates: (a) Input Condition. The electrical condition at the input terminal(s) which control the active state of the respective function. (b) Output Condition. The electrical condition existing at the output terminal(s) of an activated function. A small circle(s) at the input(s) to any element (logical or nonlogical) indicates that the relatively low (L) input signal activates the function. Conversely, the absence of a small circle indicates that the relatively high (H) input signal activates the function. A small circle at the symbol output indicates that the output terminal of the activated function is relatively low (L). This small circle shall never be drawn by itself on a diagram.

LOGIC FUNCTION	SYMBOL	EXPLANATION
AND	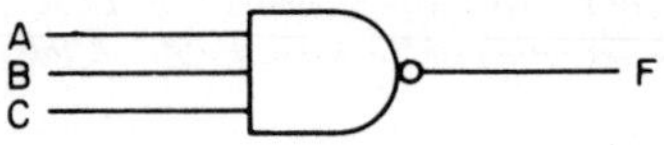	The symbol shown represents one version of the AND function. The output is low if and only if all the inputs are high. |	Input			Output
---	---	---	---
A	B	C	F
L	L	L	H
L	L	H	H
L	H	L	H
L	H	H	H
H	L	L	H
H	L	H	H
H	H	L	H
H	H	H	L	
OR	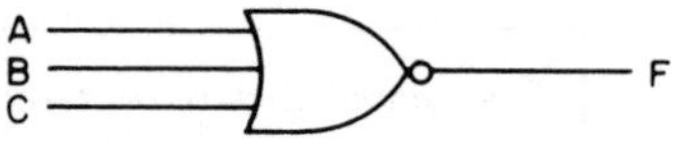	The symbol shown represents one version of the INCLUSIVE OR function. The output is low if any one or more inputs are high. |	Input			Output
---	---	---	---
A	B	C	F
L	L	L	H
L	L	H	L
L	H	L	L
L	H	H	L
H	L	L	L
H	L	H	L
H	H	L	L
H	H	H	L	
EXCLUSIVE OR.		The symbol shown represents the EXCLUSIVE OR function. NOTE A: Arc displacement determined by location of paragraph 7 template center input line guide hole. The EXCLUSIVE OR output is high if and only if any one input is high and all other inputs are low. 	Input		$F = A$ (H) and B (L) or B (H) and A (L)
A	B	
L	L	L
L	H	H
H	L	H
H	H	L | EXCLUSIVE OR may also be represented as shown in Appendix A, figure 11.

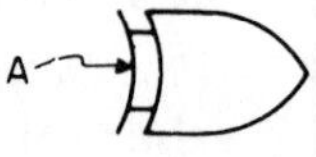

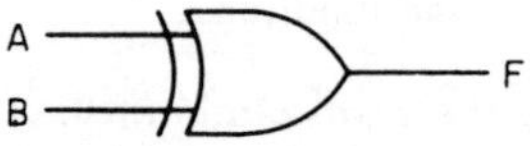

The following table of combinations illustrates
the applications and functions of two variables
and equivalents:

AND	OR	A	B	X
A, B — X	A, B — X	H H L L	H L H L	H L L L
A, B — X	A, B — X	H H L L	H L H L	L L H L
A, B — X	A, B — X	H H L L	H L H L	L H L L
A, B — X	A, B — X	H H L L	H L H L	L L L H
A, B — X	A, B — X	H H L L	H L H L	H H H L
A, B — X	A, B — X	H H L L	H L H L	H L H H
A, B — X	A, B — X	H H L L	H L H L	H H L H
A, B — X	A, B — X	H H L L	H L H L	L H H H

(Column header: TABLE OF COMBINATIONS)

FUNCTION

FLIP-FLOP.

The flip-flop is a device which stores a single
bit of information. It has three possible inputs,
set (S), clear (reset) (C), and toggle (trigger)(T),
and two possible outputs, 1 and 0.   When not
used, the trigger input may be omitted.   "S"
input shall be in proximity to the "1" output.

SYMBOL

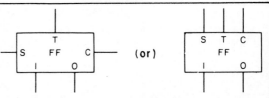

"C" input shall be in proximity to the
"0" output. The aspect ratio of the
symbol shall be 1.75 to 1.

FUNCTION	SYMBOL
BINARY REGISTER. The binary register symbol represents a group of flip- flops used in parallel to constitute a single register (as to store four bits of a char acter). It is necessary to indicate the number of "bits" or individual flip-flops in the register	Examples below show four "S" inputs grouped on one multiple input line and four each "1" and "0" grouped output lines. In some applications individual input and output lines are shown as in right hand figure. 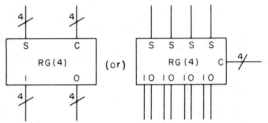 The aspect ratio of the symbol shall be 2.5 to 1 or greater, as required.
SHIFT REGISTER. The shift-register symbol represents a binary register with provision for displacing or shift ing the content of the register one stage at a time to the right or left by means of the "shift" input. The words "right shift input" shall be placed at a left corner of the symbol to indicate a shift from left to right. If the shift is from right to left, the words "left shift input" shall be placed at a right corner of the symbol.	The aspect ratio of the symbol shall be 2.5:1 or greater, as required. The choice of one of the following symbols depends on the diagram arrangement of the associated symbology 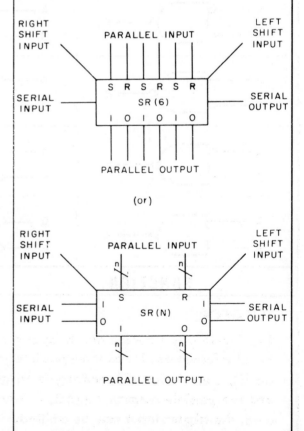

FUNCTION	SYMBOL
SINGLE SHOT FUNCTIONS. The symbols shown below are used to represent single-shot (SS) functions. Output signal shape, amplitude, duration, and polarity are determined by the circuit characteristics of the "SS," (not by the input signal) and may be shown inside or outside the symbol. The unactuated state of the "SS" is either zero or one. When actuated, it changes to the opposite state and remains in the opposite state for the duration of the active time of the device.	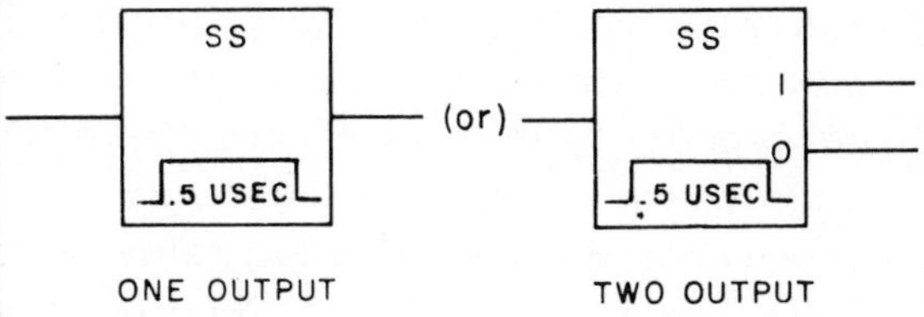 SS .5 USEC — (or) — SS 1 0 .5 USEC ONE OUTPUT TWO OUTPUT The aspect ratio of the symbol shall be 1:1.
SCHMITT TRIGGER. The symbols shown represent the Schmitt Trigger (ST) function. The device is actuated when the input signal crosses a certain "threshold" voltage. Output signal amplitude and polarity are determined by the circuit characteristics of the "ST," (not by the input signal). Stylized waveforms may be shown (inside or outside the symbol), indicating amplitude, polarity, threshold voltage and duration. The unactuated state of "ST" is either zero or one. When actuated, it changes to the opposite state and remains in the opposite state as long as the input exceeds the threshold value.	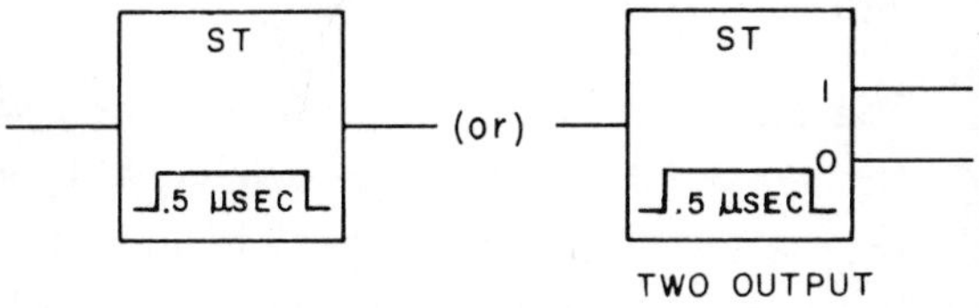 ST .5 μSEC — (or) — ST 1 0 .5 μSEC TWO OUTPUT The aspect ratio of the symbol shall be 1:1.
GENERAL LOGIC SYMBOL. Symbol for functions not elsewhere specified. The symbol shall be adequately labeled to identify the function performed. It is not intended that this symbol be used for functions which can be logically expressed by a single symbol established in this standard.	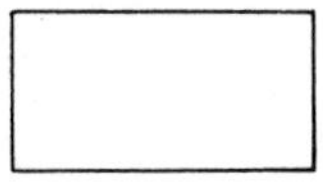 Aspect ratio shall be 2:1 or greater.

FUNCTION	SYMBOL
AMPLIFIER. Refer to MIL-STD-15-1 This symbol represents a linear or nonlinear current or voltage amplifier. This amplifier may have one or more stages and may or may not produce gain or inversion. Level changers and inverters, pulse amplifiers, emitter followers, cathode followers, relay pullers, lamp drivers, and shift register drivers are examples of devices for which this symbol is applicable.	
TIME DELAY SYMBOL. Refer to MIL-STD-15-1 The duration of the delay is included with the symbol. If the delay device is tapped, the delay time with respect to the input shall be included adjacent to the tap output. Twin vertical lines indicates the input side.	
PRACTICE Multiple inputs to a single function.	AND Function OR Function

FUNCTION	SYMBOL
Multiple inputs to physically separated functions with common outputs.	**AND Function** 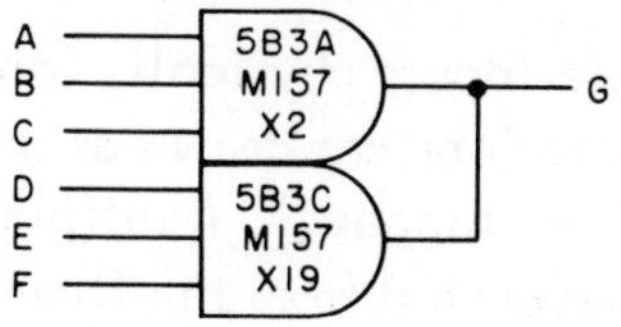 A B C → 5B3A M157 X2 D E F → 5B3C M157 X19 → G **OR Function** 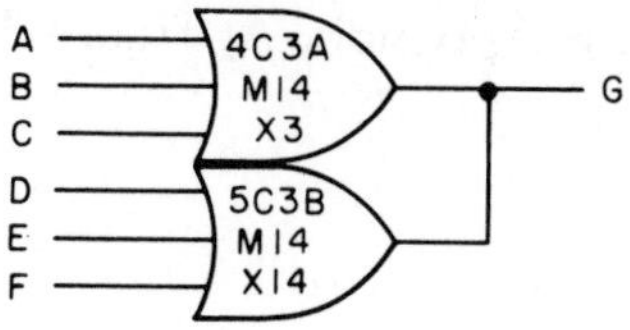 A B C → 4C3A M14 X3 D E F → 5C3B M14 X14 → G
OUTPUT COMBINATIONS Use of Separate Circuits. Where functions have the capability of being combined according to the AND (or OR) function, simply by having the outputs connected, that capability shall be shown by enveloping the branched connection with a smaller sized AND or OR symbol.	**Dot "AND"** 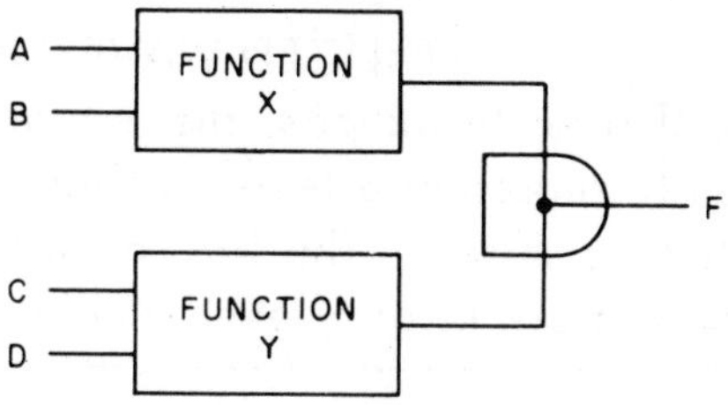 A B → FUNCTION X C D → FUNCTION Y → F **Dot "OR"** 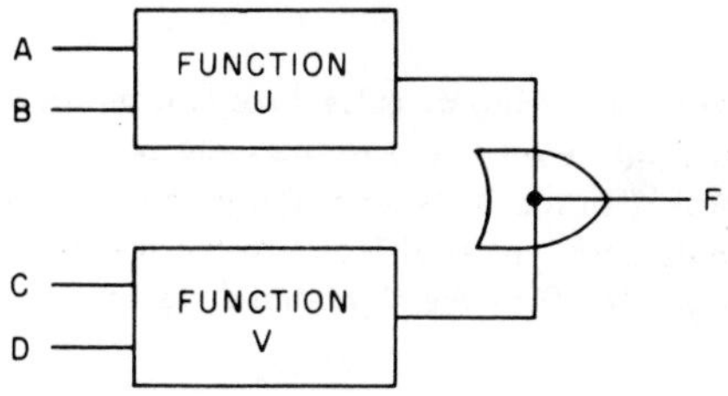 A B → FUNCTION U C D → FUNCTION V → F
EXTENDED INPUTS. In the case where a circuit is used to add inputs to another AND or OR circuit, and the connection from this second circuit to the first is made at other than a normal input or output of the first circuit, the connection will be as shown below, and will be labeled E to indicate extension of the input. See also Appendix A, figure 7. The letter R, when shown adjacent to a symbol, indicates that the output resistor is adjacent to or in the vicinity of the hardware's physical location described by the internal tagging of that symbol.	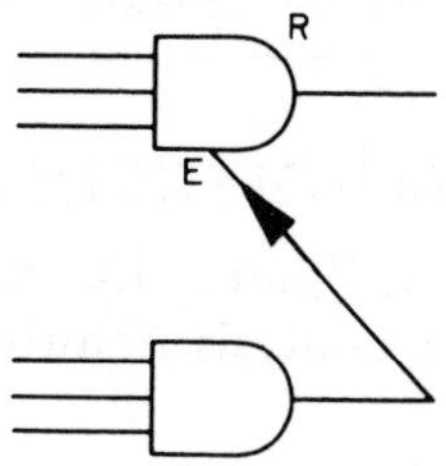 R E

FUNCTION	SYMBOL

MULTIPLE FLIP-FLOP INPUTS.

Multiple inputs physically integral with flip-flop functions are drawn as shown in Example 1, and so "tagged." Multiple inputs physically separated from the flip-flop functions are drawn as shown in Example 2, and separately tagged.

See also Appendix A, figure 12.

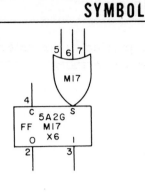
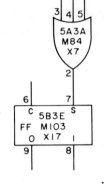

Example 1   Example 2

STYLIZED WAVEFORMS AND NOTATIONS

STYLIZED WAVEFORMS. Stylized waveforms may be placed adjacent to signal lines to indicate the nature and timing of the signals. Waveform symbols shall be used to represent a level, a single pulse, or a pulse train. Voltage levels shall be indicated, as shown. The time of occurrence of a pulse or the beginning and ending times of a pulse train or of a level may be indicated.

Level starting at pulse time A and ending at pulse time B.

Pulse occurring at pulse time C from the less positive level (-2V) to the more positive level (+5V), in the left-hand figure; and from the more positive level (+5V) to the less positive level (-2V) in the right-hand figure.

Pulse train with first pulse occurring at pulse time D and last pulse at pulse time E. (In the case of an information bearing pulse train, not all pulses are necessarily shown.)

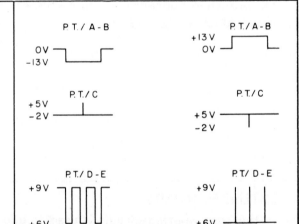

NOTE: Pulse may be represented as a single or double line, as appropriate, to clarify logic.

WAVEFORM NOTATIONS.

The following figures illustrate the application of waveform analysis notations to stylized waveforms.

PULSE CHARACTERISTIC NOTATION:

t_r	(0.2)	indicates the rise time in microseconds
t_d	(3)	indicates the duration in microseconds
t_f	(0.5)	indicates the fall time in microseconds
v_d	(10)	indicates the amplitude in volts
i_d	(10)	indicates the amplitude in amperes

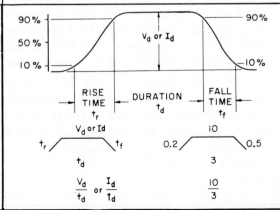

MECHANICAL AID

The template shown below illustrates the relative sizes of logic symbols.

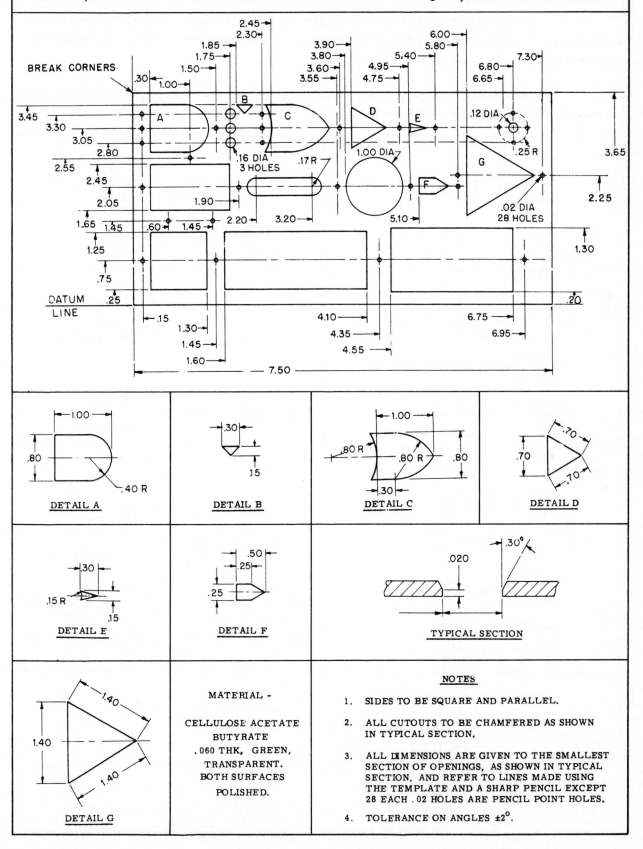

DETAIL A

DETAIL B

DETAIL C

DETAIL D

DETAIL E

DETAIL F

TYPICAL SECTION

DETAIL G

MATERIAL -

CELLULOSE ACETATE
BUTYRATE
.060 THK, GREEN,
TRANSPARENT.
BOTH SURFACES
POLISHED.

NOTES

1. SIDES TO BE SQUARE AND PARALLEL.

2. ALL CUTOUTS TO BE CHAMFERED AS SHOWN IN TYPICAL SECTION.

3. ALL DIMENSIONS ARE GIVEN TO THE SMALLEST SECTION OF OPENINGS, AS SHOWN IN TYPICAL SECTION, AND REFER TO LINES MADE USING THE TEMPLATE AND A SHARP PENCIL EXCEPT 28 EACH .02 HOLES ARE PENCIL POINT HOLES.

4. TOLERANCE ON ANGLES ±2°.

APPENDIX A   CIRCUIT AND SYMBOL CORRESPONDENCE EXAMPLES

Examples below illustrate:

(a) Basic circuitry of typical digital device hardware. In practice the hardware chosen to implement basic logic functions may be in many other forms, dependent on design criteria or the state of the art.

(b) Applications of graphic symbols relating hardware to logic functions drawn on detailed logic diagrams. Numerals on illustrations are input-output pin numbers.

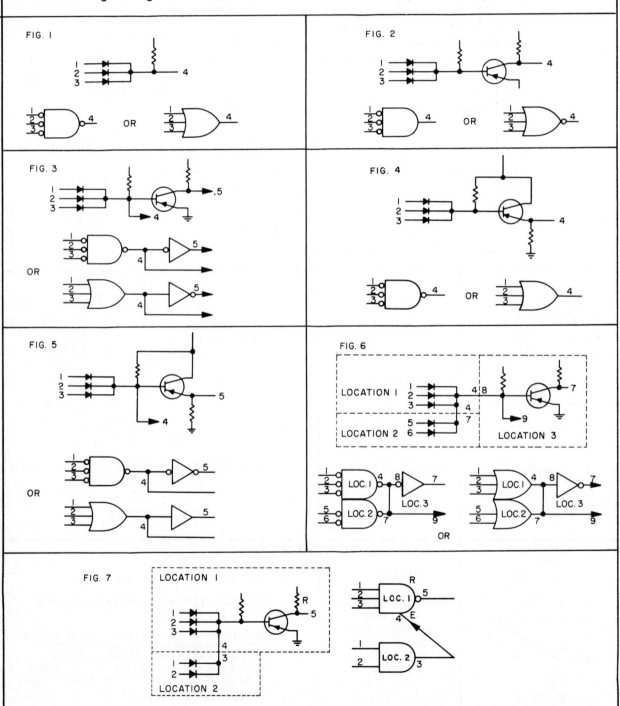

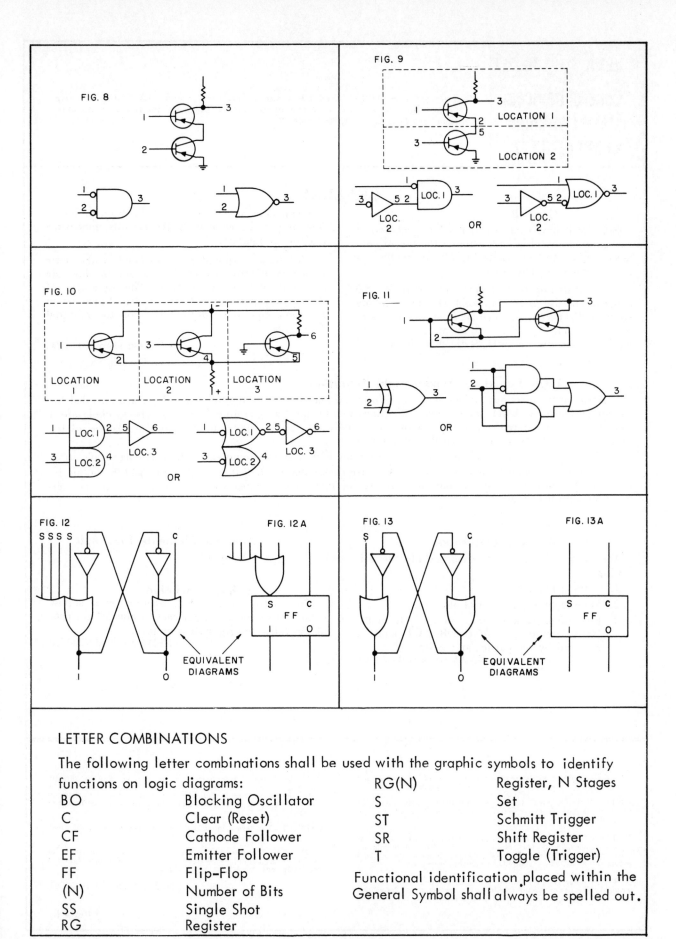

FIG. 8

FIG. 9

LOCATION 1

LOCATION 2

LOC. 1

OR

LOC. 1

LOC. 2

LOC. 2

FIG. 10

LOCATION 1

LOCATION 2

LOCATION 3

LOC. 1

LOC. 2

LOC. 3

LOC. 1

LOC. 2

LOC. 3

OR

FIG. 11

OR

FIG. 12

FIG. 12 A

S S S S   C

S   C

FF

EQUIVALENT
DIAGRAMS

FIG. 13

FIG. 13 A

S   C

S   C

FF

EQUIVALENT
DIAGRAMS

LETTER COMBINATIONS

The following letter combinations shall be used with the graphic symbols to identify
functions on logic diagrams:

BO	Blocking Oscillator	RG(N)	Register, N Stages
C	Clear (Reset)	S	Set
CF	Cathode Follower	ST	Schmitt Trigger
EF	Emitter Follower	SR	Shift Register
FF	Flip-Flop	T	Toggle (Trigger)
(N)	Number of Bits		
SS	Single Shot		
RG	Register		

Functional identification placed within the
General Symbol shall always be spelled out.

Extracted from NEMA 1C-1-1959, Control, Industrial, Section 15, Static Switching Control Devices, with the permission of the National Electrical Manufacturers Association, 155 East 44 Street, New York, N.Y.

GENERAL

General

Static switching control is defined as a method of switching electrical circuits without the use of contacts (the control primarily includes magnetic amplifiers and solid-state devices).

Static switching control performs similar to the conventional use of relays except without switching contacts. Relays convert a single input to a coil into various outputs by means of its moving armature closing or opening contacts. Static switching control elements convert a single or combination of inputs into outputs by controlling the circuits impedance and/or modulation.

The logic terminology associated with static switching control is included herein to illustrate some operating logic functions. The same type of device may perform different control functions in the same equipment depending upon the required functions.

NEMA Standard 11-17-1960.

Logic Functions, Symbols and Definitions♦

Device logic functions and symbols are illustrated and defined by the following. They are intended for use on electrical elementary or schematic diagrams to indicate the operating functions. The symbols are a shorthand graphical representation and not necessarily intended to represent the physical likeness of the device nor certain complete electrical connections.

The symbols may be combined into various circuit adaptations as required by the particular application.

Input terminals on symbols and truth tables are designated by the letters A, B and C, and the output by the letter X. These markings are only for purposes of reference, to explain the functions, and are not terminal or wire markings.

Device Identification

Markings on static units shall include the following:

1. Catalog number.
2. Manufacturer's identification.
3. Functional marking (does not apply to multi-function units; e.g., AND, OR, NOT, etc.) as required by the particular application.

NEMA Standard 11-17-1960.

General Elements for Logic Diagram

Voltage Variation

The control system shall operate on a supply voltage from minus 10 per cent to plus 10 per cent of the rated control system voltage.

NEMA Standard 9-29-1960.

NOTE I—Input terminals are shown on the left side of symbols and output terminals are shown on the right side of symbols.

NOTE II—The number of the symbol inputs may vary because of different designs. They represent typical examples and are not all-inclusive.

NOTE III—With reference to memory, retentive memory and off return memory, the memory input and output "ON" terminals are the upper lines on the symbols. The "OFF" input terminals (and output terminals, when required) are on the lower lines.

NOTE IV—For GATE symbols, the control input is the top left terminal. The power circuit terminals are the right and lower left terminals. (See gate (non-isolated and isolated.)

NOTE V—Return circuit terminals are not shown when directly connected to common or ground. When return circuits need to be shown, the control circuit shall be connected as a top vertical terminal. (For example, see gates and signal converter with return circuits.)

NOTE VI—The term "input" or "output" denotes a signal which is useful or significant to elements of the system.

NOTE VII—The terms "on" and "off" denote the presence or absence of an output, respectively. The "off" condition does not necessarily mean that there is no signal.

NEMA Standard 7-12-1961.

♦ Revised.

Logic Function	Symbol	Definitions	Truth Tables
AND	A, B, C → X	A device which produces an output only when every input is energized.	**Truth Table—AND** A B C X 0 0 0 0 0 0 1 0 0 1 0 0 0 1 1 0 1 0 0 0 1 0 1 0 1 1 0 0 1 1 1 1
NOT	A → X	A device which produces an output only when the input is not energized.	**Truth Table—NOT** A X 0 1 1 0
NOR	A, B, C → X	A device which produces an output only when every input is not energized.	**Truth Table—NOR** A B C X 0 0 0 1 0 0 1 0 0 1 0 0 0 1 1 0 1 0 0 0 1 0 1 0 1 1 0 0 1 1 1 0
OR	A, B, C → X	A device which produces an output when one input (or more) is energized.	**Truth Table—OR** A B C X 0 0 0 0 0 0 1 1 0 1 0 1 0 1 1 1 1 0 0 1 1 0 1 1 1 1 0 1 1 1 1 1

Logic Function	Symbol	Definitions
MEMORY		A device which retains the condition of output corresponding to the input last energized as long as power is maintained.
RETENTIVE MEMORY		A device which retains the conditions of output corresponding to the input last energized.
OFF RETURN MEMORY		A device which retains the condition of output corresponding to the input last energized, except upon interruption of power it returns to the off condition.
TIME DELAY ENERGIZING		A device which produces an output following definite intentional time delay after its input is energized.

Logic Function	Symbol	Definitions
TIME DELAY DE-ENERGIZING		A device whose output is de-energized following a definite intentional time delay after its input is de-energized.
TIME DELAY ENERGIZING AND DE-ENERGIZING		A device which produces an output following a definite intentional time delay after its input is energized and whose output is de-energized following a definite intentional time delay after its input is de-energized.
ADJUSTABLE TIME DELAY		Otherwise similar to time delay energizing, time delay de-energizing, and time delay energizing and de-energizing.
AMPLIFIER		A device in which an input signal controls a local source of power to produce an output enlarged relative to the input.
GATE (NON-ISOLATED)		A device which permits current flow in a non-isolated circuit when the control input is energized.
GATE (ISOLATED)		A device which permits current flow in an isolated circuit when the control input is energized.
SIGNAL CONVERTER		A device for changing a pilot signal to a logic input.
GATES AND SIGNAL CONVERTER WITH RETURN CIRCUITS		
GATE		A device which permits current flow in a non-isolated circuit when the control input is energized.
GATE		A device which permits current flow in an isolated circuit when the control input is energized.
SIGNAL CONVERTER		A device for changing a pilot signal to a logic input.
		(Continued)

IC 1-15.04 General Elements for Logic Diagram

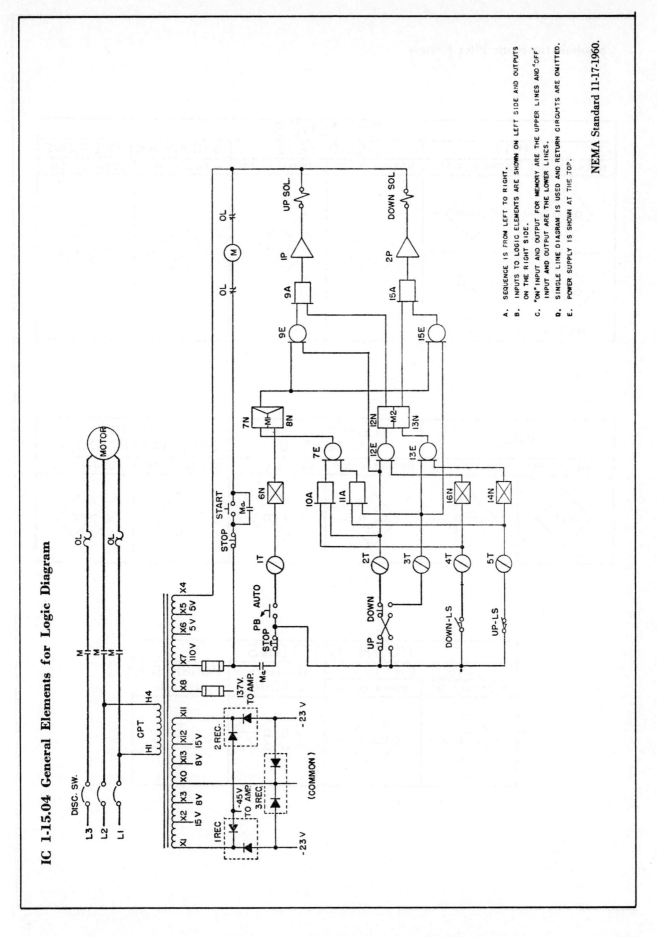

A. SEQUENCE IS FROM LEFT TO RIGHT.

B. INPUTS TO LOGIC ELEMENTS ARE SHOWN ON LEFT SIDE AND OUTPUTS ON THE RIGHT SIDE.

C. "ON" INPUT AND OUTPUT FOR MEMORY ARE THE UPPER LINES AND "OFF" INPUT AND OUTPUT ARE THE LOWER LINES.

D. SINGLE LINE DIAGRAM IS USED AND RETURN CIRCUITS ARE OMITTED.

E. POWER SUPPLY IS SHOWN AT THE TOP.

NEMA Standard 11-17-1960.

SWITCHES					
LIMIT		LIQUID LEVEL		VACUUM AND PRESSURE	
NORMALLY OFF	NORMALLY ON	NORMALLY OFF	NORMALLY ON	NORMALLY OFF	NORMALLY ON
HELD ON	HELD OFF				

FOOT		TEMPERATURE ACTUATED		FLOW (AIR, WATER, ETC.)	
NORMALLY OFF	NORMALLY ON	NORMALLY OFF	NORMALLY ON	NORMALLY OFF	NORMALLY ON

PUSH BUTTONS			
SINGLE CIRCUIT		DOUBLE CIRCUIT	MUSHROOM HEAD
NORMALLY OFF	NORMALLY ON		

Logic Function (BOOLEAN)

Reproduced from "Digital Applications of Magnetic Devices," by Albert J. Meyerhoff, published by John Wiley & Sons, Inc., New York, 1960.

Truth Table, Boolean Functions of Two Binary Variables

Formal Name of Function	Truth Table a 0 0 1 1 / b 0 1 0 1				Symbol	Formula f (AND, OR, NOT)	To Be Read as:	Common Name of Function
Falsity	0	0	0	0	0	$f = 0$		(trivial)
Conjunction	0	0	0	1		$f = ab$	a and b	AND
Inhibition	0	0	1	0	$\not\Rightarrow$	$f = ab'$	a and not b	INHIBIT
(a)	0	0	1	1		$f = a$	a	(trivial)
Reverse inhibition	0	1	0	0	$\not\Leftarrow$	$f = a'b$	not a and b	INHIBIT
(b)	0	1	0	1		$f = b$	b	(trivial)
Nonequivalence	0	1	1	0	$\not\Leftrightarrow$	$f = ab' \vee a'b$	a not equivalent to b	EXCLUSIVE OR
Disjunction	0	1	1	1	$\vee$	$f = a \vee b$	a or b	OR, INCLUSIVE OR
Conjunctive negation	1	0	0	0	$\downarrow$	$f = a'b'$	not a and not b	Peirce stroke, JOINT DENIAL
Equivalence	1	0	0	1	$\Leftrightarrow$	$f = ab \vee a'b'$	a equivalent to b	MATERIAL EQUIVALENCE
Negation of a	1	0	1	0	$'$	$f = a'$	not a	NOT
Reverse implication	1	0	1	1	$\Leftarrow$	$f = a \vee b'$	a or not b	(not used directly)
Negation of b	1	1	0	0	$'$	$f = b'$	not b	NOT
Implication	1	1	0	1	$\Rightarrow$	$f = a' \vee b$	not a or b	(not used directly)
Disjunctive negation	1	1	1	0	$\uparrow$	$f = a' \vee b'$	not a or not b	Sheffer stroke
Tautology	1	1	1	1	1	$f = 1$		(trivial)

LOGIC (PMA)
(Parallel Magnetic Pulse Amplifier-Basic-Delay)

Reproduced from "Digital Applications of Magnetic Devices," by Albert J. Meyerhoff, published by John Wiley & Sons, Inc., New York, 1960.

Basic PMA Logic Symbols

Name	Symbol	Denotation	
Basic circuit or stage	$T1$ ◯	A wound core of square-loop magnetic material is assumed,	and is uniquely designated as indicated.
Pulse line	→	Signal flow (not necessarily current) follows the arrow.	
Transfer loop	$S3$)→(	A symbol is used to uniquely designate a particular SD (S)	or SW (B) loop.
D-c line	→	Input d-c level (or pulse of long duration relative to control	pulses) is applied as indicated.
Pulse override	→→	Input signal predominates over simultaneously applied pulses	or levels.
D-c override	→▶	Input d-c level predominates over simultaneously applied	pulses or levels.
OR connection	⌐→	Pulses in the two left lines are mixed to produce pulses in a single line. Series connection	in a single transfer loop is implied.
INHIBIT	⊥	Pulse in lower line inhibits pulse in upper line.	
Branching	⌐→	Pulse in left line is transferred to separate destinations.	Series connection in a single transfer loop is implied.
Clock pulse	t_3 → ①$T1$	A prime, clear, or read pulse ensures the storage specifically of a ONE (or a ZERO, as other-	wise indicated) at every t_3, leaving the core in either the prime or the clear state.
Insert	a_3 → ①$T1$	An insert pulse at t_3, unless overridden, ensures the storage of a ONE (representing a_3 input information) in core $T1$, or the absence of an insert pulse at t_3	implies a ZERO a_3 insert (or vice versa, as otherwise indicated), and either insert is possible at any t_3.
Unconditional transfer	D_2↓ a_1→ ①$T1$ →◯$T2$ ↑t_3	Data transfer from $T1$ to $T2$ is caused by read at t_3, or by D_2 at t_2.	

Name	Symbol	Denotation	
Conditional transfer		Data transfer from $T1$ to $T2$ is caused by read at t_3 only; read by D_2 is prevented at t_2.	
Drivers and other non-magnetic circuits		A buffer driver (or other non-magnetic circuit, as otherwise indicated) is energized at t_3, and is designated by appro-	priate letter symbols. (Clock drivers are generally not shown on logic diagrams.)
Diode OR element		The symbol indicates a diode OR circuit.	

Basic Delay PMA Logic Symbols

Name	Symbol	Denotation
Basic circuit or stage		A wound core of square-loop material, a diode or transistor, and delay networks, as required.
Data transfer line		Signal flow follows the arrow; a lower-case letter identifies inputs and outputs (in this case, a and b, respectively).
Drive or read pulse		A drive or read pulse is indicated by the hook symbol, usually shown only for stages driven by buffer drivers.
Branching		Pulse in left line is transferred to separate destinations.
OR connection		The OR function is performed by the core (upper symbol), or by the diodes (lower symbol).
INHIBIT connection		The INHIBIT function is performed by input line b.
ONE generator		The stage produces a ONE output every drive time.

*Reproduced from "Digital Applications of Magnetic Devices," by Albert J. Meyerhoff,
published by John Wiley & Sons, Inc., New York, 1960.*

SMA Logic Symbols

Name	Symbol	Denotation
Complementing SMA (NOT function).	I Ph-*A*	The circuit of Fig. 16.1[*] or its equivalent is implied; the drive phase employed is indicated by the symbol at upper right (in this case Ph-*A* indicates phase *A*).
Asserting SMA	Ph-*B*	The circuit of Fig. 16.3[*] or its equivalent is implied; the drive phase employed is indicated by the symbol at upper right (in this case Ph-*B* indicates phase *B*).
Pulse line	*a* — Ph-*B* — *a'*	Pulse line as shown provides input to asserting SMA; second pulse line shown receives output; no arrows are used; a lower case letter identifies inputs and outputs (in this case *a* and NOT *a* respectively).
Multiple inputs	*a b c d* — *e*	Any of the input pulses will be amplified; the SMA shown performs an OR function ($e = a \lor b \lor c \lor d$).
Pulse line to INHIBIT input	*a* ———o	An open circle on the SMA symbol indicates that the pulse line terminating at the circle performs an INHIBIT function on the other inputs of the SMA.

[*] NEXT PAGE

Name	Symbol	Denotation
Special INHIBIT element	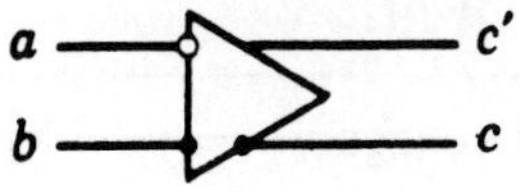	The circuit of Fig. 16.3 used as described in the text is implied; drive phase may be indicated as with any other SMA; dots are used to indicate positive polarity; function performed is INHIBIT ($c = a'b$).
Special shifting element	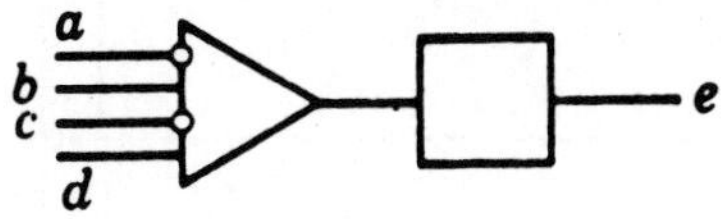	A circuit with two input windings is implied; a inhibits b, c inhibits d ($e = a'b \lor c'd$); the rectangle represents an additional passive delay of one-half cycle.
Special delay element		An element logically equivalent to the asserting SMA is implied; the notation represents a more economical design capable of driving only one other element.
Diode AND gate	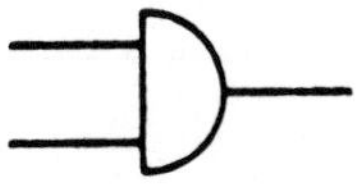	The usual diode AND gate is implied.
Diode OR gate	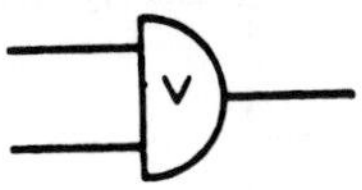	Diodes connected in the usual fashion for performing OR are implied.

FIG. 16.1. Basic complementing amplifier.

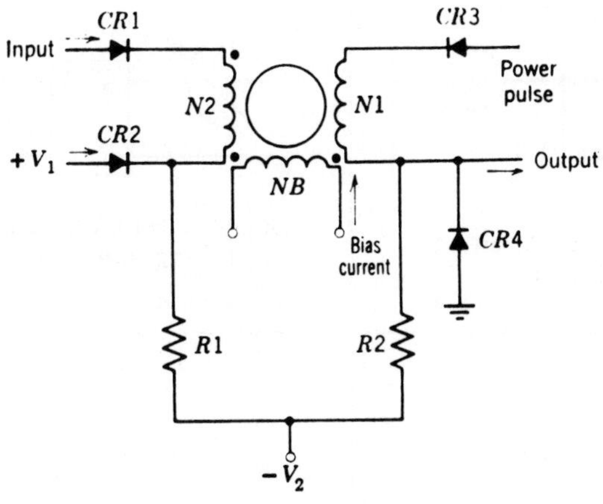

FIG. 16.3. Two-output asserting amplifier.

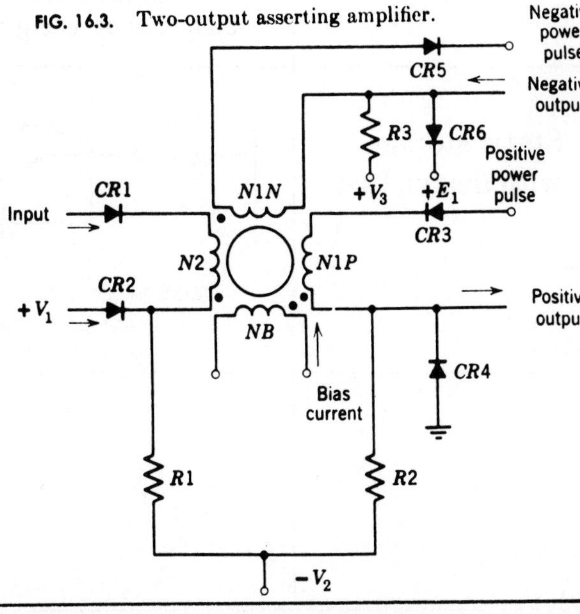

Relay-SMA Equivalent Symbols

Element	Relay Circuit	SMA Element
Logic Elements		
OR	Control voltage — Relay coil a — Output $= a \vee b$	$a \vee b$
AND	a — Output $= ab$	ab
NOT	a — Output $= a'$	a — I — a'
Storage Elements		
Static storage	Stop — Start — a. Start: Contact holds relay after start button is released. Stop: Coil de-energizer, opening contact	S 1 / R 0. After $S = 1$, Output $= 1$. After $R = 1$, Output $= 0$
Static storage with delayed set	Stop — Slow start — a. Delay in start caused by escapement or pneumatic device	S 1 / R 0. Delay in set caused by timing element

Reproduced from "Digital Applications of Magnetic Devices," by Albert J. Meyerhoff, published by John Wiley & Sons, Inc., New York, 1960.

TMA Logic Symbols

Name	Symbol	Denotation
Base circuit or stage	*TM2*	A square-loop core and transistor are implied; a designation of the element can be inscribed in the symbol as shown; the legend "ED" inscribed in the symbol denotes an enabling pulse driver.
Delay	D	A time delay, using passive circuit elements, is implied.
Input designations, TMA one-shot	a_n	One-shot is triggered at ripple time RTn by input a.
	RTn	One-shot is triggered at ripple time RTn by ripple driver.
Input designations, square TMA	b_n — 0	Square TMA is triggered to ZERO at RTn by input b.
	RTn — 1	Square TMA is triggered to ONE at RTn by ripple driver.
Output designations, TMA one-shot	$+1$ -2	One-shot produces outputs on two separate windings; the numbers and signs indicate the value and sense of each output voltage.
	c_{n+1} a_n → TM1 $+1$ b_n → TM2 -1 0 $RT(n+1)$	One-shots with output windings in series; outputs are of unit value but opposite sense so that when b_n is ONE, TM2 inhibits output of TM1. Ripple pulse $RT'(n+1)$ enables input to next stage (c_{n+1}). Active bias is zero. $c = ab'$. Short notation is $c = 0, a, -b$.

Name	Symbol	Denotation
(Output designations, continued)		One-shots with output windings in series; the outputs all have unit value and positive sense. The ripple pulse $RT(n + 1)$ has active bias of -2 so that three inputs must be ONE to produce trigger on input line to next stage (d_{n+1}). $d = abc$. Short notation is $d = -2, a, b, c$.
		A TMA one-shot is triggered at time RTn, and its delayed output enabled at a later time $RT(n + p)$.
Output designation, square TMA		Square TMA produces output pulse when switched to ZERO; numbers and signs indicate value and sense of each output voltage.
Driver		A current driver for switching cores is implied; the trigger pulse is designated, in this case ripple pulse RTn.
Diode OR		The usual diode OR is implied.

ABA Pub No 147

BANKING (COMMON MACHINE LANGUAGE, CHECKS)

Extracted from BMP 147 (Automation of Bank Operating Procedure) — The Common Machine Language for Mechanized Check Handling, through the courtesy of the Bank Management Commission, American Bankers Association, 12 East 36 Street, New York, N.Y.

Character Configuration

A. *Designation:* E-13B (comprising 14 characters—10 numeric figures 0-9 and 4 symbols)

B. *Description:*

1. Ten digits   Strokes 0-9
2. Four symbols

    ⑆ Transit Number Symbol   Stroke 10

    ⑈ Amount Symbol   Stroke 11

    ⑇ On Us Symbol   Stroke 12

    ⑉ Dash Symbol   Stroke 13

[*Note:* In the following text these three words refer to the start-stop signals illustrated rather than the normal terminology of transit number-routing symbol.]

3. Nominal Character Height   .117 inches

Nominal Character Width varies

     .052; .065; .078; .091 inches

Nominal Width of Horizontal and Vertical Bars   .013 inches

C. *Dimensions:* Detailed dimensions and the horizontal centerline (₵$_H$) of the *Printed* Character are shown on drawings covering Strokes 0 through 13. These drawings, dated November 21, 1958,

Common Language Standard-Design, Dimensions

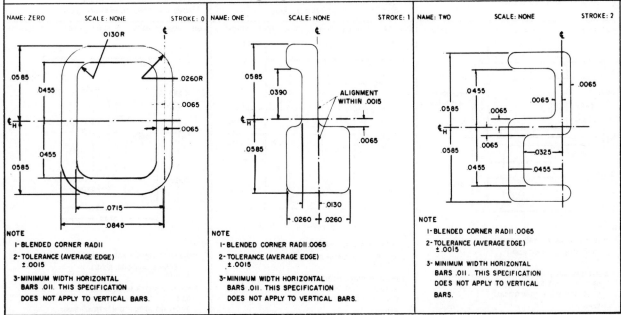

NOTE

1- BLENDED CORNER RADII

2- TOLERANCE (AVERAGE EDGE) ±.0015

3- MINIMUM WIDTH HORIZONTAL BARS .011. THIS SPECIFICATION DOES NOT APPLY TO VERTICAL BARS.

NOTE

1- BLENDED CORNER RADII .0065

2- TOLERANCE (AVERAGE EDGE) ±.0015

3- MINIMUM WIDTH HORIZONTAL BARS .011. THIS SPECIFICATION DOES NOT APPLY TO VERTICAL BARS.

NOTE

1- BLENDED CORNER RADII .0065

2- TOLERANCE (AVERAGE EDGE) ±.0015

3- MINIMUM WIDTH HORIZONTAL BARS .011. THIS SPECIFICATION DOES NOT APPLY TO VERTICAL BARS.

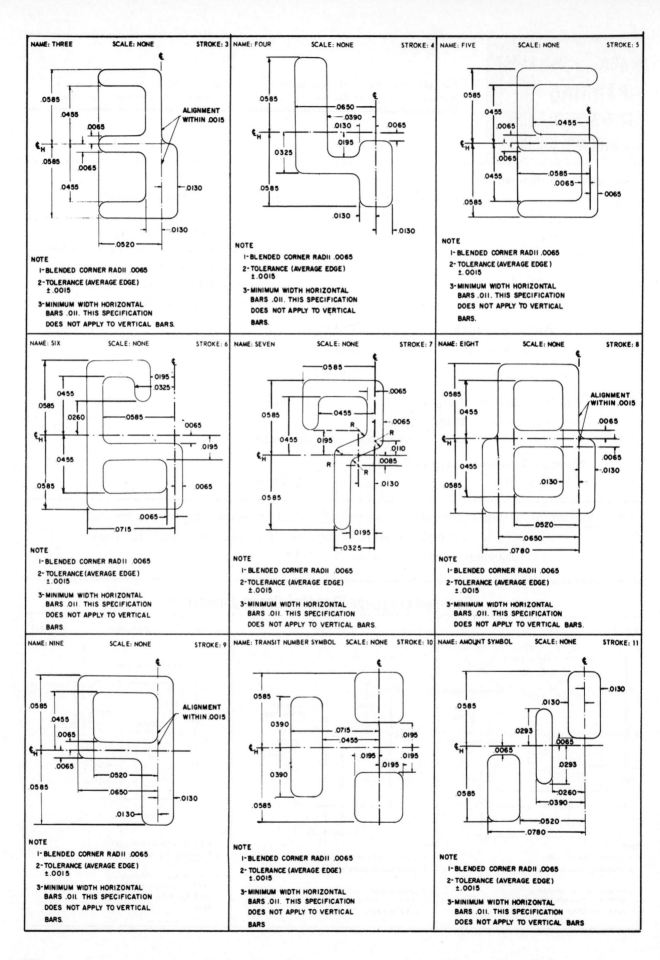

NAME: THREE   SCALE: NONE   STROKE: 3

.0585
.0455
.0065
.0065
.0455
.0130
.0130
.0520

ALIGNMENT
WITHIN .0015

NOTE

1- BLENDED CORNER RADII .0065

2- TOLERANCE (AVERAGE EDGE)
± .0015

3- MINIMUM WIDTH HORIZONTAL
BARS .011. THIS SPECIFICATION
DOES NOT APPLY TO VERTICAL BARS.

NAME: FOUR   SCALE: NONE   STROKE: 4

.0585
.0650
.0390
.0130
.0065
.0325
.0195
.0585
.0130
.0130

NOTE

1- BLENDED CORNER RADII .0065

2- TOLERANCE (AVERAGE EDGE)
± .0015

3- MINIMUM WIDTH HORIZONTAL
BARS .011. THIS SPECIFICATION
DOES NOT APPLY TO VERTICAL
BARS.

NAME: FIVE   SCALE: NONE   STROKE: 5

.0585
.0455
.0065
.0455
.0065
.0585
.0065
.0585
.0065

NOTE

1- BLENDED CORNER RADII .0065

2- TOLERANCE (AVERAGE EDGE)
± .0015

3- MINIMUM WIDTH HORIZONTAL
BARS .011. THIS SPECIFICATION
DOES NOT APPLY TO VERTICAL
BARS.

NAME: SIX   SCALE: NONE   STROKE: 6

.0195
.0325
.0455
.0585
.0260
.0585
.0065
.0455
.0195
.0585
.0065
.0065
.0715

NOTE

1- BLENDED CORNER RADII .0065

2- TOLERANCE (AVERAGE EDGE)
± .0015

3- MINIMUM WIDTH HORIZONTAL
BARS .011 THIS SPECIFICATION
DOES NOT APPLY TO VERTICAL
BARS.

NAME: SEVEN   SCALE: NONE   STROKE: 7

.0585
.0065
.0585
.0455
.0065
.0455
.0195
R
R
.0110
.0085
.0130
R
.0585
.0195
.0325

NOTE

1- BLENDED CORNER RADII .0065

2- TOLERANCE (AVERAGE EDGE)
± .0015

3- MINIMUM WIDTH HORIZONTAL
BARS .011. THIS SPECIFICATION
DOES NOT APPLY TO VERTICAL BARS.

NAME: EIGHT   SCALE: NONE   STROKE: 8

.0585
.0455
.0065
.0065
.0455
.0130
.0585
.0130
.0520
.0650
.0780

ALIGNMENT
WITHIN .0015

NOTE

1- BLENDED CORNER RADII .0065

2- TOLERANCE (AVERAGE EDGE)
± .0015

3- MINIMUM WIDTH HORIZONTAL
BARS .011. THIS SPECIFICATION
DOES NOT APPLY TO VERTICAL BARS.

NAME: NINE   SCALE: NONE   STROKE: 9

.0585
.0455
.0065
.0065
.0520
.0650
.0585
.0130
.0130

ALIGNMENT
WITHIN .0015

NOTE

1- BLENDED CORNER RADII .0065

2- TOLERANCE (AVERAGE EDGE)
± .0015

3- MINIMUM WIDTH HORIZONTAL
BARS .011. THIS SPECIFICATION
DOES NOT APPLY TO VERTICAL
BARS.

NAME: TRANSIT NUMBER SYMBOL   SCALE: NONE   STROKE: 10

.0585
.0390
.0715
.0455
.0195
.0195
.0195
.0195
.0390
.0585

NOTE

1- BLENDED CORNER RADII .0065

2- TOLERANCE (AVERAGE EDGE)
± .0015

3- MINIMUM WIDTH HORIZONTAL
BARS .011. THIS SPECIFICATION
DOES NOT APPLY TO VERTICAL
BARS

NAME: AMOUNT SYMBOL   SCALE: NONE   STROKE: 11

.0130
.0585
.0130
.0293
.0065
.0065
.0293
.0585
.0260
.0390
.0520
.0780

NOTE

1- BLENDED CORNER RADII .0065

2- TOLERANCE (AVERAGE EDGE)
± .0015

3- MINIMUM WIDTH HORIZONTAL
BARS .011. THIS SPECIFICATION
DOES NOT APPLY TO VERTICAL BARS

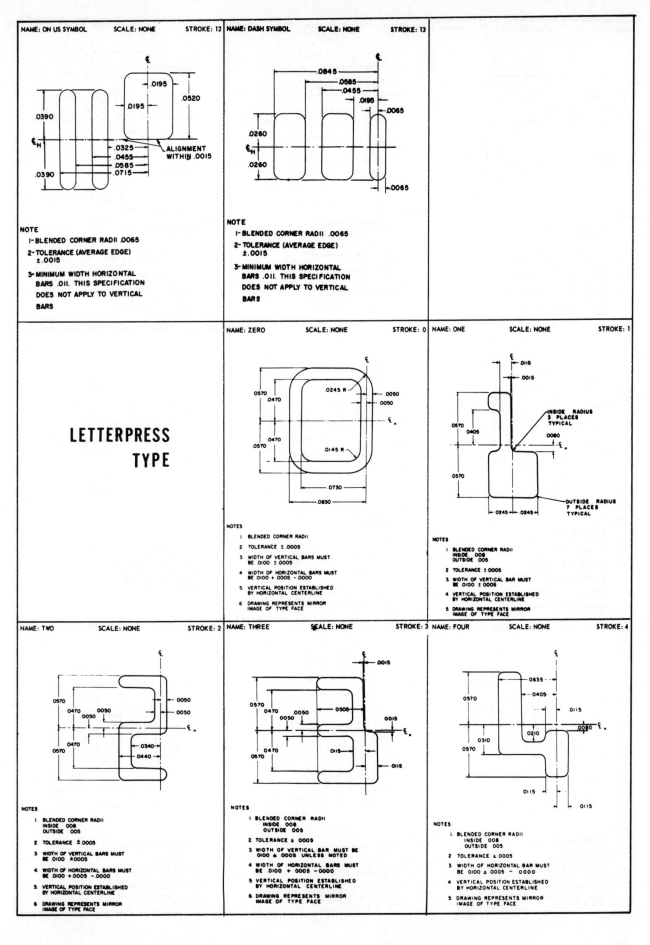

NAME: ON US SYMBOL   SCALE: NONE   STROKE: 12

.0195
.0195
.0520
.0390
.0325
.0455
.0585
.0715
.0390
ℓH
ALIGNMENT WITHIN .0015

NOTE
1- BLENDED CORNER RADII .0065
2- TOLERANCE (AVERAGE EDGE) ±.0015
3- MINIMUM WIDTH HORIZONTAL BARS .011. THIS SPECIFICATION DOES NOT APPLY TO VERTICAL BARS

NAME: DASH SYMBOL   SCALE: NONE   STROKE: 13

.0845
.0585
.0455
.0195
.0065
.0260
.0260
.0065
ℓH

NOTE
1- BLENDED CORNER RADII .0065
2- TOLERANCE (AVERAGE EDGE) ±.0015
3- MINIMUM WIDTH HORIZONTAL BARS .011. THIS SPECIFICATION DOES NOT APPLY TO VERTICAL BARS

LETTERPRESS TYPE

NAME: ZERO   SCALE: NONE   STROKE: 0

.0570
.0470
.0245 R
.0050
.0050
.0470
.0570
.0145 R
.0730
.0830
ℓH

NOTES
1. BLENDED CORNER RADII
2. TOLERANCE ±.0005
3. WIDTH OF VERTICAL BARS MUST BE .0100 ±.0005
4. WIDTH OF HORIZONTAL BARS MUST BE .0100 +.0005 -.0000
5. VERTICAL POSITION ESTABLISHED BY HORIZONTAL CENTERLINE
6. DRAWING REPRESENTS MIRROR IMAGE OF TYPE FACE

NAME: ONE   SCALE: NONE   STROKE: 1

.0115
.0015
.0570
.0405
INSIDE RADIUS 3 PLACES TYPICAL
.0080
.0570
ℓH
.0245
.0245
OUTSIDE RADIUS 7 PLACES TYPICAL

NOTES
1 BLENDED CORNER RADII INSIDE .008 OUTSIDE .005
2 TOLERANCE ±.0005
3. WIDTH OF VERTICAL BAR MUST BE .0100 ±.0005
4. VERTICAL POSITION ESTABLISHED BY HORIZONTAL CENTERLINE
5 DRAWING REPRESENTS MIRROR IMAGE OF TYPE FACE

NAME: TWO   SCALE: NONE   STROKE: 2

.0570
.0470
.0050
.0050
.0050
.0050
.0470
.0570
.0340
.0440
ℓH

NOTES
1. BLENDED CORNER RADII INSIDE .008 OUTSIDE .005
2. TOLERANCE ±.0005
3. WIDTH OF VERTICAL BARS MUST BE .0100 ±.0005
4. WIDTH OF HORIZONTAL BARS MUST BE .0100 +.0005 -.0000
5. VERTICAL POSITION ESTABLISHED BY HORIZONTAL CENTERLINE
6. DRAWING REPRESENTS MIRROR IMAGE OF TYPE FACE

NAME: THREE   SCALE: NONE   STROKE: 3

.0015
.0570
.0470
.0050
.0050
.0505
.0015
.0470
.0570
.0115
ℓH
.0115

NOTES
1 BLENDED CORNER RADII INSIDE .008 OUTSIDE .005
2. TOLERANCE ±.0005
3. WIDTH OF VERTICAL BAR MUST BE .0100 ±.0005 UNLESS NOTED
4 WIDTH OF HORIZONTAL BARS MUST BE .0100 +.0005 -.0000
5. VERTICAL POSITION ESTABLISHED BY HORIZONTAL CENTERLINE
6. DRAWING REPRESENTS MIRROR IMAGE OF TYPE FACE

NAME: FOUR   SCALE: NONE   STROKE: 4

.0635
.0570
.0405
.0115
.0080
.0210
ℓH
.0310
.0570
.0115
.0115

NOTES
1. BLENDED CORNER RADII INSIDE .008 OUTSIDE .005
2 TOLERANCE ±.0005
3. WIDTH OF HORIZONTAL BAR MUST BE .0100 ±.0005 -.0000
4 VERTICAL POSITION ESTABLISHED BY HORIZONTAL CENTERLINE
5. DRAWING REPRESENTS MIRROR IMAGE OF TYPE FACE

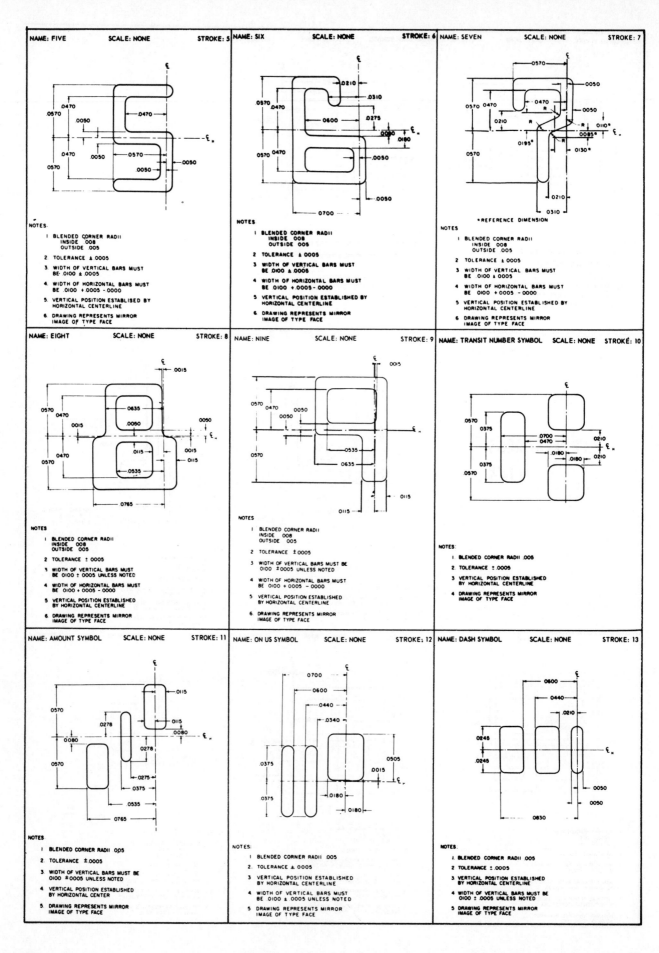

NAME: FIVE   SCALE: NONE   STROKE: 5

NOTES.

1. BLENDED CORNER RADII
   INSIDE .008
   OUTSIDE .005

2. TOLERANCE ±.0005

3. WIDTH OF VERTICAL BARS MUST
   BE .0100 ±.0005

4. WIDTH OF HORIZONTAL BARS MUST
   BE .0100 +.0005 -.0000

5. VERTICAL POSITION ESTABLISHED BY
   HORIZONTAL CENTERLINE

6. DRAWING REPRESENTS MIRROR
   IMAGE OF TYPE FACE

NAME: SIX   SCALE: NONE   STROKE: 6

NOTES

1. BLENDED CORNER RADII
   INSIDE .008
   OUTSIDE .005

2. TOLERANCE ±.0005

3. WIDTH OF VERTICAL BARS MUST
   BE .0100 ±.0005

4. WIDTH OF HORIZONTAL BARS MUST
   BE .0100 +.0005 -.0000

5. VERTICAL POSITION ESTABLISHED BY
   HORIZONTAL CENTERLINE

6. DRAWING REPRESENTS MIRROR
   IMAGE OF TYPE FACE

NAME: SEVEN   SCALE: NONE   STROKE: 7

*REFERENCE DIMENSION

NOTES

1. BLENDED CORNER RADII
   INSIDE .008
   OUTSIDE .005

2. TOLERANCE ±.0005

3. WIDTH OF VERTICAL BARS MUST
   BE .0100 ±.0005

4. WIDTH OF HORIZONTAL BARS MUST
   BE .0100 +.0005 -.0000

5. VERTICAL POSITION ESTABLISHED BY
   HORIZONTAL CENTERLINE

6. DRAWING REPRESENTS MIRROR
   IMAGE OF TYPE FACE

NAME: EIGHT   SCALE: NONE   STROKE: 8

NOTES

1. BLENDED CORNER RADII
   INSIDE .008
   OUTSIDE .005

2. TOLERANCE ±.0005

3. WIDTH OF VERTICAL BARS MUST
   BE .0100 ±.0005 UNLESS NOTED

4. WIDTH OF HORIZONTAL BARS MUST
   BE .0100 +.0005 -.0000

5. VERTICAL POSITION ESTABLISHED
   BY HORIZONTAL CENTERLINE

6. DRAWING REPRESENTS MIRROR
   IMAGE OF TYPE FACE

NAME: NINE   SCALE: NONE   STROKE: 9

NOTES

1. BLENDED CORNER RADII
   INSIDE .008
   OUTSIDE .005

2. TOLERANCE ±.0005

3. WIDTH OF VERTICAL BARS MUST BE
   .0100 ±.0005 UNLESS NOTED

4. WIDTH OF HORIZONTAL BARS MUST
   BE .0100 +.0005 -.0000

5. VERTICAL POSITION ESTABLISHED
   BY HORIZONTAL CENTERLINE

6. DRAWING REPRESENTS MIRROR
   IMAGE OF TYPE FACE

NAME: TRANSIT NUMBER SYMBOL   SCALE: NONE   STROKE: 10

NOTES:

1. BLENDED CORNER RADII .005

2. TOLERANCE ±.0005

3. VERTICAL POSITION ESTABLISHED
   BY HORIZONTAL CENTERLINE

4. DRAWING REPRESENTS MIRROR
   IMAGE OF TYPE FACE

NAME: AMOUNT SYMBOL   SCALE: NONE   STROKE: 11

NOTES.

1. BLENDED CORNER RADII .005

2. TOLERANCE ±.0005

3. WIDTH OF VERTICAL BARS MUST BE
   .0100 ±.0005 UNLESS NOTED

4. VERTICAL POSITION ESTABLISHED
   BY HORIZONTAL CENTER

5. DRAWING REPRESENTS MIRROR
   IMAGE OF TYPE FACE

NAME: ON US SYMBOL   SCALE: NONE   STROKE: 12

NOTES:

1. BLENDED CORNER RADII .005

2. TOLERANCE ±.0005

3. VERTICAL POSITION ESTABLISHED
   BY HORIZONTAL CENTERLINE

4. WIDTH OF VERTICAL BARS MUST
   BE .0100 ±.0005 UNLESS NOTED

5. DRAWING REPRESENTS MIRROR
   IMAGE OF TYPE FACE

NAME: DASH SYMBOL   SCALE: NONE   STROKE: 13

NOTES.

1. BLENDED CORNER RADII .005

2. TOLERANCE ±.0005

3. VERTICAL POSITION ESTABLISHED
   BY HORIZONTAL CENTERLINE

4. WIDTH OF VERTICAL BARS MUST BE
   .0100 ±.0005 UNLESS NOTED

5. DRAWING REPRESENTS MIRROR
   IMAGE OF TYPE FACE

Character Spacing and Alignment

A. *Spacing*

1. Amount Field and Transit Number Field:

   a. The distance between the right average edge of adjacent characters is to be .125″ plus or minus .010″. This applies to the Amount Field and the Transit Number Field. (Average edge is defined and discussed under "Character Tolerances.")

   b. The accumulation of spacing tolerances in the Amount Field and Transit Number Field is limited to the extent that the accumulation does not infringe upon the boundaries defining these fields.

2. Minimum Space—Any Field:

   The minimum space between the right average edge of adjacent characters, whether they be in the same field or adjoining fields, can never be less than .115″.

   This also applies to both On Us Fields. Maximum or other spacing requirements in both On Us Fields are to be specified by the individual machine manufacturer involved.

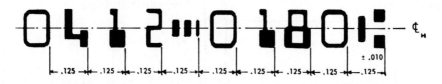

B. *Alignment*

The horizontal centerline of each character is indicated on any drawings of the printed character (₵ H).
These centerlines serve to establish vertical alignment of all characters since all characters are designed about the same horizontal centerline.

Vertical alignment tolerance is that which is consistent with good printing practice. *For example,* alignment of the bottom edge of a line of characters, within any group printed at one time (such as Account Number in On Us Field), should be such that adjacent characters do not vary vertically more than .007″.

On characters that do not come down to the "base" line the same tolerance will be applied to the horizontal centerline.

IBM   **C20-8008**

Data Processing
(Flow Charting and
Block Diagramming)

Reproduced from Reference Manual, Flow Charting and Block Diagramming Techniques, through the courtesy of International Business Machines Corporation, Data Processing Division, 112 East Post Road, White Plains, N.Y.

Flow Charting

Direction of Flow

In flow charting, solid lines are normally used, but occasionally it is desirable to differentiate between the physical movement of work and the mere transfer of information. This can be done by using solid lines in the first case and dotted lines in the second. For example, dotted lines are used to illustrate accounting control functions.

Direction of Flow

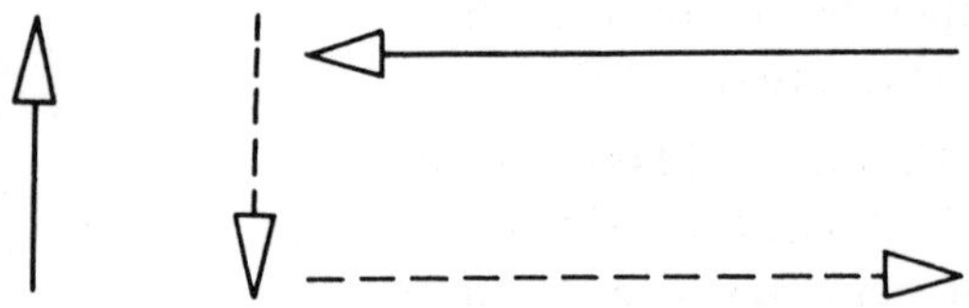

Document Symbols

The various types of documents encountered in data processing applications are represented by the symbols shown   Two sizes of each are provided. Normally, a single diagram will use either the small or the large symbols but not both.

Source Document

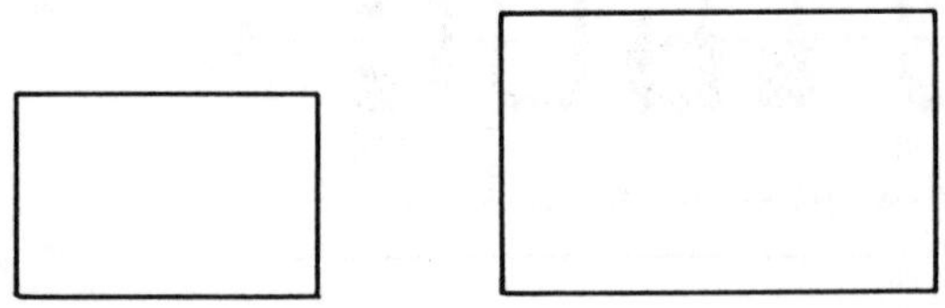

Transmittal Tape

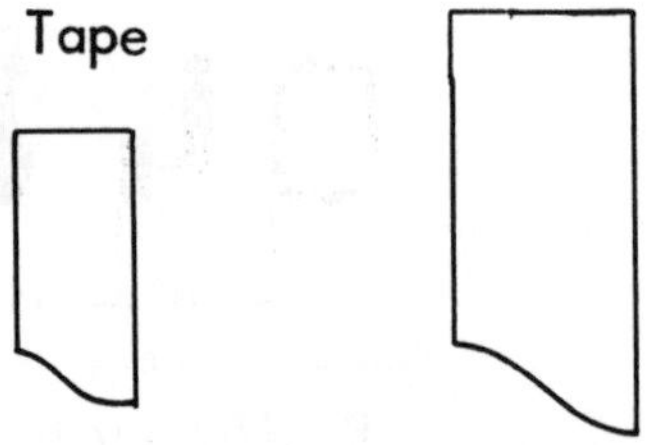

Punched Card

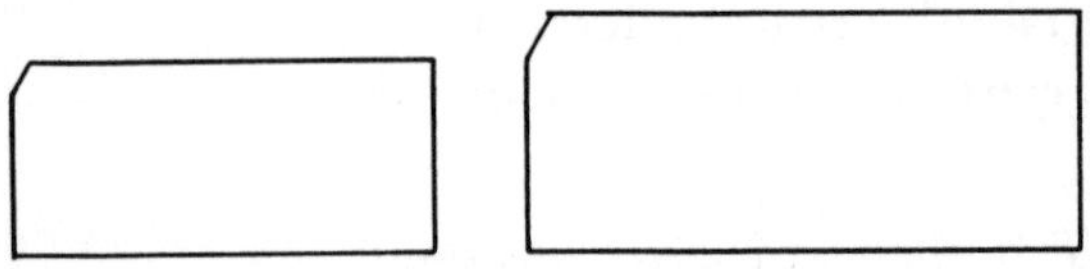

Report

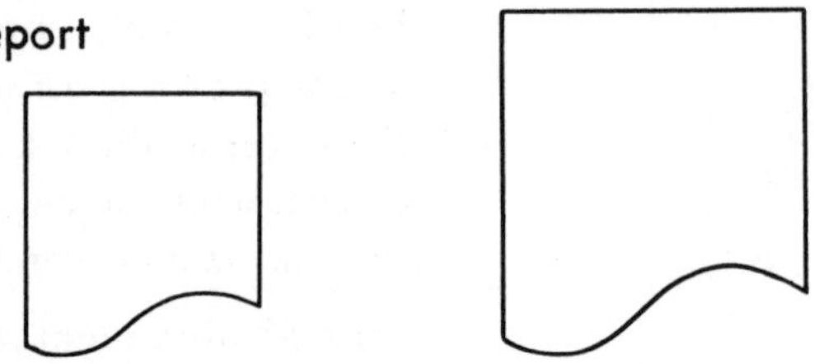

Paper Tape

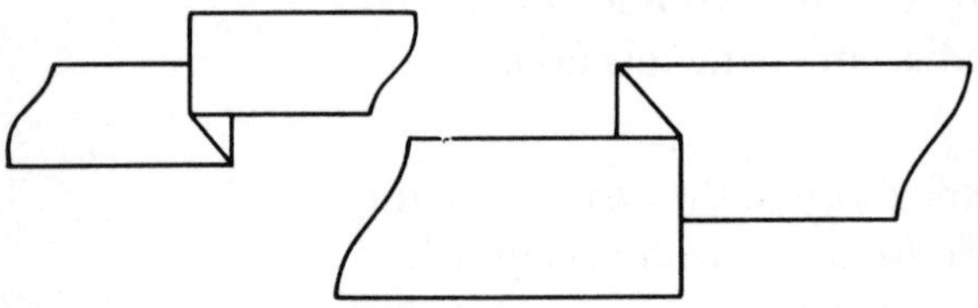

Magnetic Tape

Basic File Symbol

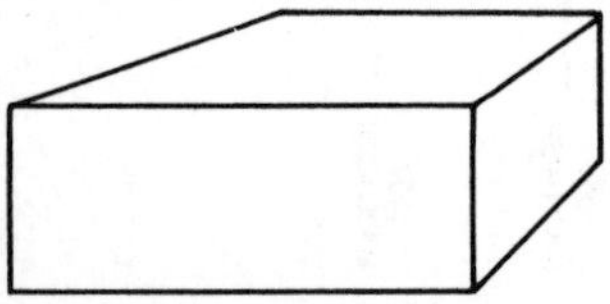

Two-Drawer File

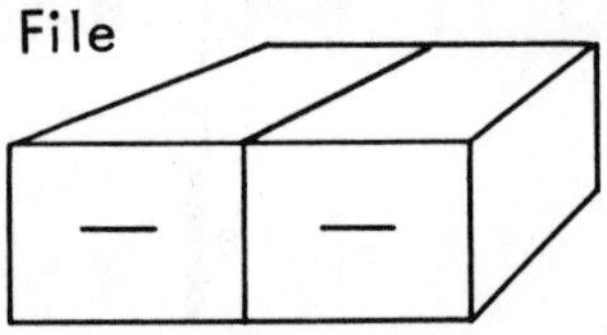

Four-Drawer File

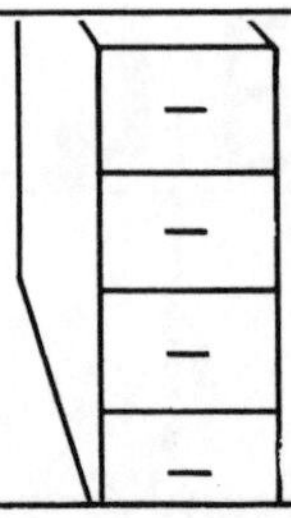

Clerical Function Symbol

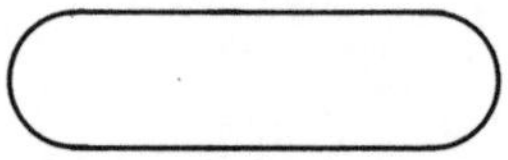

Clerical Function

Clerical Function Symbol			
(Balance and File)	(Payroll Clerk)	(Position 12)	
Operation Described	Position Title	Position Code	
Unit Record Machine Symbols	Card Punch, Card Verifier, and Other Key-Driven Devices	Sorter and Collator	Auxiliary Machines
Accounting Machines	*Data Processing System Symbols*	Central Processing Unit	Auxiliary Machine (Off-Line)
Input/Output Control	Auxiliary Drum Storage	Auxiliary Disk Storage	Inquiry Station
	Card Reader or Card Punch	Magnetic Tape Unit	Paper Tape Reader or Punch
Printer	Typewriter	**Block Diagramming**	*Block Diagramming Symbols, Stored-Wired Program*
Direction of Flow		Program Exit	Branch Identification

Stored Program Step		Control Panel Functions	
Step Connector	**Communication Line**	*Block Diagramming Symbols, Stored Program*	Direction of Flow
Console Operation or Halt	Connector or Step Identification	650 Table Lookup	7070 Priority Routine Identification
Input-Output Function	Program Modification Function	Decision Function	Processing Function

GRAPHIC SYMBOLS FOR MECHANICAL DRAWINGS

MIL-STD 17 AERONAUTICAL (HYDRAULIC EQUIPMENT)	**General.** The hydraulic symbols shown merely present outlines. The schematic diagram should show the cutaway section of each unit at least in schematic form.		Accumulator
Air bottle, emergency	Brake control	Bungee, air-oil	Coupling, self-sealing
Cylinder, actuating	Debooster, brake	Filter or strainer	Fitting, swivel
Gage, pressure	Gage and snubber, pressure	Pump, hand	Pump, power driven
Reservoir	Valve, check, automatic	Valve, check, manual	Valve, brake control
Valve, gun charger control	Valve, pressure regulating (unloading) automatic	Valve, pressure regulating (unloading) manual	Valve, relief
Valve, restrictor, both ways	Valve, restrictor, partial one-way	Valve, shuttle	Valve or selector, directional control

MIL-STD 17
AERONAUTICAL
(LINES)

GENERAL

Scope. The following establishes an approved list of mechanical symbols for use on aeronautical drawings where it is desired to represent aeronautical equipment diagrammatically.

TUBE AND HOSE LINES

Power plant, instrument, fire extinguisher and miscellaneous tube and hose line symbols.

Service	Riser or stack	Symbol
Bellows		—◇◇◇◇—
Bleed return	(BR)	— — — — — BR — — — — —
Drain	(D)	——————— D ———————
Engine coolant	(EC)	——————— EC ———————
Foam solution	(FO)	——————— FOAM ———————
Fuel oil vent	(FOV)	— — — — — FOV — — — — —
Fuel supply	(F)	——————— F ———————
Lubricating oil	(LO)	——————— LO ———————
Oil breather	(OB)	— — — — — OB — — — — —
Oil dilution	(OD)	——————— OD ———————

Service	Riser or stack	Symbol
Pneumatic	PN	—————— PN ——————
Self-sealing		▨▨▨▨▨▨▨▨▨▨▨
Vacuum	▽	—————— V ——————
Vent	V	— — — — V — — — —
Vent pressure	PV	— — — — PV — — — —
Vent return	VR	— — — — VR — — — —
Water injection	WI	—————— WI ——————
Water, cold	◴	— — — — — — —
Water, hot	◑	— —·— — —·— —

Hydraulic tube and hose line symbols

Service	Symbol
Brake	▭▭▭▭▭▭▭▭
Down (or close)	▰▰▰▰▰▰▰
Emergency pressure	——————————

Service	Symbol
Hose connection, rigid tubing	
Hose, flexible	
Return	
Supply fluid, pump suction	
Suction gravity	
Supply pressure	
Up (or open)	
Vent	

Oxygen tube and hose line symbols

Distribution (high pressure)	
Distribution (low pressure)	
Filler	
Flexible	

MIL-STD 17 AERONAUTICAL (OXYGEN EQUIPMENT)	Converter, liquid oxygen	Coupling, automatic	Cylinder, oxygen
Fitting, swivel	Gage, pressure	Indicator, oxygen flow	Oxygen recharger, portable
Oxygen unit, portable (continuous flow)	Oxygen unit, portable (demand)	Reducer, pressure	Regulator, automatic tinuous flow
Regulator, demand	Regulator tubing, oxygen mask	Valve, check, style A	Valve, check, style B
Valve, check, style C	Valve, check, style D	Valve, check, style E	Valve, check, style F
Valve, check, style G	Valve, check, style H	Valve, cylinder	Valve, filler
Valve, line			

MIL-STD 17 AERONAUTICAL POWER PLANT EQUIPMENT	Cooler, oil	Detector, carbon monoxide	Filler neck
Filter, fuel	Filter, induction air	Flowmeter	Gage glass
Gear box	Governor, propeller	Indicator, quantity	Motor, pneumatic
Pump	Pump, air	Pump, auxiliary fuel, electric driven	Pump, coolant
Pump, primer, hand	Pump, primer, motor driven	Pump, scavenger	Pump, wobble
Pump and motor, propeller feather	Radiator, coolant	Scupper	Separator, oil
Strainer	Sump	Tank	Tank, droppable

185

Tank, expansion	Tank, self-sealing	Trap, water	Valve, defueling
	GALS		
Valve, fuel selector			
2 WAY 3 WAY 4 WAY			

MIL-STD 17 AERONAUTICAL VACUUM INST·MISC VALVES & FITTINGS	Air Filter, turn and bank indicator	Boot de-icer	Filter, air
Gage, vacuum	Indicator, directional gyro	Indicator, gyro horizon	Indicator, turn and bank
Outlet, vacuum	Pilot, automatic	Pump, vacuum	Selector, static pressure
Thermometor	Valve air check	Valve, selector, four-way	Valve, vacuum, control, turn and bank indicator
Valve, vacuum relief	Valve, vacuum throttling	Venturi tube	MISCELLANEOUS VALVES
Back pressure	Cross feed	Drain	Dump
Float operated	Gate	Gate, motor operated	Globe

See Control Valves, page 245

Globe, motor operated	Needle	Poppet	Pressure regulator ADJUSTABLE
Solenoid	Supercharger regulator	Temperature control	Water regulator
FITTINGS	Banjo	Bulkhead fitting	Bushing
Cap	Connector, hose	Connector, nut and sleeve	Coupling, female
Cross	Elbow, 45 degrees	Elbow, 90 degrees	Elbow, reducing
Expansion joint, bellows	Expansion joint, sliding	Flange, reducing	Nipple
Reducer, concentric	Tee	Union, flanged	Union, screwed

Extracted from publications and catalogs on Bearing (Ball, Roller) through the courtesy of Fafnir Bearing, SKF Industries, Timken Roller Bearing Company.

bearing type	symbol	characteristics and abilities
single row radial K *non-filling slot type*		Designed to carry radial and combined loads and thrust in either direction. High speed. Preferred where specific characteristics of other type bearings are not required.
single row radial W *filling slot type*		Higher radial capacity than K type; moderate thrust capacity in either direction; moderate high speed ability. Long life.
single row WI type M and MM precision		Heavy radial and one-direction thrust capacities. Seldom used for pure radial loads when mounted singly. Best for duplex mounting and high speeds and offer extreme rigidity when duplexed.
single row WO type MM precision		Designed primarily for extremely high-speed applications where the centrifugal force of the balls becomes important.
single row angular-contact W and PW types		Well suited for duplex mountings, these bearings have heavy one-direction thrust and moderate radial capacity. Offer high axial and moderate radial rigidity when duplexed.
double row angular-contact		Heavy radial capacity and moderate thrust capacity in either direction with moderate speed ability. Good radial and axial rigidity. For reversing thrust loads, duplex pairs of single row angular-contact bearings are preferred.
one and two shields D and DD types		Same characteristics as K and W single row radial types. Offer effective grease retention and exclusion of coarse dirt. DD types (two shields) are prelubricated. (Some double row bearings available with one shield).
felt-seal T, TD, TT types		Same features as single row radial K type, with effective grease retention and dirt exclusion. Prelubricated; moderate high speed ability.
Mechani-Seal L, LD, LL, W-LL types		Highest speed ability of any sealed type, with other advantages of single row radial K type. Prelubricated; effective grease retention and dirt exclusion.
Plya-Seal P, PP, W-PP types		Offers most effective grease retention and dirt exclusion, plus all features of single row radial K type bearings. Moderate speed ability. Prelubricated. Seals are removable for inspection and/or relubrication.

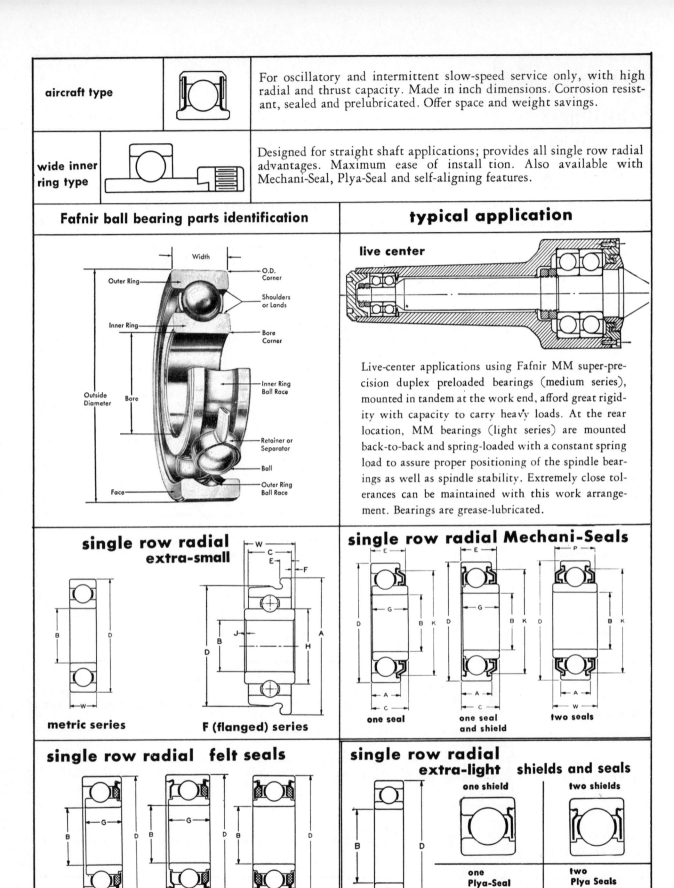

| aircraft type | | For oscillatory and intermittent slow-speed service only, with high radial and thrust capacity. Made in inch dimensions. Corrosion resistant, sealed and prelubricated. Offer space and weight savings. |

| wide inner ring type | | Designed for straight shaft applications; provides all single row radial advantages. Maximum ease of install tion. Also available with Mechani-Seal, Plya-Seal and self-aligning features. |

Fafnir ball bearing parts identification

Width
Outer Ring
O.D. Corner
Shoulders or Lands
Inner Ring
Bore Corner
Outside Diameter
Bore
Inner Ring Ball Race
Retainer or Separator
Ball
Outer Ring Ball Race
Face

typical application

live center

Live-center applications using Fafnir MM super-precision duplex preloaded bearings (medium series), mounted in tandem at the work end, afford great rigidity with capacity to carry heavy loads. At the rear location, MM bearings (light series) are mounted back-to-back and spring-loaded with a constant spring load to assure proper positioning of the spindle bearings as well as spindle stability. Extremely close tolerances can be maintained with this work arrangement. Bearings are grease-lubricated.

single row radial
extra-small

metric series   F (flanged) series

single row radial Mechani-Seals

one seal   one seal and shield   two seals

single row radial   felt seals

one seal   one seal and shield   two seals

single row radial
extra-light   shields and seals

one shield   two shields

one Plya-Seal   two Plya Seals

190

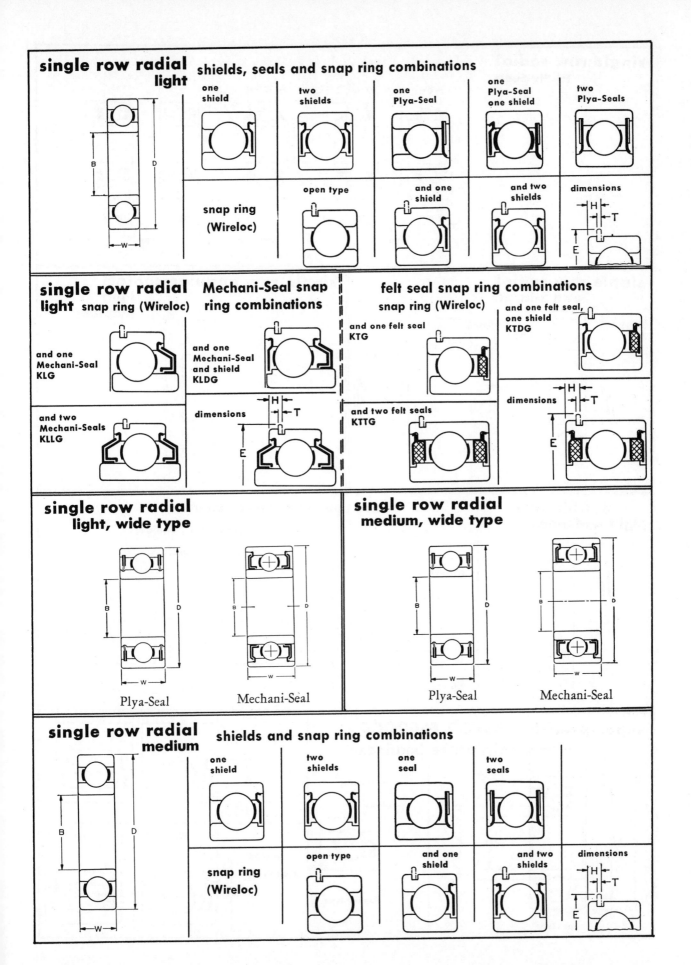

single row radial light

shields, seals and snap ring combinations

one shield

two shields

one Plya-Seal

one Plya-Seal one shield

two Plya-Seals

snap ring (Wireloc)

open type

and one shield

and two shields

dimensions

single row radial light snap ring (Wireloc)

and one Mechani-Seal KLG

and two Mechani-Seals KLLG

Mechani-Seal snap ring combinations

and one Mechani-Seal and shield KLDG

dimensions

felt seal snap ring combinations

snap ring (Wireloc)

and one felt seal KTG

and two felt seals KTTG

and one felt seal, one shield KTDG

dimensions

single row radial light, wide type

Plya-Seal

Mechani-Seal

single row radial medium, wide type

Plya-Seal

Mechani-Seal

single row radial medium

shields and snap ring combinations

one shield

two shields

one seal

two seals

snap ring (Wireloc)

open type

and one shield

and two shields

dimensions

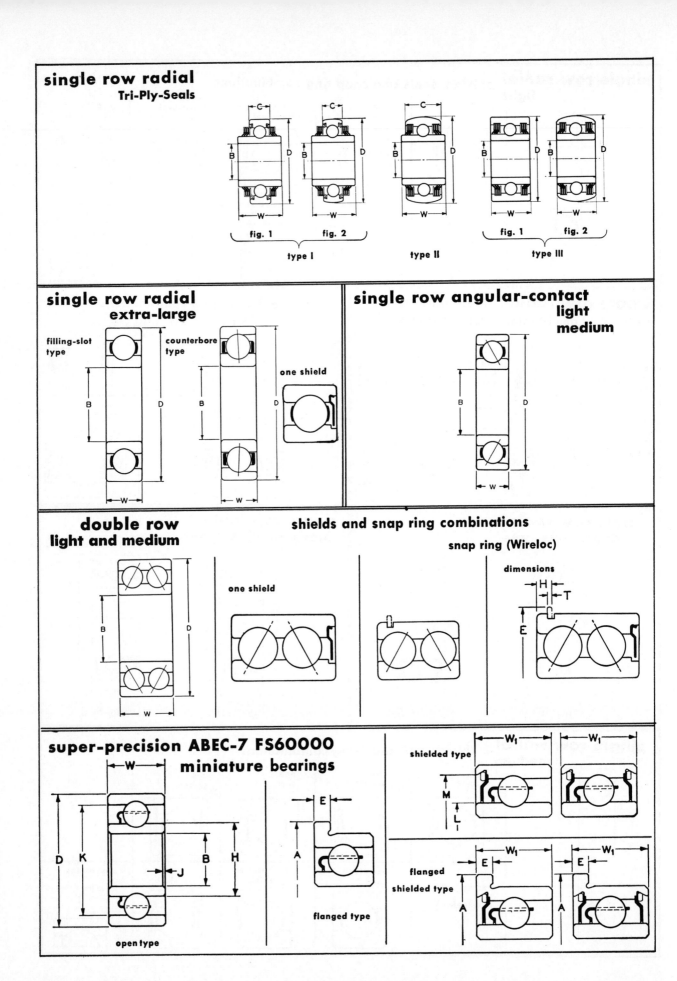

single row radial
Tri-Ply-Seals

fig. 1   fig. 2

type I   type II   type III

single row radial
extra-large

filling-slot type

counterbore type

one shield

single row angular-contact
light
medium

double row
light and medium

shields and snap ring combinations

snap ring (Wireloc)

dimensions

one shield

super-precision ABEC-7 FS60000
miniature bearings

open type

flanged type

shielded type

flanged shielded type

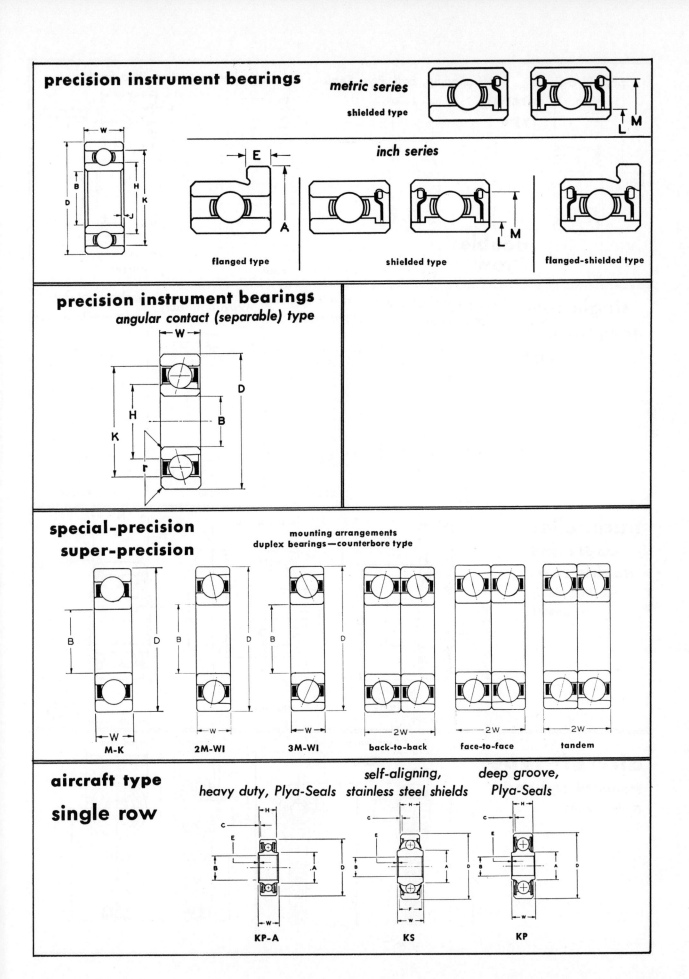

precision instrument bearings

metric series

shielded type

inch series

flanged type

shielded type

flanged-shielded type

precision instrument bearings
angular contact (separable) type

special-precision
super-precision

mounting arrangements
duplex bearings—counterbore type

M-K

2M-WI

3M-WI

back-to-back

face-to-face

tandem

aircraft type

single row

heavy duty, Plya-Seals

self-aligning, stainless steel shields

deep groove, Plya-Seals

KP-A

KS

KP

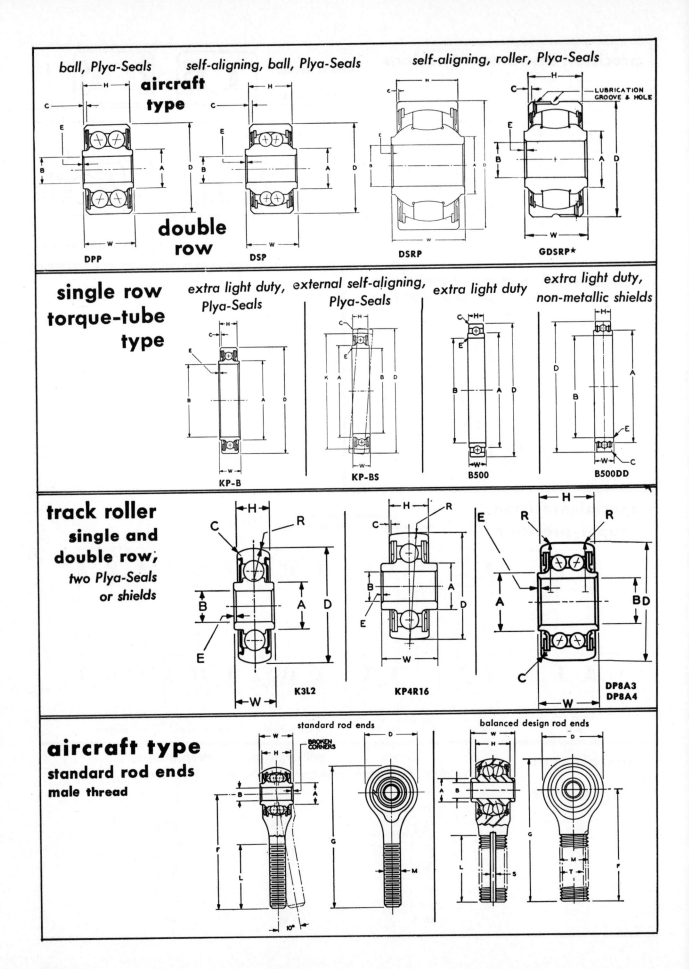

aircraft type

double row

ball, Plya-Seals   self-aligning, ball, Plya-Seals   self-aligning, roller, Plya-Seals

DPP   DSP   DSRP   GDSRP★

LUBRICATION GROOVE & HOLE

single row torque-tube type

extra light duty, Plya-Seals   external self-aligning, Plya-Seals   extra light duty   extra light duty, non-metallic shields

KP-B   KP-BS   B500   B500DD

track roller
single and double row; *two Plya-Seals or shields*

K3L2   KP4R16   DP8A3 DP8A4

aircraft type
standard rod ends
male thread

standard rod ends   balanced design rod ends

BROKEN CORNERS

194

standard rod ends

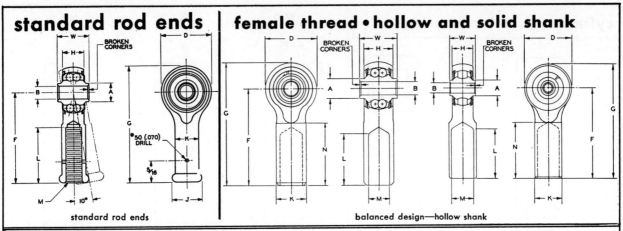

standard rod ends

female thread • hollow and solid shank

balanced design—hollow shank

helicopter • pulley

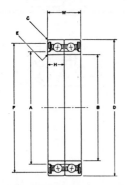

pulley type, *Plya-Seals*

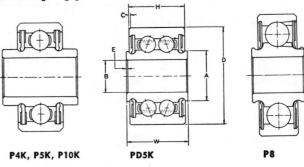

P4K, P5K, P10K   PD5K   P8

wide inner ring

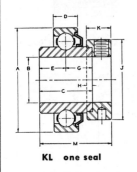

KL   one seal

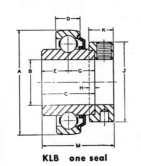

KLB   one seal

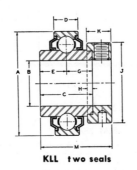

KLL   two seals

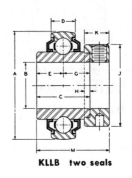

KLLB   two seals

single pillow blocks

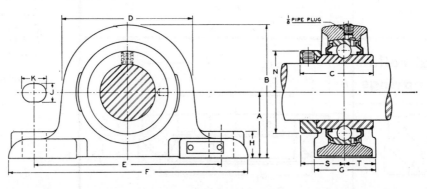

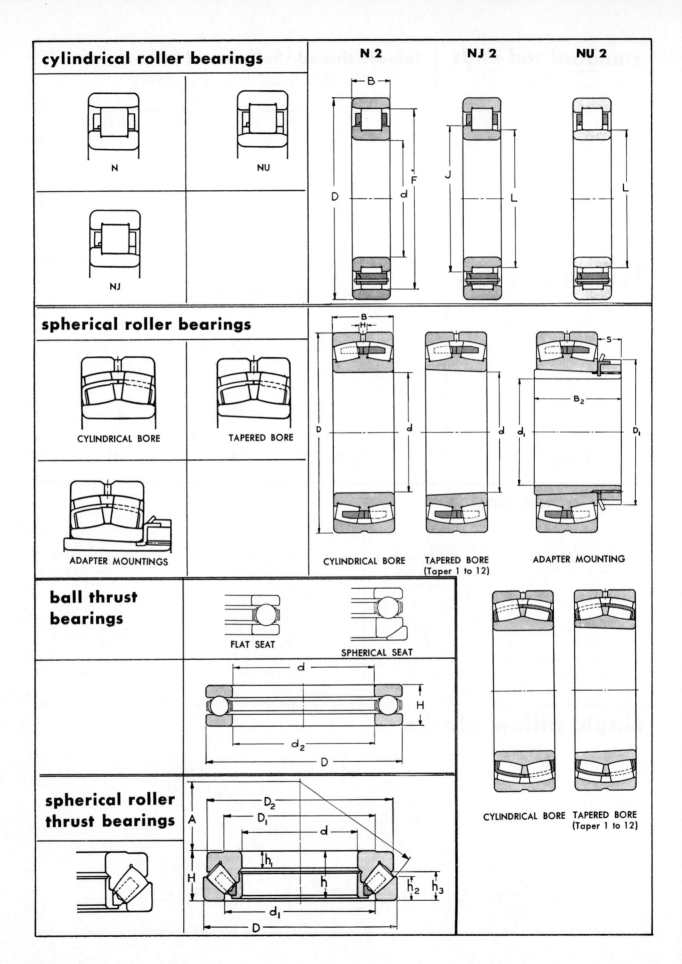

cylindrical roller bearings

N

NU

NJ

N 2   NJ 2   NU 2

spherical roller bearings

CYLINDRICAL BORE

TAPERED BORE

ADAPTER MOUNTINGS

CYLINDRICAL BORE

TAPERED BORE
(Taper 1 to 12)

ADAPTER MOUNTING

ball thrust bearings

FLAT SEAT

SPHERICAL SEAT

spherical roller thrust bearings

CYLINDRICAL BORE   TAPERED BORE
(Taper 1 to 12)

single row, tapered roller bearings	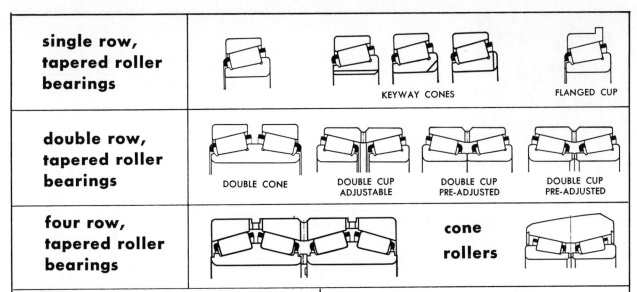 KEYWAY CONES FLANGED CUP
double row, tapered roller bearings	DOUBLE CONE DOUBLE CUP ADJUSTABLE DOUBLE CUP PRE-ADJUSTED DOUBLE CUP PRE-ADJUSTED
four row, tapered roller bearings	**cone rollers**

single row, tapered roller bearings

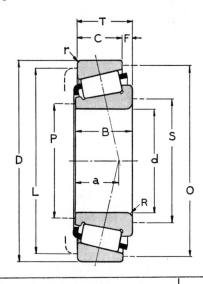

double row, tapered roller bearings

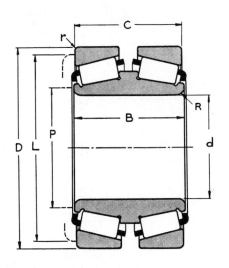

four row, tapered roller bearings

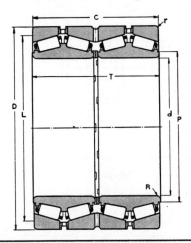

tapered roller bearing cone rollers

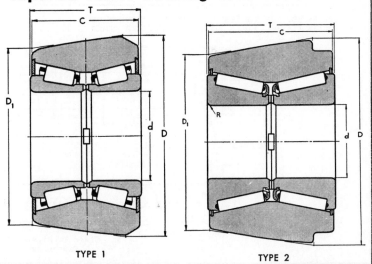

TYPE 1   TYPE 2

197

Extracted from MIL-STD-423-1958, Chain, Roller; Conveyor, Standard and Large Rollers, Flat Link Plates, Double Pitch, Single Strand; Connecting Links and Attaching Links, with the permission of the Office of the Secretary of Defense, Public Affairs Department, Washington.

TYPE 3 RC, CHAIN ROLLER: CONVEYOR, STANDARD ROLLERS, FLAT LINK PLATES, DOUBLE PITCH, SINGLE STRAND STEEL

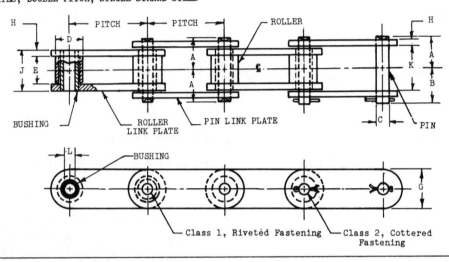

TYPE 1CL, LINK OFFSET, ROLLER CHAIN: CONVEYOR, STANDARD ROLLERS, DOUBLE PITCH, SINGLE STRAND, STEEL.

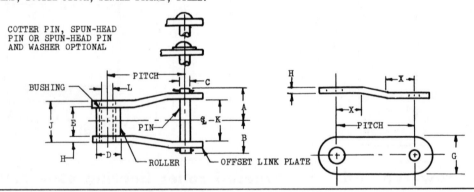

TYPE 3a RC, CHAIN ROLLER: CONVEYOR, LARGE ROLLERS. FLAT LINK PLATES, DOUBLE PITCH, SINGLE STRAND STEEL.

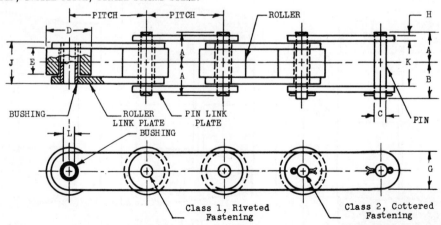

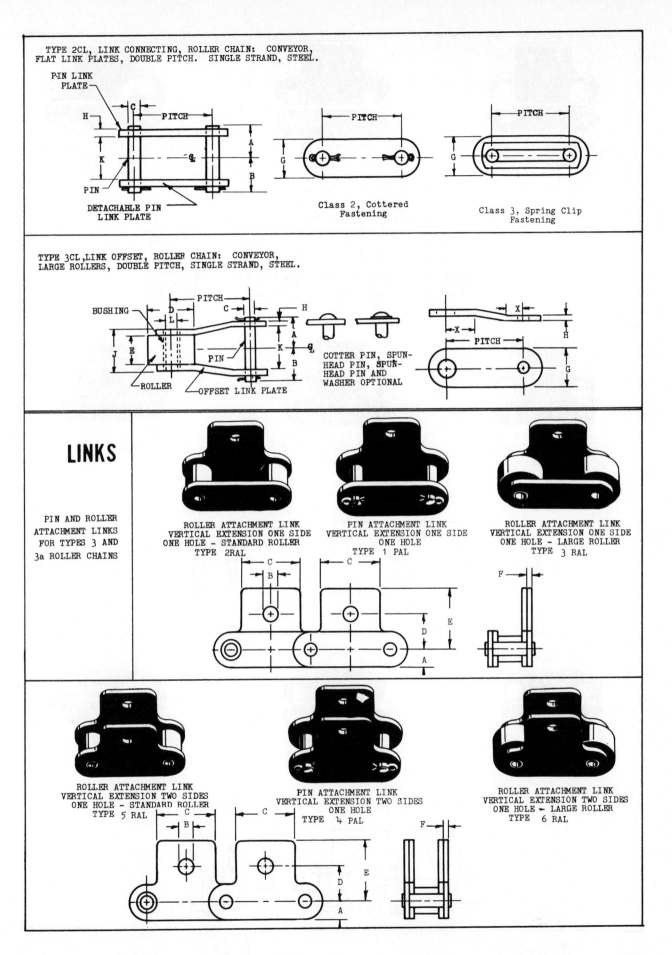

TYPE 2CL, LINK CONNECTING, ROLLER CHAIN: CONVEYOR, FLAT LINK PLATES, DOUBLE PITCH. SINGLE STRAND, STEEL.

PIN LINK PLATE

PITCH

DETACHABLE PIN LINK PLATE

PITCH

Class 2, Cottered Fastening

PITCH

Class 3, Spring Clip Fastening

TYPE 3CL, LINK OFFSET, ROLLER CHAIN: CONVEYOR, LARGE ROLLERS, DOUBLE PITCH, SINGLE STRAND, STEEL.

BUSHING

PITCH

PIN

ROLLER

OFFSET LINK PLATE

COTTER PIN, SPUN-HEAD PIN, SPUN-HEAD PIN AND WASHER OPTIONAL

PITCH

LINKS

PIN AND ROLLER ATTACHMENT LINKS FOR TYPES 3 AND 3a ROLLER CHAINS

ROLLER ATTACHMENT LINK VERTICAL EXTENSION ONE SIDE ONE HOLE - STANDARD ROLLER TYPE 2RAL

PIN ATTACHMENT LINK VERTICAL EXTENSION ONE SIDE ONE HOLE TYPE 1 PAL

ROLLER ATTACHMENT LINK VERTICAL EXTENSION ONE SIDE ONE HOLE - LARGE ROLLER TYPE 3 RAL

ROLLER ATTACHMENT LINK VERTICAL EXTENSION TWO SIDES ONE HOLE - STANDARD ROLLER TYPE 5 RAL

PIN ATTACHMENT LINK VERTICAL EXTENSION TWO SIDES ONE HOLE TYPE 4 PAL

ROLLER ATTACHMENT LINK VERTICAL EXTENSION TWO SIDES ONE HOLE - LARGE ROLLER TYPE 6 RAL

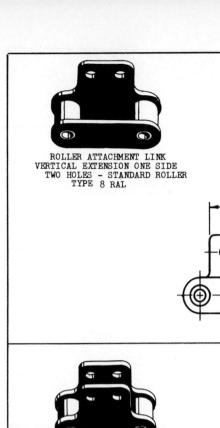

ROLLER ATTACHMENT LINK
VERTICAL EXTENSION ONE SIDE
TWO HOLES - STANDARD ROLLER
TYPE 8 RAL

PIN ATTACHMENT LINK
VERTICAL EXTENSION ONE SIDE
TWO HOLES
TYPE 7 PAL

ROLLER ATTACHMENT LINK
VERTICAL EXTENSION ONE SIDE
TWO HOLES - LARGE ROLLER
TYPE 9 RAL

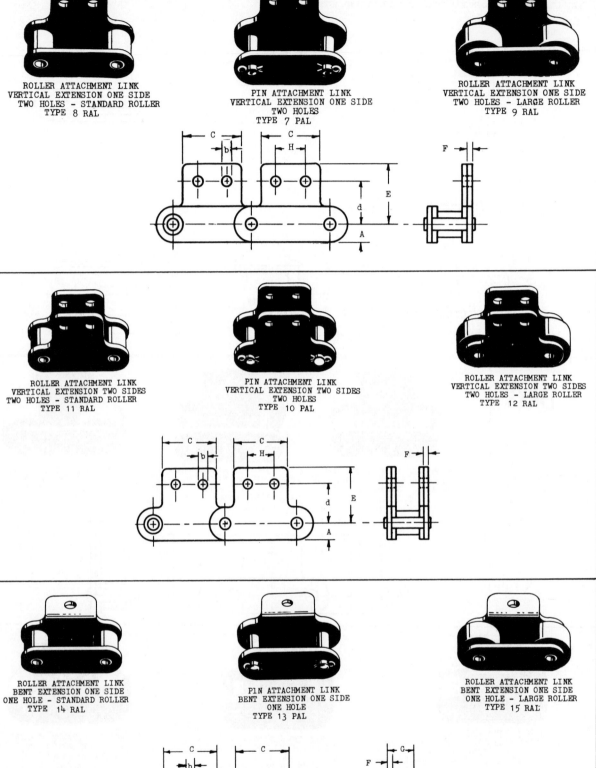

ROLLER ATTACHMENT LINK
VERTICAL EXTENSION TWO SIDES
TWO HOLES - STANDARD ROLLER
TYPE 11 RAL

PIN ATTACHMENT LINK
VERTICAL EXTENSION TWO SIDES
TWO HOLES
TYPE 10 PAL

ROLLER ATTACHMENT LINK
VERTICAL EXTENSION TWO SIDES
TWO HOLES - LARGE ROLLER
TYPE 12 RAL

ROLLER ATTACHMENT LINK
BENT EXTENSION ONE SIDE
ONE HOLE - STANDARD ROLLER
TYPE 14 RAL

PIN ATTACHMENT LINK
BENT EXTENSION ONE SIDE
ONE HOLE
TYPE 13 PAL

ROLLER ATTACHMENT LINK
BENT EXTENSION ONE SIDE
ONE HOLE - LARGE ROLLER
TYPE 15 RAL

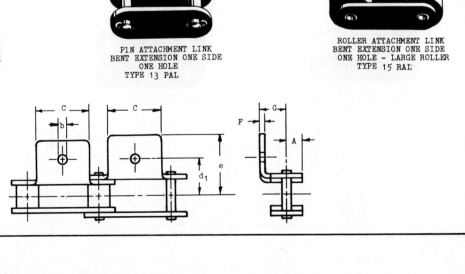

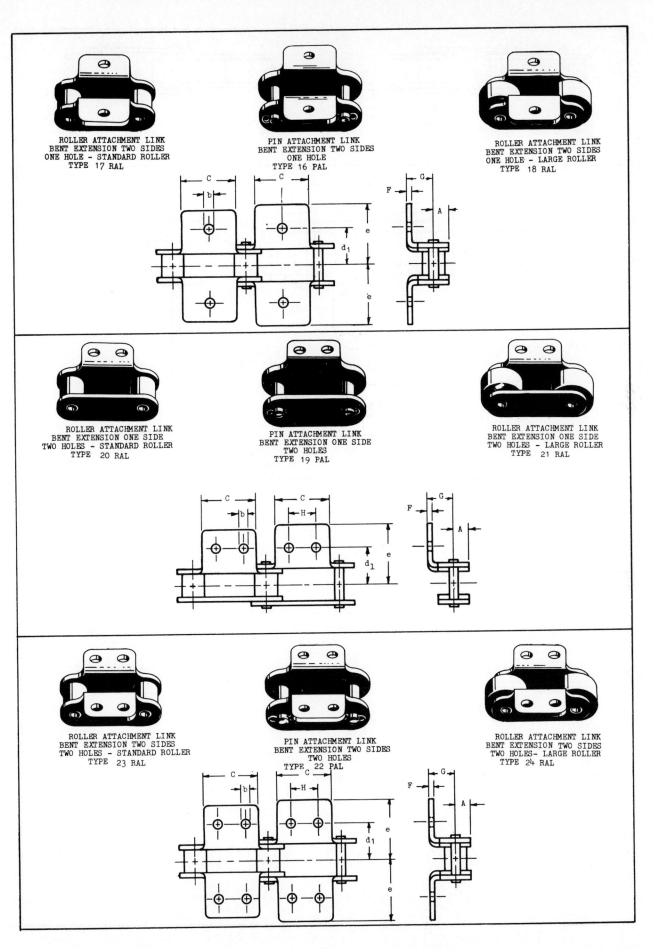

ROLLER ATTACHMENT LINK
BENT EXTENSION TWO SIDES
ONE HOLE – STANDARD ROLLER
TYPE 17 RAL

PIN ATTACHMENT LINK
BENT EXTENSION TWO SIDES
ONE HOLE
TYPE 16 PAL

ROLLER ATTACHMENT LINK
BENT EXTENSION TWO SIDES
ONE HOLE – LARGE ROLLER
TYPE 18 RAL

ROLLER ATTACHMENT LINK
BENT EXTENSION ONE SIDE
TWO HOLES – STANDARD ROLLER
TYPE 20 RAL

PIN ATTACHMENT LINK
BENT EXTENSION ONE SIDE
TWO HOLES
TYPE 19 PAL

ROLLER ATTACHMENT LINK
BENT EXTENSION ONE SIDE
TWO HOLES – LARGE ROLLER
TYPE 21 RAL

ROLLER ATTACHMENT LINK
BENT EXTENSION TWO SIDES
TWO HOLES – STANDARD ROLLER
TYPE 23 RAL

PIN ATTACHMENT LINK
BENT EXTENSION TWO SIDES
TWO HOLES
TYPE 22 PAL

ROLLER ATTACHMENT LINK
BENT EXTENSION TWO SIDES
TWO HOLES– LARGE ROLLER
TYPE 24 RAL

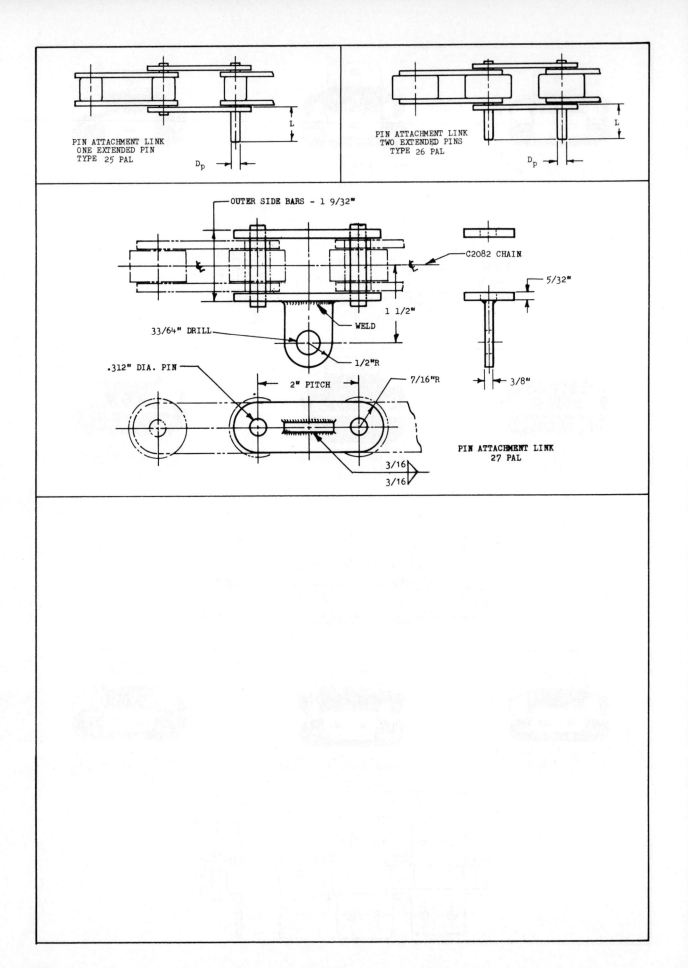

PIN ATTACHMENT LINK
ONE EXTENDED PIN
TYPE 25 PAL

PIN ATTACHMENT LINK
TWO EXTENDED PINS
TYPE 26 PAL

D_p

L

D_p

L

OUTER SIDE BARS - 1 9/32"

C2082 CHAIN

5/32"

WELD

1 1/2"

33/64" DRILL

1/2"R

3/8"

.312" DIA. PIN

2" PITCH

7/16"R

PIN ATTACHMENT LINK
27 PAL

3/16

3/16

Extracted from ASA B18.3-1961, TM 5-230- to 00-25-103, and miscellaneous publications that present graphic representation and symbology in relation to fasteners. This material reproduced through the courtesy of the Department of the Army, Department of the Air Force, Office of the Secretary of Defense; American Standards Association. Extracted from ASA B18.3-1961, with the permission of the American Society of Mechanical Engineers.

FASTENERS (SCREWS, BOLTS, PINS, RIVETS, etc.)

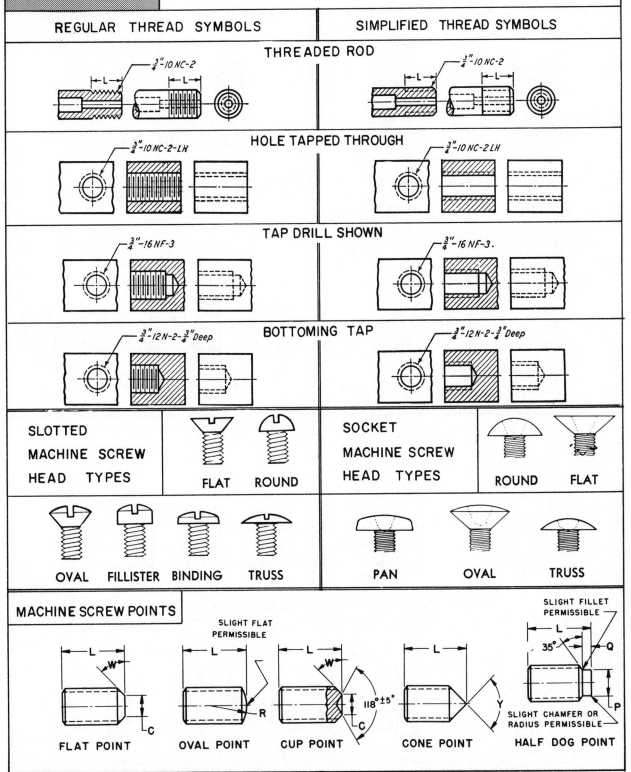

REGULAR THREAD SYMBOLS

SIMPLIFIED THREAD SYMBOLS

THREADED ROD

$\frac{3}{4}$"-10 NC-2

HOLE TAPPED THROUGH

$\frac{3}{4}$"-10 NC-2-LH

TAP DRILL SHOWN

$\frac{3}{4}$"-16 NF-3

BOTTOMING TAP

$\frac{3}{4}$"-12 N-2-$\frac{3}{4}$" Deep

SLOTTED MACHINE SCREW HEAD TYPES — FLAT ROUND

SOCKET MACHINE SCREW HEAD TYPES — ROUND FLAT

OVAL FILLISTER BINDING TRUSS

PAN OVAL TRUSS

MACHINE SCREW POINTS

SLIGHT FLAT PERMISSIBLE

SLIGHT FILLET PERMISSIBLE

SLIGHT CHAMFER OR RADIUS PERMISSIBLE

FLAT POINT OVAL POINT CUP POINT CONE POINT HALF DOG POINT

118°±5°

35°

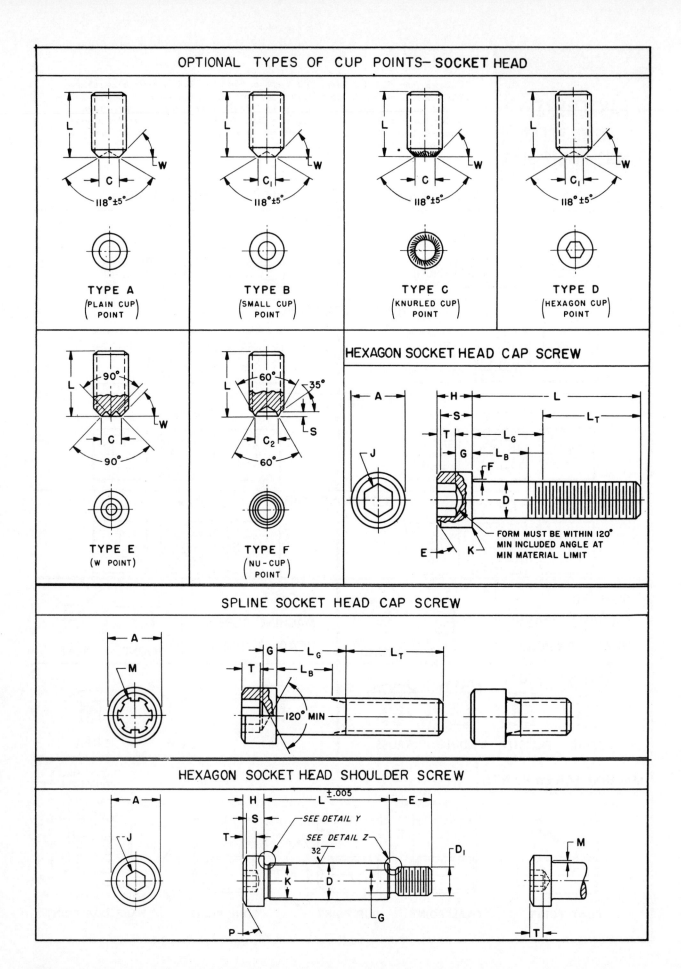

OPTIONAL TYPES OF CUP POINTS— SOCKET HEAD

TYPE A
(PLAIN CUP POINT)

TYPE B
(SMALL CUP POINT)

TYPE C
(KNURLED CUP POINT)

TYPE D
(HEXAGON CUP POINT)

TYPE E
(W POINT)

TYPE F
(NU-CUP POINT)

HEXAGON SOCKET HEAD CAP SCREW

FORM MUST BE WITHIN 120°
MIN INCLUDED ANGLE AT
MIN MATERIAL LIMIT

SPLINE SOCKET HEAD CAP SCREW

120° MIN

HEXAGON SOCKET HEAD SHOULDER SCREW

SEE DETAIL Y
SEE DETAIL Z

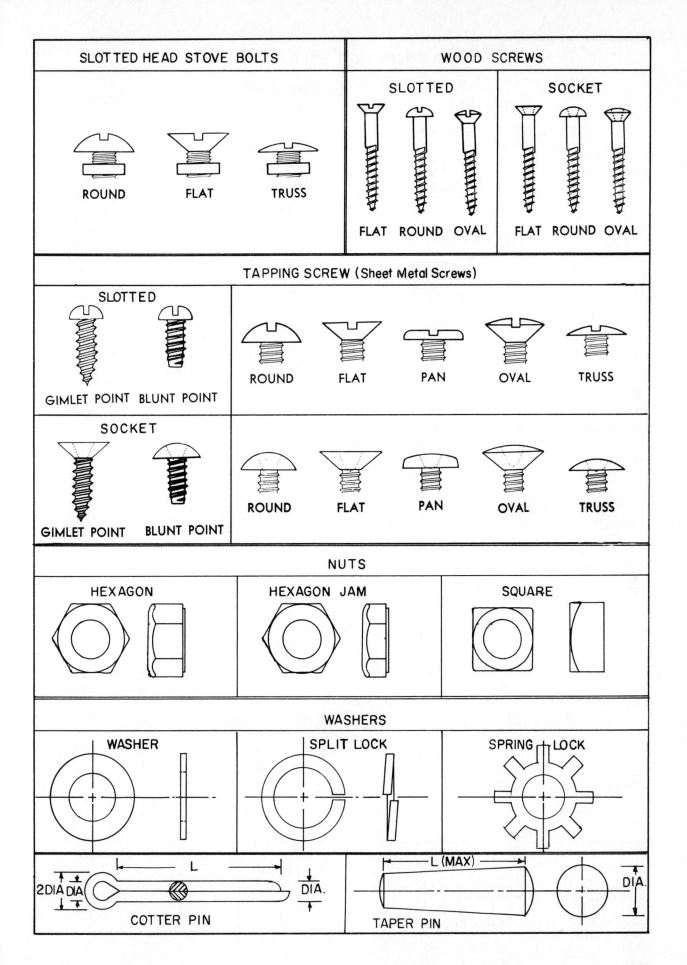

SLOTTED HEAD STOVE BOLTS	WOOD SCREWS

SLOTTED HEAD STOVE BOLTS

ROUND   FLAT   TRUSS

WOOD SCREWS

SLOTTED   SOCKET

FLAT ROUND OVAL   FLAT ROUND OVAL

TAPPING SCREW (Sheet Metal Screws)

SLOTTED

GIMLET POINT   BLUNT POINT

ROUND   FLAT   PAN   OVAL   TRUSS

SOCKET

GIMLET POINT   BLUNT POINT

ROUND   FLAT   PAN   OVAL   TRUSS

NUTS

HEXAGON   HEXAGON JAM   SQUARE

WASHERS

WASHER   SPLIT LOCK   SPRING LOCK

2DIA DIA   L   DIA.

COTTER PIN

L (MAX)   DIA.

TAPER PIN

205

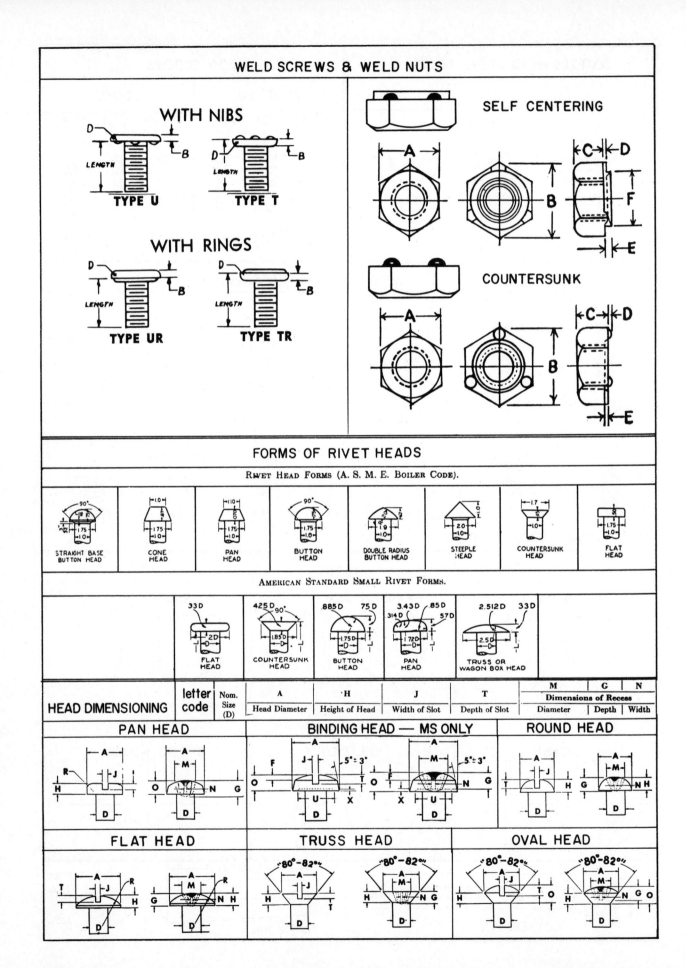

WELD SCREWS & WELD NUTS

WITH NIBS

TYPE U

TYPE T

WITH RINGS

TYPE UR

TYPE TR

SELF CENTERING

COUNTERSUNK

FORMS OF RIVET HEADS

RIVET HEAD FORMS (A. S. M. E. BOILER CODE).

| STRAIGHT BASE BUTTON HEAD | CONE HEAD | PAN HEAD | BUTTON HEAD | DOUBLE RADIUS BUTTON HEAD | STEEPLE HEAD | COUNTERSUNK HEAD | FLAT HEAD |

AMERICAN STANDARD SMALL RIVET FORMS.

| FLAT HEAD | COUNTERSUNK HEAD | BUTTON HEAD | PAN HEAD | TRUSS OR WAGON BOX HEAD |

HEAD DIMENSIONING	letter code	Nom. Size (D)	A	H	J	T	M	G	N
							Dimensions of Recess		
			Head Diameter	Height of Head	Width of Slot	Depth of Slot	Diameter	Depth	Width

PAN HEAD

BINDING HEAD — MS ONLY

ROUND HEAD

FLAT HEAD

TRUSS HEAD

OVAL HEAD

206

TIMBER CONSTRUCTION CONNECTORS

DESCRIPTION	SYMBOL	ILLUSTRATED USE	PICTORIAL	DESCRIPTION	SYMBOL	ILLUSTRATED USE	PICTORIAL
SPLIT RING	SR	$2\frac{1}{2}$ SR		CIRCULAR SPIKE	CS	$3\frac{1}{8}$ CS	
TOOTHED RING	TR	2TR		CLAMPING PLATE, PLAIN	CPP	5 x 5 CPP	
CLAW PLATE, MALE	CPM	$2\frac{5}{8}$ CPM		CLAMPING PLATE, FLANGED	CPFL	5 x 8 CPFL	
CLAW PLATE, FEMALE	CPF	$3\frac{1}{8}$ CPF		SPIKE GRID, FLAT	SGF	$4\frac{1}{8}$ x $4\frac{1}{8}$ SGF	
SHEAR PLATE	SP	4SP		SPIKE GRID, SINGLE CURVE	SGSC	$4\frac{1}{8}$ x $4\frac{1}{8}$ SGSC	
BULLDOG, ROUND	BR	$3\frac{3}{4}$ BR		SPIKE GRID, DOUBLE CURVE	SGDC	$4\frac{1}{8}$ x $4\frac{1}{8}$ SGDC	
BULLDOG, SQUARE	BS	5BS		WOOD SPLICE PLATES			

ASME IEEE FLUID POWER	Flow Lines And Flow Line Functions Lines, Working —————————	Lines, Pilot — — — — — Length of dash shall be at least 20 line widths with space approximately 5 line widths.	Lines, Liquid Drain or Air Exhaust - - - - - - - - - - - - - Length of dash and space shall be approximately equal, each less than 5 line widths.
Lines, Crossing			Lines, Joining Connector dot shall be approximately 5 widths of associated lines.
		Lines, Flexible	Lines to Reservoir *Below Fluid Level*
Above Fluid Level	Flow, Direction of	Plug or Plugged Connection ✕	*Testing Station*
Fluid Power Take-off Station	Restriction, Fixed	Quick Disconnect *Without Checks*	*With Checks* Disconnected
With One Check	With Two Checks	Pumps, Compressors And Rotary Motors Basic Symbol *Envelope*	*Ports* Lines outside envelope are not part of symbol, but represent flow lines connected thereto.
Shafts, Rotating Arrow indicates direction of rotation by assuming it is on near side of shaft	*Controls* *Appropriate letter combinations	* AIR MOT — Motor, Air Rotary CENT — Centrifugal COMP — Compensator CYL — Cylinder (Motor, Linear) DET — Detent (Associated with other controls) ELEC MOT — Motor, Electric HYD MOT — Motor, Hydraulic Cont	

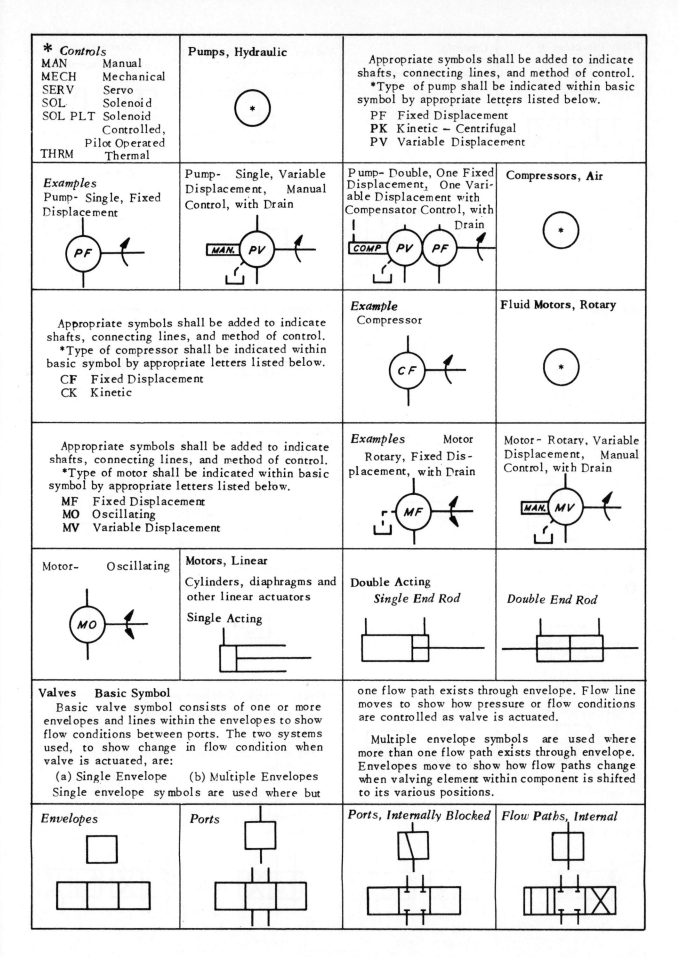

* *Controls*
 MAN   Manual
 MECH   Mechanical
 SERV   Servo
 SOL   Solenoid
 SOL PLT   Solenoid
             Controlled,
       Pilot Operated
 THRM   Thermal
	Pumps, Hydraulic	Appropriate symbols shall be added to indicate shafts, connecting lines, and method of control.
		    *Type of pump shall be indicated within basic symbol by appropriate letters listed below.
		    PF Fixed Displacement
		    PK Kinetic – Centrifugal
		    PV Variable Displacement

Examples
Pump- Single, Fixed Displacement

Pump- Single, Variable Displacement, Manual Control, with Drain

Pump- Double, One Fixed Displacement, One Variable Displacement with Compensator Control, with Drain

Compressors, Air

Appropriate symbols shall be added to indicate shafts, connecting lines, and method of control.
   *Type of compressor shall be indicated within basic symbol by appropriate letters listed below.
   CF   Fixed Displacement
   CK   Kinetic

Example
Compressor

Fluid Motors, Rotary

Appropriate symbols shall be added to indicate shafts, connecting lines, and method of control.
   *Type of motor shall be indicated within basic symbol by appropriate letters listed below.
   MF   Fixed Displacement
   MO   Oscillating
   MV   Variable Displacement

Examples   Motor Rotary, Fixed Displacement, with Drain

Motor- Rotary, Variable Displacement, Manual Control, with Drain

Motor-   Oscillating

Motors, Linear

Cylinders, diaphragms and other linear actuators

Single Acting

Double Acting
Single End Rod

Double End Rod

Valves   Basic Symbol
   Basic valve symbol consists of one or more envelopes and lines within the envelopes to show flow conditions between ports. The two systems used, to show change in flow condition when valve is actuated, are:

   (a) Single Envelope   (b) Multiple Envelopes
Single envelope symbols are used where but

one flow path exists through envelope. Flow line moves to show how pressure or flow conditions are controlled as valve is actuated.

   Multiple envelope symbols are used where more than one flow path exists through envelope. Envelopes move to show how flow paths change when valving element within component is shifted to its various positions.

Envelopes   *Ports*   *Ports, Internally Blocked*   *Flow Paths, Internal*

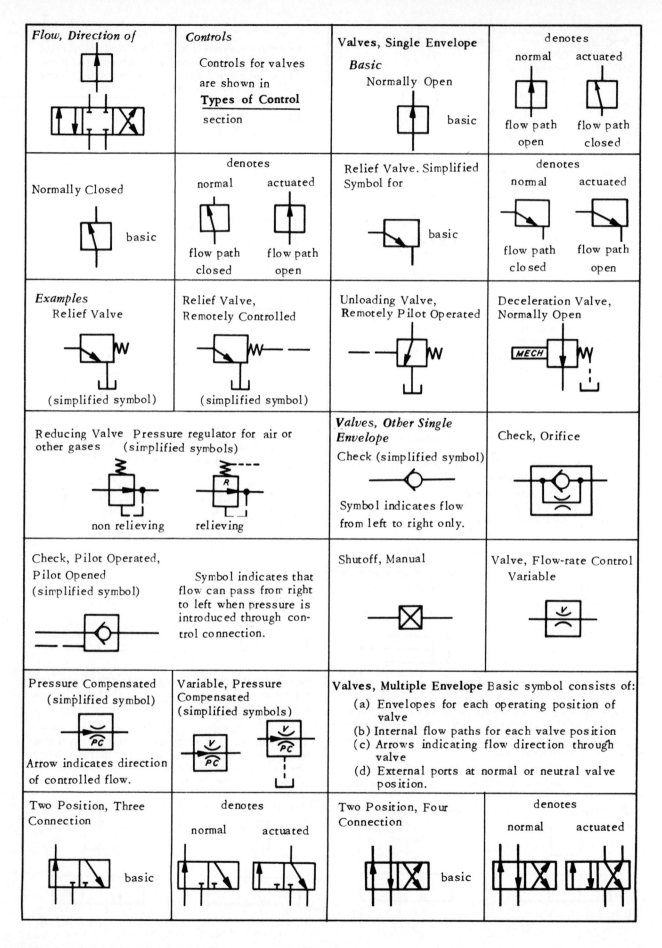

Flow, Direction of	*Controls* Controls for valves are shown in **Types of Control** section	Valves, Single Envelope *Basic* Normally Open basic	denotes normal actuated flow path flow path open closed
Normally Closed basic	denotes normal actuated flow path flow path closed open	Relief Valve. Simplified Symbol for basic	denotes normal actuated flow path flow path closed open
Examples Relief Valve (simplified symbol)	Relief Valve, Remotely Controlled (simplified symbol)	Unloading Valve, Remotely Pilot Operated	Deceleration Valve, Normally Open MECH
Reducing Valve Pressure regulator for air or other gases (simplified symbols) non relieving relieving		*Valves, Other Single Envelope* Check (simplified symbol) Symbol indicates flow from left to right only.	Check, Orifice
Check, Pilot Operated, Pilot Opened (simplified symbol)	Symbol indicates that flow can pass from right to left when pressure is introduced through control connection.	Shutoff, Manual	Valve, Flow-rate Control Variable
Pressure Compensated (simplified symbol) Arrow indicates direction of controlled flow.	Variable, Pressure Compensated (simplified symbols) PC PC	**Valves, Multiple Envelope** Basic symbol consists of: (a) Envelopes for each operating position of valve (b) Internal flow paths for each valve position (c) Arrows indicating flow direction through valve (d) External ports at normal or neutral valve position.	
Two Position, Three Connection basic	denotes normal actuated	Two Position, Four Connection basic	denotes normal actuated

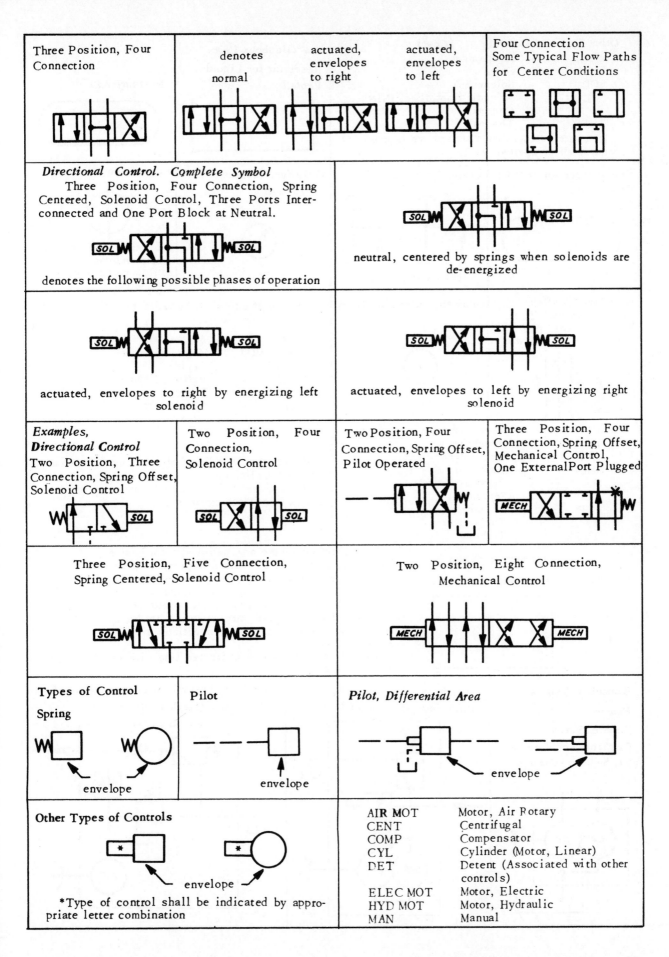

Three Position, Four Connection

denotes normal

actuated, envelopes to right

actuated, envelopes to left

Four Connection
Some Typical Flow Paths for Center Conditions

Directional Control. Complete Symbol
Three Position, Four Connection, Spring Centered, Solenoid Control, Three Ports Interconnected and One Port Block at Neutral.

denotes the following possible phases of operation

neutral, centered by springs when solenoids are de-energized

actuated, envelopes to right by energizing left solenoid

actuated, envelopes to left by energizing right solenoid

Examples,
Directional Control
Two Position, Three Connection, Spring Offset, Solenoid Control

Two Position, Four Connection, Solenoid Control

Two Position, Four Connection, Spring Offset, Pilot Operated

Three Position, Four Connection, Spring Offset, Mechanical Control, One External Port Plugged

Three Position, Five Connection, Spring Centered, Solenoid Control

Two Position, Eight Connection, Mechanical Control

Types of Control

Spring

Pilot

Pilot, Differential Area

envelope

envelope

envelope

Other Types of Controls

*Type of control shall be indicated by appropriate letter combination

AIR MOT	Motor, Air Rotary
CENT	Centrifugal
COMP	Compensator
CYL	Cylinder (Motor, Linear)
DET	Detent (Associated with other controls)
ELEC MOT	Motor, Electric
HYD MOT	Motor, Hydraulic
MAN	Manual

211

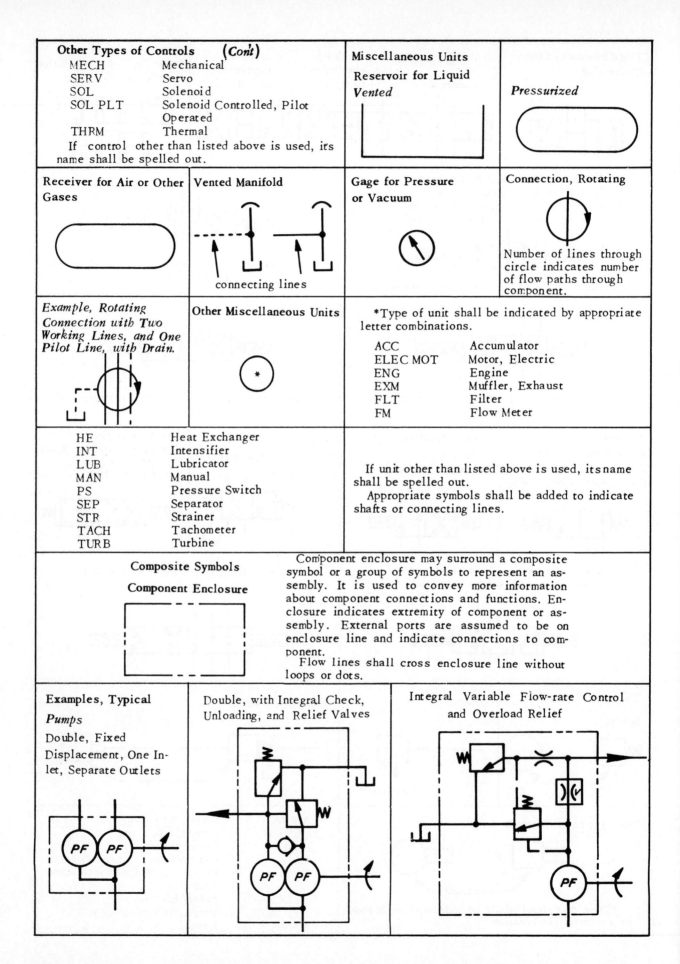

Other Types of Controls *(Cont)*

MECH	Mechanical
SERV	Servo
SOL	Solenoid
SOL PLT	Solenoid Controlled, Pilot Operated
THRM	Thermal

If control other than listed above is used, its name shall be spelled out.

Miscellaneous Units

Reservoir for Liquid

Vented

Pressurized

Receiver for Air or Other Gases

Vented Manifold

connecting lines

Gage for Pressure or Vacuum

Connection, Rotating

Number of lines through circle indicates number of flow paths through component.

Example, Rotating Connection with Two Working Lines, and One Pilot Line, with Drain.

Other Miscellaneous Units

*Type of unit shall be indicated by appropriate letter combinations.

ACC	Accumulator
ELEC MOT	Motor, Electric
ENG	Engine
EXM	Muffler, Exhaust
FLT	Filter
FM	Flow Meter

HE	Heat Exchanger
INT	Intensifier
LUB	Lubricator
MAN	Manual
PS	Pressure Switch
SEP	Separator
STR	Strainer
TACH	Tachometer
TURB	Turbine

If unit other than listed above is used, its name shall be spelled out.

Appropriate symbols shall be added to indicate shafts or connecting lines.

Composite Symbols

Component Enclosure

Component enclosure may surround a composite symbol or a group of symbols to represent an assembly. It is used to convey more information about component connections and functions. Enclosure indicates extremity of component or assembly. External ports are assumed to be on enclosure line and indicate connections to component.

Flow lines shall cross enclosure line without loops or dots.

Examples, Typical

Pumps

Double, Fixed Displacement, One Inlet, Separate Outlets

Double, with Integral Check, Unloading, and Relief Valves

Integral Variable Flow-rate Control and Overload Relief

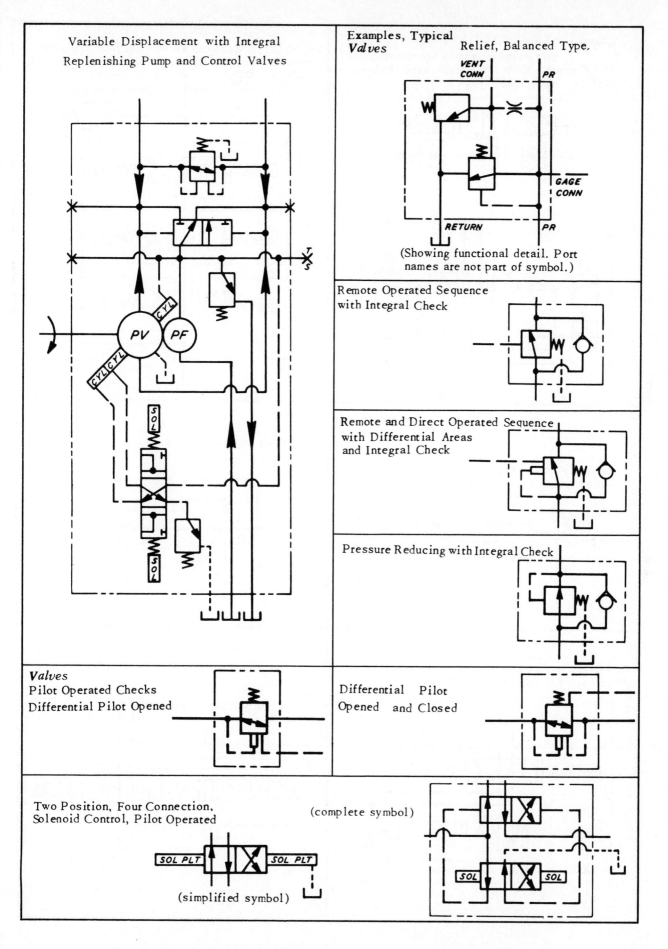

Variable Displacement with Integral
Replenishing Pump and Control Valves

Examples, Typical
Valves
Relief, Balanced Type.

VENT CONN
PR
GAGE CONN
RETURN
PR

(Showing functional detail. Port
names are not part of symbol.)

Remote Operated Sequence
with Integral Check

Remote and Direct Operated Sequence
with Differential Areas
and Integral Check

Pressure Reducing with Integral Check

Valves
Pilot Operated Checks
Differential Pilot Opened

Differential Pilot
Opened and Closed

Two Position, Four Connection,
Solenoid Control, Pilot Operated

(complete symbol)

SOL PLT   SOL PLT

SOL   SOL

(simplified symbol)

Two Position, Five Connection, Solenoid Control, Pilot Operated with Exhaust
Throttles   (simplified symbol)

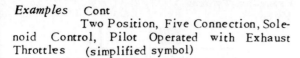
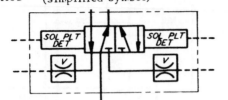

Multiple, Three Position, Manual Directional Control, with Integral Check and Relief
Valves   **ED**

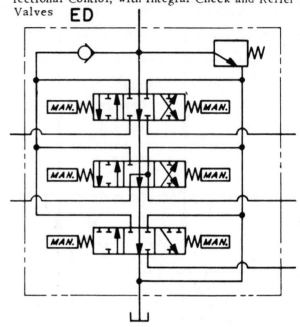

(complete symbol)

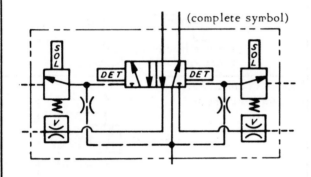

Variable Pressure Compensated Flow-
rate Control and Overload Relief

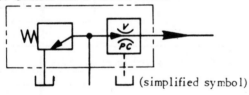

(simplified symbol)

Flow Rate Control, Pressure Compensated with Integral Check

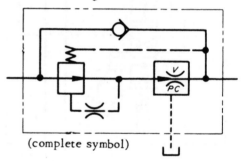

(complete symbol)

Panel Mounted Separate Units Fur-
nished as a Package (Relief, Two 4-way, Two
Check and Flow-rate Control Valves)

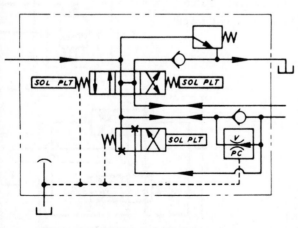

Cycle Control Panel, Five Position

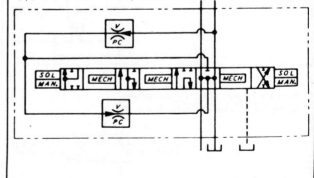

J.I.C. HYDRAULICS (Fluid Legend Code)

Extracted from JIC — Hydraulic Standards, Hydraulic Legend Code, presently published by Hydraulics and Pneumatic publication and Hydraulics Standards for Industrial Equipment, with permission of General Motors Corporation, Manufacturing Development, GM Technical Center, Warren, Mich.

FUNCTION	Color Code	Patt No.	Pattern (Zip-A-Tone)	DEFINITION
Intensified Pressure	Black	7R		Pressure in excess of supply pressure which is induced by a booster or intensifier.
Supply Pressure	Red	177		Power-actuating fluid.
Charging Pressure	Intmt Red	52		Pump-inlet pressure that is higher than atmospheric pressure.
Pilot Pressure	Intmt Red	52		Auxiliary pressure which is lower than supply pressure.
Reduced Pressure	Intmt Red	52		Control-actuating pressure.
Metered Flow	Yellow	63		Fluid at controlled flow rate, other than pump delivery.
Exhaust	Blue	75		Return of power and control fluid to reservoir.
Intake	Green	16		Sub-atmospheric pressure, usually on intake side of pump.
Drain	Green	16		Return of leakage fluid to reservoir.
Inactive	Blank			Fluid which is within the circuit, but which does not serve a functional purpose during the phase being represented.

J.I.C.
PNEUMATIC
(AIR LEGEND CODE)

Extracted from JIC — Pneumatic Standards, Air Legend Code, presently published by Hydraulics and Pneumatic publication and Pneumatic Standards for Industrial Equipment, with permission of General Motors Corporation, Manufacturing Development, GM Technical Center, Warren, Mich.

FUNCTION	Color Code	Patt No	Pattern (Zip-A-Tone)	DEFINITION
Intensified Pressure	Black	7R		Pressure in excess of supply pressure and which is increased by a booster or intensifier.
Supply Pressure	Red	177		Power actuating air.
Charging Pressure	Intmt Red	52		Compressor-inlet pressure that is higher than atmospheric pressure.
Reduced Pressure	Intmt Red	52		Auxiliary pressure which is lower than supply pressure.
Metered Flow	Yellow	63		Controlled flow rate.
Exhaust	Blue	75		Return of power actuating medium to atmosphere.
Intake	Green	16		Sub-atmospheric pressure, usually on intake side of compressor.
Inactive	Blank			Air pressure which is within the circuit but which does not serve a functional purpose during the phase being represented.

MIL—STD 17. GAGES THERMOMETERS MISCELLANEOUS	**General.** The following symbols shall be used where graphic representation of gages, thermometers, and certain miscellaneous units listed herein is desired.		**Gages** Absolute pressure
Differential	Draft	Duplex	Liquid level
Pressure	Vacuum	Vacuum-pressure	
Thermometers Thermometer	Thermometer, distant reading, bare bulb type	Thermometer, distant reading, separate socket type	
Miscellaneous Air chamber	Bulkhead joint, expansion	Bulkhead joint, fixed	Deck box, for deck operating gear or sounding
Eductor	Funnel, closed	Funnel, open	Gage glass
Meter, area type (other than electrical)	Meter, displacement type (other than electrical)	Recorder (other than electrical)	Salinity cell

Sea chest, discharge	Sea chest, suction	Sight flow	Test casting, sprinkler system
Thermostat, remote bulb	Vent	Water seal	Zinc box

AGA ASME
GEARS
Representation
Nomenclature

Extracted from American Standard Gear Nomenclature—Terms, Definitions and Illustrations (ASA B6.10-1954), with the permission of the publisher, the American Society of Mechanical Engineers, United Engineering Center, 345 East 47 Street, New York, N.Y., and the American Gear Manufacturers Association, One Thomas Circle, Washington, D.C.

KINDS OF GEARS

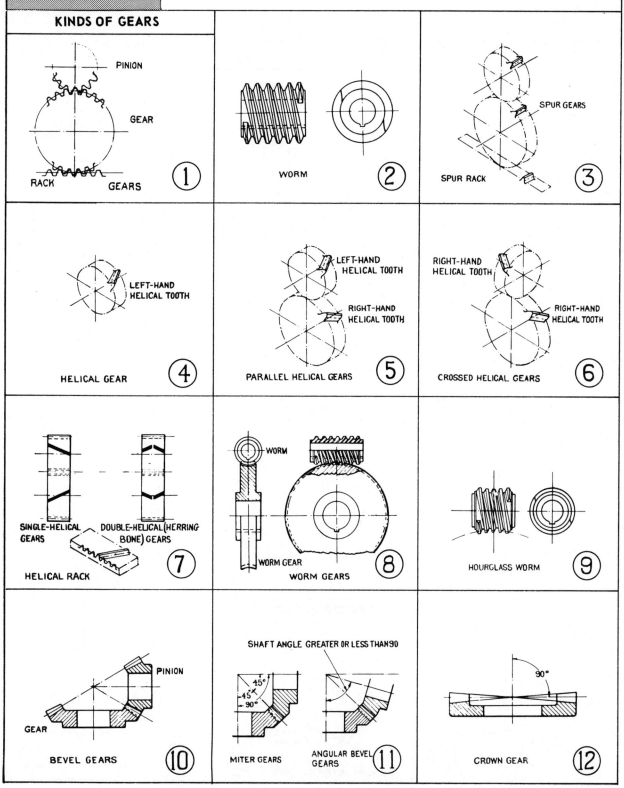

1. PINION, GEAR, RACK GEARS

2. WORM

3. SPUR GEARS, SPUR RACK

4. HELICAL GEAR — LEFT-HAND HELICAL TOOTH

5. PARALLEL HELICAL GEARS — LEFT-HAND HELICAL TOOTH, RIGHT-HAND HELICAL TOOTH

6. CROSSED HELICAL GEARS — RIGHT-HAND HELICAL TOOTH, RIGHT-HAND HELICAL TOOTH

7. HELICAL RACK — SINGLE-HELICAL GEARS, DOUBLE-HELICAL (HERRING BONE) GEARS

8. WORM GEARS — WORM, WORM GEAR

9. HOURGLASS WORM

10. BEVEL GEARS — PINION, GEAR

11. SHAFT ANGLE GREATER OR LESS THAN 90 — MITER GEARS, ANGULAR BEVEL GEARS — 45°, 45°, 90°

12. CROWN GEAR — 90°

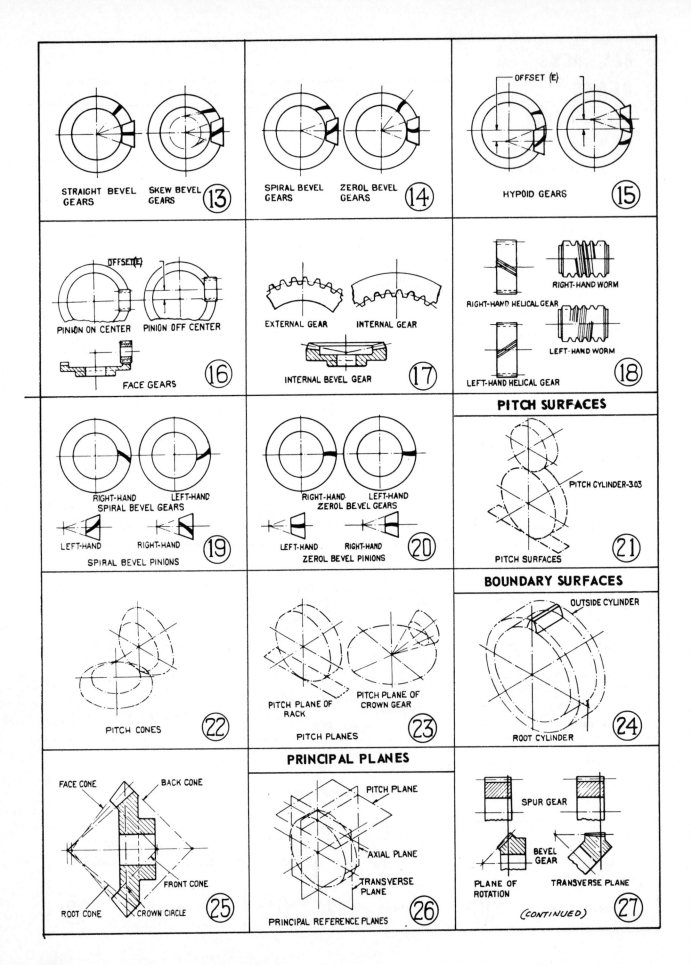

STRAIGHT BEVEL GEARS   SKEW BEVEL GEARS   ⑬

SPIRAL BEVEL GEARS   ZEROL BEVEL GEARS   ⑭

OFFSET (E)

HYPOID GEARS   ⑮

OFFSET (E)

PINION ON CENTER   PINION OFF CENTER

FACE GEARS   ⑯

EXTERNAL GEAR   INTERNAL GEAR

INTERNAL BEVEL GEAR   ⑰

RIGHT-HAND HELICAL GEAR   RIGHT-HAND WORM

LEFT-HAND HELICAL GEAR   LEFT-HAND WORM   ⑱

RIGHT-HAND   LEFT-HAND
SPIRAL BEVEL GEARS

LEFT-HAND   RIGHT-HAND

SPIRAL BEVEL PINIONS   ⑲

RIGHT-HAND   LEFT-HAND
ZEROL BEVEL GEARS

LEFT-HAND   RIGHT-HAND

ZEROL BEVEL PINIONS   ⑳

PITCH SURFACES

PITCH CYLINDER-3.03

PITCH SURFACES   ㉑

PITCH CONES   ㉒

PITCH PLANE OF RACK   PITCH PLANE OF CROWN GEAR

PITCH PLANES   ㉓

BOUNDARY SURFACES

OUTSIDE CYLINDER

ROOT CYLINDER   ㉔

FACE CONE   BACK CONE

FRONT CONE

ROOT CONE   CROWN CIRCLE   ㉕

PRINCIPAL PLANES

PITCH PLANE

AXIAL PLANE

TRANSVERSE PLANE

PRINCIPAL REFERENCE PLANES   ㉖

SPUR GEAR

BEVEL GEAR

PLANE OF ROTATION   TRANSVERSE PLANE

(CONTINUED)   ㉗

220

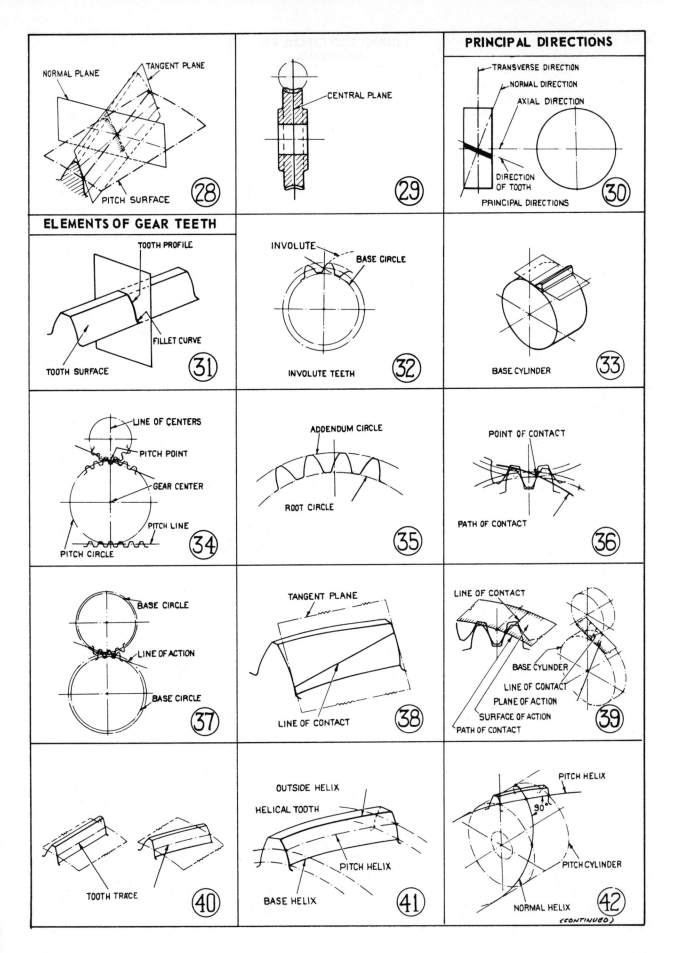

PRINCIPAL DIRECTIONS

28 — NORMAL PLANE / TANGENT PLANE / PITCH SURFACE

29 — CENTRAL PLANE

30 — TRANSVERSE DIRECTION / NORMAL DIRECTION / AXIAL DIRECTION / DIRECTION OF TOOTH / PRINCIPAL DIRECTIONS

ELEMENTS OF GEAR TEETH

31 — TOOTH PROFILE / FILLET CURVE / TOOTH SURFACE

32 — INVOLUTE / BASE CIRCLE / INVOLUTE TEETH

33 — BASE CYLINDER

34 — LINE OF CENTERS / PITCH POINT / GEAR CENTER / PITCH LINE / PITCH CIRCLE

35 — ADDENDUM CIRCLE / ROOT CIRCLE

36 — POINT OF CONTACT / PATH OF CONTACT

37 — BASE CIRCLE / LINE OF ACTION / BASE CIRCLE

38 — TANGENT PLANE / LINE OF CONTACT

39 — LINE OF CONTACT / BASE CYLINDER / LINE OF CONTACT / PLANE OF ACTION / SURFACE OF ACTION / PATH OF CONTACT

40 — TOOTH TRACE

41 — OUTSIDE HELIX / HELICAL TOOTH / PITCH HELIX / BASE HELIX

42 — PITCH HELIX / 90° / PITCH CYLINDER / NORMAL HELIX / *(CONTINUED)*

221

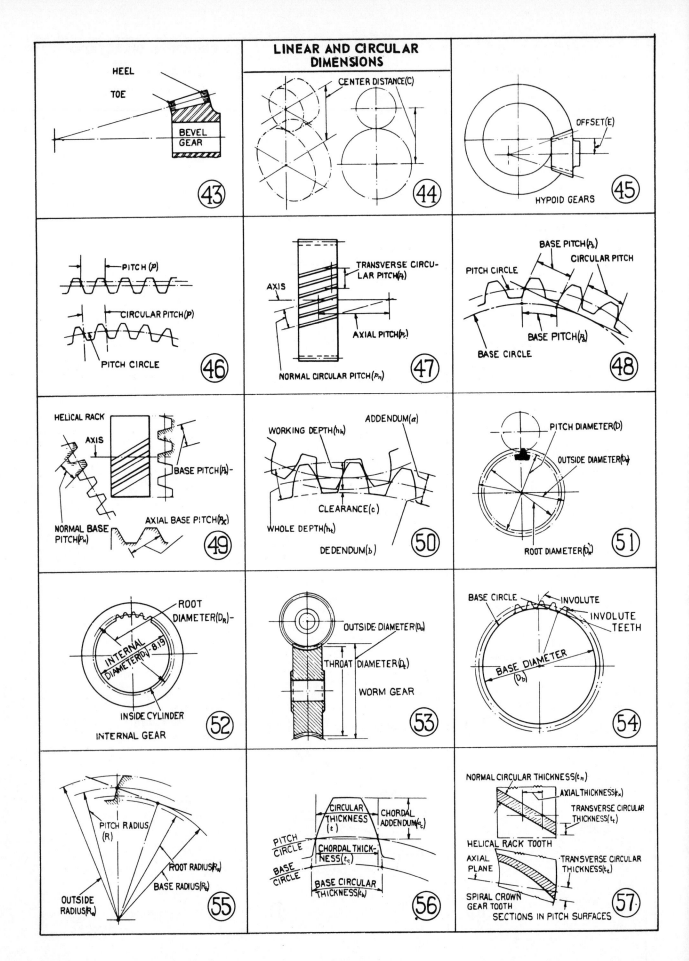

HEEL
TOE
BEVEL GEAR
43

LINEAR AND CIRCULAR DIMENSIONS
CENTER DISTANCE(C)
44

OFFSET(E)
HYPOID GEARS
45

PITCH (P)
CIRCULAR PITCH(P)
PITCH CIRCLE
46

AXIS
TRANSVERSE CIRCULAR PITCH(P₁)
AXIAL PITCH(P₂)
NORMAL CIRCULAR PITCH(Pₙ)
47

BASE PITCH(P₆)
CIRCULAR PITCH
PITCH CIRCLE
BASE PITCH(P₆)
BASE CIRCLE
48

HELICAL RACK
AXIS
BASE PITCH(P₆)
NORMAL BASE PITCH(Pₙ)
AXIAL BASE PITCH(Pₓ)
49

WORKING DEPTH(hₖ)
ADDENDUM(a)
CLEARANCE(c)
WHOLE DEPTH(hₜ)
DEDENDUM(b)
50

PITCH DIAMETER(D)
OUTSIDE DIAMETER(Dₒ)
ROOT DIAMETER(Dᵣ)
51

ROOT DIAMETER(Dᵣ)
INTERNAL DIAMETER(D₁=8.19)
INSIDE CYLINDER
INTERNAL GEAR
52

OUTSIDE DIAMETER(Dₒ)
THROAT DIAMETER(Dₜ)
WORM GEAR
53

BASE CIRCLE
INVOLUTE
INVOLUTE TEETH
BASE DIAMETER (D₆)
54

PITCH RADIUS (R)
ROOT RADIUS(Rᵣ)
BASE RADIUS(R₆)
OUTSIDE RADIUS(Rₒ)
55

CIRCULAR THICKNESS (t)
CHORDAL ADDENDUM(aₒ)
PITCH CIRCLE
CHORDAL THICKNESS(tₒ)
BASE CIRCLE
BASE CIRCULAR THICKNESS(t₆)
56

NORMAL CIRCULAR THICKNESS(tₙ)
AXIAL THICKNESS(tₓ)
TRANSVERSE CIRCULAR THICKNESS(tₜ)
HELICAL RACK TOOTH
AXIAL PLANE
TRANSVERSE CIRCULAR THICKNESS(tₜ)
SPIRAL CROWN GEAR TOOTH
SECTIONS IN PITCH SURFACES
57

222

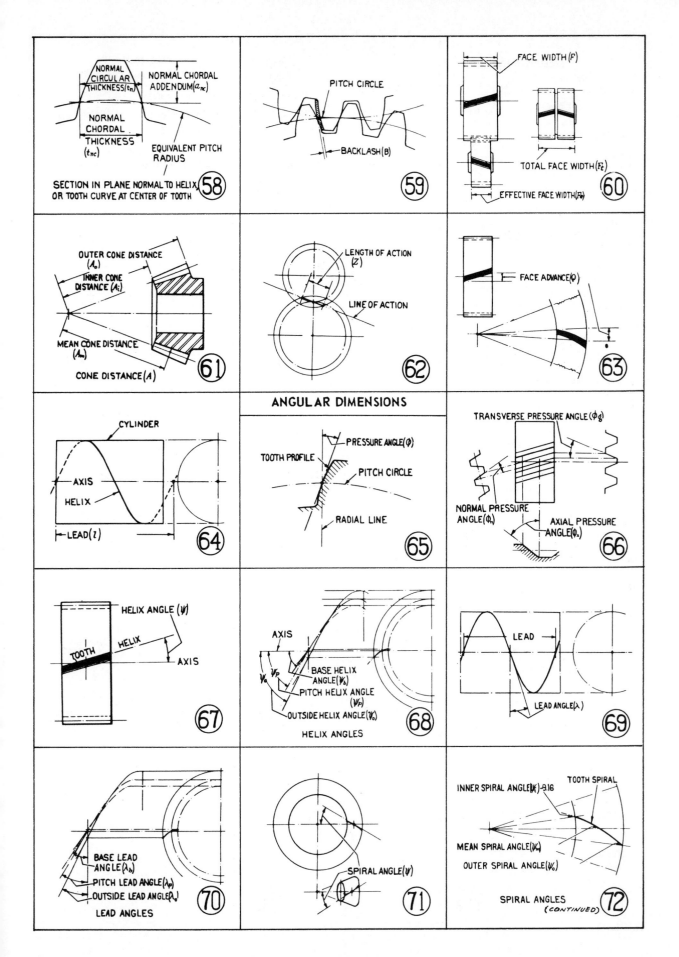

58 SECTION IN PLANE NORMAL TO HELIX OR TOOTH CURVE AT CENTER OF TOOTH

NORMAL CIRCULAR THICKNESS(t_n)
NORMAL CHORDAL ADDENDUM(a_{nc})
NORMAL CHORDAL THICKNESS (t_{nc})
EQUIVALENT PITCH RADIUS

59 PITCH CIRCLE
BACKLASH(B)

60 FACE WIDTH (F)
TOTAL FACE WIDTH(F_t)
EFFECTIVE FACE WIDTH(F_e)

61 CONE DISTANCE (A)
OUTER CONE DISTANCE (A_o)
INNER CONE DISTANCE (A_i)
MEAN CONE DISTANCE (A_m)

62 LENGTH OF ACTION (Z)
LINE OF ACTION

63 FACE ADVANCE($φ$)

64 CYLINDER
AXIS
HELIX
LEAD(l)

ANGULAR DIMENSIONS

65 PRESSURE ANGLE($φ$)
TOOTH PROFILE
PITCH CIRCLE
RADIAL LINE

66 TRANSVERSE PRESSURE ANGLE($φ_g$)
NORMAL PRESSURE ANGLE($φ_n$)
AXIAL PRESSURE ANGLE($φ_x$)

67 HELIX ANGLE ($ψ$)
TOOTH HELIX
AXIS

68 HELIX ANGLES
AXIS
BASE HELIX ANGLE($ψ_b$)
PITCH HELIX ANGLE ($ψ_p$)
OUTSIDE HELIX ANGLE($ψ_o$)

69 LEAD
LEAD ANGLE($λ$)

70 LEAD ANGLES
BASE LEAD ANGLE($λ_b$)
PITCH LEAD ANGLE($λ_p$)
OUTSIDE LEAD ANGLE($λ_o$)

71 SPIRAL ANGLE($ψ$)

72 SPIRAL ANGLES (CONTINUED)
INNER SPIRAL ANGLE($ψ_i$)-9.16
TOOTH SPIRAL
MEAN SPIRAL ANGLE($ψ_m$)
OUTER SPIRAL ANGLE($ψ_o$)

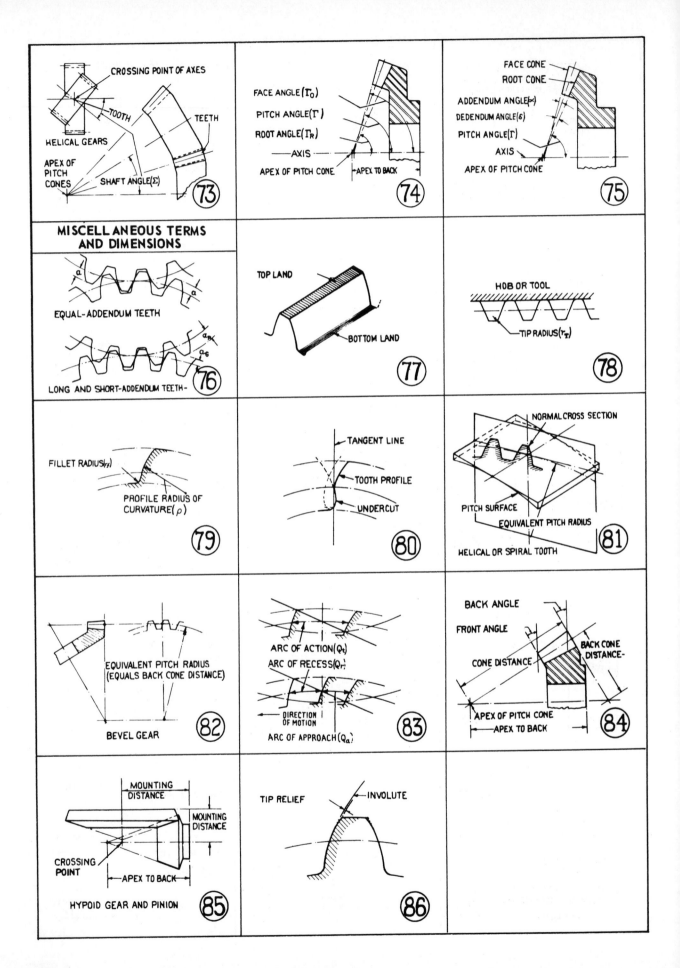

MISCELLANEOUS TERMS AND DIMENSIONS

73 — CROSSING POINT OF AXES / TOOTH / TEETH / HELICAL GEARS / APEX OF PITCH CONES / SHAFT ANGLE(Σ)

74 — FACE ANGLE(Γ_O) / PITCH ANGLE(Γ) / ROOT ANGLE(Γ_R) / AXIS / APEX OF PITCH CONE / APEX TO BACK

75 — FACE CONE / ROOT CONE / ADDENDUM ANGLE(α) / DEDENDUM ANGLE(δ) / PITCH ANGLE(Γ) / AXIS / APEX OF PITCH CONE

76 — EQUAL-ADDENDUM TEETH / LONG AND SHORT-ADDENDUM TEETH-

77 — TOP LAND / BOTTOM LAND

78 — HOB OR TOOL / TIP RADIUS(r_T)

79 — FILLET RADIUS(r_f) / PROFILE RADIUS OF CURVATURE(ρ)

80 — TANGENT LINE / TOOTH PROFILE / UNDERCUT

81 — NORMAL CROSS SECTION / PITCH SURFACE / EQUIVALENT PITCH RADIUS / HELICAL OR SPIRAL TOOTH

82 — EQUIVALENT PITCH RADIUS (EQUALS BACK CONE DISTANCE) / BEVEL GEAR

83 — ARC OF ACTION(Q_t) / ARC OF RECESS(Q_r) / DIRECTION OF MOTION / ARC OF APPROACH(Q_a)

84 — BACK ANGLE / FRONT ANGLE / CONE DISTANCE / BACK CONE DISTANCE / APEX OF PITCH CONE / APEX TO BACK

85 — MOUNTING DISTANCE / MOUNTING DISTANCE / CROSSING POINT / APEX TO BACK / HYPOID GEAR AND PINION

86 — TIP RELIEF / INVOLUTE

224

U.S. Army Ord. Corps

MECHANICAL

(Gear & Mechanism Schematic Illustration)

Extracted from the "Draftsman's Handbook," Ordinance Corps, Department of the Army, with the permission of the Office of the Secretary of Defense, Public Affairs Department, Washington.

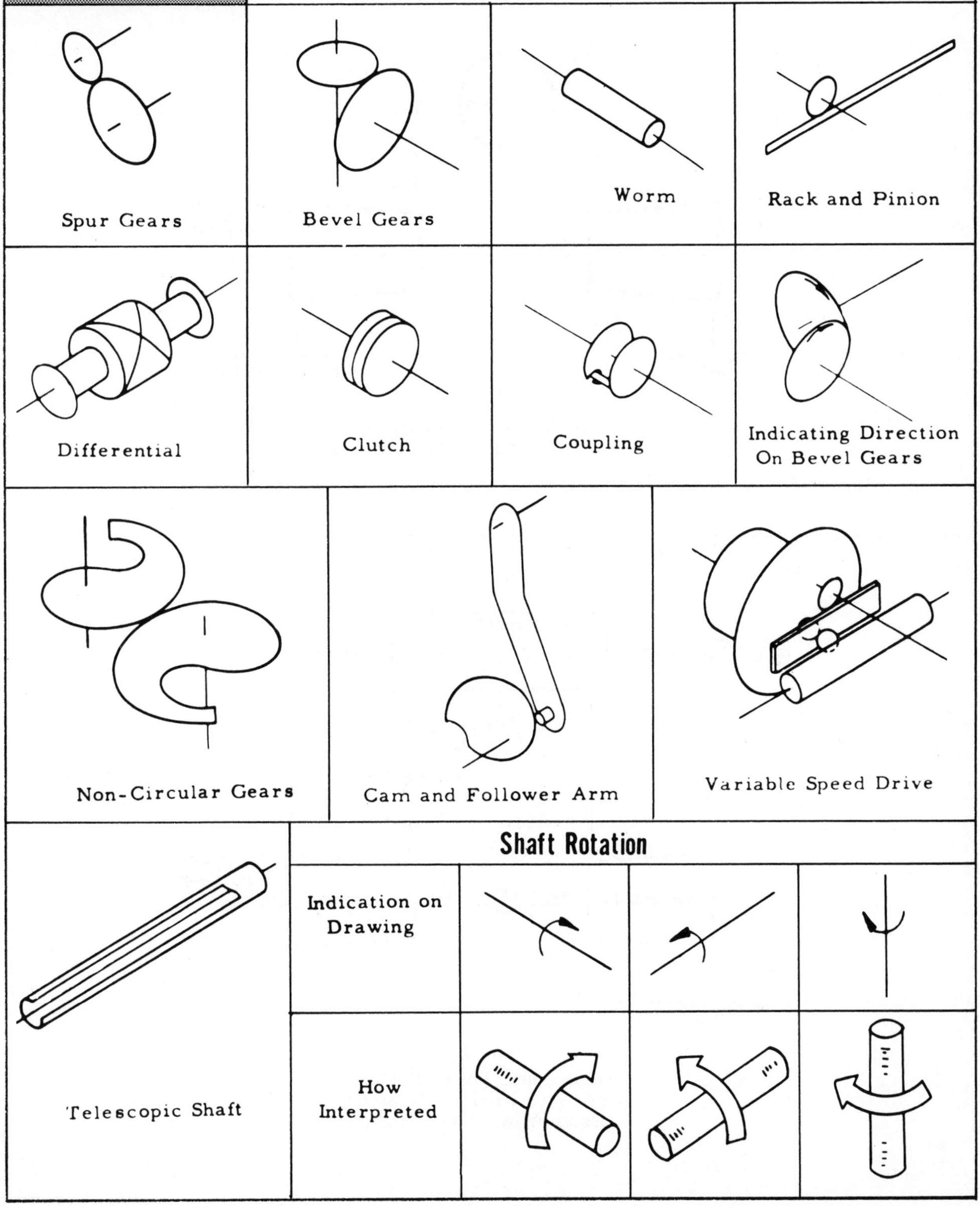

Spur Gears

Bevel Gears

Worm

Rack and Pinion

Differential

Clutch

Coupling

Indicating Direction On Bevel Gears

Non-Circular Gears

Cam and Follower Arm

Variable Speed Drive

Telescopic Shaft

Shaft Rotation

Indication on Drawing

How Interpreted

Extracted from NEMA 48-134, Definitions for Marine Propulsion, Gas Turbines, with the permission of the National Electrical Manufacturers Association, 155 East 44 Street, New York, N.Y.

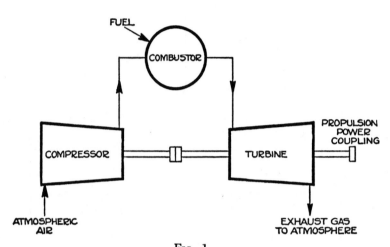

FIG. 1
GAS TURBINE POWER PLANT,
OPEN CYCLE, SERIES FLOW, SINGLE SHAFT

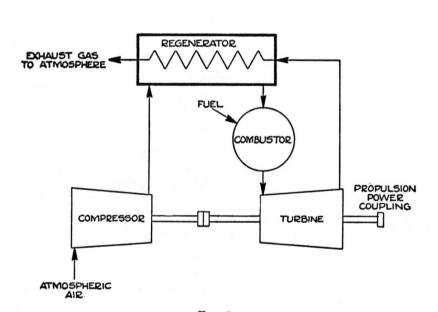

FIG. 2
GAS TURBINE POWER PLANT,
OPEN CYCLE WITH REGENERATOR,
SERIES FLOW, SINGLE SHAFT

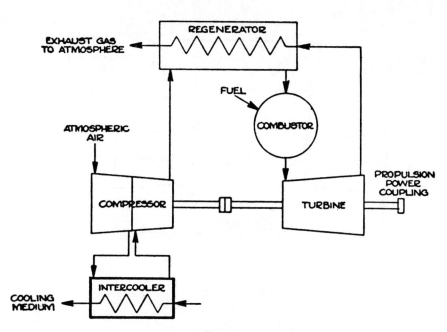

Fig. 3

Gas Turbine Power Plant,
Open Cycle with Regenerator and Intercooler,
Series Flow, Single Shaft

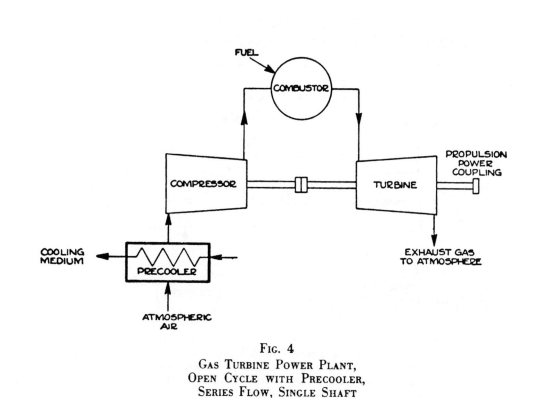

Fig. 4

Gas Turbine Power Plant,
Open Cycle with Precooler,
Series Flow, Single Shaft

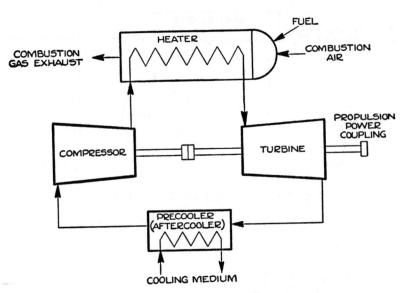

FIG. 5
GAS TURBINE POWER PLANT,
CLOSED CYCLE WITH PRECOOLER,
SERIES FLOW, SINGLE SHAFT

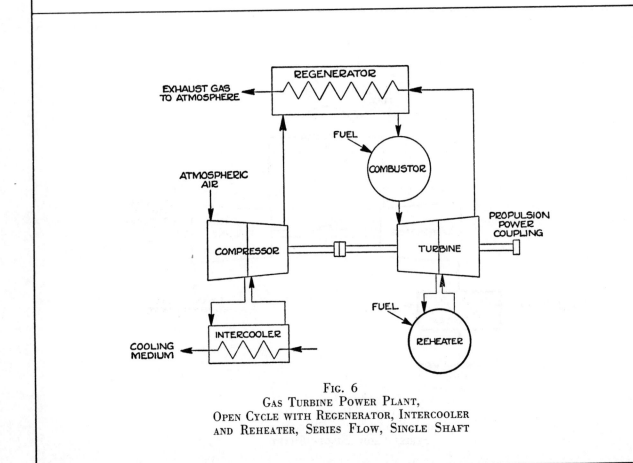

FIG. 6
GAS TURBINE POWER PLANT,
OPEN CYCLE WITH REGENERATOR, INTERCOOLER
AND REHEATER, SERIES FLOW, SINGLE SHAFT

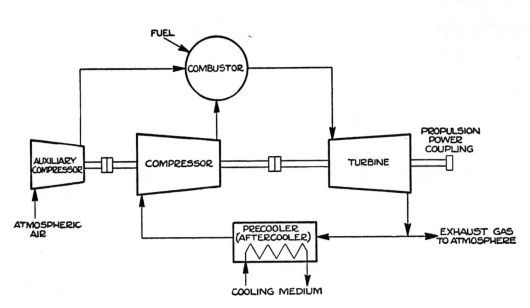

FIG. 7

GAS TURBINE POWER PLANT,
SEMI-CLOSED CYCLE WITH PRECOOLER,
SERIES FLOW, SINGLE SHAFT

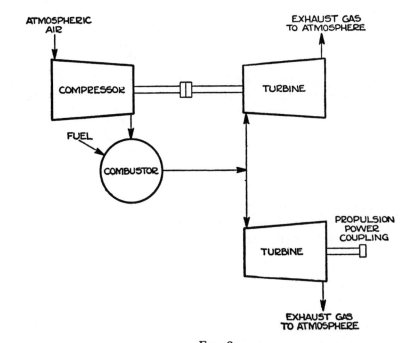

FIG. 8

GAS TURBINE POWER PLANT,
OPEN CYCLE, SERIES-PARALLEL FLOW
(PARALLEL TURBINES), MULTIPLE SHAFT

Extracted from NEMA SM40-1961, Marine Propulsion, Steam Turbines and Gears, with the permission of the National Electrical Manufacturers Association, 155 East 44 Street, New York, N.Y.

TYPES OF TURBINES	SYMBOL
Fig. 1-1 High-Pressure Turbine is the high-pressure element of a compound turbine.	
Fig. 1-2 Intermediate-Pressure Turbine is the intermediate pressure element of a compound turbine.	
Fig. 1-3 Low-Pressure Turbine, Single Flow, is the low-pressure element of a compound turbine. It has a single steam path from the initial stage through the final stage.	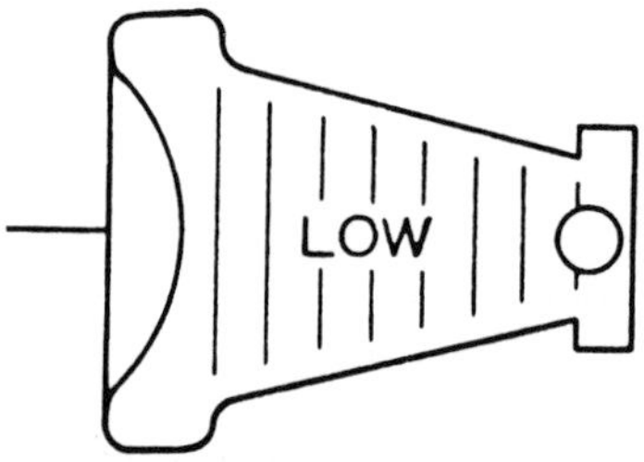
Fig. 1-4 Low-Pressure Turbine, Double Flow, is the low-pressure element of a compound turbine. It has a divided steam path.	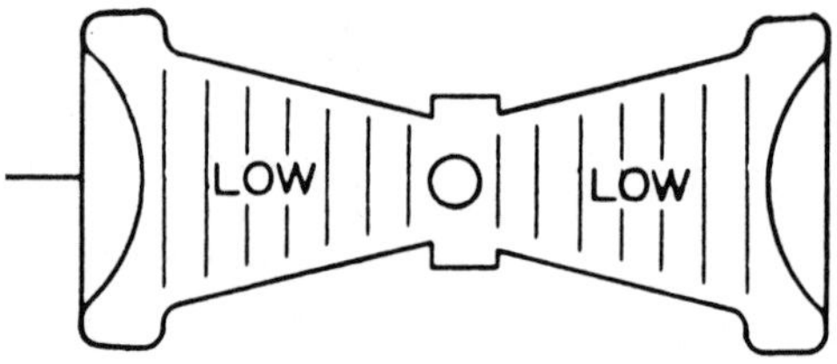
Fig. 1-5 Single-Cylinder Turbine is a single-element turbine in which the steam expansion is complete within a single casing.	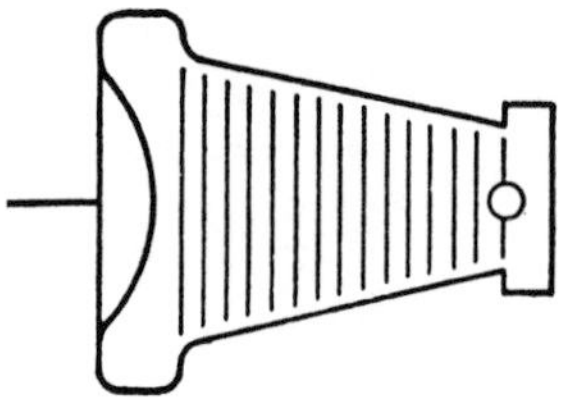
Fig. 1-6 Astern Turbine consists of those elements of the turbine that normally function to drive the ship astern. It may be arranged in the same casing as the ahead turbine or within its own casing.	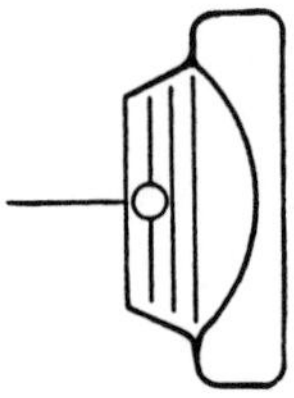

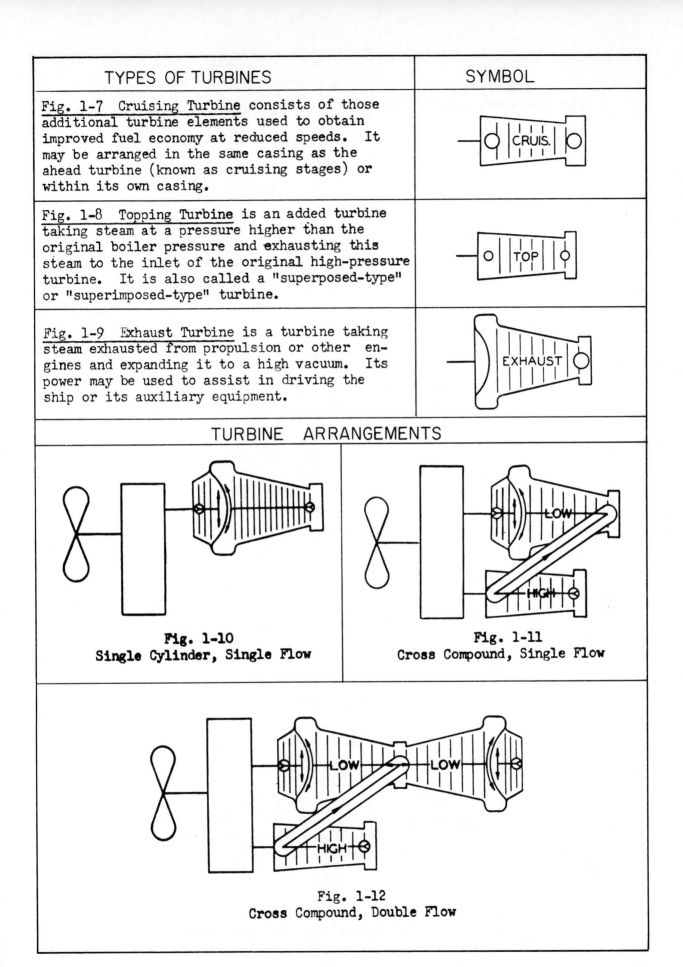

TYPES OF TURBINES	SYMBOL
Fig. 1-7 Cruising Turbine consists of those additional turbine elements used to obtain improved fuel economy at reduced speeds. It may be arranged in the same casing as the ahead turbine (known as cruising stages) or within its own casing.	CRUIS.
Fig. 1-8 Topping Turbine is an added turbine taking steam at a pressure higher than the original boiler pressure and exhausting this steam to the inlet of the original high-pressure turbine. It is also called a "superposed-type" or "superimposed-type" turbine.	TOP
Fig. 1-9 Exhaust Turbine is a turbine taking steam exhausted from propulsion or other engines and expanding it to a high vacuum. Its power may be used to assist in driving the ship or its auxiliary equipment.	EXHAUST

TURBINE   ARRANGEMENTS

Fig. 1-10
Single Cylinder, Single Flow

Fig. 1-11
Cross Compound, Single Flow

Fig. 1-12
Cross Compound, Double Flow

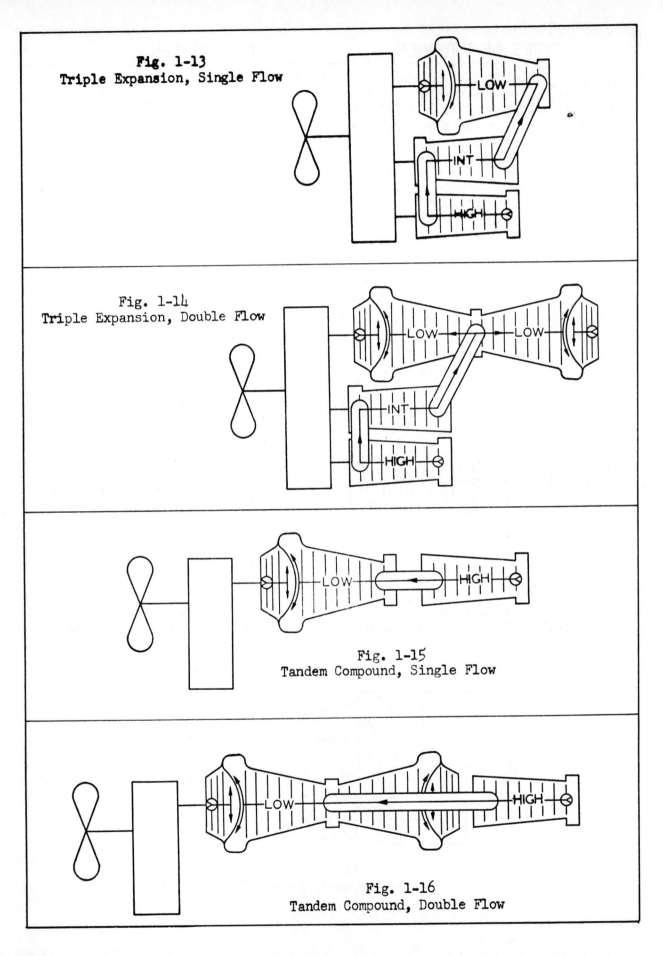

Fig. 1-13
Triple Expansion, Single Flow

Fig. 1-14
Triple Expansion, Double Flow

Fig. 1-15
Tandem Compound, Single Flow

Fig. 1-16
Tandem Compound, Double Flow

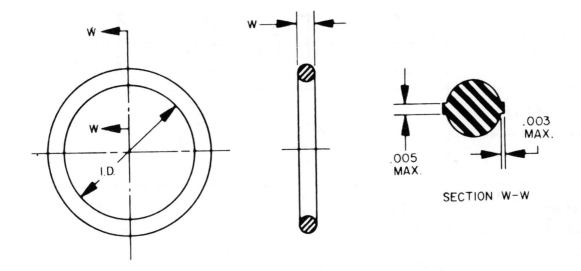

O-rings are measured by cross section width (W) and inside diameter (ID).

Dimensions are given in inches.

Graphical Symbols For Pipe Fittings, Valves and Piping (ASA-ASME 232.23).*

	Flanged	Screwed	Bell & Spigot	Welded	Soldered
Bushing					
Cap					
Cross Reducing					
Straight size					
Crossover					
Elbow 45 degrees					
90 degrees					
Turned down / Turned up					
Base					

*See p. 235.

Extracted from ASA Z32.2.3-1953, Graphical Symbols for Pipe Fitting, Valves and Piping, with the permission of the publisher, the American Society of Mechanical Engineers, United Engineering Center, 345 East 47 Street, New York, N.Y.

	Flanged	Screwed	Bell & Spigot	Welded	Soldered
Elbow (con't)					
Double branch					
Long radius					
Reducing					
Side outlet (outlet down)					
Side outlet (outlet up)					
Street					
Joint					
Connecting pipe					
Expansion					
Lateral					

	Flanged	Screwed	Bell & Spigot	Welded	Soldered
Orifice Flange					
Reducing Flange					
Plugs					
Bull plug					
Pipe plug					
Reducer					
Concentric					
Eccentric					
Sleeve					
Tee					
Straight size					

	Flanged	Screwed	Bell & Spigot	Welded	Soldered
Tee (con't)					
Outlet up					
Outlet down					
Double sweep					
Reducing					
Single sweep					
Side outlet (outlet down)					
Side outlet (outlet up)					
Union					
Angle Valve					
Check					

Graphical Symbols for Valves (ASA-ASME 232.2.3)

	Flanged	Screwed	Bell & Spigot	Welded	Soldered
Angle Valve (con't)					
Gate (elevation)					
Gate (plan)					
Globe (elevation)					
Globe (plan)					
Hose angle		Same as hose valve (angle)			
Automatic					
Bypass					
Governor-operated					
Reducing					
Check					
Angle check		Same as angle valve (check)			

	Flanged	Screwed	Bell & Spigot	Welded	Soldered
Check (con't) Straight way					
Cock					
Diaphragm					
Float					
Gate Also used for general stop valve when amplified by specification					
Angle gate		Same as angle valve—gate (elevation, plan)			
Hose gate		Same as hose valve—gate			
Motor-operated					
Globe					
Angle globe		Same as angle valve—globe (elevation, plan)			
Hose globe		Same as hose valve—globe			

	Flanged	Screwed	Bell & Spigot	Welded	Soldered
Globe (con't) Motor-operated					
Hose Angle					
Gate					
Globe					
Lockshield					
Quick Opening					
Safety					
Stop		Same as globe plan			

Air Conditioning

BRINE RETURN	— — —BR— — —
BRINE SUPPLY	—————B—————
CIRCULATING CHILLED OR HOT-WATER FLOW	—————CH—————
CIRCULATING CHILLED OR HOT-WATER RETURN	— — —CHR— — —
CONDENSER WATER FLOW	—————C—————
CONDENSER WATER RETURN	— — —CR— — —
DRAIN	—————D—————
HUMIDIFICATION LINE	—— - —— H —— - ——
MAKE-UP WATER	—— - —— - —— - ——
REFRIGERANT DISCHARGE	—————RD—————
REFRIGERANT LIQUID	—————RL—————
REFRIGERANT SUCTION	— — —RS— — —

Heating

AIR-RELIEF LINE	— — — — —
BOILER BLOW OFF	— — — — —
COMPRESSED AIR	—————A—————
CONDENSATE OR VACUUM PUMP DISCHARGE	—o— —o— —o—
FEEDWATER PUMP DISCHARGE	—oo— —oo— —oo—
FUEL-OIL FLOW	—————FOF—————
FUEL-OIL RETURN	— — —FOR— — —
FUEL-OIL TANK VENT	— — —FOV— — —
HIGH-PRESSURE RETURN	—#— —#— —#—
HIGH-PRESSURE STEAM	—#— —#— —#—
HOT-WATER HEATING RETURN	— — — — —
HOT-WATER HEATING SUPPLY	—————————

Heating (cont)

LOW-PRESSURE RETURN	— — — — —
LOW-PRESSURE STEAM	————————
MAKE-UP WATER	—·—·—·—
MEDIUM PRESSURE RETURN	—+—+—+—
MEDIUM PRESSURE STEAM	—/—/—/—

Plumbing

ACID WASTE	——— ACID ———
COLD WATER	—·—·—·—
COMPRESSED AIR	——— A ———
DRINKING-WATER FLOW	—— — —— —
DRINKING-WATER RETURN	—— —— ——
FIRE LINE	—F———F—
GAS	—G———G—
HOT WATER	—— —— ——
HOT-WATER RETURN	—— ··· —— ··· ——
SOIL, WASTE OR LEADER (ABOVE GRADE)	————————
SOIL, WASTE OR LEADER (BELOW GRADE)	— — — — —
VACUUM CLEANING	—V———V—
VENT	– – – – – –

Pneumatic

TUBE RUNS	════════

Sprinklers

BRANCH AND HEAD	—o———o—
DRAIN	—S— — —S—
MAIN SUPPLIES	———S———

MIL-STD 17 **PIPE FITTINGS**	**General.** The following symbols shall be used in connection with the piping symbols when graphic representation of pipe fittings is required.	**Type of connections.** The various types of connections or joints shall be represented as follows:

Screwed ends Flanged ends Bell-and-spigot ends Welded and brazed ends Soldered ends		The screwed representation may be used to indicate all types of connections provided the type of connection is covered by a note on the drawing or by specifications. In the standard symbols listed below the screwed connection is used in all illustrations for convenience.

Elbows

Elbow, 90 degrees	Elbow, 45 degrees	Elbow, other than 90 or 45 degrees, specify angle	Elbow, base
		30°	

Elbow, double branch, or plain double T–Y	Elbow, long radius	Elbow, reducing	Elbow, side outlet, outlet down
	LR		

Elbow, side outlet, outlet up	Elbow, turned down	Elbow, turned up	Elbow, union

Tees

Tee	Tee, double sweep	Tee, outlet down	Tee, outlet up

Tee, single sweep, or plain T–Y	**Tee, side outlet, outlet down**	Tee, side outlet, outlet up	Tee, union

Other pipe fittings Blank flange	Bulkhead flange	Bushing	Cap
Coupling	Cross	Expansion joint, bellows	Expansion joint, sliding
Lateral, or Y	Plug	Reducer, concentric	Reducer, eccentric
Reducing flange	Return bend	Sleeve	Spectacle flange
Through double T–Y	Through double Y	True Y	Union, flanged
Union, screwed			

MIL–STD 17 VALVES	**General.** The following symbols shall be used when graphic representation of valve symbols is required.	**Types of connections.** The various types of connections or joints shall be represented as follows:

		The screwed representation may be used to indicate all types of connections provided the type of connection is covered by a note on the drawing or by specifications. In the standard symbols listed below the screwed connection is used in all illustrations for convenience.
Screwed ends		
Flanged ends		
Bell-and-spigot ends		
Welded and brazed ends		
Soldered ends		

Control valves

Valve

Symbol

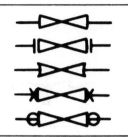

General symbol. This general symbol may be used to represent any control valve where the specific type of valve, features of construction, operation or other identification is not known or required to be shown at time of preparation of plan, or where option as to type of control valve is involved. The following listed specific control valve symbols should be used where applicable.

Angle	Angle, air operated, spring closing	Angle, air operated, spring opening	Angle, deck operated
Angle, high lift	Angle, hose	Angle, hydraulically operated	Angle, key operated
Angle, locked closed	Angle, locked open	Angle, motor operated	Angle, needle
Angle, operated at place and adjacent space	Boiler bottom blow	Boiler surface blow	Butterfly

Chronometer	Cross	Gate	Gate, angle
Gate, deck operated	Gate, hose	Gate, locked closed	Gate, locked open
Gate, motor operated	Gate, operated at place and adjacent space	Gate, quick closing	Gate, quick opening
Gate, sluice	Globe	Globe, air operated, spring closing	Globe, air operated, spring opening
Globe, deck operated	Globe, hose	Globe, hydraulically operated	Globe, key operated
Globe, locked closed	Globe, locked open	Globe, motor operated	Globe, operated at place and adjacent space
Micrometer	Needle	Piston actuated valve (suitable for addition of control piping)	Stop cock, plug or cylinder valve, 2 way

Stop cock, plug or cylinder valve, 3 way, 2 port 	Stop cock, plug or cylinder valve, 3 way, 3 port 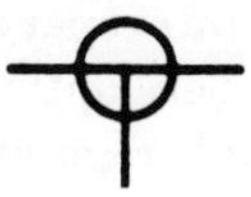	Stop cock, plug or cylinder valve, 4 way, 4 port 	

Check valves

Symbol

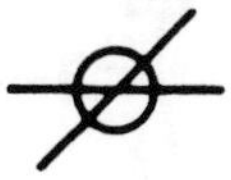

General symbol. This general symbol may be used to represent any check·valve where the specific type of valve, features of construction, operation or other identification is not known or required to be shown at time of preparation of plan, or where option as to type of check valve is involved. The following listed specific check valve symbols should be used where applicable.

Angle, stop check 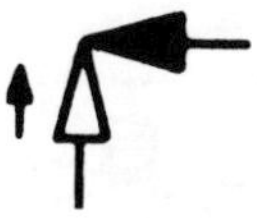	Angle, stop check, air operated, spring closing 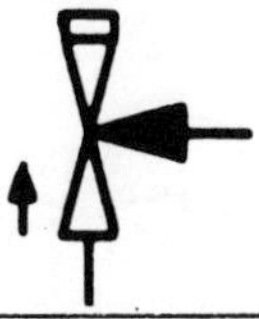	Angle, stop check, deck operated 	Angle, stop check hose 

Angle, stop check, hydraulically operated 	Angle, stop lift check 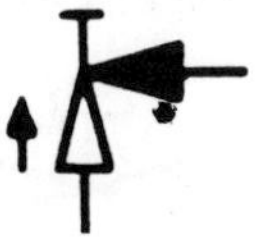	Boiler feed, stop and check combined 	Check, angle 

Check, ball 	Check, lift 	Check, swing 	Check, weight type 

Foot 	Globe, stop check 	Globe, stop check, air operated, spring closing 	Globe, stop check, deck operated 

Globe, stop check, hose 	Globe, stop check, hydraulically operated 	Globe, stop lift check 	

Relief, regulating, and safety valves

Symbol   General symbol. This general symbol may be used to represent any relief, regulating or safety valve where the specific type of valve, features of construction, operation or other identification is not known or required to be shown at time of preparation of plan, or where option as to type of relief, regulating or safety valve is involved. The following listed specific relief regulating or safety valve symbols should be used where applicable.

Show pressure settings for all relief, regulating and safety valves where applicable. See example shown 125 PSI 65 PSI		Angle, relief	Angle, relief adjustable, or angle spring loaded reducing valve
Back pressure	Boiler feed regulator	Globe, relief	Globe, relief adjustable, or spring loaded reducing
Globe, relief pilot actuated	Pressure reducing or pressure regulating, increased actuating pressure closes valve	Pressure reducing or pressure regulating, increased actuating pressure opens valve	Pressure regulating, weight-loaded
Safety, boiler	Safety, boiler pilot actuator	Safety, superheater pilot actuated	
Other valves Automatic	Automatic, operated by governor	Diaphragm	Faucet
Float operated	Lock and shield	Manifold	Manifold, deck operated

Manifold, globe check	Manifold, globe check, deck operated	Pet cock	Pilot
Pneumatic, three-way	Proportioning, three-way	Pump governor	Solenoid control
Thermostatically controlled	Try cock		

PIPING

General. The following symbols shall be used to distinguish the various lines of piping or systems shown on a diagrammatic piping plan. Two methods are shown; method I is covered on 251 and method II on 255. The method adopted must be used throughout on each plan. In using method I, the principal system on each drawing may be indicated by a solid line (in lieu of its symbolic representation listed below) if by so doing there is no confusion with other symbols on the drawing. The piping symbols listed are to be used, when applicable, without regard to their grouping under the general headings of plumbing, heating, and power, etc. In using method II, the riser or stack symbols, where required, shall be in accordance with method I. In using either method, a legend shall appear on each drawing, unless the drawing contains only a single system.

Intersections and crossovers. In those cases where fitting symbols are not used in the diagrammatic representations the intersection (joining) of any two piping runs shall be represented by actual contact between the symbols as follows:

Typical intersections
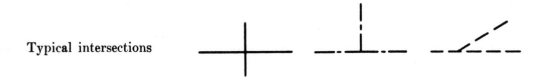

Cross-overs (no connection between piping) shall be represented by a break in one of the lines as follows:

Typical cross-overs
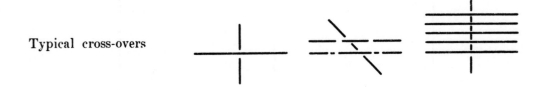

Pipe systems (method I)   Miscellaneous systems

Service	Riser or stack	Symbol
Acetylene	(AC)	——— AC ———
Air, compressed	(A)	——— A ———
Drain, building*	(D)	———————————
Drain, storm or roof	(O)	— — — — — — —
Drain, subsoil	⊕	▶——▶——▶——▶——▶
Fuel supply (except gasoline)	(F)	——— FUEL ———
Gas	(G)	——— G ———
Gasoline	(GN)	——— GASO ———
Hydrogen	(HY)	——— HY ———
Oxygen	(OX)	——— OX ———
Sewer, sanitary*	◯	———————————
Sewerage, combined	⦶	— + — + — + — +
Soil*	(S)	———————————
Vacuum	▽	——— V ———
Vent	(V)	– – – – – – –
Vent, acid	◔	– – – – ACID – – – –

*Above or below grade.

Service	Riser or stack	Symbol
Waste*	(W)	————————————
Waste, acid or chemical	(◁)	——— ACID ———
Waste, indirect	(Y)	→—→—→—→—→—
Water, chilled drinking	(◕)	——— DW ———
Water, chilled drinking return	(◕)	——— DWR ———
Water, cold	(◔)	— · — · — · — · —
Water, fresh	(FW)	——— FW ———
Water, hot	(◐)	— · · — · · — · · —
Water, hot return	(◕)	— · — · — · — · —
Water, raw	(R)	——— RW ———
Water, salt	(⊗)	——— SW ———
Water, tempered	(T)	——— T ———

Pneumatic tube run systems

Tube runs, pneumatic	(PN)	——— PN ———

Fire and sprinkler systems

Carbon dioxide system		——— CO2 ———
Fire line	(◑)	——— F ———

*Above or below grade.

Service	Riser or stack	Symbol
Foam solution	(FO)	—————— FOAM ——————
Sprinkler branch and head		—o———o———o———o—
Sprinkler drain		—S——— — ——S—
Sprinkler main supply		——————— S ———————

Heating and power systems

Service	Riser or stack	Symbol
Boiler blow-off		—— —— BBO —— —
Capillary tubing		—××——××——××—
Condensate or vacuum pump discharge		——————— CD ———————
Exhaust, internal combustion engine		——————— EE ———————
Exhaust, steam		——————— ES ———————
Feedwater pump discharge		——————— FD ———————
Fuel oil overflow		——————— FOO ———————
Fuel oil return		— — — FOR — — —
Fuel oil service		——————— FOS ———————
Fuel oil supply		——————— FO ———————
Fuel oil transfer		——————— FOT ———————
Fuel oil vent		— — — —FOV— — — —
Gage line		—×——×——×—

Service	Symbol
Lubricating oil	———— LO ————
Relief, air line	— — — AR — — —
Return (condensate), high pressure	– // — // — // –
Return (condensate), low pressure	— — —LPR— — —
Return (condensate), medium pressure	–/– /– /–
Steam, high pressure	—//——//——//—
Steam, low pressure	——— LP ———
Steam, medium pressure	—/——/——/—
Water, hot heating return	— — —HWR— — —
Water, hot heating supply	——— HW ———

Refrigerating and air conditioning systems

Service	Symbol
Brine return	— — —BR— — —
Brine supply	——— B ———
Drain line	——— D ———
Humidification line	—— – –H—— – –
Refrigerant discharge	——— RD ———
Refrigerant liquid	——— RL ———

Service	Symbol
Refrigerant suction	— — — RS — — —
Water return, chilled	— — — CWR — — —
Water return, condenser	— — — CR — — —
Water supply, chilled	—————— CW ——————
Water supply, condenser	—————— C ——————

Pipe systems (method II)

Service	Symbol
Principal system	————————————
Second system in importance	— — · — — · — —
Third system in importance	— — — — — —
Fourth system in importance	— — — — — —
Fifth system in importance	— — — — — —
Invisible lines (adequately labeled as to system)	- - - - - - - - - -

MIL-STD 17 STRAINERS and TRAPS	General. The following symbols shall be used where graphic representation of strainers and traps is desired.	Types of connections. The applicable types of connections or joints shall be as indicated for valves The screwed representation may be used to indicate all types of connections provided the type of connection is covered by a note on the drawing or by specifications.	
Strainers Box strainer	Duplex oil filter	Duplex strainer	Macomb strainer
Magnetic strainer	Metal edge strainer	Plate strainer	Self cleaning strainer
Steam (basket) strainer	Strainer	Y strainer	
Traps Air eliminator	Boiler return trap	Bucket trap	Float and thermostatic trap
Float trap	Impulse trap	P trap	Running trap
Scale trap	Thermostatic blast trap	Thermostatic trap	Trap Vacuum trap

Reproduced from Morse, "Mechanical Power Transmission Manual," through the courtesy of Morse, a Borg Warner Industry, Ithaca, N.Y. This section shows graphic representation of speed reducers and shaft position. Complete data are to be found in the above-described manual. Similar data are to be found in the "Boston Handbook No. 58," which can be obtained from the Boston Gear Works, Quincy, Mass., or from a local representative.

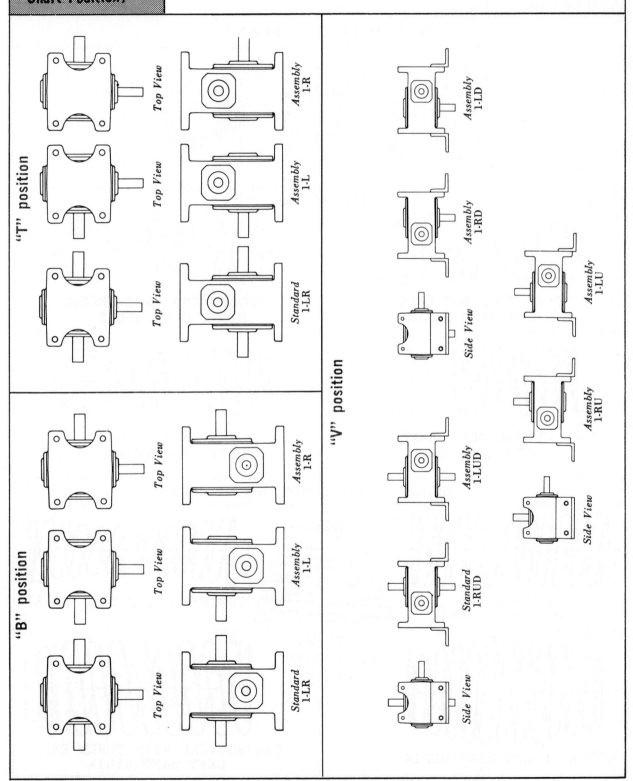

Extracted from MIL-STD-29-1958, Mechanical Drawing Requirements for Springs, with the permission of the Office of the Secretary of Defense, Public Affairs Department, Washington. This standard is coincidental to standards established by the Spring Manufacturers Association, Bristol, Conn. Other portions of this section were extracted from the "Handbook of Mechanical Spring Design," published by the Associated Spring Corporation, Bristol, Conn.

HELICAL COMPRESSION SPRINGS

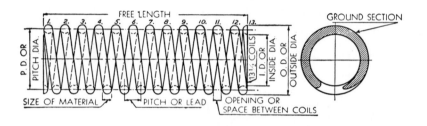

Type of Ends

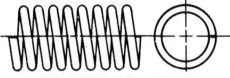

OPEN ENDS NOT GROUND RIGHT HAND HELIX

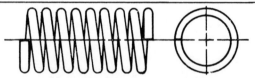

CLOSED ENDS NOT GROUND RIGHT HAND HELIX

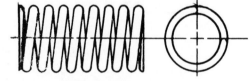

CLOSED ENDS GROUND LEFT HAND HELIX

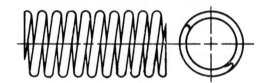

OPEN ENDS GROUND LEFT HAND HELIX

HELICAL COMPRESSION SPRING FORMS

CYLINDRICAL RIGHT HAND HELIX

CONICAL RIGHT HAND HELIX

CONCAVE RIGHT HAND HELIX

CONVEX RIGHT HAND HELIX

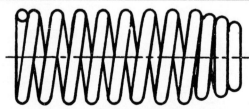

CYLINDRICAL WITH CONED END LEFT HAND HELIX

HELICAL EXTENSION SPRINGS

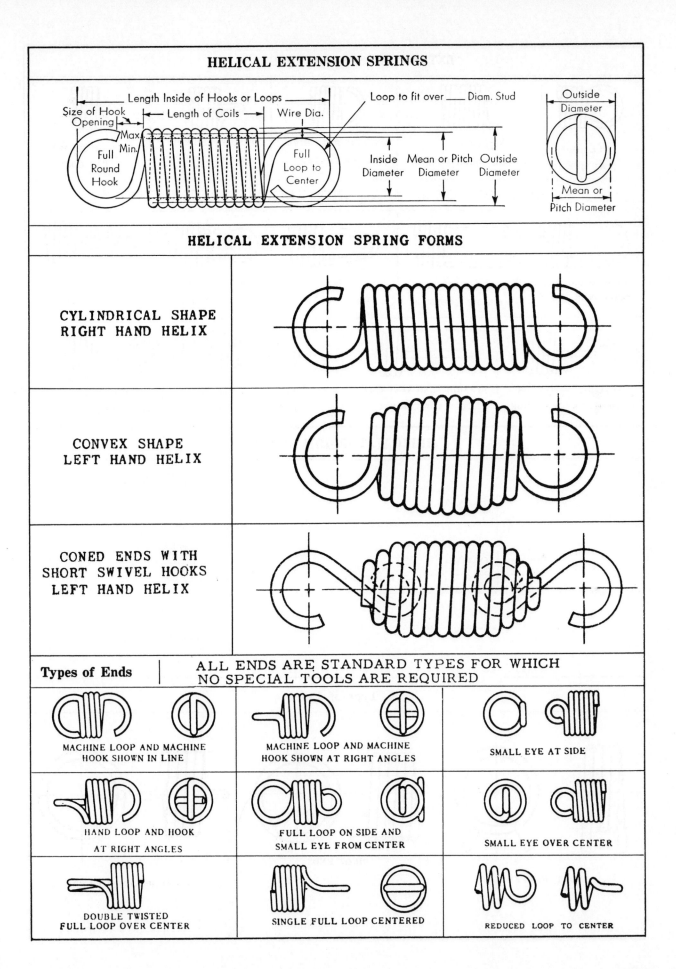

Length Inside of Hooks or Loops

Length of Coils

Size of Hook Opening

Max. Min.

Full Round Hook

Wire Dia.

Loop to fit over ____ Diam. Stud

Full Loop to Center

Inside Diameter

Mean or Pitch Diameter

Outside Diameter

Outside Diameter

Mean or Pitch Diameter

HELICAL EXTENSION SPRING FORMS

CYLINDRICAL SHAPE RIGHT HAND HELIX	
CONVEX SHAPE LEFT HAND HELIX	
CONED ENDS WITH SHORT SWIVEL HOOKS LEFT HAND HELIX	

Types of Ends	ALL ENDS ARE STANDARD TYPES FOR WHICH NO SPECIAL TOOLS ARE REQUIRED

MACHINE LOOP AND MACHINE HOOK SHOWN IN LINE

MACHINE LOOP AND MACHINE HOOK SHOWN AT RIGHT ANGLES

SMALL EYE AT SIDE

HAND LOOP AND HOOK AT RIGHT ANGLES

FULL LOOP ON SIDE AND SMALL EYE FROM CENTER

SMALL EYE OVER CENTER

DOUBLE TWISTED FULL LOOP OVER CENTER

SINGLE FULL LOOP CENTERED

REDUCED LOOP TO CENTER

EXTENSION SPRING ENDS

**FULL LOOP
AT SIDE**

**SMALL
OFF-SET HOOK AT SIDE**

**MACHINE HALF HOOK
OVER CENTER**

**HAND HALF LOOP
OVER CENTER**

**PLAIN SQUARE
CUT ENDS**

THIS GROUP OF SPECIAL ENDS REQUIRE SPECIAL TOOLS

**LONG ROUND END
HOOK OVER CENTER**

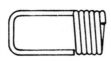

**LONG SQUARE END
HOOK OVER CENTER**

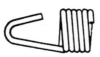

**V HOOK
OVER CENTER**

**CONED END WITH
SHORT SWIVEL EYE**

**CONED END WITH
SWIVEL BOLT**

**EXTENDED EYE FROM
EITHER CENTER OR SIDE**

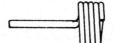

**STRAIGHT END ANNEALED
TO ALLOW FORMING**

**CONED END TO HOLD
LONG SWIVEL EYE**

**CONED END
WITH SWIVEL HOOK**

HELICAL TORSION SPRINGS

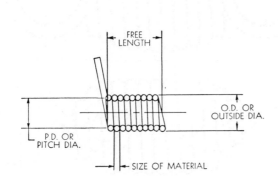

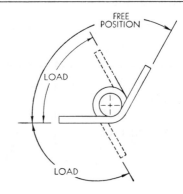

Type of Ends.

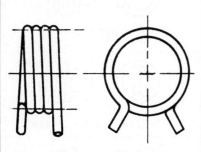

SHORT HOOK ENDS

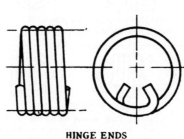

HINGE ENDS

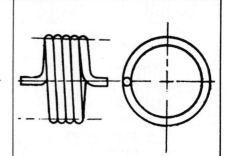

STRAIGHT OFFSET ENDS

HELICAL TORSION SPRING FORMS

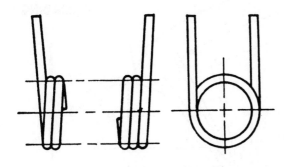

LEFT HAND HELIX

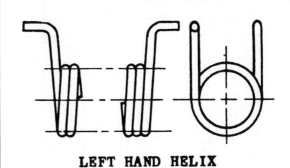

LEFT HAND HELIX

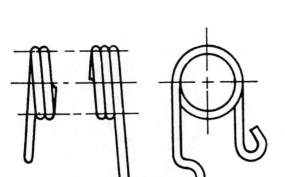

RIGHT HAND HELIX

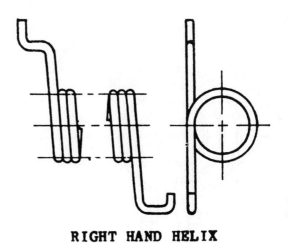

RIGHT HAND HELIX

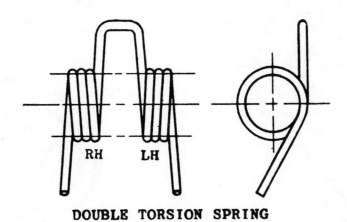

RH   LH

DOUBLE TORSION SPRING

SPIRAL TORSION SPRINGS

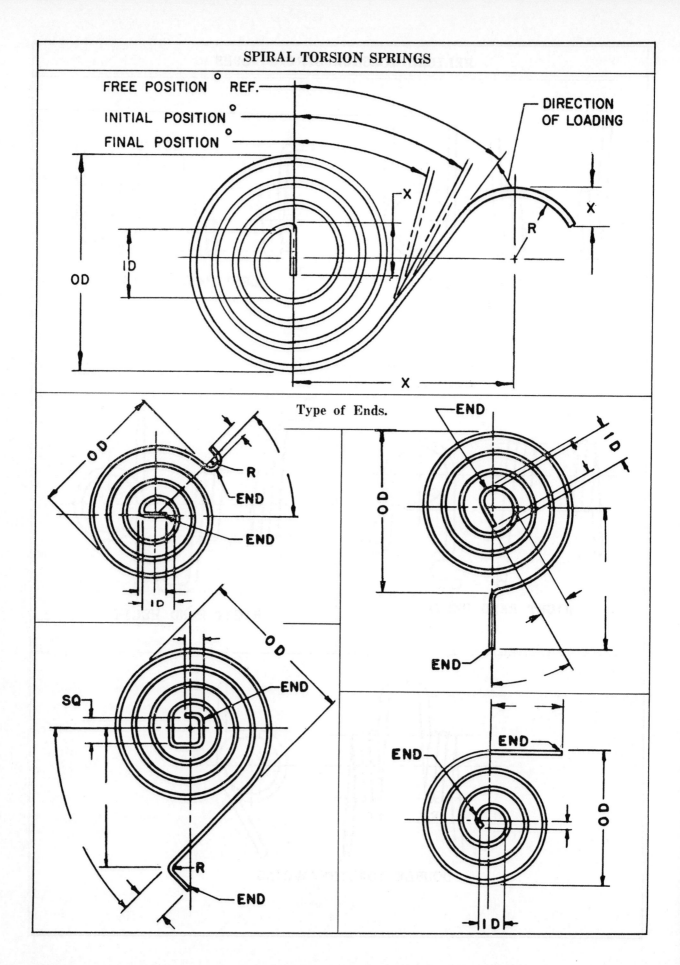

Type of Ends.

TORSION BAR SPRINGS

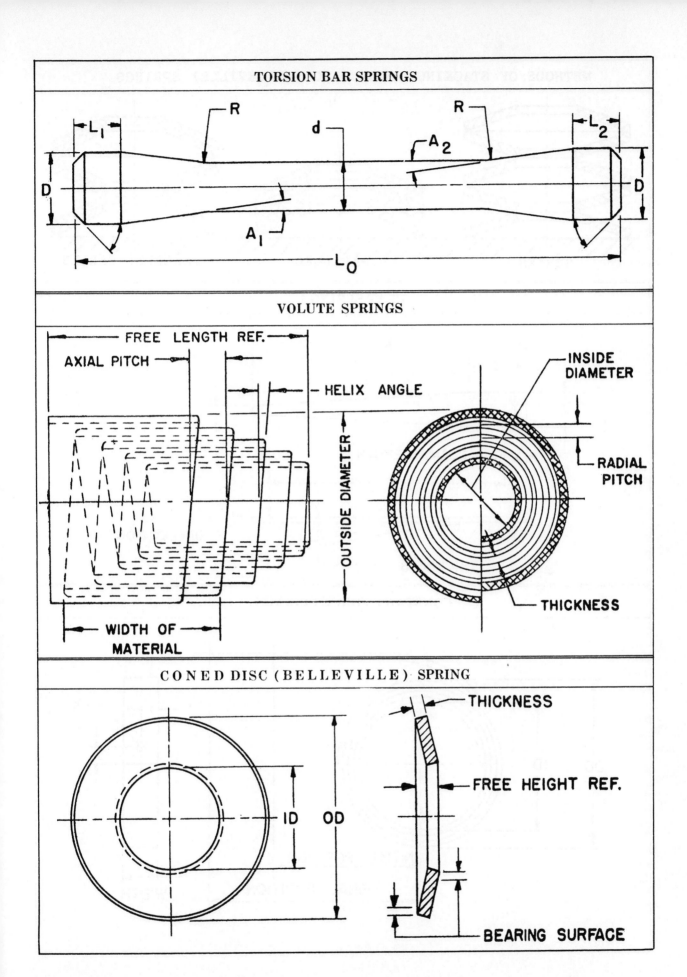

VOLUTE SPRINGS

CONED DISC (BELLEVILLE) SPRING

METHODS OF STACKING CONED DISC (BELLEVILLE) SPRINGS

SERIES   PARALLEL   PARALLEL-SERIES

FLAT SPRINGS

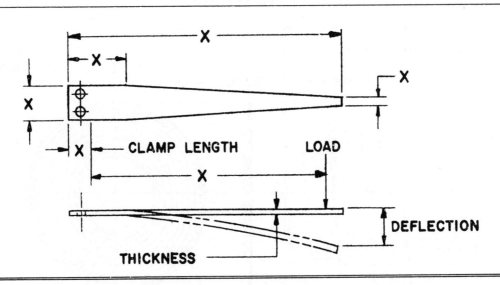

X

X

X

X

CLAMP LENGTH   LOAD

X

DEFLECTION

THICKNESS

CONSTANT FORCE SPRINGS

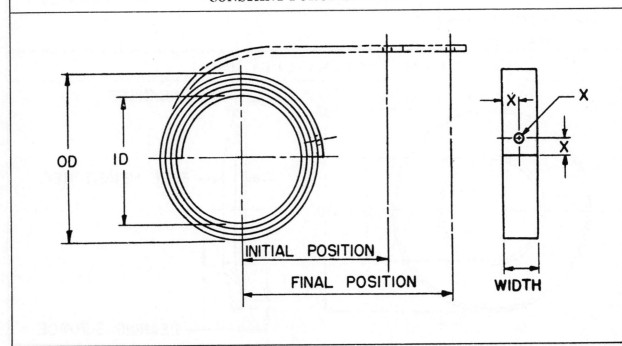

OD

ID

X

X

INITIAL POSITION

FINAL POSITION

WIDTH

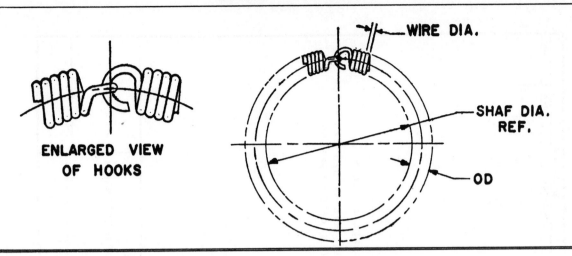

ENLARGED VIEW
OF HOOKS

WIRE DIA.

SHAF DIA.
REF.

OD

Power Springs *Clock or Motor Type*

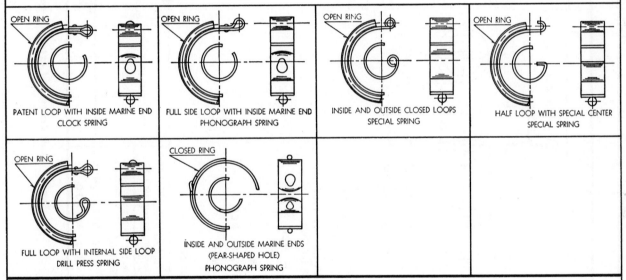

OPEN RING

PATENT LOOP WITH INSIDE MARINE END
CLOCK SPRING

OPEN RING

FULL SIDE LOOP WITH INSIDE MARINE END
PHONOGRAPH SPRING

OPEN RING

INSIDE AND OUTSIDE CLOSED LOOPS
SPECIAL SPRING

OPEN RING

HALF LOOP WITH SPECIAL CENTER
SPECIAL SPRING

OPEN RING

FULL LOOP WITH INTERNAL SIDE LOOP
DRILL PRESS SPRING

CLOSED RING

INSIDE AND OUTSIDE MARINE ENDS
(PEAR-SHAPED HOLE)
PHONOGRAPH SPRING

Hairsprings

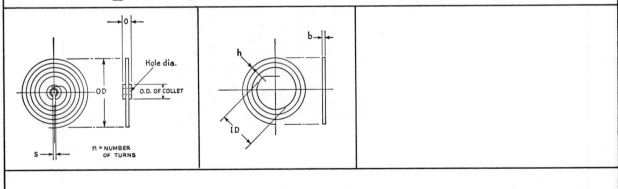

O

Hole dia.

OD

O.D. OF COLLET

S

n = NUMBER
OF TURNS

b

h

ID

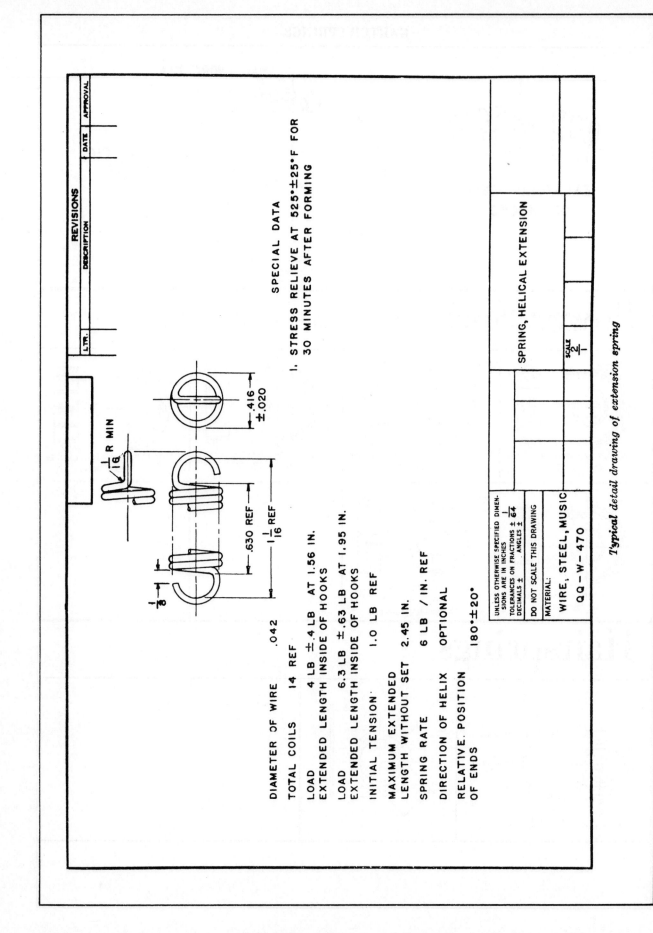

Typical detail drawing of extension spring

AWS A2.0 WELDING

Extracted from ASA Y32.3-1959, Graphical Symbols for Welding, with the permission of the publisher, the American Society of Mechanical Engineers, United Engineering Center, 345 East 47 Street, New York, N.Y. Reproduced from AWS A2.0-58, Welding Symbols, published by the American Welding Society, 33 West 39 Street, New York, N.Y.

Arc and Gas Weld Symbols

FILLET	PLUG or SLOT	ARC-SPOT or ARC-SEAM

GROOVE

SQUARE	V	BEVEL	U	J	FLANGE V	FLARE BEVEL

BACK or BACKING	MELT-THRU	SURFACING	FLANGE EDGE	FLANGE CORNER	

Resistance Weld Symbols

RESISTANCE SPOT	PROJECTION	RESISTANCE SEAM	FLASH or UPSET

Supplementary Symbols

Supplementary symbols to be used in connection with weld symbols

WELD ALL AROUND	FIELD WELD	CONTOUR FLUSH	CONTOUR CONVEX

Brazing, Forge, Thermit, Induction and Flow Welding Symbols

Brazing, forge, thermit, induction and flow welding shall be indicated by using a process or specification reference in the tail of the welding symbol.

Standard Location of Elements of a Welding Symbol

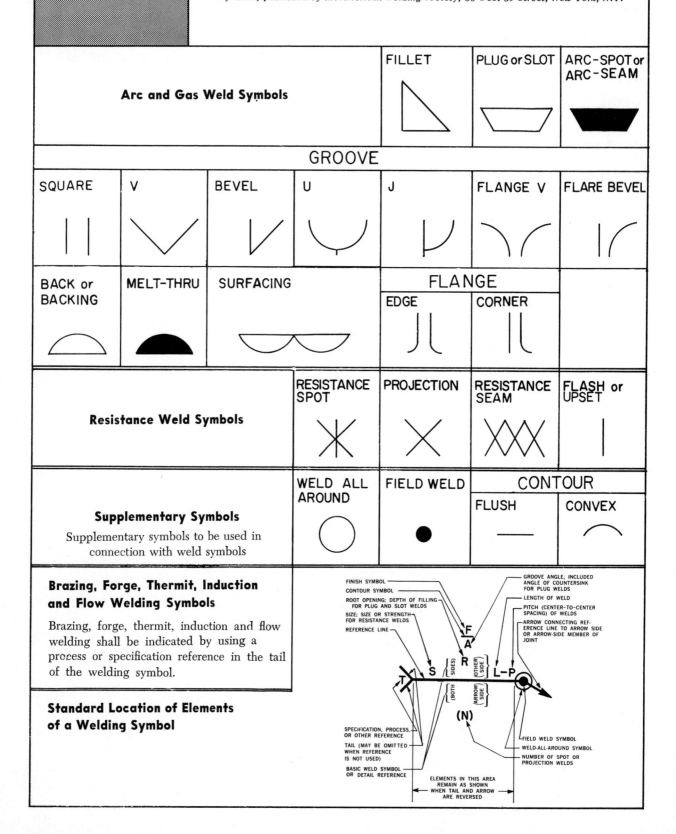

FINISH SYMBOL
CONTOUR SYMBOL
ROOT OPENING; DEPTH OF FILLING FOR PLUG AND SLOT WELDS
SIZE; SIZE OR STRENGTH FOR RESISTANCE WELDS
REFERENCE LINE
GROOVE ANGLE; INCLUDED ANGLE OF COUNTERSINK FOR PLUG WELDS
LENGTH OF WELD
PITCH (CENTER-TO-CENTER SPACING) OF WELDS
ARROW CONNECTING REFERENCE LINE TO ARROW SIDE OR ARROW-SIDE MEMBER OF JOINT
SPECIFICATION, PROCESS, OR OTHER REFERENCE
TAIL (MAY BE OMITTED WHEN REFERENCE IS NOT USED)
BASIC WELD SYMBOL OR DETAIL REFERENCE
FIELD WELD SYMBOL
WELD-ALL-AROUND SYMBOL
NUMBER OF SPOT OR PROJECTION WELDS
ELEMENTS IN THIS AREA REMAIN AS SHOWN WHEN TAIL AND ARROW ARE REVERSED

F / A / S / R / T / L-P / (N) / (BOTH SIDES) / (OTHER SIDE) / (ARROW SIDE)

Elements of a Welding Symbol

This standard makes a distinction between the terms *weld symbol and welding symbol.* The *weld symbol* is the ideograph used to indicate the desired type of weld. The assembled *welding symbol* consists of the following eight elements, or such of these elements as are necessary:

Reference line.
Arrow.
Basic weld symbols.
Dimensions and other data.
Supplementary symbols.
Finish symbols.
Tail.
Specification, process, or other references.

BASIC SYMBOLS (Weld) and Location Significance

LOCATION SIGNIFICANCE	ARROW-SIDE	OTHER-SIDE	BOTH-SIDES	NO ARROW-SIDE OR OTHER-SIDE SIGNIFICANCE	LOCATION SIGNIFICANCE	ARROW-SIDE	OTHER-SIDE	BOTH-SIDES	NO ARROW-SIDE OR OTHER-SIDE SIGNIFICANCE
ARC AND GAS WELD SYMBOLS					ARC AND GAS WELD SYMBOLS				
FILLET				NOT USED	BACK OR BACKING	GROOVE WELD SYMBOL	GROOVE WELD SYMBOL	NOT USED	NOT USED
PLUG OR SLOT			NOT USED	NOT USED	MELT-THRU	GROOVE OR FLANGE WELD SYMBOL	GROOVE OR FLANGE WELD SYMBOL	NOT USED	NOT USED
ARC-SEAM OR ARC-SPOT			NOT USED	NOT USED	SURFACING	NOT USED	NOT USED	NOT USED	
ARC AND GAS WELD SYMBOLS					FLANGE				
GROOVE					EDGE			NOT USED	NOT USED
SQUARE				NOT USED					
V				NOT USED	CORNER			NOT USED	NOT USED
					RESISTANCE WELD SYMBOLS				
BEVEL				NOT USED	RESISTANCE SPOT	NOT USED	NOT USED	NOT USED	
U				NOT USED	PROJECTION			NOT USED	NOT USED
J				NOT USED	RESISTANCE-SEAM	NOT USED	NOT USED	NOT USED	
FLARE-V				NOT USED	FLASH OR UPSET	NOT USED	NOT USED	NOT USED	
FLARE-BEVEL				NOT USED					

BASIC JOINTS

Identification of *arrow-side* and *other-side* of joint and *arrow-side* and *other-side* member of joint

ARROW OF WELDING SYMBOL — ARROW SIDE OF JOINT — JOINT — OTHER SIDE OF JOINT
BUTT JOINT

ARROW SIDE OF JOINT — OTHER SIDE OF JOINT — ARROW OF WELDING SYMBOL
CORNER JOINT

ARROW SIDE OF JOINT — JOINT — OTHER SIDE OF JOINT — ARROW OF WELDING SYMBOL

ARROW OF WELDING SYMBOL — ARROW SIDE OF JOINT — OTHER SIDE OF JOINT
TEE JOINT

OTHER SIDE OF JOINT — ARROW SIDE OF JOINT — ARROW OF WELDING SYMBOL
LAP JOINT

ARROW-SIDE MEMBER OF JOINT — OTHER-SIDE MEMBER OF JOINT — ARROW OF WELDING SYMBOL

ARROW SIDE OF JOINT — ARROW OF WELDING SYMBOL — JOINT — OTHER SIDE OF JOINT
EDGE JOINT

TYPICAL WELDING SYMBOLS

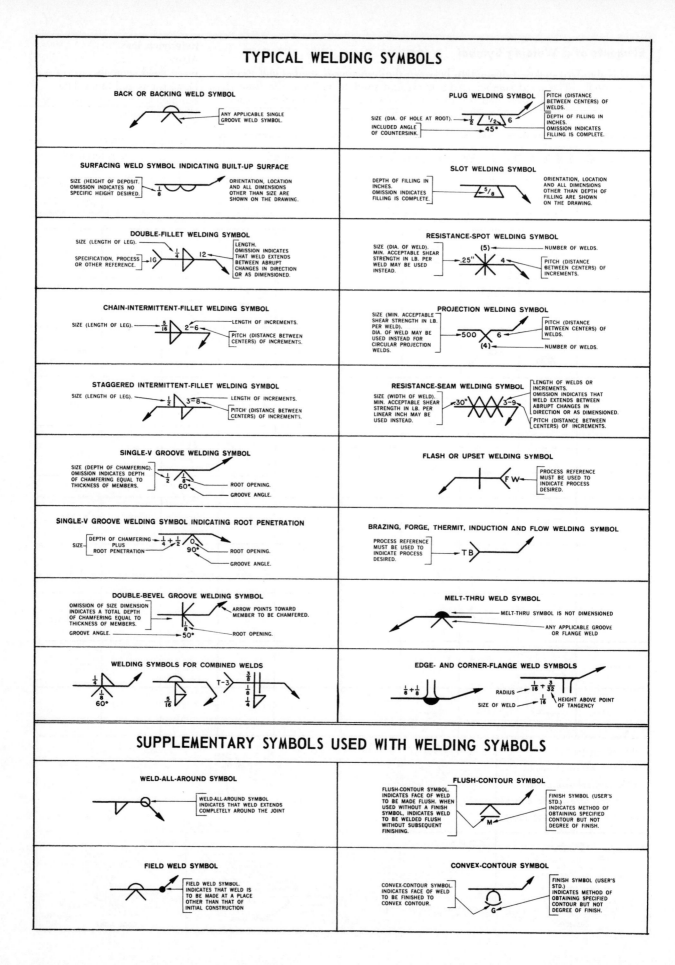

BACK OR BACKING WELD SYMBOL

ANY APPLICABLE SINGLE GROOVE WELD SYMBOL.

PLUG WELDING SYMBOL

PITCH (DISTANCE BETWEEN CENTERS) OF WELDS.
SIZE (DIA. OF HOLE AT ROOT).
INCLUDED ANGLE OF COUNTERSINK.
DEPTH OF FILLING IN INCHES. OMISSION INDICATES FILLING IS COMPLETE.

SURFACING WELD SYMBOL INDICATING BUILT-UP SURFACE

SIZE (HEIGHT OF DEPOSIT. OMISSION INDICATES NO SPECIFIC HEIGHT DESIRED.
ORIENTATION, LOCATION AND ALL DIMENSIONS OTHER THAN SIZE ARE SHOWN ON THE DRAWING.

SLOT WELDING SYMBOL

DEPTH OF FILLING IN INCHES. OMISSION INDICATES FILLING IS COMPLETE.
ORIENTATION, LOCATION AND ALL DIMENSIONS OTHER THAN DEPTH OF FILLING ARE SHOWN ON THE DRAWING.

DOUBLE-FILLET WELDING SYMBOL

SIZE (LENGTH OF LEG).
SPECIFICATION, PROCESS OR OTHER REFERENCE.
LENGTH. OMISSION INDICATES THAT WELD EXTENDS BETWEEN ABRUPT CHANGES IN DIRECTION OR AS DIMENSIONED.

RESISTANCE-SPOT WELDING SYMBOL

SIZE (DIA. OF WELD). MIN. ACCEPTABLE SHEAR STRENGTH IN LB. PER WELD MAY BE USED INSTEAD.
(5) NUMBER OF WELDS.
PITCH (DISTANCE BETWEEN CENTERS) OF INCREMENTS.

CHAIN-INTERMITTENT-FILLET WELDING SYMBOL

SIZE (LENGTH OF LEG).
LENGTH OF INCREMENTS.
PITCH (DISTANCE BETWEEN CENTERS) OF INCREMENTS.

PROJECTION WELDING SYMBOL

SIZE (MIN. ACCEPTABLE SHEAR STRENGTH IN LB. PER WELD). DIA. OF WELD MAY BE USED INSTEAD FOR CIRCULAR PROJECTION WELDS.
PITCH (DISTANCE BETWEEN CENTERS) OF WELDS.
NUMBER OF WELDS.

STAGGERED INTERMITTENT-FILLET WELDING SYMBOL

SIZE (LENGTH OF LEG).
LENGTH OF INCREMENTS.
PITCH (DISTANCE BETWEEN CENTERS) OF INCREMENTS.

RESISTANCE-SEAM WELDING SYMBOL

SIZE (WIDTH OF WELD). MIN. ACCEPTABLE SHEAR STRENGTH IN LB. PER LINEAR INCH MAY BE USED INSTEAD.
LENGTH OF WELDS OR INCREMENTS. OMISSION INDICATES THAT WELD EXTENDS BETWEEN ABRUPT CHANGES IN DIRECTION OR AS DIMENSIONED.
PITCH (DISTANCE BETWEEN CENTERS) OF INCREMENTS.

SINGLE-V GROOVE WELDING SYMBOL

SIZE (DEPTH OF CHAMFERING). OMISSION INDICATES DEPTH OF CHAMFERING EQUAL TO THICKNESS OF MEMBERS.
ROOT OPENING.
GROOVE ANGLE.

FLASH OR UPSET WELDING SYMBOL

F W
PROCESS REFERENCE MUST BE USED TO INDICATE PROCESS DESIRED.

SINGLE-V GROOVE WELDING SYMBOL INDICATING ROOT PENETRATION

SIZE—DEPTH OF CHAMFERING PLUS ROOT PENETRATION
ROOT OPENING.
GROOVE ANGLE.

BRAZING, FORGE, THERMIT, INDUCTION AND FLOW WELDING SYMBOL

PROCESS REFERENCE MUST BE USED TO INDICATE PROCESS DESIRED.
T B

DOUBLE-BEVEL GROOVE WELDING SYMBOL

OMISSION OF SIZE DIMENSION INDICATES A TOTAL DEPTH OF CHAMFERING EQUAL TO THICKNESS OF MEMBERS.
GROOVE ANGLE.
ARROW POINTS TOWARD MEMBER TO BE CHAMFERED.
ROOT OPENING.

MELT-THRU WELD SYMBOL

MELT-THRU SYMBOL IS NOT DIMENSIONED
ANY APPLICABLE GROOVE OR FLANGE WELD

WELDING SYMBOLS FOR COMBINED WELDS

EDGE- AND CORNER-FLANGE WELD SYMBOLS

RADIUS
SIZE OF WELD
HEIGHT ABOVE POINT OF TANGENCY

SUPPLEMENTARY SYMBOLS USED WITH WELDING SYMBOLS

WELD-ALL-AROUND SYMBOL

WELD-ALL-AROUND SYMBOL INDICATES THAT WELD EXTENDS COMPLETELY AROUND THE JOINT

FLUSH-CONTOUR SYMBOL

FLUSH-CONTOUR SYMBOL. INDICATES FACE OF WELD TO BE MADE FLUSH. WHEN USED WITHOUT A FINISH SYMBOL, INDICATES WELD TO BE WELDED FLUSH WITHOUT SUBSEQUENT FINISHING.
FINISH SYMBOL (USER'S STD.) INDICATES METHOD OF OBTAINING SPECIFIED CONTOUR BUT NOT DEGREE OF FINISH.

FIELD WELD SYMBOL

FIELD WELD SYMBOL. INDICATES THAT WELD IS TO BE MADE AT A PLACE OTHER THAN THAT OF INITIAL CONSTRUCTION

CONVEX-CONTOUR SYMBOL

CONVEX-CONTOUR SYMBOL. INDICATES FACE OF WELD TO BE FINISHED TO CONVEX CONTOUR.
FINISH SYMBOL (USER'S STD.) INDICATES METHOD OF OBTAINING SPECIFIED CONTOUR BUT NOT DEGREE OF FINISH.

270

BUTT JOINT

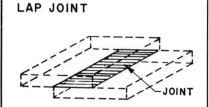

JOINT

APPLICABLE WELDS

Square-Groove	Flare-Bevel-Groove
V-Groove	Melt-Thru
Bevel-Groove	Edge-Flange
U-Groove	Flash
J-Groove	Upset
Flare-V-Groove	

CORNER JOINT

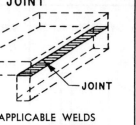

JOINT

APPLICABLE WELDS

Fillet	Flare-Bevel-Groove
Arc-Spot	Melt-Thru
Arc-Seam	Edge-Flange
Square-Groove	Corner-Flange
V-Groove	Resistance-Spot
Bevel-Groove	Projection
U-Groove	Resistance-Seam
J-Groove	Flash
Flare-V-Groove	

TEE JOINT

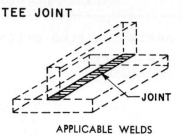

JOINT

APPLICABLE WELDS

Fillet	Flare-Bevel-Groove
Plug	Melt-Thru
Slot	Resistance-Spot
Arc-Spot	Projection
Arc-Seam	Resistance-Seam
Bevel-Groove	Flash
J-Groove	

LAP JOINT

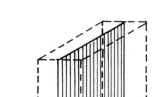

JOINT

APPLICABLE WELDS

Fillet	J-Groove
Plug	Flare-Bevel-Groove
Slot	Resistance-Spot
Arc-Spot	Projection
Arc-Seam	Resistance-Seam
Bevel-Groove	

EDGE JOINT

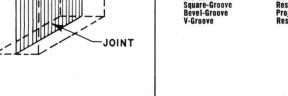

JOINT

APPLICABLE WELDS

Plug	U-Groove
Slot	J-Groove
Arc-Spot	Edge-Flange
Arc-Seam	Corner-Flange
Square-Groove	Resistance-Spot
Bevel-Groove	Projection
V-Groove	Resistance-Seam

ARROW-SIDE FILLET WELDING SYMBOL

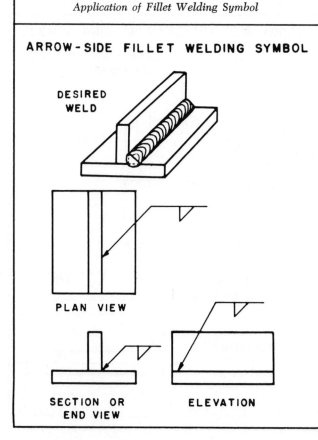

DESIRED WELD

PLAN VIEW

SECTION OR END VIEW

ELEVATION

OTHER-SIDE FILLET WELDING SYMBOL

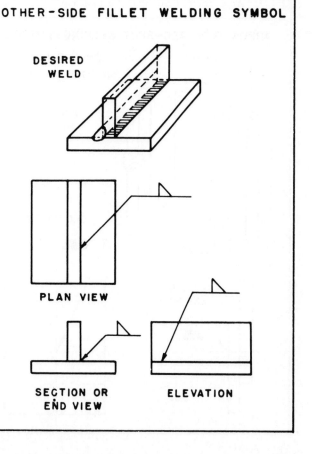

DESIRED WELD

PLAN VIEW

SECTION OR END VIEW

ELEVATION

271

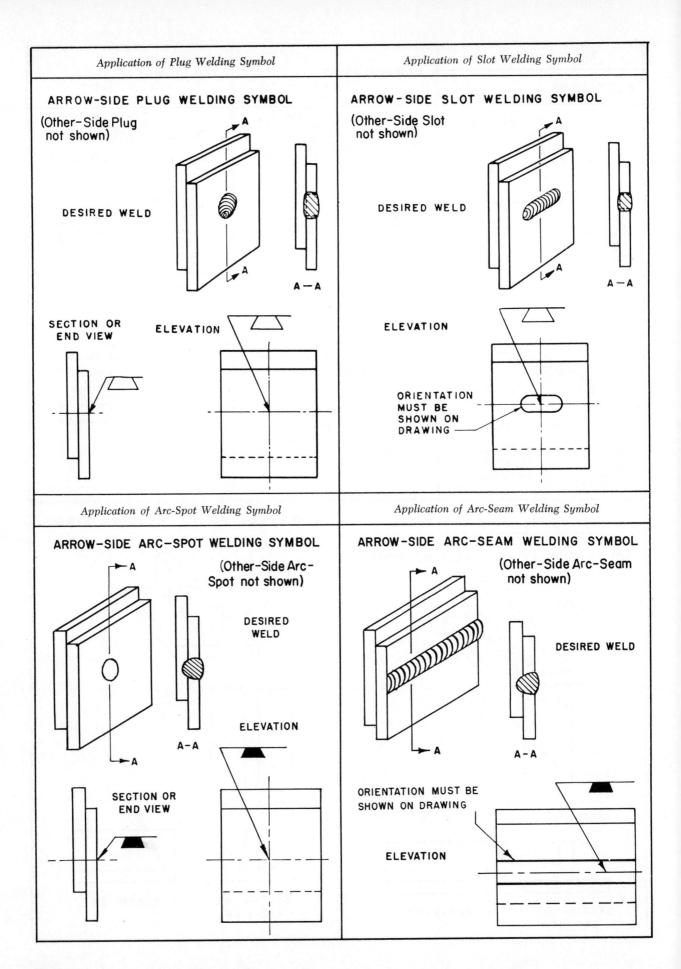

Application of Plug Welding Symbol

ARROW-SIDE PLUG WELDING SYMBOL

(Other-Side Plug not shown)

DESIRED WELD

A

A — A

SECTION OR END VIEW

ELEVATION

Application of Slot Welding Symbol

ARROW-SIDE SLOT WELDING SYMBOL

(Other-Side Slot not shown)

DESIRED WELD

A

A — A

ELEVATION

ORIENTATION MUST BE SHOWN ON DRAWING

Application of Arc-Spot Welding Symbol

ARROW-SIDE ARC-SPOT WELDING SYMBOL

(Other-Side Arc-Spot not shown)

DESIRED WELD

A

A

A-A

SECTION OR END VIEW

ELEVATION

Application of Arc-Seam Welding Symbol

ARROW-SIDE ARC-SEAM WELDING SYMBOL

(Other-Side Arc-Seam not shown)

A

A

A-A

DESIRED WELD

ORIENTATION MUST BE SHOWN ON DRAWING

ELEVATION

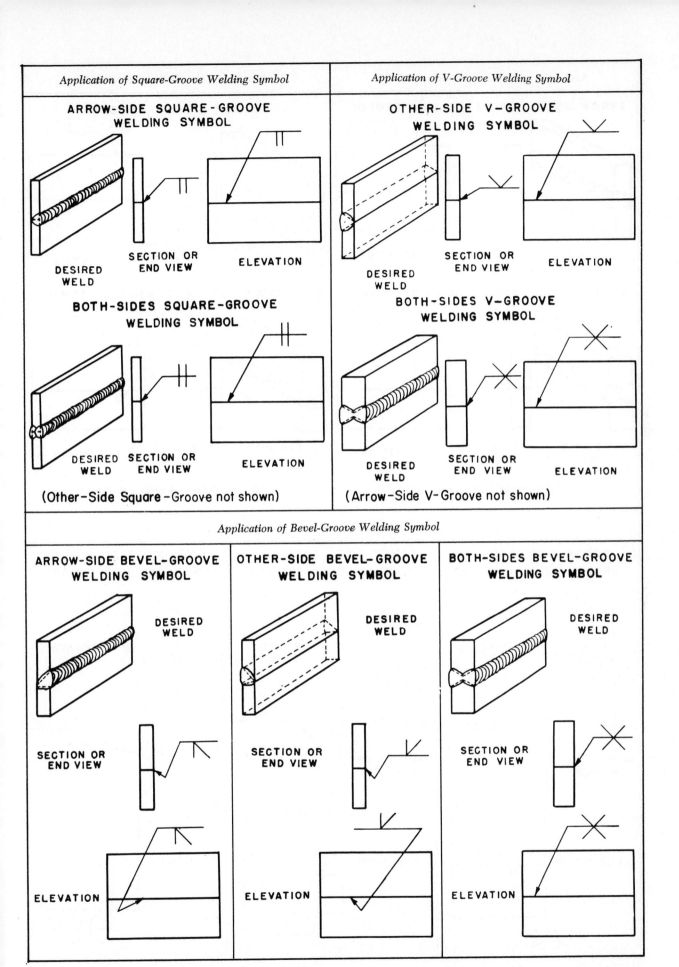

Application of Square-Groove Welding Symbol

ARROW-SIDE SQUARE-GROOVE WELDING SYMBOL

DESIRED WELD

SECTION OR END VIEW

ELEVATION

BOTH-SIDES SQUARE-GROOVE WELDING SYMBOL

DESIRED WELD

SECTION OR END VIEW

ELEVATION

(Other-Side Square-Groove not shown)

Application of V-Groove Welding Symbol

OTHER-SIDE V-GROOVE WELDING SYMBOL

DESIRED WELD

SECTION OR END VIEW

ELEVATION

BOTH-SIDES V-GROOVE WELDING SYMBOL

DESIRED WELD

SECTION OR END VIEW

ELEVATION

(Arrow-Side V-Groove not shown)

Application of Bevel-Groove Welding Symbol

ARROW-SIDE BEVEL-GROOVE WELDING SYMBOL

DESIRED WELD

SECTION OR END VIEW

ELEVATION

OTHER-SIDE BEVEL-GROOVE WELDING SYMBOL

DESIRED WELD

SECTION OR END VIEW

ELEVATION

BOTH-SIDES BEVEL-GROOVE WELDING SYMBOL

DESIRED WELD

SECTION OR END VIEW

ELEVATION

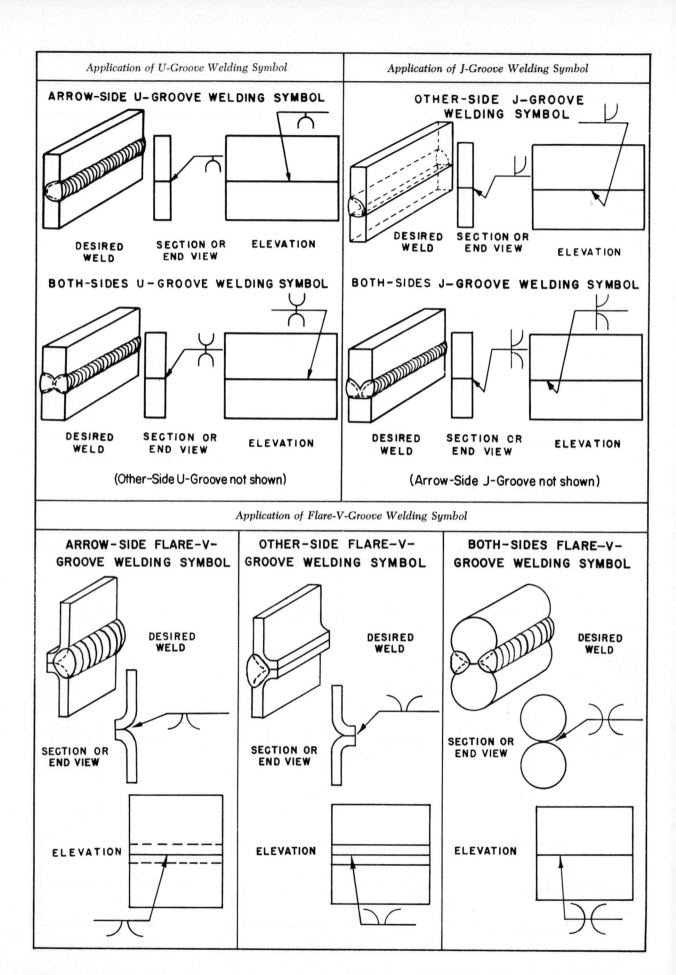

Application of U-Groove Welding Symbol

ARROW-SIDE U-GROOVE WELDING SYMBOL

DESIRED WELD   SECTION OR END VIEW   ELEVATION

BOTH-SIDES U-GROOVE WELDING SYMBOL

DESIRED WELD   SECTION OR END VIEW   ELEVATION

(Other-Side U-Groove not shown)

Application of J-Groove Welding Symbol

OTHER-SIDE J-GROOVE WELDING SYMBOL

DESIRED WELD   SECTION OR END VIEW   ELEVATION

BOTH-SIDES J-GROOVE WELDING SYMBOL

DESIRED WELD   SECTION OR END VIEW   ELEVATION

(Arrow-Side J-Groove not shown)

Application of Flare-V-Groove Welding Symbol

ARROW-SIDE FLARE-V-GROOVE WELDING SYMBOL

DESIRED WELD

SECTION OR END VIEW

ELEVATION

OTHER-SIDE FLARE-V-GROOVE WELDING SYMBOL

DESIRED WELD

SECTION OR END VIEW

ELEVATION

BOTH-SIDES FLARE-V-GROOVE WELDING SYMBOL

DESIRED WELD

SECTION OR END VIEW

ELEVATION

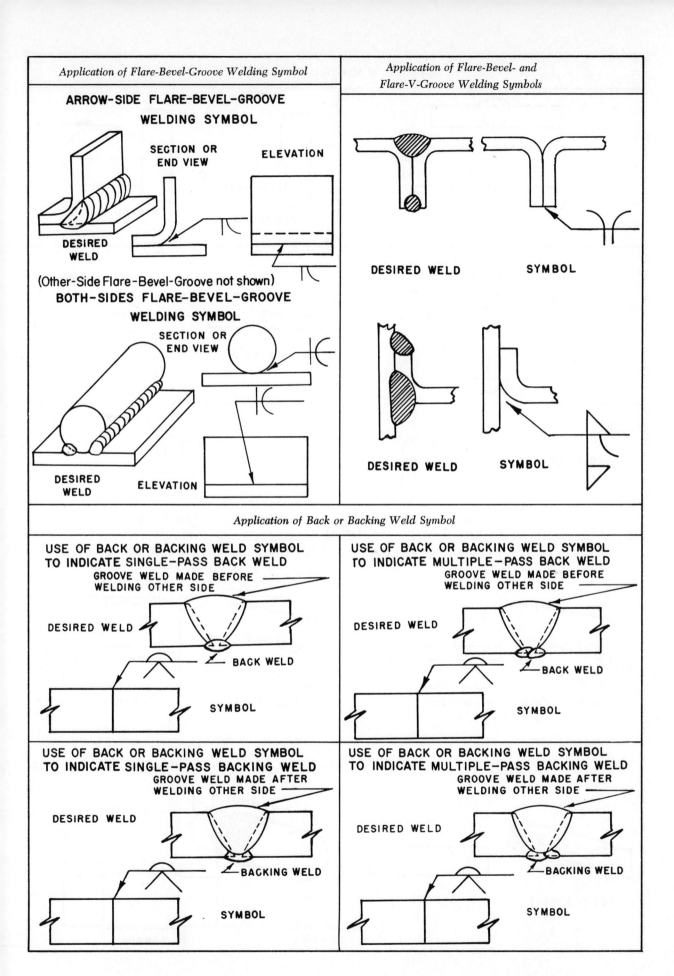

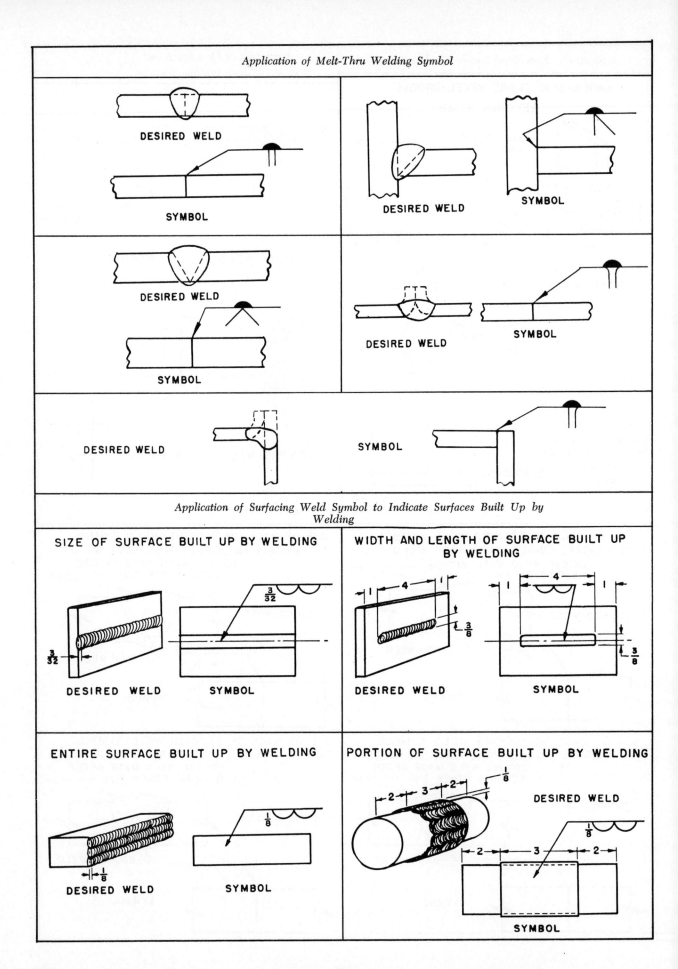

Application of Melt-Thru Welding Symbol

Application of Surfacing Weld Symbol to Indicate Surfaces Built Up by Welding

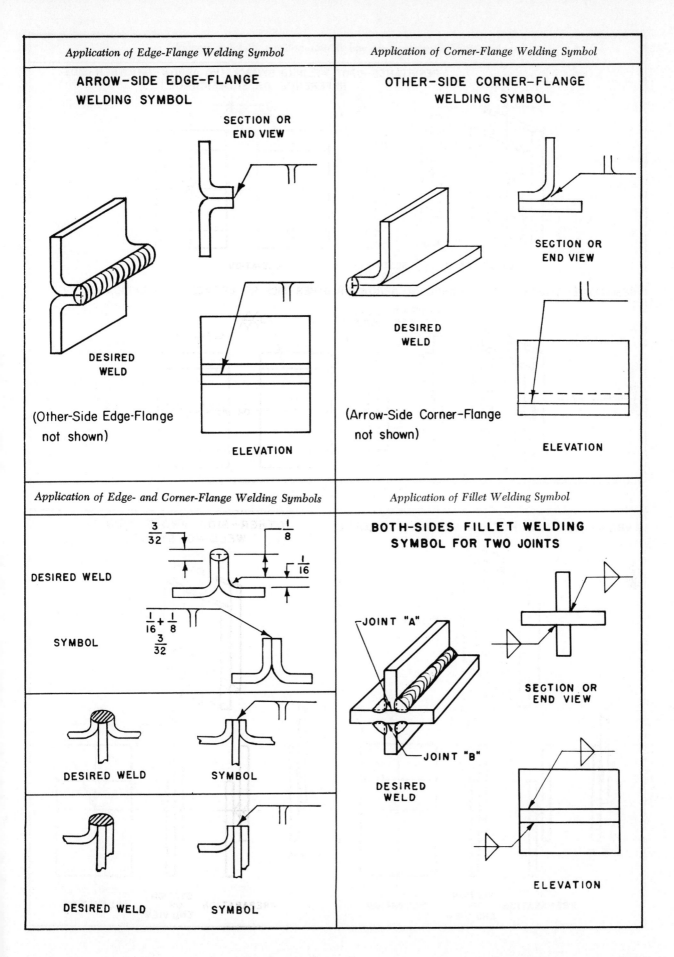

Application of Edge-Flange Welding Symbol

ARROW–SIDE EDGE–FLANGE WELDING SYMBOL

SECTION OR END VIEW

DESIRED WELD

ELEVATION

(Other-Side Edge-Flange not shown)

Application of Corner-Flange Welding Symbol

OTHER–SIDE CORNER–FLANGE WELDING SYMBOL

SECTION OR END VIEW

DESIRED WELD

(Arrow-Side Corner-Flange not shown)

ELEVATION

Application of Edge- and Corner-Flange Welding Symbols

DESIRED WELD

$\frac{3}{32}$ $\frac{1}{8}$ $\frac{1}{16}$

SYMBOL

$\frac{1}{16}+\frac{1}{8}$
$\frac{3}{32}$

DESIRED WELD   SYMBOL

DESIRED WELD   SYMBOL

Application of Fillet Welding Symbol

BOTH–SIDES FILLET WELDING SYMBOL FOR TWO JOINTS

JOINT "A"

JOINT "B"

DESIRED WELD

SECTION OR END VIEW

ELEVATION

RESISTANCE-SPOT WELDING SYMBOL (NO ARROW- OR OTHER-SIDE REFERENCE OR SIGNIFICANCE.)

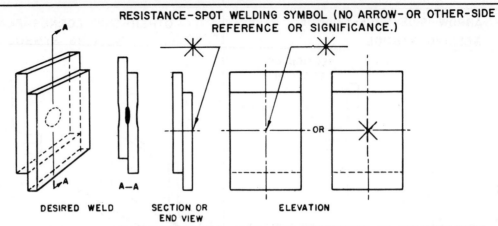

DESIRED WELD   SECTION OR END VIEW   ELEVATION

RESISTANCE-SEAM WELDING SYMBOL (NO ARROW- OR OTHER-SIDE REFERENCE OR SIGNIFICANCE.)

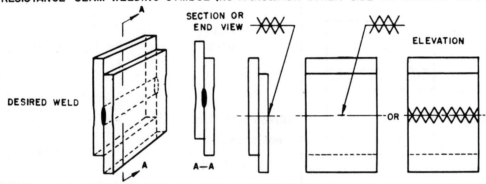

DESIRED WELD   SECTION OR END VIEW   ELEVATION

ARROW-SIDE PROJECTION WELDING SYMBOL

OTHER-SIDE PROJECTION WELDING SYMBOL

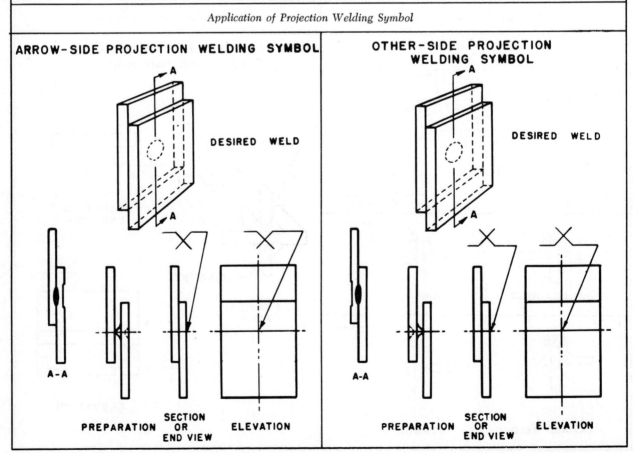

DESIRED WELD

PREPARATION   SECTION OR END VIEW   ELEVATION

DESIRED WELD

PREPARATION   SECTION OR END VIEW   ELEVATION

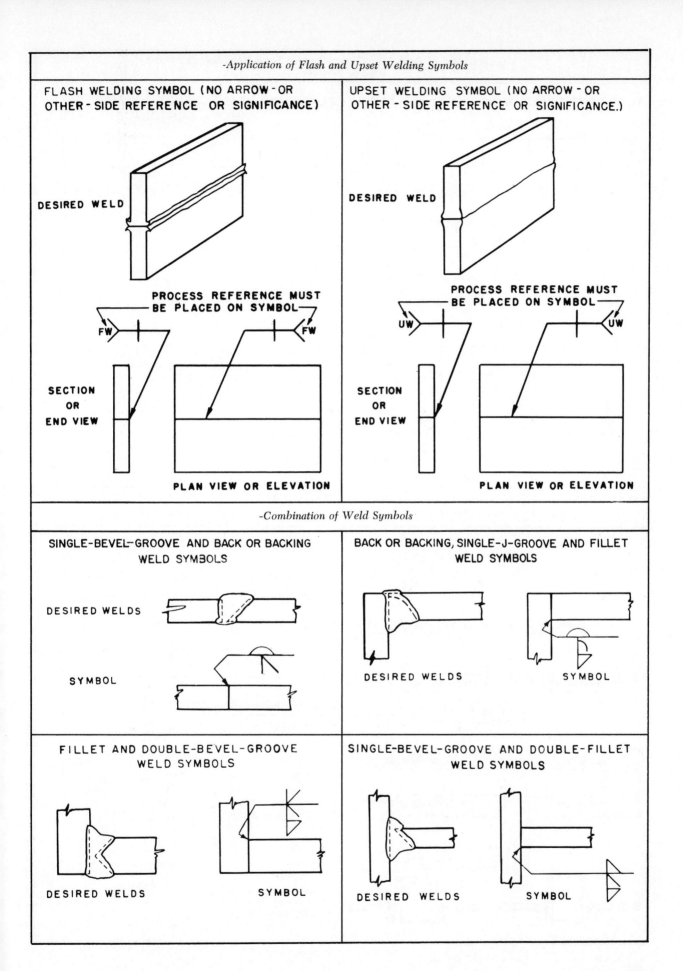

-Application of Flash and Upset Welding Symbols

FLASH WELDING SYMBOL (NO ARROW - OR OTHER - SIDE REFERENCE OR SIGNIFICANCE)

UPSET WELDING SYMBOL (NO ARROW - OR OTHER - SIDE REFERENCE OR SIGNIFICANCE.)

DESIRED WELD

DESIRED WELD

PROCESS REFERENCE MUST BE PLACED ON SYMBOL

FW   FW

UW   UW

SECTION OR END VIEW

SECTION OR END VIEW

PLAN VIEW OR ELEVATION

PLAN VIEW OR ELEVATION

-Combination of Weld Symbols

SINGLE-BEVEL-GROOVE AND BACK OR BACKING WELD SYMBOLS

BACK OR BACKING, SINGLE-J-GROOVE AND FILLET WELD SYMBOLS

DESIRED WELDS

SYMBOL

DESIRED WELDS   SYMBOL

FILLET AND DOUBLE-BEVEL-GROOVE WELD SYMBOLS

SINGLE-BEVEL-GROOVE AND DOUBLE-FILLET WELD SYMBOLS

DESIRED WELDS   SYMBOL

DESIRED WELDS   SYMBOL

279

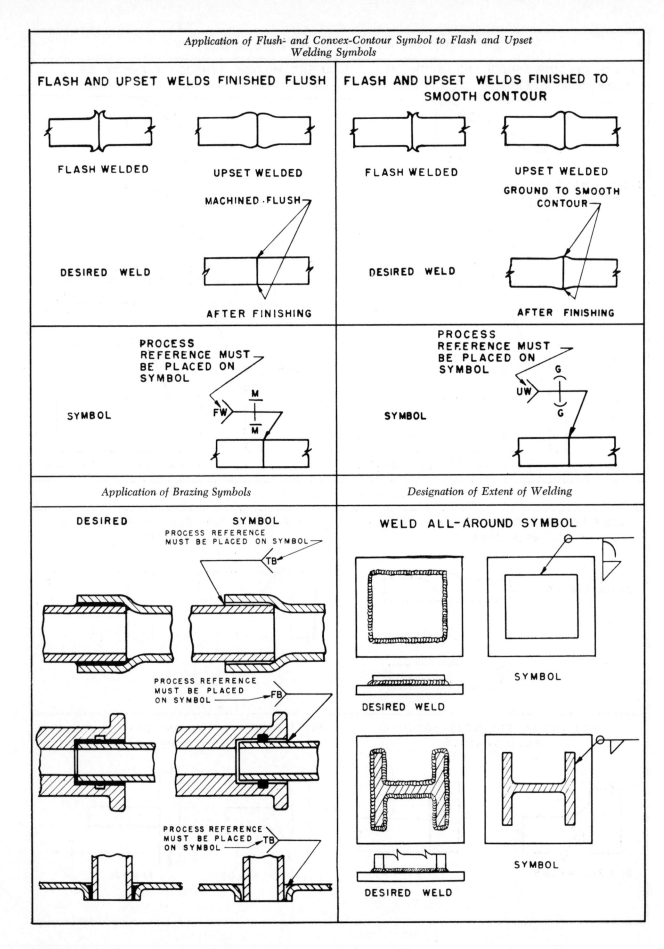

Application of Flush- and Convex-Contour Symbol to Flash and Upset Welding Symbols

FLASH AND UPSET WELDS FINISHED FLUSH

FLASH WELDED

UPSET WELDED

MACHINED FLUSH

DESIRED WELD

AFTER FINISHING

SYMBOL

PROCESS REFERENCE MUST BE PLACED ON SYMBOL

M / FW / M

FLASH AND UPSET WELDS FINISHED TO SMOOTH CONTOUR

FLASH WELDED

UPSET WELDED

GROUND TO SMOOTH CONTOUR

DESIRED WELD

AFTER FINISHING

SYMBOL

PROCESS REFERENCE MUST BE PLACED ON SYMBOL

G / UW / G

Application of Brazing Symbols

DESIRED

SYMBOL

PROCESS REFERENCE MUST BE PLACED ON SYMBOL

TB

PROCESS REFERENCE MUST BE PLACED ON SYMBOL

FB

PROCESS REFERENCE MUST BE PLACED ON SYMBOL

TB

Designation of Extent of Welding

WELD ALL-AROUND SYMBOL

SYMBOL

DESIRED WELD

SYMBOL

DESIRED WELD

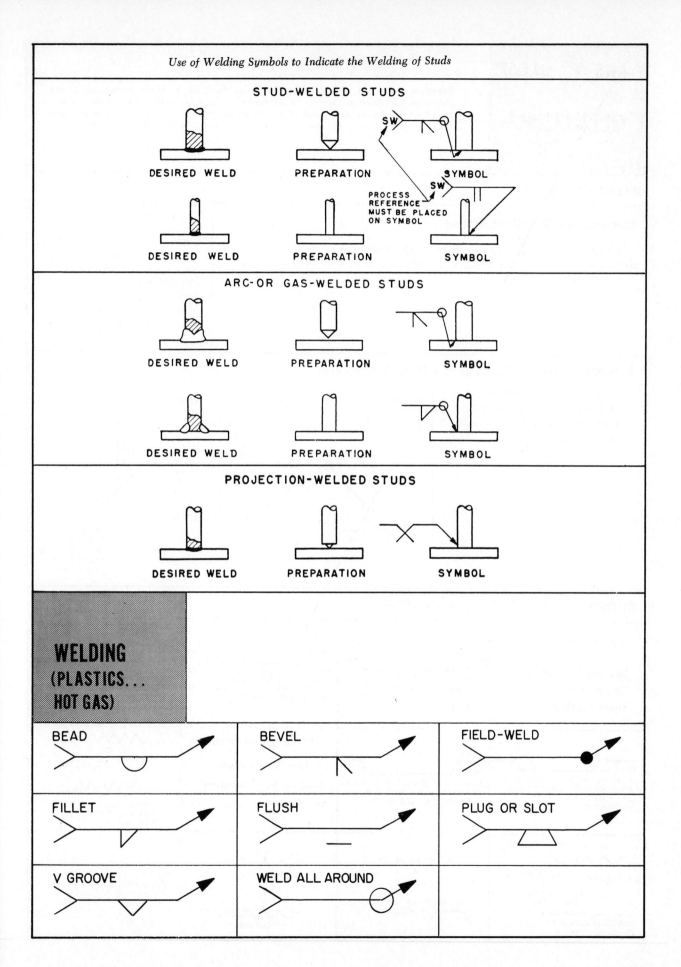

Use of Welding Symbols to Indicate the Welding of Studs

STUD-WELDED STUDS

DESIRED WELD · PREPARATION · SYMBOL

DESIRED WELD · PREPARATION · SYMBOL

PROCESS REFERENCE MUST BE PLACED ON SYMBOL

ARC- OR GAS-WELDED STUDS

DESIRED WELD · PREPARATION · SYMBOL

DESIRED WELD · PREPARATION · SYMBOL

PROJECTION-WELDED STUDS

DESIRED WELD · PREPARATION · SYMBOL

WELDING (PLASTICS... HOT GAS)

BEAD

BEVEL

FIELD-WELD

FILLET

FLUSH

PLUG OR SLOT

V GROOVE

WELD ALL AROUND

AWS C2.6-57T METALLIZING	*Extracted from ASA Y32.12-1960, Metallizing Symbols, with the permission of the publisher, the American Society of Mechanical Engineers, United Engineering Center, 345 East 47 Street, New York, N.Y. Reproduced from AWS C2.6-57T, Metallizing Symbols, published by the American Welding Society, 33 West 39 Street, New York, N.Y.*

BASIC SYMBOLS

Elements of a Metallizing Symbol

A metallizing symbol shall consist of the following elements, or such of these elements as are necessary to prescribe the required operations.

Reference Line
Arrow
Surface Preparation Symbol
Dimensions and other data
Supplementary Symbols
Finish Symbols
Tail
Metallizing Designator, (M)
Specification, process,
      or other references

Standard Location of Elements of a Metallizing Symbol

The elements of a metallizing symbol shall have standard locations with respect to each other as shown

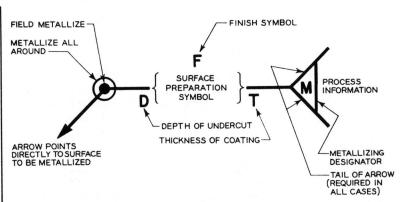

FIELD METALLIZE

METALLIZE ALL AROUND

ARROW POINTS DIRECTLY TO SURFACE TO BE METALLIZED

SURFACE PREPARATION SYMBOL

DEPTH OF UNDERCUT

THICKNESS OF COATING

FINISH SYMBOL

PROCESS INFORMATION

METALLIZING DESIGNATOR

TAIL OF ARROW (REQUIRED IN ALL CASES)

SURFACE PREPARATION SYMBOLS

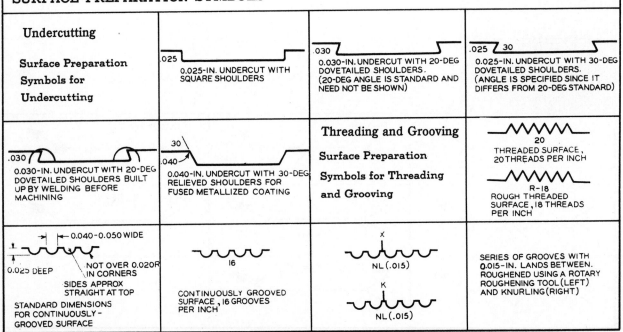

Undercutting

Surface Preparation Symbols for Undercutting

.025
0.025-IN. UNDERCUT WITH SQUARE SHOULDERS

.030
0.030-IN. UNDERCUT WITH 20-DEG DOVETAILED SHOULDERS. (20-DEG ANGLE IS STANDARD AND NEED NOT BE SHOWN)

.025 30
0.025-IN. UNDERCUT WITH 30-DEG DOVETAILED SHOULDERS. (ANGLE IS SPECIFIED SINCE IT DIFFERS FROM 20-DEG STANDARD)

.030
0.030-IN. UNDERCUT WITH 20-DEG DOVETAILED SHOULDERS BUILT UP BY WELDING BEFORE MACHINING

30
.040
0.040-IN. UNDERCUT WITH 30-DEG RELIEVED SHOULDERS FOR FUSED METALLIZED COATING

Threading and Grooving

Surface Preparation Symbols for Threading and Grooving

20
THREADED SURFACE, 20 THREADS PER INCH

R-18
ROUGH THREADED SURFACE, 18 THREADS PER INCH

0.040-0.050 WIDE
NOT OVER 0.020R IN CORNERS
SIDES APPROX STRAIGHT AT TOP
0.025 DEEP
STANDARD DIMENSIONS FOR CONTINUOUSLY-GROOVED SURFACE

16
CONTINUOUSLY GROOVED SURFACE, 16 GROOVES PER INCH

X
NL (.015)

K
NL (.015)

SERIES OF GROOVES WITH 0.015-IN. LANDS BETWEEN. ROUGHENED USING A ROTARY ROUGHENING TOOL (LEFT) AND KNURLING (RIGHT)

Blasting Symbol for Surface Preparation by Blasting	B BLASTING PROCEDURE TO BE REFERENCED IN TAIL OF ARROW OR DETAILS INSERTED THEREIN	**Electric Bonding and Metallic Spray Bonding** Symbol for Surface Preparation by Electric Bonding or Metallic Spray Bonding	FINE ELECTRIC BOND DEPOSIT EB(F)
METALLIC SPRAY BOND DEPOSIT MSB			

SUPPLEMENTARY SYMBOLS

Metallizing Designator	All metallizing symbols shall include an M located in the tail of the arrow (This symbol is known as the *metallizing designator* and serves to distinguish metallizing symbols from welding symbols or other symbols which may be similarly drawn.)

Metallize-All-Around ——————— **Field Metallize Symbol**	Metallizing which is to extend over a complete surface between abrupt changes in dimension shall be designated by use of the *metallize-all- around symbol* Metallizing to be done on a member or part which is installed and in service shall be designated by use of the *field metallize symbol*	METALLIZE ALL AROUND $\bigcirc$	FIELD METALLIZE $\bullet$	MACHINE FLAT (✻)
		✻ INDICATE HERE WHETHER GROUND (G), MACHINED (M), WIRE BRUSHED (WB) OR BUFFED (B)		

Thickness of **Sprayed Metal**	The thickness of the sprayed metal coating shall be placed to the right of the surface preparation symbol as shown Where the diameter to which the part is to be built up, rather than the thickness of coating, is to be specified, this dimension shall be placed to the right of the surface preparation symbol followed by the letter D Thickness of Coating .030 6.50D

Finishing Symbols	All metallized surfaces shall be left as metallized unless the *machined flat symbol* is used. Where the machined flat symbol is used it shall be placed above the surface preparation symbol, as shown ———— together with one of the following letters designating how the surface is to be finished: G—Ground; M—Machined; WB—Wire Brushed; B—Buffed. Use of Finishing Symbol W B / B M

Procedure Information	The procedure to be followed in metallizing, including wire size, rate of spraying, type of flame and spraying distance shall be identified by placing a reference in the tail of the arrow to that procedure. Alternatively, all details of the procedure may be placed directly in the tail of the arrow.

Example of Use

of Metallizing Symbols

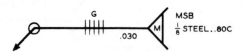

This symbol specifies: No undercut. Metallic spraybond surface preparation. Spray all around with $^1/_8$ in. diam., 0.80 carbon steel wire to a thickness of 0.030 in. Finish by grinding.

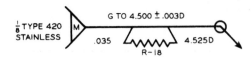

This symbol specifies: 0.035-in. undercut. Rough threading, 18 threads per in. 20-deg dovetailed shoulders. Spray to 4.525 in. diam. with $^1/_8$-in., Type 420 stainless steel wire. Grind to 4.500 ± 0.003-in diam.

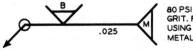

This symbol specifies: Pressure blast with 80 psi air and G-14 angular steel grit. Flash spray immediately after blasting using $^1/_8$-in., 0.10 C steel wire. Metallize all around 0.025-in. thick with $^1/_8$-in. aluminum wire.

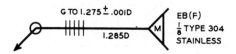

This symbol specifies: No undercut. Electric bond (fine) surface preparation. Spray all around to 1.285-in. diam. with $^1/_8$-in., Type 304 stainless steel wire. Finish grind to 1.275 ± 0.001 diam.

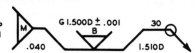

This symbol specifies: Undercut 0.040-in. deep with 30-deg. relieved shoulders. Grit blast with 25 mesh angular steel grit. Buildup to 1.510-in. with powder metallizing using number 66 alloy after preheating to 600° F. Fuse with oxyacetylene flame. Finish grind to 1.500 ± 0.001 diameter.

Extracted from ASA Y32.17-1962, Nondestructive Testing Symbols, with the permission of the publisher, the American Society of Mechanical Engineers, United Engineering Center, 345 East 47 Street, New York, N.Y. Reproduced from AWS A2.2-58, published by the American Welding Society, 33 West.39 Street, New York, N.Y.

BASIC TESTING SYMBOLS

Basic Nondestructive Testing symbols shall be as follows:

TYPE OF TEST	SYMBOL
RADIOGRAPHIC	*RT*
MAGNETIC-PARTICLE	*MT*
PENETRANTS	*PT*
ULTRASONIC	*UT*

ELEMENTS OF THE TESTING SYMBOL

The assembled testing symbol consists of the following elements. Such of these elements as are necessary shall be used and shall have standard locations with respect to each other as shown below.

Reference Line   Tail
Arrow   Extent of test
Basic Testing symbol   Specification, process,
Test-all-around symbol   or other reference
(N) Number of Tests

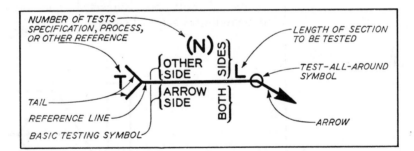

SIGNIFICANCE OF ARROW

The arrow shall connect the reference line to the part to be tested. The side of the part to be tested, to which the arrow points shall be considered the arrow side of the part. The side opposite the arrow side of the part shall be considered the other side.

LOCATION OF TESTING SYMBOL

(a) Tests to be made on the arrow side of the part shall be indicated by the test symbol on the side of the reference line toward the reader as follows:

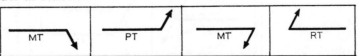

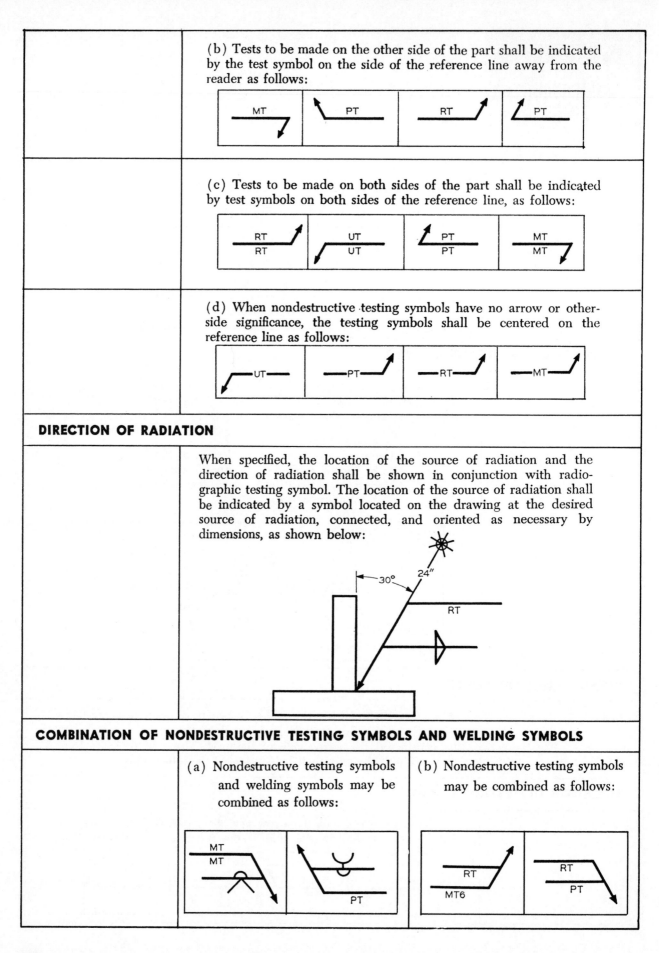

(b) Tests to be made on the other side of the part shall be indicated by the test symbol on the side of the reference line away from the reader as follows:

(c) Tests to be made on both sides of the part shall be indicated by test symbols on both sides of the reference line, as follows:

(d) When nondestructive testing symbols have no arrow or other-side significance, the testing symbols shall be centered on the reference line as follows:

DIRECTION OF RADIATION

When specified, the location of the source of radiation and the direction of radiation shall be shown in conjunction with radiographic testing symbol. The location of the source of radiation shall be indicated by a symbol located on the drawing at the desired source of radiation, connected, and oriented as necessary by dimensions, as shown below:

COMBINATION OF NONDESTRUCTIVE TESTING SYMBOLS AND WELDING SYMBOLS

(a) Nondestructive testing symbols and welding symbols may be combined as follows:

(b) Nondestructive testing symbols may be combined as follows:

USE OF REFERENCES	
	Specifications, process, classification, or other references need not be used on testing symbols when the testing procedure is prescribed elsewhere. When a specification,. process, classification, or other reference is used with a testing symbol, the reference shall be placed in the tail, as follows: 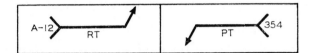

SPECIFYING LENGTH OF SECTION TO BE TESTED	
	(a) To specify tests of welds or parts where only length of section need be considered, the length in inches shall be shown to the right of the basic test symbol, as follows: 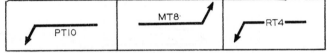
	(b) To show the exact location of a section to be tested as well as its length, dimension lines shall be used as follows: 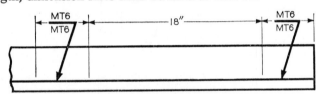 (c) When the full length of a part is to be tested, no length dimension need be shown on the testing symbol.

SPECIFYING NUMBER OF TESTS	
	To specify a. number of tests to be taken at random, the number of desired tests shall be shown in parenthesis, as follows: 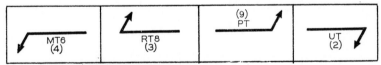

SPECIFYING TESTS MADE ALL AROUND A PART	
	To specify tests to be made all around a part, the test-all-around symbol shall be used, as follows: 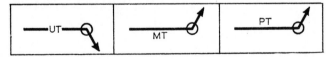

SPECIFYING TESTS OF AREAS	
	When required, nondestructive tests of areas shall be indicated by one of the following methods: (a) For nondestructive testing of an area represented as a plane on

the drawing, the area to be tested shall be enclosed by straight broken lines having a circle at each change of direction. The testing symbol specifying the kind of nondestructive test shall be used in connection with these lines, as shown below. When necessary, these inclosures shall be located by dimensions.

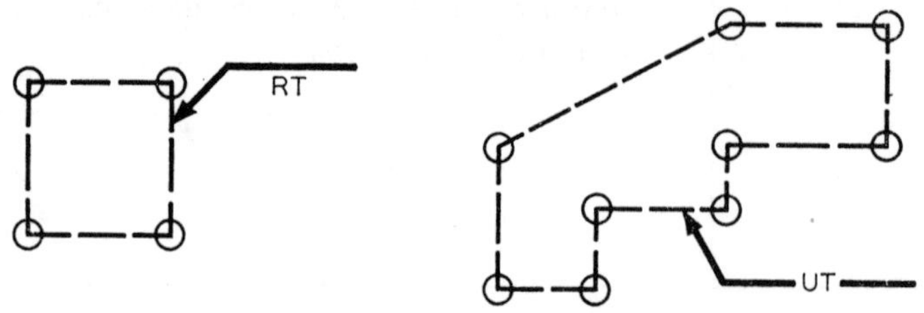

(b) For nondestructive testing areas of revolution, the area shall be indicated by using the test-all-around symbol as follows:

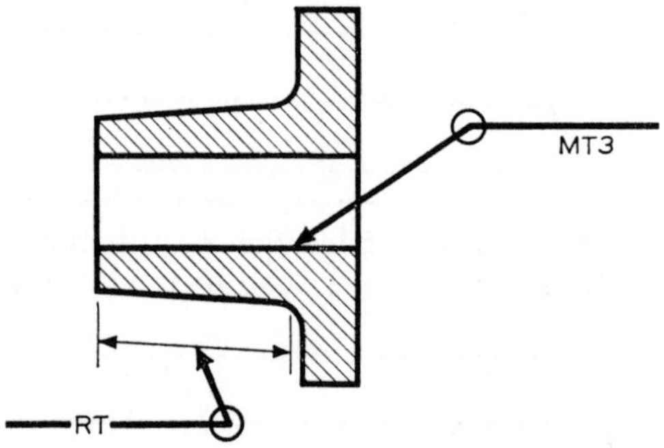

The symbol at left indicates that the bore of the flange is to be subjected to a magnetic-particle examination for a distance of three inches from the face, all the way around.

The above symbol indicates an area of revolution to be subjected to radiographic examination where dimensions are not available on drawing.

MIL·STD 8B GEOMETRIC TOLERANCE	*Extracted from MIL-STD-8B-1959 (superceding MIL-STD-8A), Dimensioning and Tolerancing, with the permission of the Office of the Secretary of Defense, Public Affairs Department, Washington.*		
FLATNESS & STRAIGHTNESS	ANGULARITY	PERPENDIC-ULARITY	PARALLELISM
CONCENTRICITY	TRUE POSITION	ROUNDNESS	SYMMETRY
	(MMC) MAXIMUM MATERIAL CONDITION	(RFS) REGARDLESS OF FEATURE SIZE	

Feature control symbol.

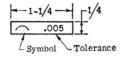
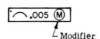

└ Symbol └ Tolerance   └ Modifier

Feature control symbol. When symbols are used, a positional or form tolerance shall be stated by means of the feature control symbol illustrated The geometric characteristic symbol shall be followed by the permissible tolerance, and in some cases by the modifier Ⓜ or Ⓢ.

The height of the box outline of the symbol shall be ¼ inch, and the length shall be 1¼ inches, excepting that when characters in addition to the characteristic symbol, datum reference, and tolerance must be specified, the length of the box should be increased as necessary to avoid crowding.

The feature control symbols shall be associated with the feature(s) being toleranced by one of the following methods:

    (a) Adding the symbol to a note pertaining to the feature(s).

    (b) Running a leader line from the symbol to the feature.

    (c) Attaching a side, end or corner of the box to an extension line from the feature.

    (d) Attaching a side or end of the box to the dimension line pertaining to the feature when it is cylindrical.

Datum identifying symbol.

├─ 5/8 ─┤

─ B ─

└ Identifying Letter

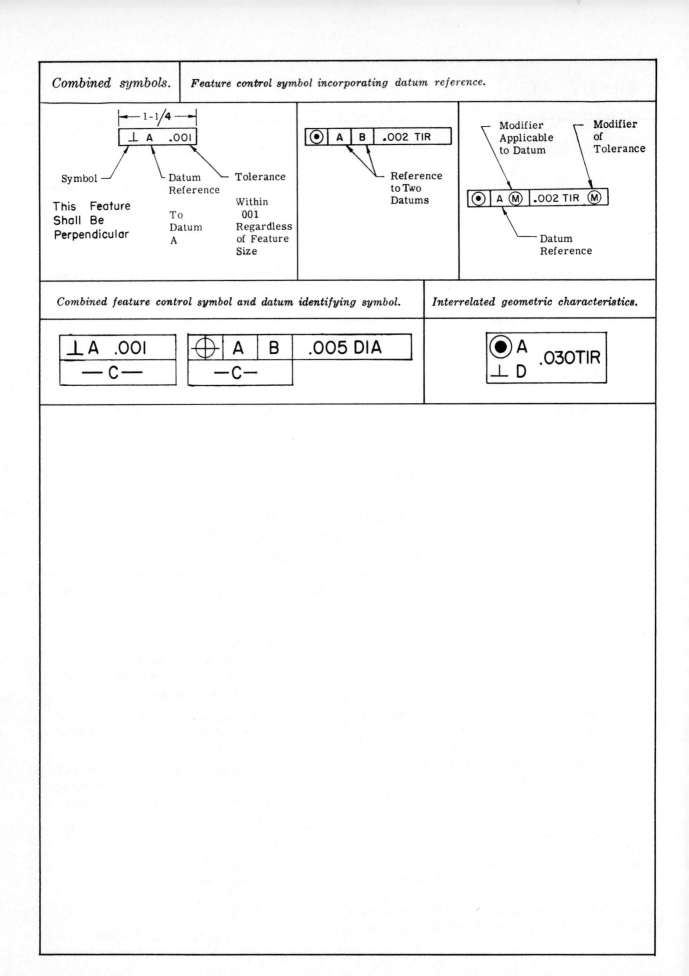

Combined symbols. | **Feature control symbol incorporating datum reference.**

|← 1-1/4 →|

⊥ A .001

Symbol —   Datum   Tolerance
      Reference

This Feature   Within
Shall Be   To   001
Perpendicular   Datum   Regardless
            A   of Feature
                     Size

⊙ | A | B | .002 TIR

Reference
to Two
Datums

Modifier   **Modifier**
Applicable   of
to Datum   Tolerance

⊙ | A Ⓜ | .002 TIR Ⓜ

Datum
Reference

Combined feature control symbol and datum identifying symbol. | **Interrelated geometric characteristics.**

⊥ A .001
— C —

⊕ | A | B | .005 DIA
— C —

⊙ A
⊥ D   .030 TIR

DIFFERENCES IN AMERICAN–BRITISH–CANADIAN STANDARDS

ITEM	AMERICAN *ASA Y14.5 AND MIL-STD-8B		BRITISH	CANADIAN
	NOTES	SYMBOLS		
ROUNDNESS	ROUND WITHIN .002 ON DIA	○ .002	ENTIRE SURFACE MUST LIE INSIDE ANNULAR TOLERANCE ZONE .001 WIDE	ENTIRE SURFACE MUST LIE INSIDE ANNULAR TOLERANCE ZONE .001 WIDE
TRUE POSITION DIMENSION	BASIC OR BSC	BASIC OR BSC	(TP)	(TP)
TRUE POSITION AT MMC	LOCATED AT TRUE POSITION WITHIN .010 DIA	⊕ .010 DIA	POSN TOL .010 DIA (MMC)	LOCATE WITHIN .010 DIA MMC
TRUE POSITION RFS WITH DATUM RFS	LOCATED AT TRUE POSITION WITHIN .010 DIA RFS IN RELATION TO DATUM A RFS	⊕ A Ⓢ .010 DIA Ⓢ	POSN TOL .010 DIA DATUM–A	LOCATE WITHIN .010 DIA DATUM–A
TRUE POSITION AT MMC WITH DATUM AT MMC	LOCATED AT TRUE POSITION WITHIN .010 DIA IN RELATION TO DATUM A	⊕ A .010 DIA	POSN TOL .010 DIA (MMC) DATUM–A (MMC)	LOCATE WITHIN .010 MMC DATUM A MMC
TRUE POSITION WITH TWO DATUMS	LOCATED AT TRUE POSITION WITHIN .005 DIA AT MMC IN RELATION TO DATUM A AT MMC AND DATUM B RFS	⊕ AⓂ BⓈ .005 DIAⓂ	POSN TOL .005 DIA (MMC) DATUM–A (MMC) AND B	LOCATE WITHIN .005 DIA MMC DATUMS A, MMC AND B
TRUE POSITION OF SLOTS OR TABS	LOCATED AT TRUE POSITION WITHIN .002 WIDE ZONE RFS IN RELATION TO DATUM A AT MMC	⊕ AⓂ .002 TOTAL Ⓢ	POSN TOL .002 WIDE, DATUM–A (MMC)	LOCATE WITHIN .002 WIDE ZONE WITH RESPECT TO DATUM A AT MMC

DIFFERENCES IN AMERICAN-BRITISH-CANADIAN STANDARDS

ITEM	AMERICAN *ASA Y14.5 AND MIL-STD-8B		BRITISH	CANADIAN
	NOTES	SYMBOLS		
AUXILIARY INFORMATION	REF		(XX)	REF
DEC DIM.	1.005		1.005	1.005
TRUE PROFILE DIMENSIONING	BASIC		(TP)	(TP)
STRAIGHTNESS	STRAIGHT WITHIN .003 TOTAL	⌒ .003	STR TOL .003 DIA	STRAIGHT WITHIN .003
FLATNESS	FLAT WITHIN .003 TOTAL	⌒ .003	FLAT TOL .003 WIDE	FLAT WITHIN .003
PARALLELISM	PARALLEL TO A WITHIN .005 TOTAL	∥ A .005	PAR TOL .005 WIDE (OR DIA) DATUM–FACE A	PARALLEL TO FACE A WITHIN .005
PERPENDICULARITY	PERPENDICULAR TO A WITHIN .002 TOTAL	⊥ A .002	SQ TOL .002 WIDE (OR DIA) DATUM–FACE A	SQUARE WITH FACE A WITHIN .002
ANGULARITY	ANGULAR TOL .006 TOTAL, DATUM A	∠ A .006	ANG TOL .006 WIDE DATUM–FACE A	ANG. TOL .006 DATUM–FACE A
CONCENTRICITY	CONCENTRIC TO A WITHIN .003 TIR	⊙ A .003 TIR	CONC TOL .003 DIA DATUM–A	CONC TO CYL A WITHIN .003 FIM
SYMMETRY	SYMMETRICAL WITH A WITHIN .004 TOTAL	≡ A .004	SYM TOL .004 WIDE DATUM–A	SYMMETRICAL WITH WIDTH A WITHIN .004

* Tentative pending final adoption of symbols by ASA membership

Extracted from MIL-STD-10A-1955 (superceding MIL-STD-10), Surface Roughness, Waviness and Lay, with the permission of the Office of the Secretary of Defense, Public Affairs Department, Washington.

Proportions for Basic Symbol.

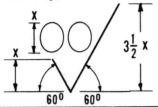

Basic surface roughness symbol. The basic symbol √ shall be used to designate surfaced roughness. Convenient proportions for the basic symbol are shown

TABLE I

Preferred Roughness Height Ratings*

¼	2	16	125	1000
½	4	32	250	....
1	8	63	500	....

TABLE II

Waviness Height Values (Inches)

0.00002	0.00008	0.0003	0.001	0.005	0.015
0.00003	0.0001	0.0005	0.002	0.008	0.020
0.00005	0.0002	0.0008	0.003	0.010	....

TABLE III

Roughness-Width Cutoff Values (Inches)

| .003 | .010 | .030[1] | .100 | .300 | 1.000 |

* Known also as Arithmetical Average (AA) ratings and Centre Line Average (CLA) index numbers.

1 The .030 cutoff value shall be standard unless otherwise specified. When the .030 cutoff value applies, it need not be shown in the symbol, or specified in specifications, etc.

LAY SYMBOLS

LAY SYMBOL	DESIGNATION	EXAMPLE
═══	Lay parallel to the boundary line representing the surface to which the symbol applies.	Direction of tool MARKS
⊥	Lay perpendicular to the boundary line representing the surface to which the symbol applies.	DIRECTION OF TOOL MARKS
✕	Lay angular in both directions to boundary line representing the surface to which symbol applies.	DIRECTION OF TOOL MARKS

LAY SYMBOL	DESIGNATION	EXAMPLE
M	Lay multidirectional	
C	Lay approximately circular relative to the center of the surface to which the symbol applies.	
R	Lay approximately radial relative to the center of the surface to which the symbol applies.	

Application of symbols and ratings. Surface roughness, waviness and lay requirements shall be represented on drawings in the manner illustrated in figures 2 through 10. Care should be exercised to insert numerical values in the precise positions shown. Waviness, lay, and roughness-width cutoff, designations may, when warranted by special requirements, be specified in NOTES.

Figure 2 — **Surface Roughness Symbol (Basic).**— Designation of symbol only indicates requirements governing surface irregularities detailed in NOTES.

Figure 3 — **Roughness Height Rating.**—The surface roughness height, expressed by a numerical rating, placed adjacent to and at the left of long leg as shown. The specification of one number indicates the maximum permissible sustained roughness height rating. Any lesser rating shall be acceptable.

Figure 4 — **Maximum and Minimum Ratings.**— Maximum and minimum roughness height ratings shall indicate permissible range. The maximum rating shall be placed above the minimum as shown.

Figure 5 — **Waviness Height.**—Waviness height value, in inches, shall be placed above extension line as shown. The value shown shall indicate maximum allowable waviness height.

Figure 6 — **Waviness Width.** — Waviness width value, in inches, shall be placed above the extension line at the right of the waviness height value as shown. The value shown shall indicate the maximum allowable waviness width. NOTE —This designation will not be used when percentage of contact area is specified.

Figure 7 — **Contact Area.** — Minimum requirements for contact or bearing area shall be indicated by a percentage value placed above the extension line as shown. Further requirements may be controlled by NOTES.

Figure 8 — **Lay.**—The lay designation is indicated by the symbol placed to the right and slightly above the point of the surface roughness symbol as shown.

Figure 9 — **Surface Roughness Width.**—The surface roughness width value, in inches, shall be placed at the right and parallel to the lay symbol as shown. The value shown shall indicate maximum allowable roughness width.

Figure 10 — **Roughness-Width Cutoff.**—The roughness-width cutoff value, other than the preferred .030 cutoff value, shall be placed immediately below the extension and to the right of the long leg as shown.

Roughness Height Rating	General Application of Roughness Height Ratings	Roughness Height Rating	General Application of Roughness Height Ratings
1000 √	Very rough, low grade surface resulting from sand casting, torch or saw cutting, chipping or rough forgings. Machine operations are not required as appearance is not objectionable. This finish, rarely specified, is suitable for unmachined clearance areas on machinery, jigs, and other rough construction items.		economically produced on lathes, milling machines, shapers, grinders, etc. The surface finish may also be obtained on permanent mold castings, die castings, extrusions, and rolled surfaces.
500 √	Very rough, low grade surfaces, where smoothness is of no object, resulting from heavy cuts and coarse feeds in milling, turning, shaping, boring, and from very rough filing, rough disc grinding and snagging. This surface is suitable for clearance areas on machinery, jigs, and fixtures. This surface roughness may be obtained by natural processes of sand casting or rough forging.	63 √	A good machine finish produced under controlled production procedures using relatively high speeds and fine feeds in taking light cuts with well-sharpened cutters. This surface value may be specified where close fits are required and may be used for all stressed parts, except for fast rotating shafts, axles, and parts subject to severe vibration or extreme tension. This surface roughness is satisfactory for bearing surfaces when the motion is slow and the loads are light or infrequent. This surface roughness may also be obtained on extrusions, rolled surfaces, die castings, and permanent mold castings when rigidly controlled.
250 √	Coarse production surfaces, for unimportant clearance and cleanup operations, resulting from very coarse surface grind, rough file, disc grind, and from rapid feeds in turning, milling, shaping, drilling, boring, grinding, etc., where definite tool marks are not objectionable. This roughness may also be produced on the natural surfaces of forgings, permanent mold castings, extrusions and rolled surfaces. Surfaces with this roughness value can be produced very economically and is used to a great extent on parts where stress requirements, appearance, and conditions of operations and design permit.	32 √	A high-grade machine finish requiring close control when produced by lathes, shapers, milling machines, etc., but relatively easy to produce by centerless, cylindrical or surface grinders. This surface may be specified in parts where stress concentration is present. This surface finish is satisfactory for bearing surfaces when motion is not continuous and loads are light. When finer finishes than this are specified, production costs rise rapidly, therefore, such finishes must be analyzed carefully by the engineer or designer. Also processes such as extruding, rolling, or die casting may produce a comparable surface roughness when such processes are rigidly controlled.
125 √	This is the roughest surface recommended for parts subject to leads, vibration, and high stress. This surface roughness is also permitted for bearing surfaces when the motion is slow and the loads are light or infrequent, but not to be specified for fast rotating shafts, axles, and parts subject to severe vibration or extreme tension. This surface is a medium, commercial machine finish in which relatively high speeds and fine feeds are used in taking light cuts with well-sharpened tools, and may be	16 √	A high quality surface produced by fine cylindrical grinding, emery buffing, coarse honing or lapping. A surface of this value is specified where smoothness is of primary importance for proper functioning of the part, such as rapidly rotating shaft bearing, heavily loaded bearings, and extreme tension members.

Continued |

Roughness Height Rating	General Application of Roughness Height Ratings
8 ✓	Very fine surfaces produced by special finishing operations such as honing, lapping, or buffing. Surfaces refined to this degree are specified where packings and rings must slide across the direction of the surface grain, maintaining or withstanding pressures; the interior honed surfaces of hydraulic cylinders are an example. Finishes of this value may also be required in precision gages and instrument work, on sensitive value surfaces, or on rapidly rotating shafts and on bearings where lubrication is not dependable.
4 ✓	Refined surfaces produced by special finishing operations such as honing, lapping, and buffing. This surface roughness value should be specified only when the requirements of design makes it mandatory as the cost of manufacturing is extremely high. Surfaces refined to this degree are required in instrument work, gage work and where packings and rings must slide across the direction of surface grain, such as on chrome plated piston rods, etc. where lubrication is not dependable.
2 ✓ 1 ✓ 1/2 ✓ 1/4 ✓	Very refined surfaces produced only by the finest of modern honing, lapping, buffing, and superfinishing equipment. These surfaces may have a satin or highly polished appearance depending on the finishing operation and material. Finishes of this type are only specified when design requirements make it mandatory as the cost of manufacturing is extremely high. Surfaces refined to this degree are specified on fine or very sensitive instrument parts or other laboratory items, and certain gage surfaces, such as on precision gage blocks.

STRUCTURAL SYMBOLS

Extracted from MIL-STD-18A-1953 (superceding MIL-STD-18), Structural Symbols, with the permission of the Office of the Secretary of Defense, Public Affairs Department, Washington.

Description	Symbol	Illustrated use
Tensile stress in a member	+	+ 59,000
Compressive stress in a member	−	− 64,000
Pounds	#	120,000#
Number	#	#8
Feet / Inches	' / "	3'-6"
Angular measurements — Degrees, Minutes, Seconds	° ' "	12° 36' 50"
Kip (1000#)	K	30K
Deflection	△	△ = 0.300"
Modulus of elasticity	E	E = 30,000,000
At	@	4 @ 6
Percent	%	20%
By	X	3 X 10
Round	φ	1½ φ
Square	□	2 □

Structural framing, member designations (Followed by member number, and preceded by floor designation* where applicable)

*Floor designation by number, with B for basement and R for roof.

Description	Symbol	Illustrated use
Beam	B	2 B 2
Girder	G	B G 4
Joist	J	R J 6
Slab	S	4 S 8
Column	C	C 10
Bracing	Br	Br 12
Strut	St	St 3
Footing	F	F 5
Girt	Gt	Gt 7
Knee brace	KB	KB 9
Lintel	L	L 11
Purlin	P	P 2
Rafter	R	R 4
Stair stringer	SS	SS 6
Truss	T	T 8
Wall	W	W 10

REINFORCED CONCRETE CONSTRUCTION	The following symbols are for use on drawings of reinforced concrete structures or elements thereof.	Bars, round Straight bars Plain ends	Hooked one end
Hooked both ends	Bent bars Plain ends	Hooked one end	Hooked both ends
Column ties Square or rectangular	Circular	Column spiral	**Stirrup** **"U" type**
"W" type	Tied type	Direction in which main bars extend	Limits of area covered by bars
Anchor bolt (in plan) *Illustrated use* $\frac{3}{4}\phi$X2'-6" ANCHOR BOLTS		Anchor bolt set in pipe sleeve (in plan) *Illustrated use* $\frac{3}{4}\phi$X2'-6" ANCHOR BOLTS SET IN $1\frac{1}{2}\phi$X8 PIPE SLEEVES	

Description	*Symbol*	*Illustrated use*
Ultimate compressive strength of concrete	f'_c	$f'_c = 3000$ PSI
Tensile stress in reinforcement	f_s	$f_s = 20,000$ PSI
Compressive stress in concrete	f_c	$f_c = 1050$ PSI
Area of tensile reinforcement	A_s	$A_s = 2.4$ SQ. IN.
Area of compressive reinforcement	A'_s	$A'_s = 1.8$ SQ. IN
Modulus of elasticity of concrete	E_c	$E_c = 1,500,000$ PSI
Modulus of elasticity of reinforcement steel	E_s	$E_s = 30,000,000$ PSI

REINFORCING BAR DESIGNATION	The size of the reinforcing steel bars shall be designated by number in accordance with table I. Numbers are based on the number of eighths of an inch included in the nominal diameter of the bar.

TABLE I.—*Bar size designations*

Deformed bar designation number	Unit weight, pounds per foot	Round sections—Nominal dimensions		
		Diameter, inches	Cross-sectional area, square inches	Perimeter, inches
*2	0. 167	0. 250	0. 05	0. 786
3	. 376	. 375	. 11	1. 178
4	. 668	. 500	. 20	1. 571
5	1. 043	. 625	. 31	1. 963
6	1. 502	. 750	. 44	2. 356
7	2. 044	. 875	. 60	2. 749
8	2. 670	1. 000	. 79	3. 142
**9	3. 400	1. 128	1. 00	3. 544
**10	4. 303	1. 270	1. 27	3. 990
**11	5. 313	1. 410	1. 56	4. 430

*Bar No. 2 in plain rounds only.
**Bars of designation No. 9, 10, and 11 correspond to the former 1-inch, 1⅛-inch and 1¼-inch square sizes and are equivalent to those former standard bar sizes in weight and nominal cross-sectional areas.

STRUCTURAL STEEL AND ALUMINUM CONSTRUCTION	The following symbols are for use **on drawings** involving structural steel or aluminum construction. When both aluminum **and structural steel** shapes occur on the same drawing, add suffix "AL" to all aluminum shape designations; for example 8 ⌴ 6.67 AL

Description		Symbol	Illustrated use
GENERAL	Gage	g	g = 3½
	Pitch of rivets	P	P = 2½
	Milled face	MILL	MILL ‖
			(continued)

Description	Symbol	Illustrated use
LIST OF SINGLE STRUCTURAL SHAPES		
Wide flange shape	WF	24 WF 76
Beams		
American standard	I	15 I 42.9
Light beams and joists	B	6 B 12
Standard mill	M	8 M 17
Junior	Jr	7 Jr 5.5
Light columns	M	8 X 8 M 34.3
Channels*		
American standard	⌴	9 ⌴ 13.4
Car and ship	⌴	12 X 4 ⌴ 44.5
Junior	Jr ⌴	10 Jr ⌴ 8.4
Angles*		
Equal leg	L	L 3 X 3 X $\frac{1}{4}$
Unequal leg	L	L 7 X 4 X $\frac{1}{2}$
Bulb	BULB L	BULB L 6 X 3 $\frac{1}{2}$ X 17.4
Serrated (cut from channel)**	⅄	⅄ (3+1) ⌴ 4.1
Tees		
Structural, cut from rolled shapes	ST	ST 5 WF 10.5 ST 6 I 20.4 ST 6 B 9.5 ST 6 Jr 5.90
Rolled (flange by stem)	T	T 4 X 3 X 9.2
Built up	T̅	T̅ BAR 3 X $\frac{1}{2}$ BAR 4 X $\frac{1}{4}$
Serrated (cut from beam)**	⅄	⅄ (4+1) WF 10
Bearing pile	BP	14 BP 73
Zee	Z	Z 6 X 3 $\frac{1}{2}$ X 15.7
Plate	Pl	Pl 18 X $\frac{1}{2}$ X 2-6"
Plate (alternative use)	Pl	10.2 # Pl
Floor plate, raised pattern	Fl Pl	Fl Pl $\frac{1}{2}$
Flat bar	Bar	Bar 2 $\frac{1}{2}$ X $\frac{1}{4}$
Tie rod	TR	$\frac{3}{4}$ $^\phi$ TR
Pipe column	O	O 6 $^\phi$

*Symbols for channels and angles may be oriented to agree with the position of the member being designated.

**In example given under illustrated use, the sum of the figures within the parentheses is the depth of the stem, the first figure being one-half the depth of the cut shape and the second being one-half the depth of serration.

(continued)

COMBINATIONS OF STRUCTURAL SHAPES. Except for those shapes for which the symbol is a letter or letters, symbols for single structural shapes may be combined to indicate the composition of a built up member. For instance a double-angle strut may be represented thus ⌐⌐; and a channel and angle section may be represented by ⌐⌐. Where a combination includes a shape the symbol for which is a letter or letters, a line representation of the shape may be used, as for instance in the case of a wide flange beam and a channel, the representation may be thus ⊥. The representation in each case may be accompanied by the sizes of the shapes, involved, thus ⊥ 24 W 100 / 2 PL 14 X 3/4.

RIVETING SYMBOLS

Description	Plan	Symbol	Section
Shop rivets			
Two full heads			
Countersunk & chipped NS			
Countersunk & chipped FS			
Countersunk & chipped BS			
Countersunk, not over ⅛ inch high NS			
Countersunk, not over ⅛ inch high FS			
Countersunk, not over ⅛ inch high BS			
Flattened to ¼ inch for ½ and ⅝ rivets NS			
Flattened to ¼ inch for ½ and ⅝ rivets FS			
Flattened to ¼ inch for ½ and ⅝ rivets BS			
Flattened to ⅜ inch for ¾ and over rivets NS			
Flattened to ⅜ inch for ¾ and over rivets FS			
Flattened to ⅜ inch for ¾ and over rivets BS			
Field rivets			
Two full heads			
Countersunk NS			
Countersunk FS			
Countersunk BS			

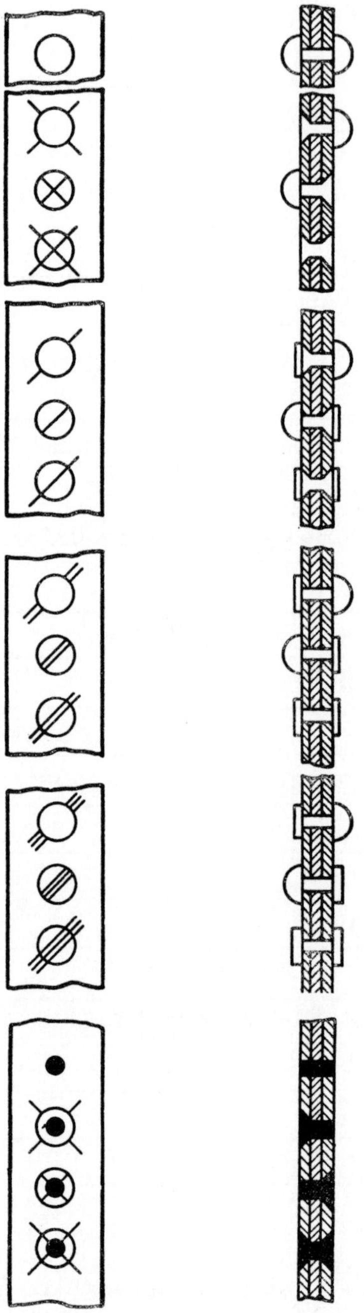

<table>
<tr><td rowspan="4">TIMBER
CONSTRUCTION</td><td colspan="2">The following symbols are for use on drawings

involving timber construction.</td></tr>
</table>

GENERAL

Description	Symbol	Illustrated use
Horizontal shearing stress	H	H=120 PSI
Compressive stress perpendicular to grain	c⊥	c⊥=455 PSI
Compressive stress parallel to grain	c	c=1450 PSI
Stress in extreme fibre for bending	f	f=1450 PSI
Tensile stress parallel to grain	t	t=1450 PSI

TIMBER CONNECTORS

Description	Symbol	Illustrated use
Split ring	SR	$2\frac{1}{2}$ SR
Toothed ring	TR	2 TR
Claw plate; male	CPM	$2\frac{5}{8}$ CPM
Claw plate; female	CPF	$3\frac{1}{8}$ CPF
Shear plate	SP	4 SP
Bulldog; round	BR	$3\frac{3}{4}$ BR
Bulldog; square	BS	5 BS
Circular spike	CS	$3\frac{1}{8}$ CS
Clamping plate; plain	CPP	5X5 CPP
Clamping plate; flanged	CPFL	5X8 CPFL
Spike grid; flat	SGF	$4\frac{1}{8}$ X $4\frac{1}{8}$ SGF
Spike grid; single curve	SGSC	$4\frac{1}{8}$ X $4\frac{1}{8}$ SGSC
Spike grid; double curve	SGDC	$4\frac{1}{8}$ X $4\frac{1}{8}$ SGDC

IDENTIFICATION OF TIMBERS FOR SPECIAL GRADING

	Symbol

Joists and planks or beams and stringer grades
    Beams, continuous over 2 spans
    Beams, continuous over 3 or more spans
	M
	N

Members in tension, or in compression parallel to grain, or in combined compression and bending	T
Post and timber grades Special size members not conforming to standard post and timber classification sizes	P

Reproduced from the "Extrusion Die List Manual" through the courtesy of the Reynolds Metal Company, Richmond, Va. The "Extrusion Die List Manual" has been compiled from various sections of Reynolds Aluminum Mill Products Catalog in order to provide a single publication, a complete reference. Illustrated here are only the basic shapes; complete technical data and other special extrusions may be found in the above-mentioned manual.

ALUMINUM STRUCTURALS

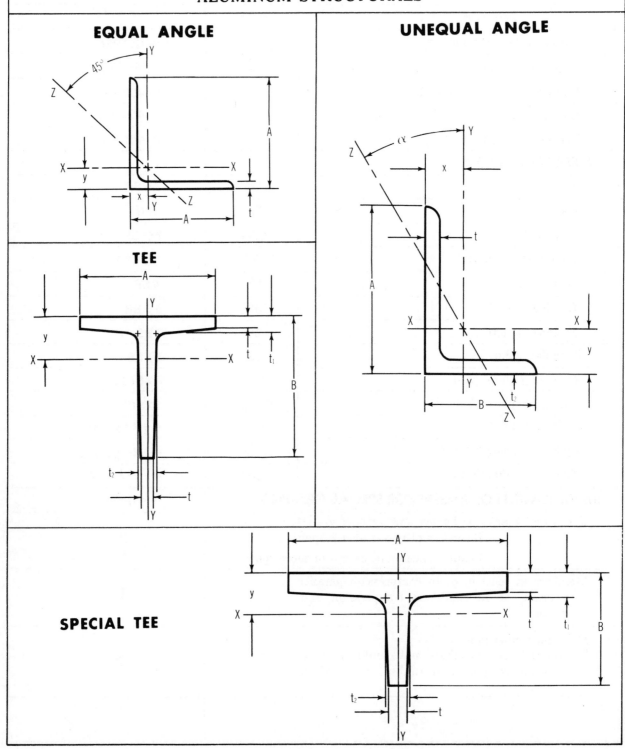

EQUAL ANGLE

UNEQUAL ANGLE

TEE

SPECIAL TEE

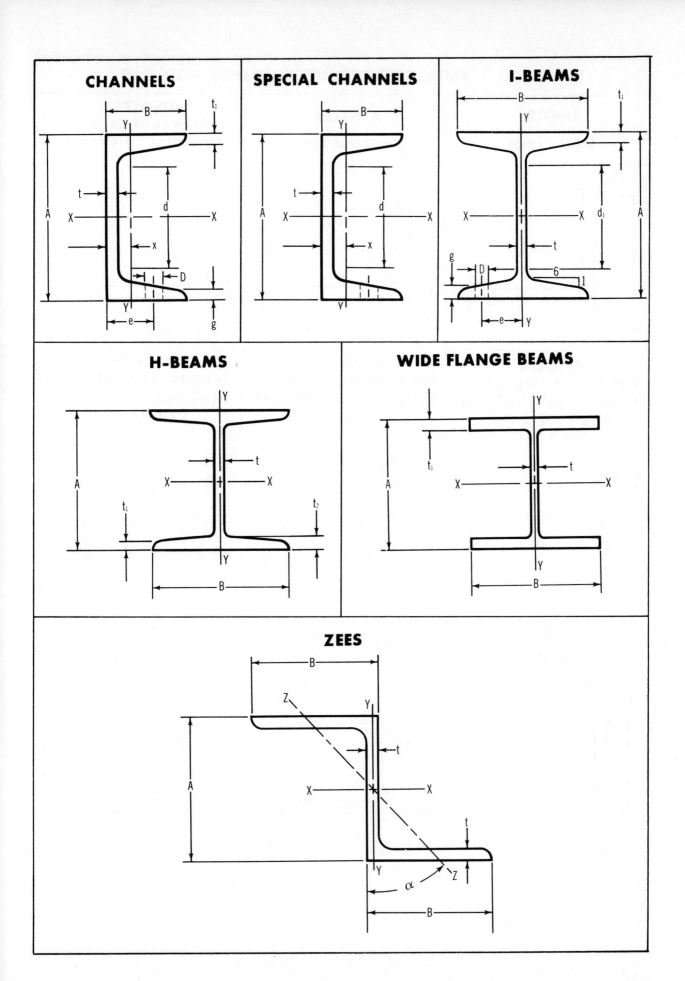

305

ANGLES
Equal Legs

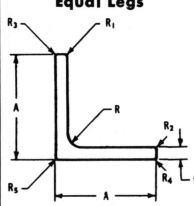

ANGLES
Unequal Legs

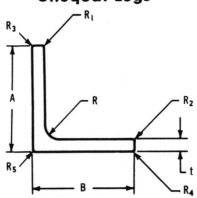

ANGLES
Unequal Legs, Unequal Thickness

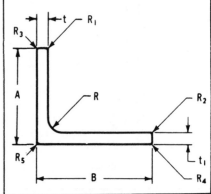

ANGLES
Equal and Unequal Legs, Equal Thickness Angles Greater Than 90°

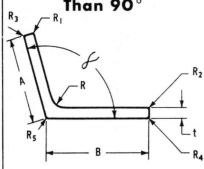

ANGLES
Unequal Legs, Unequal Thickness Angles Less Than 90°

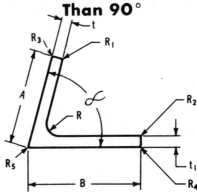

ANGLES
Unequal Legs, Unequal Thickness   Angles Greater Than 90°

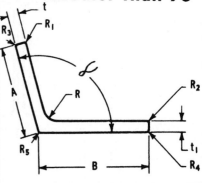

ANGLES
Bulb

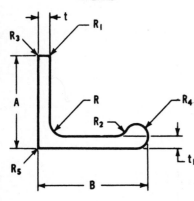

CHANNELS

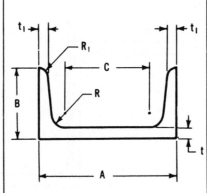

CHANNELS
Equal Thickness

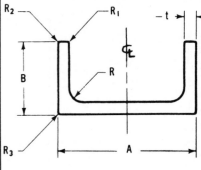

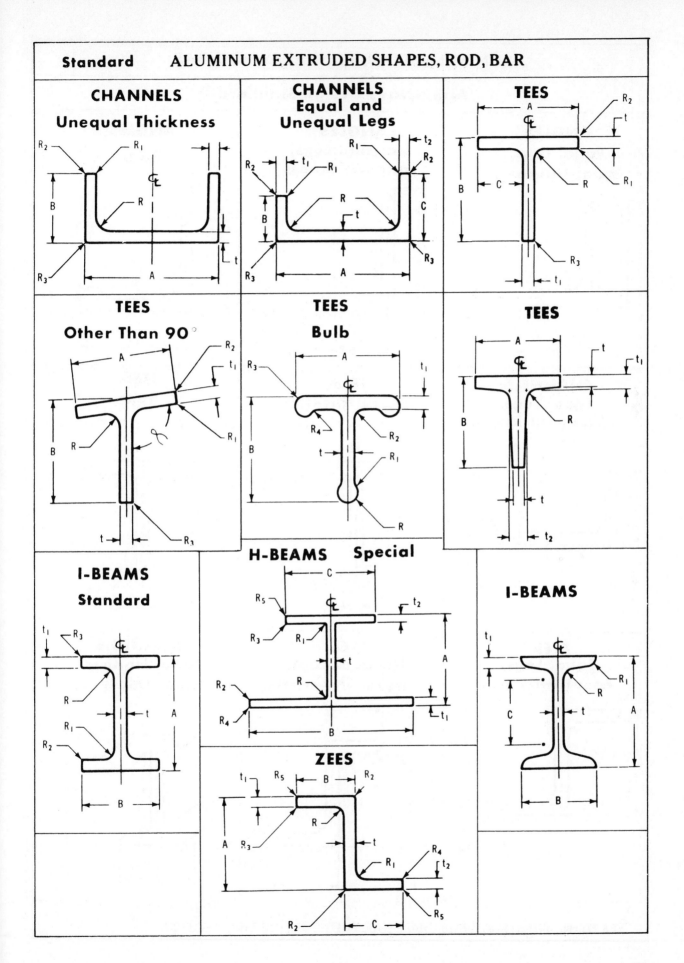

ALUMINUM EXTRUDED SHAPES, ROD, BAR

Army-Navy Design Standard [x]

ANGLES
**Equal Legs,
Equal Thickness**

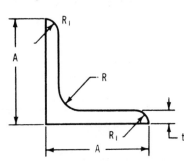

ANGLES
**Unequal Legs,
Equal Thickness**

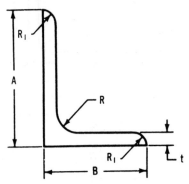

ANGLES
Bulb

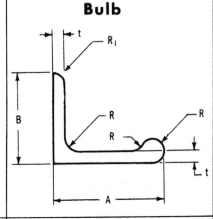

CHANNELS
**Equal Legs,
Equal Thickness**

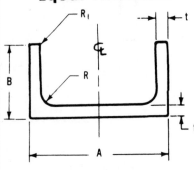

TEES
Equal Thickness

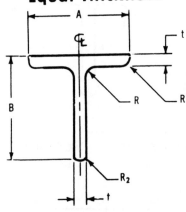

TEES
Bulb

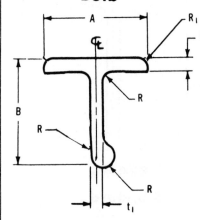

ZEES
**Equal Legs,
Equal Thickness**

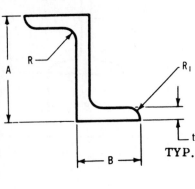

ZEES
**Unequal Legs,
Equal Thickness**

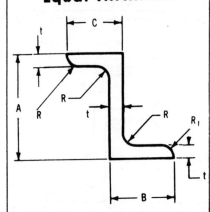

I-SECTION
**Equal Flanges,
Equal Thickness**

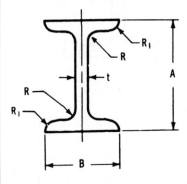

[x]SEE STANDARD STRUCTURAL SHAPES AT THE START OF THIS SECTION

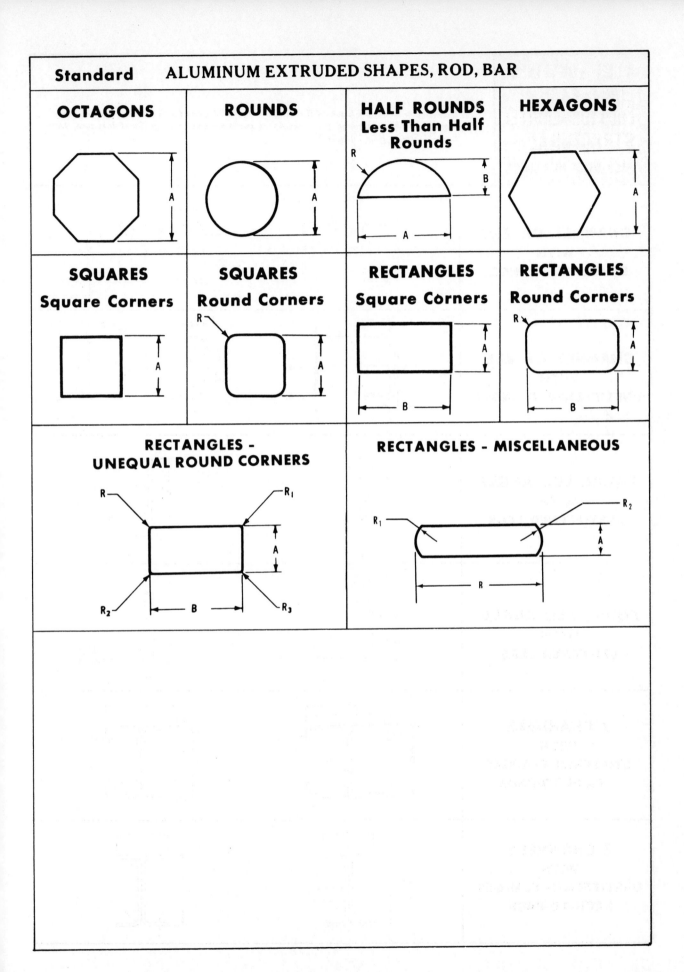

Standard   ALUMINUM EXTRUDED SHAPES, ROD, BAR

OCTAGONS

ROUNDS

HALF ROUNDS
Less Than Half Rounds

HEXAGONS

SQUARES
Square Corners

SQUARES
Round Corners

RECTANGLES
Square Corners

RECTANGLES
Round Corners

RECTANGLES - UNEQUAL ROUND CORNERS

RECTANGLES - MISCELLANEOUS

Extracted from 1962 edition of the "Light Gage Cold-formed Steel Design Manual," and reproduced herein through the courtesy of the American Iron and Steel Institute, 150 East 42 Street, New York, N.Y.

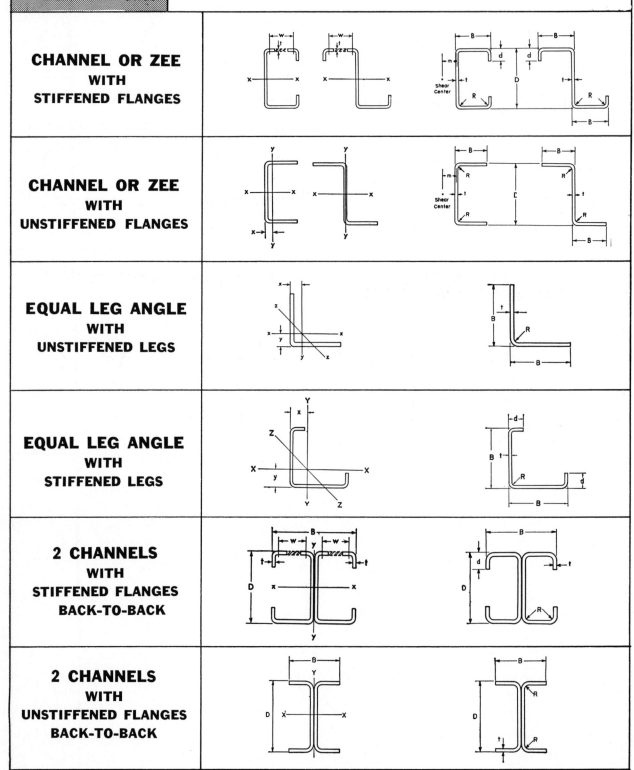

CHANNEL OR ZEE **WITH** **STIFFENED FLANGES**	
CHANNEL OR ZEE **WITH** **UNSTIFFENED FLANGES**	
EQUAL LEG ANGLE **WITH** **UNSTIFFENED LEGS**	
EQUAL LEG ANGLE **WITH** **STIFFENED LEGS**	
2 CHANNELS **WITH** **STIFFENED FLANGES** **BACK-TO-BACK**	
2 CHANNELS **WITH** **UNSTIFFENED FLANGES** **BACK-TO-BACK**	

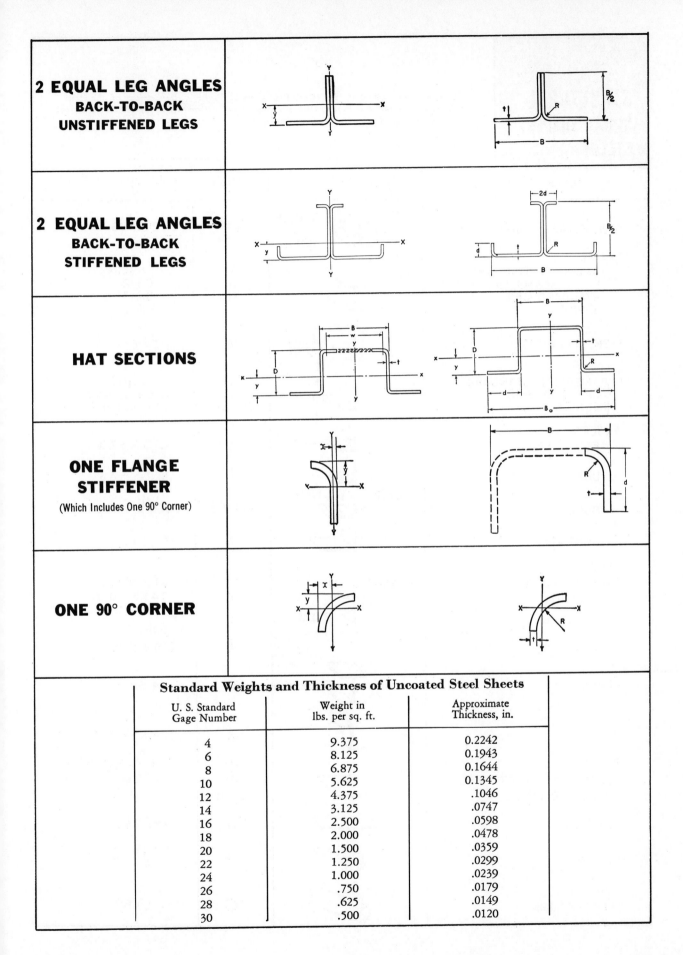

	2 EQUAL LEG ANGLES BACK-TO-BACK UNSTIFFENED LEGS	
2 EQUAL LEG ANGLES BACK-TO-BACK STIFFENED LEGS		
HAT SECTIONS		
ONE FLANGE STIFFENER (Which Includes One 90° Corner)		
ONE 90° CORNER		

Standard Weights and Thickness of Uncoated Steel Sheets

U. S. Standard Gage Number	Weight in lbs. per sq. ft.	Approximate Thickness, in.
4	9.375	0.2242
6	8.125	0.1943
8	6.875	0.1644
10	5.625	0.1345
12	4.375	.1046
14	3.125	.0747
16	2.500	.0598
18	2.000	.0478
20	1.500	.0359
22	1.250	.0299
24	1.000	.0239
26	.750	.0179
28	.625	.0149
30	.500	.0120

STRUCTURAL
(SINGLE SHAPES, STEEL)

Extracted from TM5-230; TO 00-25-103, General Drafting, Department of the Army, Department of the Air Force, with the permission of the Office of the Secretary of Defense, Public Affairs Department, Washington.

DESCRIPTION	PICTORIAL	SYMBOL	ILLUSTRATED USE
WIDE FLANGE SHAPE	FLANGE / WEB	WF	24 WF 76
BEAMS			
AMERICAN STANDARD		I	15 I 42.9
LIGHT BEAMS AND JOISTS		B	6 B 12
STANDARD MILL		M	8 M 17
JUNIOR		Jr	7 Jr 5.5
LIGHT COLUMNS	NOMINAL DEPTH	M	8 X 8M 34.3
CHANNELS			
AMERICAN STANDARD		⌐	9 ⌐ 13.4
CAR AND SHIP	DEPTH	⌐	12 X 4 ⌐ 44.5
JUNIOR		Jr ⌐	10 Jr ⌐ 8.4
ANGLES			
EQUAL LEG	LEG	L	L 3 X 3 X $\frac{1}{4}$
UNEQUAL LEG		L	L 7 X 4 X $\frac{1}{2}$
BULB	FLANGE / WEB	BULB L	BULB L 6 X $3\frac{1}{2}$ X 17.4
SERRATED		⅄	⅄ (3+1) ⌐ 4.1
TEES			
STRUCTURAL	FLANGE	ST	ST 5 WF 10.5
ROLLED		T	T 4 X 3 X 9.2
BUILT UP	STEM	T	T BAR 3 X $\frac{1}{2}$ BAR 4 X $\frac{1}{4}$
SERRATED		⅄	⅄ (4+1) WF 10
BEARING PILE		BP	14 BP 73
ZEE		Z	Z 6 X $3\frac{1}{2}$ X 15.7
PLATE		Pl	Pl 18 X $\frac{1}{2}$ X 2'-6"
PLATE (ALTERNATE USE)		Pl	10.2 # Pl
CHECKERED PLATE		CK Pl	CK Pl $\frac{1}{2}$
FLAT BAR		Bar	Bar $2\frac{1}{2}$ X $\frac{1}{4}$
TIE ROD		TR	$\frac{3}{4}$ ϕ TR
PIPE COLUMN		○	○ 6 ϕ

Extracted from American Standard Drafting Practices, Mechanical Assemblies (ASA Y14.14-1961), with the permission of the publisher, the American Society of Mechanical Engineers, United Engineering Center 345 East 47 Street, New York, N.Y.

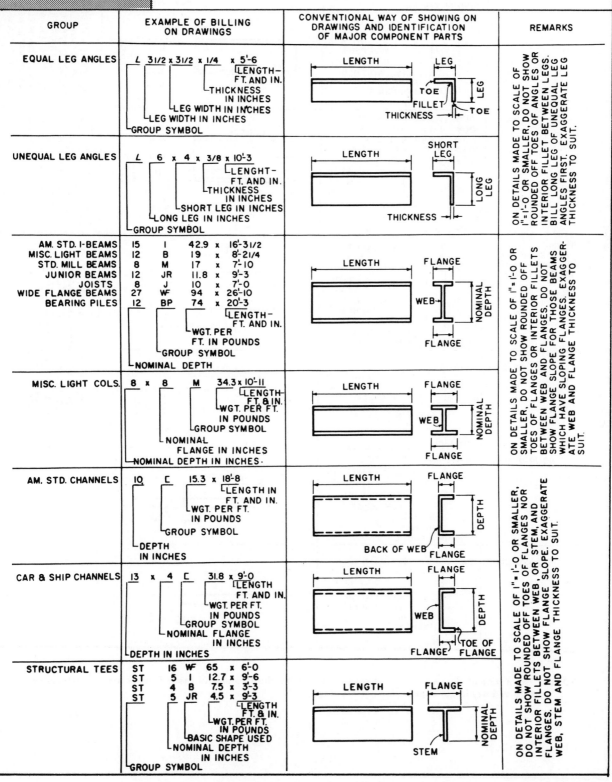

GROUP	EXAMPLE OF BILLING ON DRAWINGS	CONVENTIONAL WAY OF SHOWING ON DRAWINGS AND IDENTIFICATION OF MAJOR COMPONENT PARTS	REMARKS
EQUAL LEG ANGLES	L 31/2 x 31/2 x 1/4 x 5'-6 — LENGTH—FT. AND IN.; THICKNESS IN INCHES; LEG WIDTH IN INCHES; LEG WIDTH IN INCHES; GROUP SYMBOL	LENGTH; LEG; TOE; LEG; FILLET; THICKNESS; TOE	ON DETAILS MADE TO SCALE OF 1"=1'-0 OR SMALLER, DO NOT SHOW ROUNDED OFF TOES OF ANGLES OR INTERIOR FILLET BETWEEN LEGS. BILL LONG LEG OF UNEQUAL LEG ANGLES FIRST. EXAGGERATE LEG THICKNESS TO SUIT.
UNEQUAL LEG ANGLES	L 6 x 4 x 3/8 x 10'-3 — LENGHT—FT. AND IN.; THICKNESS IN INCHES; SHORT LEG IN INCHES; LONG LEG IN INCHES; GROUP SYMBOL	LENGTH; SHORT LEG; LONG LEG; THICKNESS	
AM. STD. I-BEAMS; MISC. LIGHT BEAMS; STD. MILL BEAMS; JUNIOR BEAMS; JOISTS; WIDE FLANGE BEAMS; BEARING PILES	15 I 42.9 x 16'-31/2; 12 B 19 x 8'-21/4; 8 M 17 x 7'-10; 12 JR 11.8 x 9'-3; 8 J 10 x 7'-0; 27 WF 94 x 26'-10; 12 BP 74 x 20'-3 — LENGTH—FT. AND IN.; WGT. PER FT. IN POUNDS; GROUP SYMBOL; NOMINAL DEPTH	LENGTH; FLANGE; WEB; NOMINAL DEPTH; FLANGE	ON DETAILS MADE TO SCALE OF 1"=1'-0 OR SMALLER, DO NOT SHOW ROUNDED OFF TOES OF FLANGES OR INTERIOR FILLETS BETWEEN WEB AND FLANGES. DO NOT SHOW FLANGE SLOPE FOR THOSE BEAMS WHICH HAVE SLOPING FLANGES. EXAGGERATE WEB AND FLANGE THICKNESS TO SUIT.
MISC. LIGHT COLS.	8 x 8 M 34.3 x 10'-11 — LENGTH—FT. & IN.; WGT. PER FT. IN POUNDS; GROUP SYMBOL; NOMINAL FLANGE IN INCHES; NOMINAL DEPTH IN INCHES	LENGTH; FLANGE; WEB; NOMINAL DEPTH; FLANGE	
AM. STD. CHANNELS	10 C 15.3 x 18'-8 — LENGTH IN FT. AND IN.; WGT. PER FT. IN POUNDS; GROUP SYMBOL; DEPTH IN INCHES	LENGTH; FLANGE; DEPTH; BACK OF WEB; FLANGE	ON DETAILS MADE TO SCALE OF 1"=1'-0 OR SMALLER, DO NOT SHOW ROUNDED OFF TOES OF FLANGES NOR INTERIOR FILLETS BETWEEN WEB, OR STEM, AND FLANGES. DO NOT SHOW FLANGE SLOPE. EXAGGERATE WEB, STEM AND FLANGE THICKNESS TO SUIT.
CAR & SHIP CHANNELS	13 x 4 C 31.8 x 9'-0 — LENGTH FT. AND IN.; WGT. PER FT. IN POUNDS; GROUP SYMBOL; NOMINAL FLANGE IN INCHES; DEPTH IN INCHES	LENGTH; FLANGE; DEPTH; WEB; TOE OF FLANGE; FLANGE	
STRUCTURAL TEES	ST 16 WF 65 x 6'-0; ST 5 I 12.7 x 9'-6; ST 4 B 7.5 x 3'-3; ST 5 JR 4.5 x 9'-3 — LENGTH FT. & IN.; WGT. PER FT. IN POUNDS; BASIC SHAPE USED; NOMINAL DEPTH IN INCHES; GROUP SYMBOL	LENGTH; FLANGE; NOMINAL DEPTH; STEM	

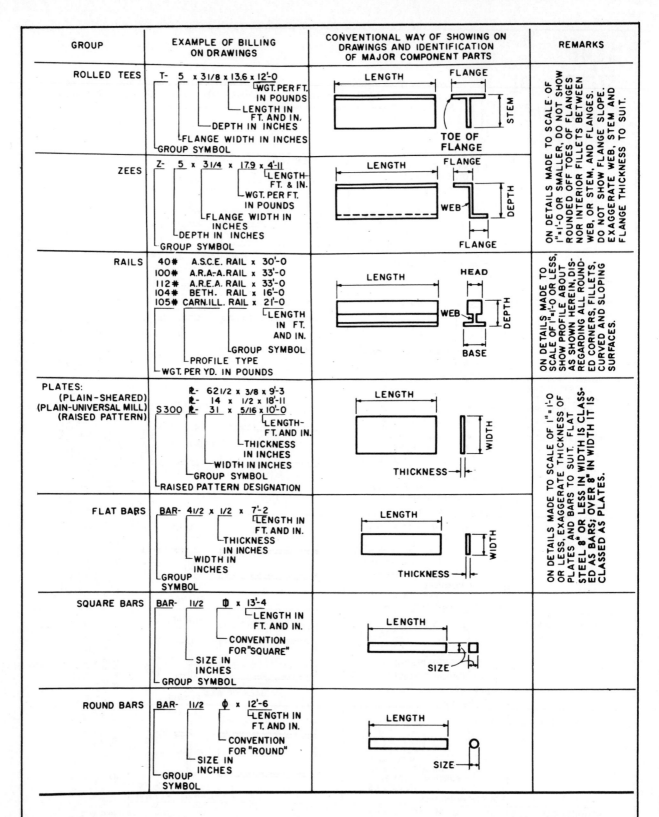

GROUP	EXAMPLE OF BILLING ON DRAWINGS	CONVENTIONAL WAY OF SHOWING ON DRAWINGS AND IDENTIFICATION OF MAJOR COMPONENT PARTS	REMARKS
ROLLED TEES	T- 5 x 31/8 x 13.6 x 12'-0	LENGTH / FLANGE / STEM / TOE OF FLANGE	ON DETAILS MADE TO SCALE OF 1"=1'-0 OR SMALLER, DO NOT SHOW ROUNDED OFF TOES OF FLANGES NOR INTERIOR FILLETS BETWEEN WEB, OR STEM, AND FLANGES. DO NOT SHOW FLANGE SLOPE. EXAGGERATE WEB, STEM AND FLANGE THICKNESS TO SUIT.
ZEES	Z- 5 x 31/4 x 17.9 x 4'-11	LENGTH / FLANGE / WEB / DEPTH / FLANGE	
RAILS	40# A.S.C.E. RAIL x 30'-0 / 100# A.R.A-A. RAIL x 33'-0 / 112# A.R.E.A. RAIL x 33'-0 / 104# BETH. RAIL x 16'-0 / 105# CARN.ILL. RAIL x 21'-0	LENGTH / HEAD / WEB / DEPTH / BASE	ON DETAILS MADE TO SCALE OF 1"=1'-0 OR LESS, SHOW PROFILE ABOUT AS SHOWN HEREIN, DISREGARDING ALL ROUNDED CORNERS, FILLETS, CURVED AND SLOPING SURFACES.
PLATES: (PLAIN-SHEARED) (PLAIN-UNIVERSAL MILL) (RAISED PATTERN)	℞- 621/2 x 3/8 x 9'-3 / ℞- 14 x 1/2 x 18'-11 / S300 ℞- 31 x 5/16 x 10'-0	LENGTH / WIDTH / THICKNESS	ON DETAILS MADE TO SCALE OF 1"=1'-0 OR LESS, EXAGGERATE THICKNESS OF PLATES AND BARS TO SUIT. FLAT STEEL 8" OR LESS IN WIDTH IS CLASSED AS BARS; OVER 8" IN WIDTH IT IS CLASSED AS PLATES.
FLAT BARS	BAR- 41/2 x 1/2 x 7'-2	LENGTH / WIDTH / THICKNESS	
SQUARE BARS	BAR- 11/2 ◻ x 13'-4	LENGTH / SIZE	
ROUND BARS	BAR- 11/2 φ x 12'-6	LENGTH / SIZE	

NOTE: The names of the parts of the shapes shown in the third column of these figures are for instruction only and would not appear on most drawings.

HEAT – POWER – HEATING – VENTILATING – AIR CONDITIONING SYMBOLS

All MIL-STD-17, extracted from MIL-STD-17-1950, Mechanical Symbols, through the courtesy of the Office of the Secretary of Defense, Public Affairs Department, Washington. MIL-STD 17A symbols will be found in this section and in the Heating, Ventilating, and Air Conditioning section of this book. MIL-STD-17-1950, included in this and other sections, is for reference only. MIL-STD-17A-1961 is coincidental with American Standards Association and the American Society of Mechanical Engineers:

   ASA Z32.2.3-1953: Graphical Symbols for Pipe Fittings, Valves and Piping (p. 234)
   ASA Y32.4-1955:   Graphical Symbols for Plumbing (p. 330)
   ASA Z32.2.4-1954: Graphical Symbols for Heating, Ventilating and Air Conditioning (p. 322)
   ASA Z32.2.6-1956: Graphical Symbols for Heat Power Apparatus (p. 320)
   ASA Y32.10-1958:   Graphical Symbols for Fluid Power Diagrams (p. 208)

These standards are extracted with the permission of the American Society of Mechanical Engineers.

Extracted from TEMA Standards, 4th ed., 1959, Nomenclature of Heat Exchanger Components, reproduced herein from the standards, with the permission of the publisher, the Tubular Exchanger Manufacturers Association, 53 Park Place, New York, N.Y.

FIGURE N-1

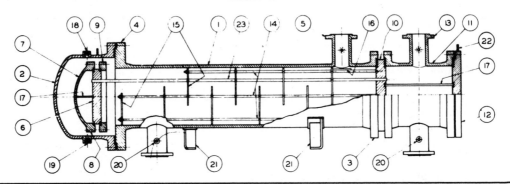

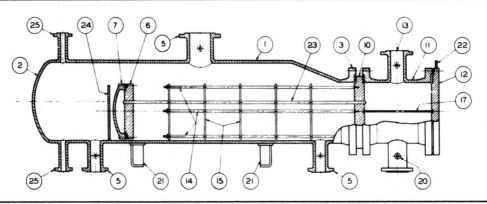

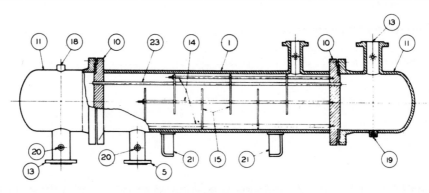

TABLE N-1

1. Shell	10. Stationary Tubesheet	19. Drain Connection
2. Shell Cover	11. Channel or Stationary Head	20. Instrument Connection
3. Shell Flange Channel End	12. Channel Cover	21. Support Saddles
4. Shell Flange Cover End	13. Channel Nozzle	22. Lifting Lugs
5. Shell Nozzle	14. Tie Rods and Spacers	23. Tubes
6. Floating Tubesheet	15. Transverse Baffles or Support Plates	24. Weir
7. Floating Head Cover	16. Impingement Baffle	25. Liquid Level Connection
8. Floating Head Flange	17. Pass Partition	
9. Floating Head Backing Device	18. Vent Connection	

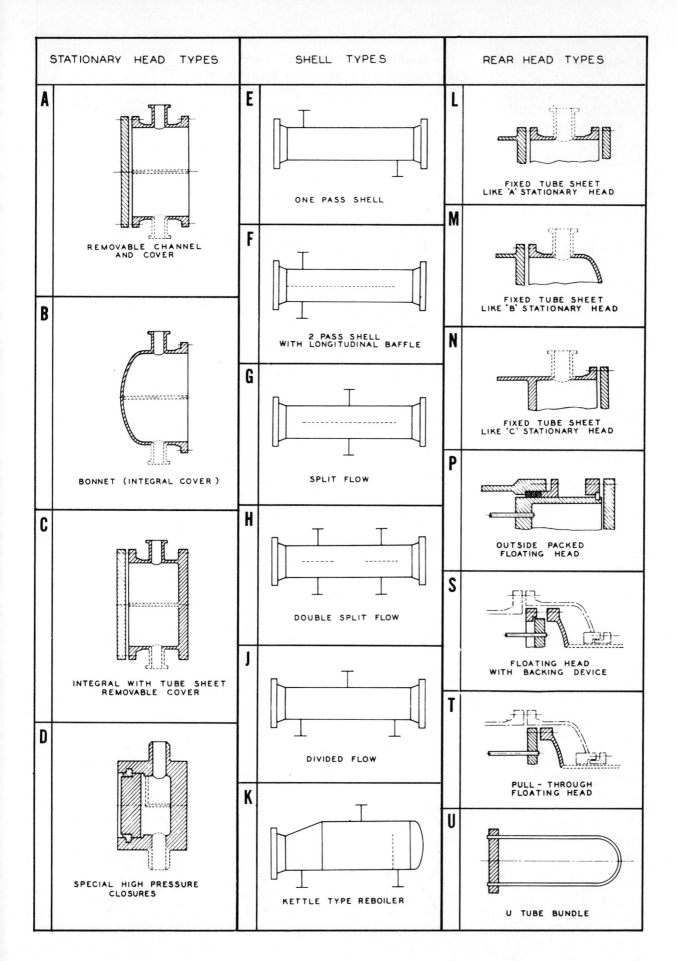

STATIONARY HEAD TYPES	SHELL TYPES	REAR HEAD TYPES

A — REMOVABLE CHANNEL AND COVER

B — BONNET (INTEGRAL COVER)

C — INTEGRAL WITH TUBE SHEET REMOVABLE COVER

D — SPECIAL HIGH PRESSURE CLOSURES

E — ONE PASS SHELL

F — 2 PASS SHELL WITH LONGITUDINAL BAFFLE

G — SPLIT FLOW

H — DOUBLE SPLIT FLOW

J — DIVIDED FLOW

K — KETTLE TYPE REBOILER

L — FIXED TUBE SHEET LIKE 'A' STATIONARY HEAD

M — FIXED TUBE SHEET LIKE 'B' STATIONARY HEAD

N — FIXED TUBE SHEET LIKE 'C' STATIONARY HEAD

P — OUTSIDE PACKED FLOATING HEAD

S — FLOATING HEAD WITH BACKING DEVICE

T — PULL-THROUGH FLOATING HEAD

U — U TUBE BUNDLE

HEAT POWER APPARATUS

Combination of symbols. Symbols for prime movers and pumps have been itemized below as separate symbols. Where it is desired to indicate the motive power of a pump these symbols may be used in combination as illustrated

Motor driven rotary pump

Designation of service. The service of a pump shall be indicated by a brief title under the symbol as illustrated below. Fuel oil service pump Boiler feed pump	Equipment symbols	Air ejector (dynamic pump)	Blower
Blower, soot	Boiler, steam generator (with economizer)	Clutch, all types	Combustion chamber, gas turbine
Compressor, axial flow, air or gas	Compressor, reciprocating	Compressor, rotary, roots blower vane type	Desuperheater
Engine, diesel DE	gas GE	steam SE	Evaporator, single effect
Evaporator, double effect	Evaporator, triple effect		Gear train, all types
Heat interchanger (gas to liquid or liquid to liquid)	Heat interchanger (gas to gas)	Heater, feed, with air outlet	Heater, feed, open or direct contact

Heater, feed (deaerator) with surge tank	Motor	Precipitator: E—Electrostatic M—Mechanical W—Wet	Pump, centrifugal
Pump, hand	Pump, reciprocating	Pump, rotary and screw	Purifier, centrifugal
Separator, oil	Separator, steam	Superheater, intermediate (flue gas reheater)	Superheater or reheater, live steam
Tank, closed	Tank, open	Turbine, bleeder	Turbine, condensing
Turbine, gas	Turbine, steam		

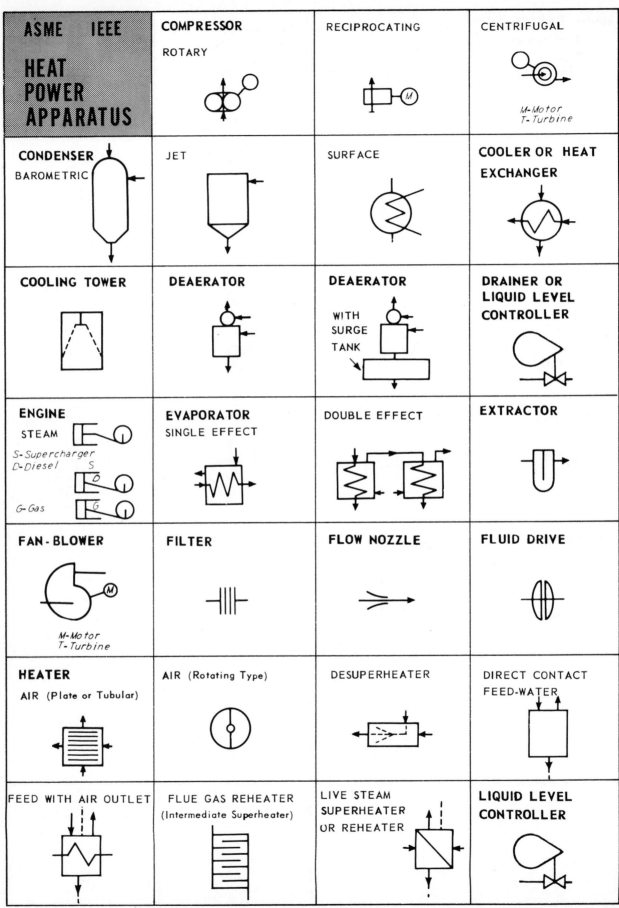

ASME IEEE **HEAT POWER APPARATUS**	**COMPRESSOR** ROTARY	RECIPROCATING	CENTRIFUGAL M-Motor T-Turbine
CONDENSER BAROMETRIC	JET	SURFACE	**COOLER OR HEAT EXCHANGER**
COOLING TOWER	**DEAERATOR**	**DEAERATOR** WITH SURGE TANK	**DRAINER OR LIQUID LEVEL CONTROLLER**
ENGINE STEAM S-Supercharger D-Diesel S G-Gas	**EVAPORATOR** SINGLE EFFECT	DOUBLE EFFECT	**EXTRACTOR**
FAN - BLOWER M-Motor T-Turbine	**FILTER**	**FLOW NOZZLE**	**FLUID DRIVE**
HEATER AIR (Plate or Tubular)	AIR (Rotating Type)	DESUPERHEATER	DIRECT CONTACT FEED-WATER
FEED WITH AIR OUTLET	FLUE GAS REHEATER (Intermediate Superheater)	LIVE STEAM SUPERHEATER OR REHEATER	**LIQUID LEVEL CONTROLLER**

Extracted from American Standard Graphical Symbols for Heat Power Apparatus (ASA Z32.2.6-1950), with the permission of the publisher, the American Society of Mechanical Engineers, United Engineering Center, 345 East 47 Street, New York, N.Y.

ORIFICE	PRECIPITATOR	PUMP	Letters Denote Service
	E-Electrostatic M-Mechanical W-Wet 	CENTRIFUGAL AND ROTARY 	F- Boiler Feed S- Service D- Condensate C- Circ. Water V- Air O- Oil
Letters Denote Service M- Motor T- Turbine E- Steam Engine G- Gas Engine D- Diesel Engine	RECIPROCATING 	DYNAMIC (Air Ejector or Eductor) 	**SEPARATOR**
STEAM GENERATOR (Boiler with Economizer) 	**STEAM TRAP** 	**STRAINER** SINGLE 	DOUBLE
TANK CLOSED 	OPEN 	FLASH OR PRESSURE 	**TURBINE** CONDENSING
STEAM TURBINE OR AXIAL COMPRESSOR 	**VENTURI TUBE** 		

ASME IEEE HEATING	AIR ELIMINATOR	ANCHOR	EXPANSION JOINT
HANGER OR SUPPORT	**HEAT EXCHANGER**	**HEAT TRANSFER SURFACE, PLAN (INDICATE TYPE SUCH AS CONVECTOR)**	**PUMP (INDICATE TYPE SUCH AS VACUUM)**
STRAINER	**TANK (DESIGNATE TYPE)**	**THERMOMETER**	**THERMOSTAT**
TRAPS BOILER RETURN	BLAST THERMOSTATIC	FLOAT	FLOAT AND THERMOSTATIC
THERMOSTATIC	**UNIT HEATER (CENTRIFUGAL FAN), PLAN**	**UNIT HEATER (PROPELLER), PLAN**	**UNIT VENTILATOR, PLAN**
VALVES CHECK	DIAPHRAGM	GATE / GLOBE	LOCK AND SHIELD
MOTOR OPERATED	REDUCING PRESSURE	RELIEF (EITHER PRESSURE OR VACUUM)	**VENT POINT**

Extracted from American Standard Graphical Symbols for Heating, Ventilating and Air Conditioning (ASA Z32.2.4-1953), with the permission of the publisher, the American Society of Mechanical Engineers, United Engineering Center, 345 East 47 Street, New York, N.Y.

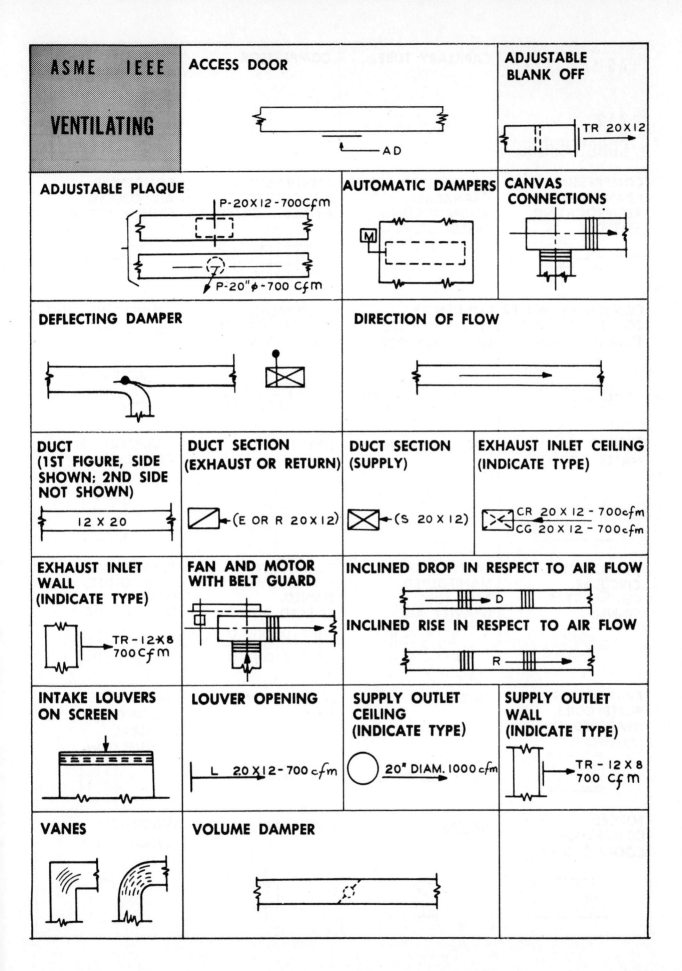

ASME   IEEE

VENTILATING

ACCESS DOOR

AD

ADJUSTABLE BLANK OFF

TR 20X12

ADJUSTABLE PLAQUE

P-20X12-700Cfm

P-20"φ-700 Cfm

AUTOMATIC DAMPERS

M

CANVAS CONNECTIONS

DEFLECTING DAMPER

DIRECTION OF FLOW

DUCT (1ST FIGURE, SIDE SHOWN; 2ND SIDE NOT SHOWN)

12 X 20

DUCT SECTION (EXHAUST OR RETURN)

(E OR R 20X12)

DUCT SECTION (SUPPLY)

(S 20X12)

EXHAUST INLET CEILING (INDICATE TYPE)

CR 20X12-700cfm

CG 20X12-700cfm

EXHAUST INLET WALL (INDICATE TYPE)

TR-12X8 700Cfm

FAN AND MOTOR WITH BELT GUARD

INCLINED DROP IN RESPECT TO AIR FLOW

D

INCLINED RISE IN RESPECT TO AIR FLOW

R

INTAKE LOUVERS ON SCREEN

LOUVER OPENING

L 20X12-700cfm

SUPPLY OUTLET CEILING (INDICATE TYPE)

20" DIAM. 1000cfm

SUPPLY OUTLET WALL (INDICATE TYPE)

TR-12X8 700 Cfm

VANES

VOLUME DAMPER

ASME IEEE AIR CONDITIONING	CAPILLARY TUBE	COMPRESSOR	COMPRESSOR, ENCLOSED, CRANK-CASE, ROTARY, BELTED
COMPRESSOR, OPEN CRANKCASE, RECIPROCATING, BELTED	COMPRESSOR, OPEN CRANKCASE, RECIPROCATING, DIRECT DRIVE	CONDENSER, AIR COOLED, FINNED, FORCED AIR	CONDENSER, AIR COOLED, FINNED, STATIC
CONDENSER, WATER COOLED, CONCENTRIC TUBE IN A TUBE	CONDENSER, WATER COOLED, SHELL AND COIL	CONDENSER, WATER COOLED, SHELL AND TUBE	CONDENSING UNIT, AIR COOLED
CONDENSING UNIT, WATER COOLED	COOLING TOWER	DRYER	EVAPORATIVE CONDENSER
EVAPORATOR, CIRCULAR, CEILING TYPE, FINNED	EVAPORATOR, MANIFOLDED, BARE TUBE, GRAVITY AIR	EVAPORATOR, MANIFOLDED, FINNED, FORCED AIR	EVAPORATOR, MANIFOLDED, FINNED, GRAVITY AIR
EVAPORATOR, PLATE COILS, HEADERED OR MANIFOLD	FILTER, LINE	FILTER & STRAINER, LINE	FINNED TYPE COOLING UNIT, NATURAL CONVECTION
FORCED CONVECTION COOLING UNIT	GAUGE	HIGH SIDE FLOAT	IMMERSION COOLING UNIT

LOW SIDE FLOAT	MOTOR-COMPRESSOR, ENCLOSEDCRANKCASE, RECIPROCATING, DIRECT CONNECTED	MOTOR-COMPRESSOR, ENCLOSED CRANKCASE, ROTARY, DIRECT CONNECTED	MOTOR-COMPRESSOR, SEALED CRANKCASE, RECIPROCATING
MOTOR-COMPRESSOR, SEALED CRANKCASE, ROTARY	PRESSURESTAT	PRESSURE SWITCH	PRESSURE SWITCH WITH HIGH PRESSURE CUT-OUT
RECEIVER, HORIZONTAL	RECEIVER, VERTICAL	SCALE TRAP	SPRAY POND
THERMAL BULB	THERMOSTAT (REMOTE BULB)	VALVES AUTOMATIC EXPANSION	COMPRESSOR SUCTION PRESSURE LIMITING, THROTTLING TYPE (COMPRESSOR SIDE)
CONSTANT PRESSURE, SUCTION	EVAPORATOR PRESSURE REGULATING, SNAP ACTION	EVAPORATOR PRESSURE REGULATING, THERMOSTATIC THROTTLING TYPE	EVAPORATOR PRESSURE REGULATING, THROTTLING TYPE (EVAPORATOR SIDE)
HAND EXPANSION	MAGNETIC STOP	SNAP ACTION	SUCTION VAPOR REGULATING
THERMO SUCTION	THERMOSTATIC EXPANSION	WATER	VIBRATION ABSORBER, LINE

MIL-STD 17 HEATING, VENTILATING & AIR CONDITIONING EQUIPMENT	**General.** The following symbols shall be used where graphic representation of heating, ventilating, and air conditioning equipment is desired.		**see...** symbol representation of ductwork used in conjunction with these symbols 327-29
Equipment symbols for general use	Cooler, unit, centrifugal fan (self contained or otherwise)	Cooler, unit, propeller type	Heat transfer surface (all types)
Heater, convection	Heater, unit, centrifugal fan	Heater, unit, propeller type	Heater and cooler, unit, combined, propeller type
Radiator, floor	Radiator, wall	Ventilator, cowl: round oval	Ventilator, gooseneck
Ventilator, rain and spray proof	Ventilator, standard roof	Ventilator, unit	Ventilator, waterproof, bucket type
Equipment symbols for use with single line representation of ducting	Cooling coil, duct type / Cooling coil, gravity type	Fan, axial, free inlet or discharge	Fan, axial, in duct
Fan, axial, with preheater free inlet	Fan, centrifugal	Fan, propeller	Heater, duct type

326

General. The following symbols shall be used for graphic representation of ductwork. Symbols have been grouped under the two headings, symbols for general use, and ... symbols for single line representation of ducting. The method of representation shall be optional with the bureau or service concerned. Dimensions and capacity following certain symbols are descriptive of size and capacity of the equipment. The vertical dimension of the equipment should be given first, followed by the horizontal dimension.

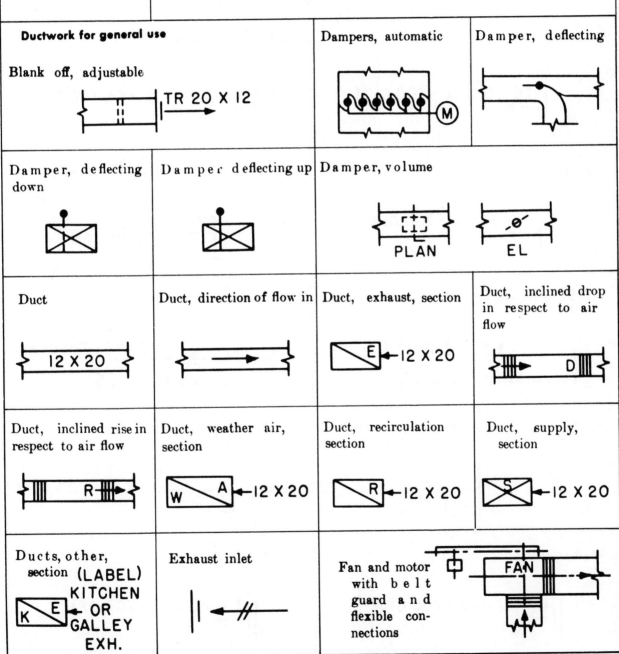

Ductwork for general use

Blank off, adjustable

TR 20 X 12

Dampers, automatic

Damper, deflecting

Damper, deflecting down

Damper deflecting up

Damper, volume

PLAN   EL

Duct

12 X 20

Duct, direction of flow in

Duct, exhaust, section

E ← 12 X 20

Duct, inclined drop in respect to air flow

D

Duct, inclined rise in respect to air flow

R

Duct, weather air, section

W   A ← 12 X 20

Duct, recirculation section

R ← 12 X 20

Duct, supply, section

S ← 12 X 20

Ducts, other, section (LABEL) KITCHEN OR GALLEY EXH.

K   E ←

Exhaust inlet

Fan and motor with belt guard and flexible connections

FAN

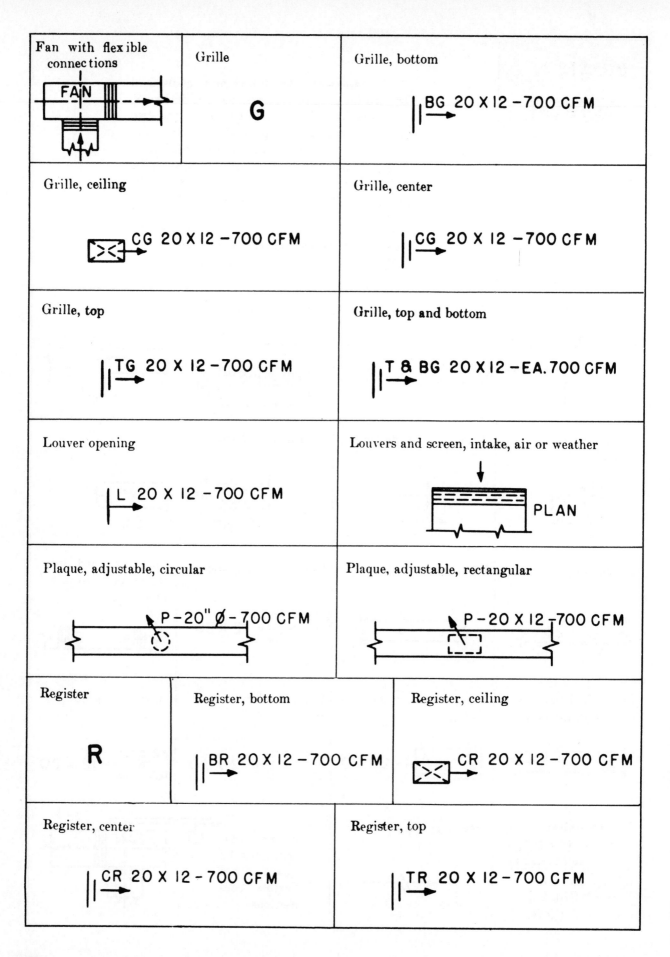

Fan with flexible connections	Grille	Grille, bottom
FAN	G	BG 20 X 12 – 700 CFM

Grille, ceiling	Grille, center
CG 20 X 12 – 700 CFM	CG 20 X 12 – 700 CFM

Grille, top	Grille, top and bottom
TG 20 X 12 – 700 CFM	T & BG 20 X 12 – EA. 700 CFM

Louver opening	Louvers and screen, intake, air or weather
L 20 X 12 – 700 CFM	PLAN

Plaque, adjustable, circular	Plaque, adjustable, rectangular
P – 20" ⌀ – 700 CFM	P – 20 X 12 – 700 CFM

Register	Register, bottom	Register, ceiling
R	BR 20 X 12 – 700 CFM	CR 20 X 12 – 700 CFM

Register, center	Register, top
CR 20 X 12 – 700 CFM	TR 20 X 12 – 700 CFM

Register, top and bottom ‖→ T & BR 20 X 12 — EA. 700 CFM	Supply outlet ‖—→	Vanes

Ductwork for single line representation	Closure, watertight, horizontal	Closure, watertight, vertical	Damper

Duct, exhaust system, nonwatertight ———< ○ ◎ 　　　DOWN　UP	Duct, exhaust system, watertight =====< ○ ◎ 　　　DOWN　UP

Duct, recirculating system, nonwatertight >——→ ○ ◎ 　　　DOWN　UP	Duct, recirculating system, watertight >==→ ○ ◎ 　　　DOWN　UP

Duct, supply system, nonwatertight ———→ ○ ◎ 　　　DOWN　UP	Duct, supply system, watertight ===→ ○ ◎ 　　　DOWN　UP

ASME PLUMBING	AUTOPSY TABLE	BATH *	BED PAN WASHER STERILIZER
	AT	B-1 B-2, etc.	BPW BPS
BIDET	**CAN WASHER**	**CLEANOUT**	**DENTAL UNIT**
B	CW	CO	DU
DISH WASHER	**DRAIN**	**DRINKING FOUNTAIN** *	**GAS OUTLET**
DW	FD	DF-1 DF-2, etc.	G
GREASE TRAP	**HOSE BIBB**	**HOSE RACK**	**HOT WATER TANK**
GT	HB	HR	HWT
LAUNDRY TRAY	**LAVATORIES** *	**METER**	**RANGE**
LT	L-1 L-2, etc. L-1 L-2, etc.	M	R
ROOF DRAIN	**SHOWER** HEAD STALL	**SINK** *	**WASH FOUNTAIN** CIRCULAR HALF CIRCULAR
RD		S-1 S-2, etc.	WF WF
URINAL *	**VACUUM OUTLET**	**WATER CLOSET** *	**WATER HEATER**
U-1 U-2, etc.		WC-1 WC-2, etc.	WH

*USE SPECIFICATION TO DESCRIBE

Extracted from American Standard Graphical Symbols for Plumbing (ASA Y32.4-1955), with the permission of the publisher, the American Society of Mechanical Engineers, United Engineering Center, 345 East 47 Street, New York, N.Y.

MIL-STD 17 PLUMBING	Autopsy table	Bath, angle tub	Bath, arm
	AT		AB
Bath, corner	**Bath, emergency**	**Bath, foot**	**Bath, hubbard**
	EB	FB	HB
Bath, infants	**Bath, leg**	**Bath, prenatal**	**Bath, recessed**
IB	LB	PB	
Bath, roll rim	**Bath, sitz**	**Bibb, hose**	**Bidet**
	SB	HB	B
Cabinet, fire hose	**Can washer**	**Clean-out**	**Cooker, steam**
FHC		C/O	STM COOK
Water, closet low tank	**Water closet, no tank**	**Water closet, wall hung**	**Dental unit**
LT		WH	DU
Dishwasher	**Dishwasher and counters**		**Drain**
DW	DW		D

Drain, deck, with valve	Drain, floor, with backwater valve	Drain, garage	Faucet, lawn hose LF HF
Fountain, drinking and electric water cooler EWC	Fountain, drinking pedestal type DF	Fountain, drinking, trough type DF	Fountain, drinking, wall type DF
Fountain, wash, circular	Fountain, wash. semicircular	Gas range R	Grinder, garbage (independent unit) GG
Heater, water WH	Kettle, steam	Lavatories in battery *Multiples of applicable unit symbol*	Lavatory, corner L
Lavatory, dental DL	Lavatory, medical ML	Lavatory, pedestal PL	Lavatory, wall WL
Outlet, gas G	Outlet, vacuum	Peeler, potato PP	Rack, hose HR
Separator, grease G	Separator, oil	Shower head	Shower, multistall

Shower, overhead gang PLAN ELEVATION		Shower, psychiatric PS	Shower, stall
Sink, kitchen S	Sink, developing	Sink, instrument IS	Sink, scullery
Sink, kitchen, left hand drain board (Reverse symbol for right hand unit)	Sink, kitchen, right and left drain board	Sink, service SS	Sink, surgeon's scrub-up SSS
Sink, table and bain-marie combination TABLE SINK BAIN MARIE	Sink, wash	Sink, wash, wall type	Sink and dishwasher, combination (Reverse symbol for opposite hand unit)
Sink and laundry tray, combination S & T	Sterilizer, bed pan BPS	Sterilizer, dressings DS	Sterilizer, instrument IS
Sterilizer, pressure PS	Sterilizer, utensil US	Straddle stand	Sump, roof
Table, steam ST	Tank, hot water HWT	Tray, laundry LT	Urinal, corner type

Urinal, pedestal type	Urinal, stall type	Urinal, trough type	Urinal, wall type
		TU	
Urinals in battery *Multiples of applicable unit symbol*	Urns, coffee and water ©Ⓦ©	Wall hydrant WH	Washer, bed pan BPW

Extracted from American Standard Graphical Symbols for Process Flow Diagrams (ASA Y32.11-1961) for the Petroleum and Chemical Industries, with the permission of the publisher, the American Society of Mechanical Engineers, United Engineering Center, 345 East 47 Street, New York, N.Y.

Graphical Symbols for
Process Flow Diagrams

1. SCOPE

This preliminary set of standard symbols has been developed for use on the basic process flow diagrams in order to represent the major items of equipment used by the petroleum and chemical industries.

A process flow diagram is the first drawing made to show the basic items of major equipment and their relation to one another in the process scheme. The more important flow lines are indicated as connecting these pieces of equipment and help to describe how the process operates.

2. BASIC PRINCIPLES

Simplicity of outline form were considered as paramount in the development of these symbols. The main idea is to preserve the general physical appearance of the equipment, with the minimum strokes to a draftsman.

No scale is applied to a process flow diagram, but the relative size of the symbols should be selected in keeping with the overall size of the completed drawing. The symbols should be arranged on the drawing in logical sequence of flow, from the charge material to the main product, with a minimum of cross-over lines.

It is suggested that the equipment outlines be drawn by heavy lines, and that the connecting piping be shown as lighter lines. For the purpose of most process flow diagrams it is not considered necessary to indicate any instrumentation or electrical symbols.

3. GENERAL

The following 79 symbols are by no means all that were suggested or that may be required; however, by adopting these as a standard the majority of present processes may be adequately represented.

In the preparation of final drawings for the detailed design, erection or operation of a unit, the process flow diagram must be supplemented by the more detailed engineering flow sheets and the final piping layout drawings.

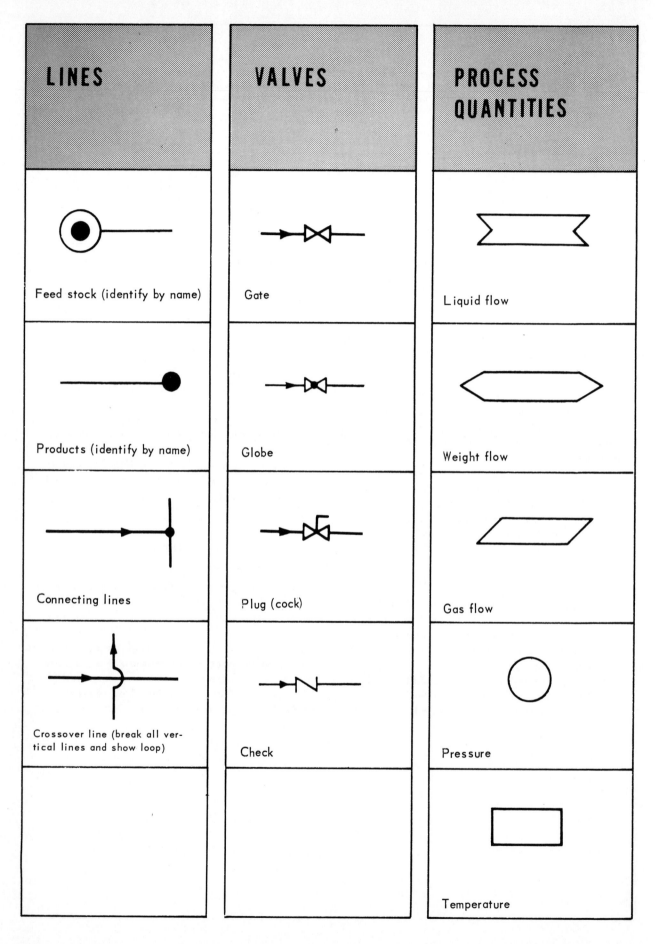

LINES	VALVES	PROCESS QUANTITIES
Feed stock (identify by name)	Gate	Liquid flow
Products (identify by name)	Globe	Weight flow
Connecting lines	Plug (cock)	Gas flow
Crossover line (break all vertical lines and show loop)	Check	Pressure
		Temperature

FURNACES & BOILERS	HEAT TRANSFER	HEAT TRANSFER continued

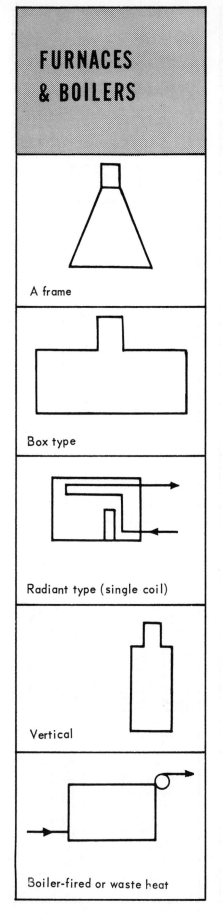

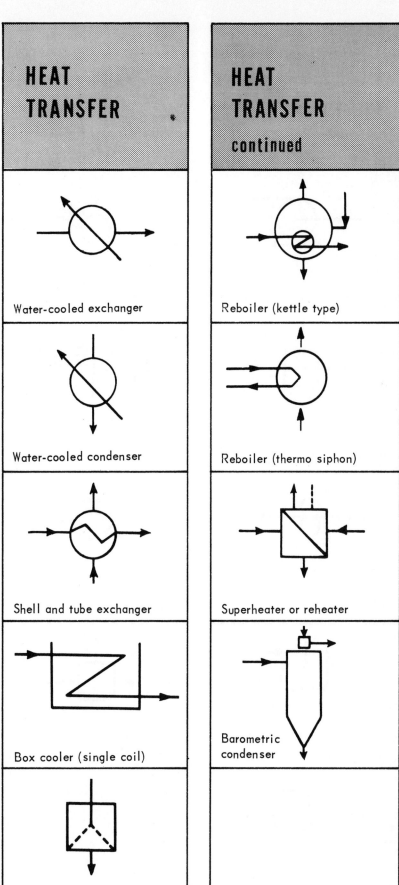

A frame

Box type

Radiant type (single coil)

Vertical

Boiler-fired or waste heat

Water-cooled exchanger

Water-cooled condenser

Shell and tube exchanger

Box cooler (single coil)

Cooling tower

Reboiler (kettle type)

Reboiler (thermo siphon)

Superheater or reheater

Barometric condenser

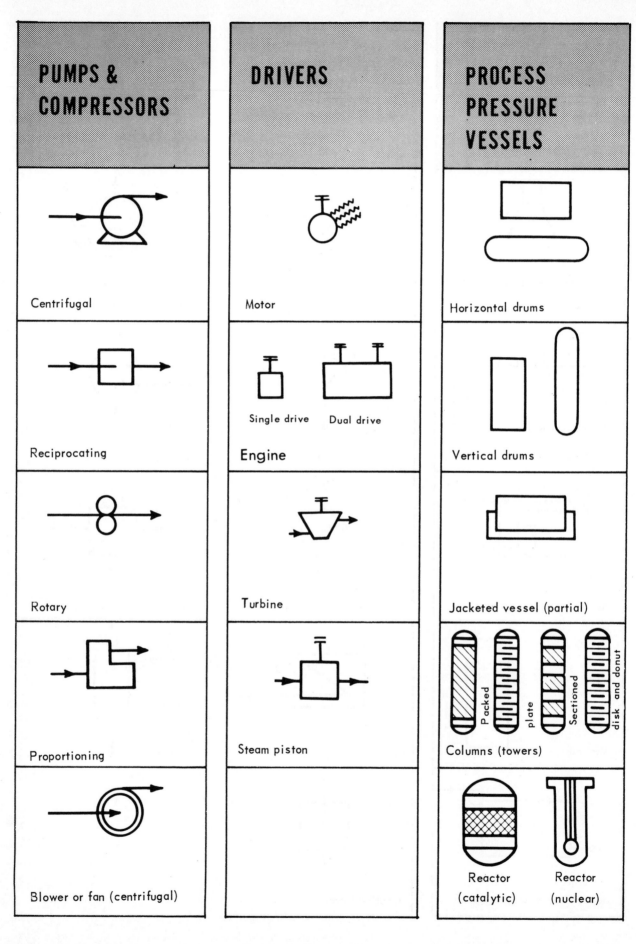

PUMPS & COMPRESSORS

Centrifugal

Reciprocating

Rotary

Proportioning

Blower or fan (centrifugal)

DRIVERS

Motor

Single drive   Dual drive

Engine

Turbine

Steam piston

PROCESS PRESSURE VESSELS

Horizontal drums

Vertical drums

Jacketed vessel (partial)

Packed   plate   Sectioned   disk and donut

Columns (towers)

Reactor
(catalytic)

Reactor
(nuclear)

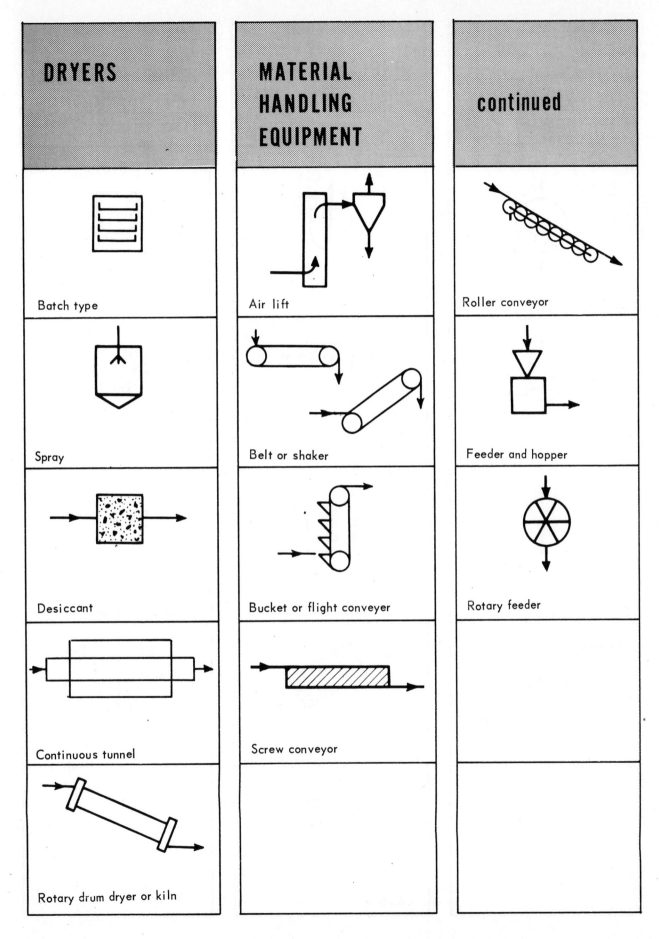

DRYERS	MATERIAL HANDLING EQUIPMENT	continued
Batch type	Air lift	Roller conveyor
Spray	Belt or shaker	Feeder and hopper
Desiccant	Bucket or flight conveyer	Rotary feeder
Continuous tunnel	Screw conveyor	
Rotary drum dryer or kiln		

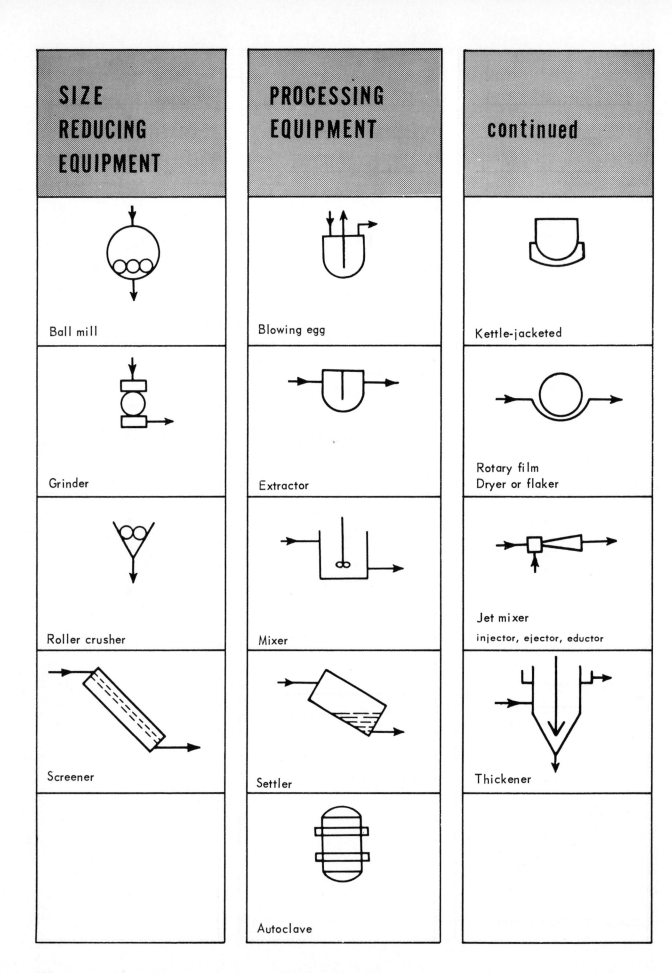

SIZE REDUCING EQUIPMENT	PROCESSING EQUIPMENT	continued
Ball mill	Blowing egg	Kettle-jacketed
Grinder	Extractor	Rotary film Dryer or flaker
Roller crusher	Mixer	Jet mixer injector, ejector, eductor
Screener	Settler	Thickener
	Autoclave	

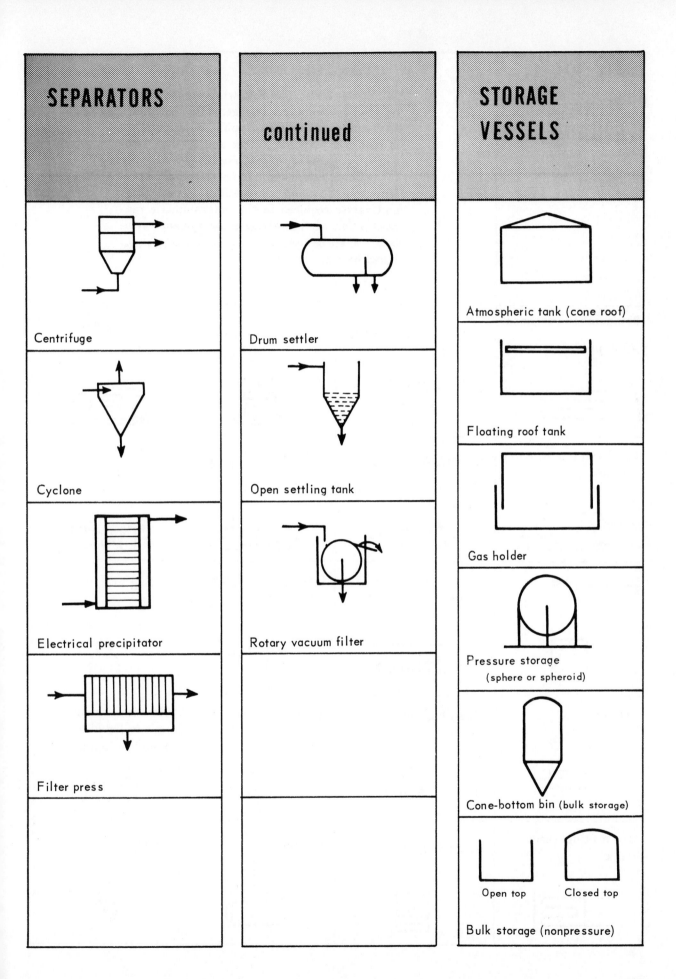

SEPARATORS

Centrifuge

Cyclone

Electrical precipitator

Filter press

continued

Drum settler

Open settling tank

Rotary vacuum filter

STORAGE VESSELS

Atmospheric tank (cone roof)

Floating roof tank

Gas holder

Pressure storage
(sphere or spheroid)

Cone-bottom bin (bulk storage)

Open top   Closed top

Bulk storage (nonpressure)

MIL-STD 17 REFRIGERATION EQUIPMENT	**General.** The following symbols shall be used to represent refrigeration machinery and equipment where graphic representation is required. Special valves and fittings associated with this equipment are listed herein for convenient reference. However, for representation of piping, conventional pipe fittings and valves required in the diagrammatic representation of the refrigeration systems, symbols shall be used in conjunction with those listed herein.

Refrigeration equipment Coil, pipe 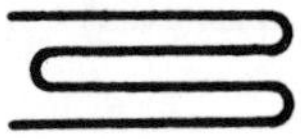	Compressor (all types) 	Condenser, evaporative 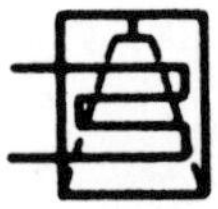	Condensing unit, air cooled 
Condensing unit, water cooled 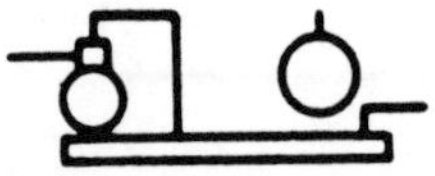	Cooler, brine 	Cooler, water, with brine coil 	Cooler, water, with direct expansion coil 
Cooling tower 	Cooling unit, finned type, natural convection 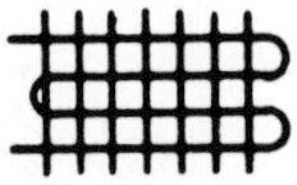	Cooling unit, forced convection 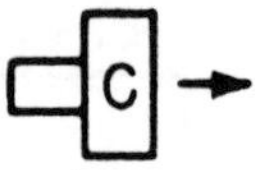	Cooling unit, immersion 
Dryer 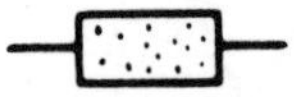	Float, high side 	Float, low side 	Heat interchanger (gas to liquid or liquid to liquid) 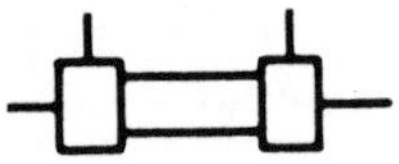
Ice making (brine tank) 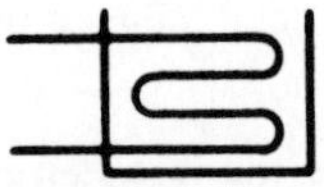	Ice making unit 	Receiver 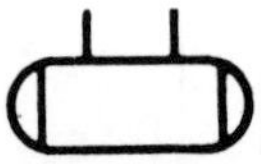	Strainer 

Switch, cut-out, combination high and low pressure	Switch, cut-out, high pressure	Switch, cut-out, low pressure	Switch, water failure
HP LP	HP	LP	WF
Thermal bulb	Trap, scale	Valve, compressor suction pressure limiting, throttling type (compressor side) CS	Valve, evaporator pressure regulating, thermostatic throttling type
Valve, evaporator pressure regulating, throttling type (evaporator side) E S	Valve, evaporator pressure regulating snap-action valve S	Valve, expansion, automatic	Valve, expansion, manually operated
Valve, expansion, thermostatic	Valve, solenoid		

GRAPHICAL SYMBOLS FOR TIME-MOTION STUDY PROCESS ANALYSIS

Extracted and redrawn for this section from the "Production Handbook," The Ronald Press Company, New York, 1958; "Tool Engineers Handbook," McGraw-Hill Book Company, Inc., New York, 1959. Complete data on this subject may be obtained from the above-mentioned publications.

WORKING AREA FOR HANDS

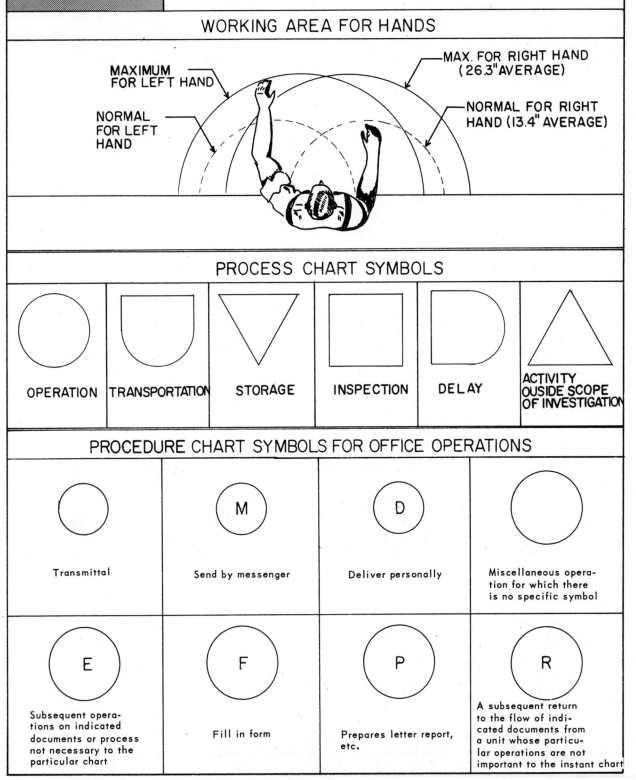

MAXIMUM FOR LEFT HAND

NORMAL FOR LEFT HAND

MAX. FOR RIGHT HAND (26.3" AVERAGE)

NORMAL FOR RIGHT HAND (13.4" AVERAGE)

PROCESS CHART SYMBOLS

OPERATION	TRANSPORTATION	STORAGE	INSPECTION	DELAY	ACTIVITY OUSIDE SCOPE OF INVESTIGATION

PROCEDURE CHART SYMBOLS FOR OFFICE OPERATIONS

	M	D	
Transmittal	Send by messenger	Deliver personally	Miscellaneous operation for which there is no specific symbol

E	F	P	R
Subsequent operations on indicated documents or process not necessary to the particular chart	Fill in form	Prepares letter report, etc.	A subsequent return to the flow of indicated documents from a unit whose particular operations are not important to the instant chart

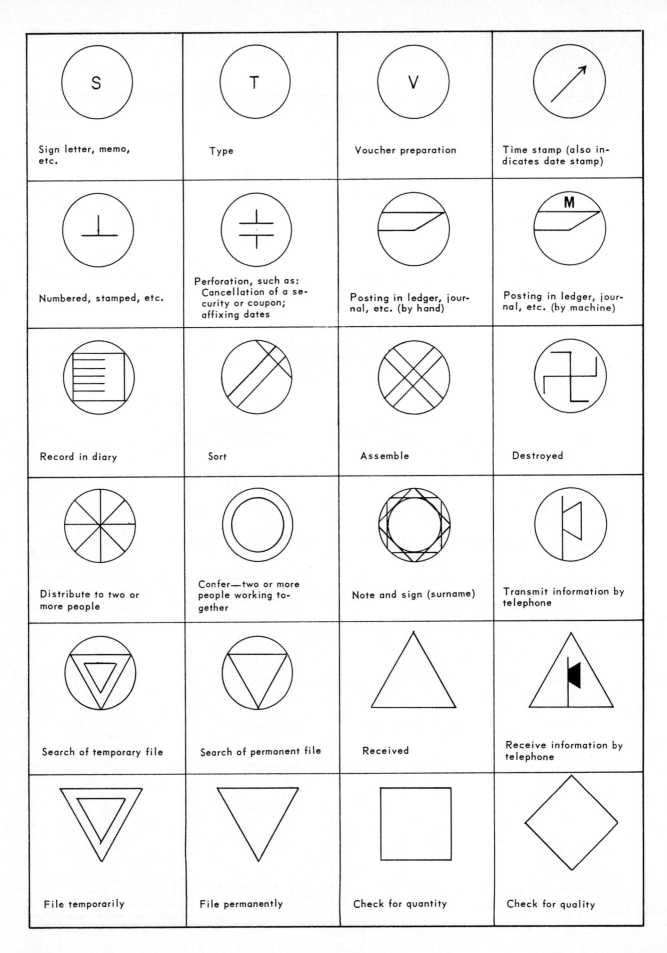

S — Sign letter, memo, etc.	**T** — Type	**V** — Voucher preparation	Time stamp (also indicates date stamp)
Numbered, stamped, etc.	Perforation, such as: Cancellation of a security or coupon; affixing dates	Posting in ledger, journal, etc. (by hand)	Posting in ledger, journal, etc. (by machine)
Record in diary	Sort	Assemble	Destroyed
Distribute to two or more people	Confer—two or more people working together	Note and sign (surname)	Transmit information by telephone
Search of temporary file	Search of permanent file	Received	Receive information by telephone
File temporarily	File permanently	Check for quantity	Check for quality

Check for both quantity and quality (examine)	Check for both quantity and quality and perform operation	Inspect for quality and perform operation (select, check, and make entry)	Approve (administrator's or division head's perfunctory signature—actual, official final approval by anyone
Extension proof or other mechanical check of an arithmetic operation	Document, form, or other paper. For example, F1-149 means original and three copies of Form F1-149	Discontinuity: intervening functions unimportant to the chart	

Chart of Typical Office Procedure

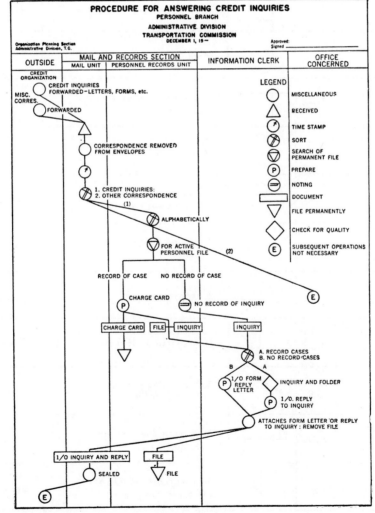

NAME OF SYMBOL	THERBLIG SYMBOL		EXPLANATION SUGGESTED BY	COLOR	COLOR SYMBOL
Search	Sh.		Eye turned as if searching	Black	
Find	F.		Eye straight as if fixed on object	Gray	
Select	St.		Reaching for object	Gray, light	
Grasp	G.		Hand open for grasping object	Lake red	
Transport loaded	T.L.		A hand with something in it	Green	
Position	P.		Object being placed by hand	Blue	
Assemble	A.		Several things put together	Violet, heavy	
Use	U.		Word "use"	Purple	
Disassemble	D.A.		One part of an assembly removed	Violet, light	
Inspect	I.		Magnifying lens	Burnt ochre	
Preposition	P.P.		A ninepin which is set up in a bowling alley	Sky-blue	
Release load	R.L.		Dropping content out of hand	Carmine red	
Transport empty	T.E.		Empty hand	Olive green	
Rest for over-coming fatigue	R.		Man seated as if resting	Orange	
Unavoidable delay	U.D.		Man bumping his nose unintentionally	Yellow ochre	
Avoidable delay	A.D.		Man lying down on job voluntarily	Lemon yellow	
Plan	Pn.		Man with his fingers at his brow thinking	Brown	
Hold	H.		Magnet holding iron bar	Gold ochre	

MICRO-MOTION TRANSFER SHEET

Film No. *U-2*   Date Filmed *May 5, 19—*   By *Conner*

Operation *Screw & Washer Assembly*   Operator *Lefgren*   Department *Radio Cabinet Assembly*

Sheet No. *1* of *1*   Date Made *May 12*   By *C. x L.*

Clock Reading No. Frames	Subtracted Time	Therblig Symbol	DESCRIPTION LEFT HAND	Clock Reading No. Frames	Subtracted Time	Therblig Symbol	DESCRIPTION RIGHT HAND	Clock Reading No. Frames	Subtracted Time	NOTES
4661			Start	4669			Start			Time – Wink
77	16	⌣	To L_1	86	17	⌣	To R_1			
82	5	∩	Screw T, 1, 2	94	8	∩	Steel Washer, T, 1, 2			
94	12	⌣	To Center	4703	9	⌣	To left hand above center			
4703	9	⌢	For right hand	32	29	9	With screw			
36	33	Ω	T, 1, 2	45	13	U	On screw to head			
37	1	⌢		46	1	⌣				
42	5	∩	1, Washer	56	10	⌣	To R_2			
45	3	Ω	1, "	62	6	∩	Rubber Washer T, 1, 2			
75	30	⌢	For right hand T, 1, 2	75	13	⌣	To left hand above center			
98	23	Ω	T, 1, 2	89	14	9	With screw			
99	1	⌢	1	4810	21	U	On screw to Steel Washer			
4804	5	∩	1, Rubber Washer	11	1	⌣				
05	1	⌢	2,	22	11	⌣	To L_2			
10	5	∩	2, Rubber Washer	28	6	∩	Rubber bushing T, 1, 2			
40	30	⌢	For right hand T, 1, 2	40	12	⌣	To left hand above center			
63	23	Ω	T, 1, 2	49	9	9	With screw			
64	1	⌢		63	14	U	On screw			
				71	8	⌣	To R_3			
				72	1	⌢				

Fig. 31. Micromotion Transfer Sheet

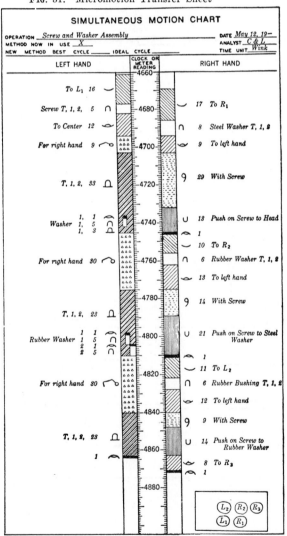

Simultaneous-Motion Cycle Chart Plotted from Data on the
Transfer Sheet, Fig. 31

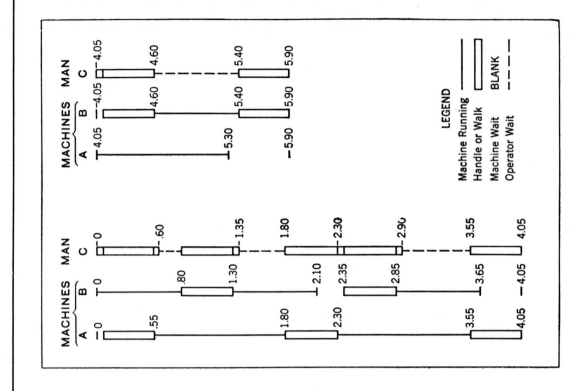

Man-Machine Chart with Worker Waiting for Automatics to Finish Operations

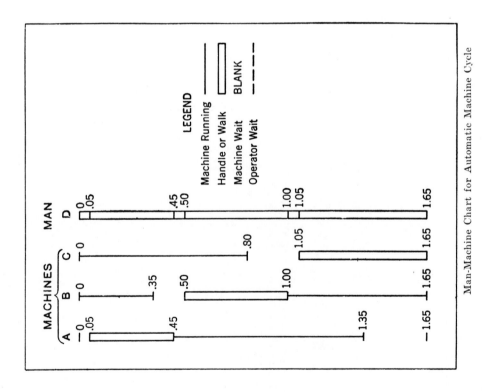

Man-Machine Chart for Automatic Machine Cycle

SWI - AIA File - 16E

ARCHITECTURE
(STEEL WINDOWS & CURTAIN WALLS)

Extracted from Recommended Standard for Steel Windows (AIA File No. 16-E), with the permission of the publisher, the Steel Window Institute, 18455 Harvest Lane, Brookfield, Wis.

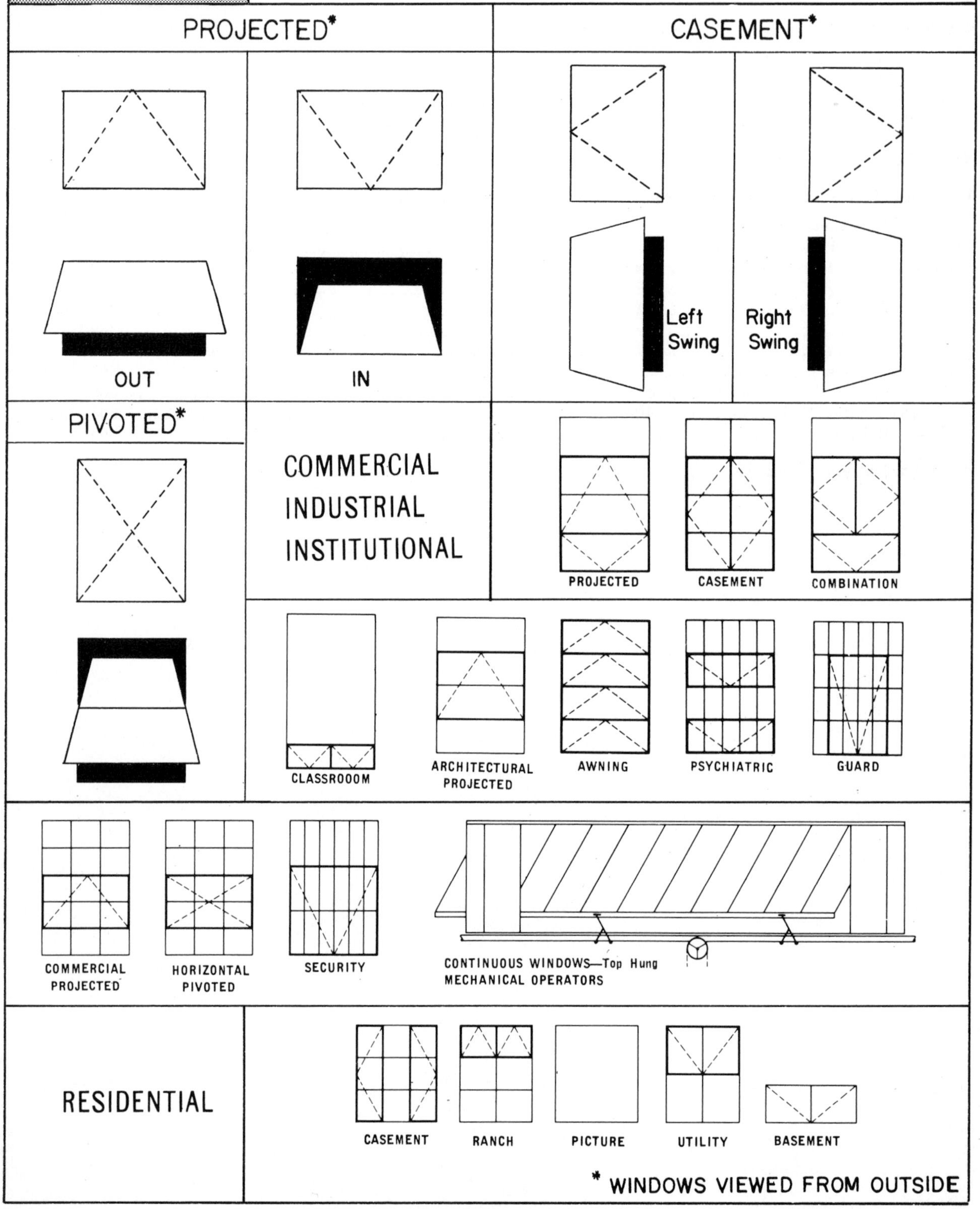

PROJECTED*

OUT

IN

CASEMENT*

Left Swing

Right Swing

PIVOTED*

COMMERCIAL INDUSTRIAL INSTITUTIONAL

PROJECTED

CASEMENT

COMBINATION

CLASSROOOM

ARCHITECTURAL PROJECTED

AWNING

PSYCHIATRIC

GUARD

COMMERCIAL PROJECTED

HORIZONTAL PIVOTED

SECURITY

CONTINUOUS WINDOWS—Top Hung MECHANICAL OPERATORS

RESIDENTIAL

CASEMENT

RANCH

PICTURE

UTILITY

BASEMENT

* WINDOWS VIEWED FROM OUTSIDE

352

| RESIDENTIAL | |
| CURTAIN WALLS | |

DOUBLE HUNG

Type A Type B Type E Type F COLONIAL

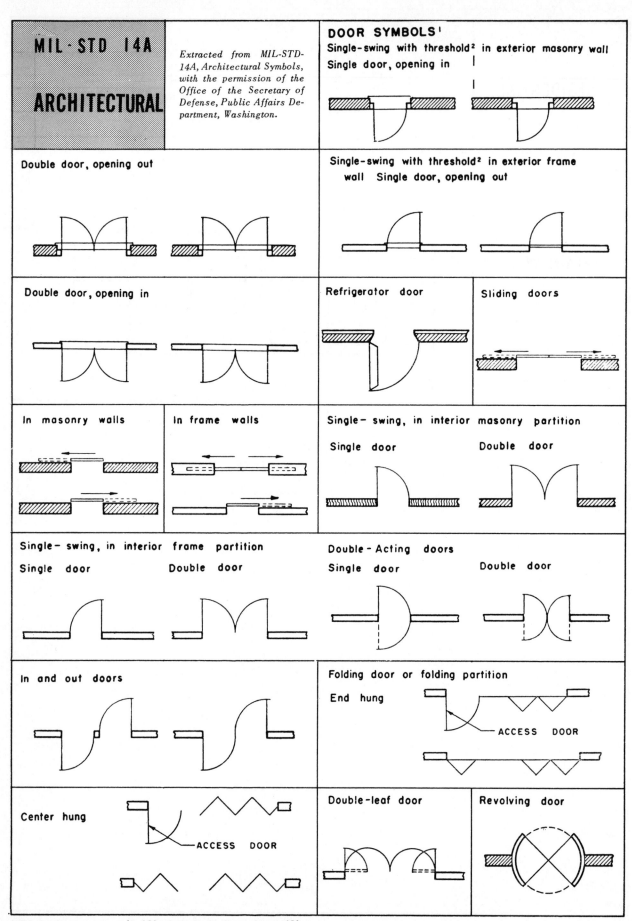

MIL-STD 14A

ARCHITECTURAL

Extracted from MIL-STD-14A, Architectural Symbols, with the permission of the Office of the Secretary of Defense, Public Affairs Department, Washington.

DOOR SYMBOLS[1]

Single-swing with threshold[2] in exterior masonry wall
Single door, opening in

Double door, opening out

Single-swing with threshold[2] in exterior frame wall   Single door, opening out

Double door, opening in

Refrigerator door

Sliding doors

In masonry walls

In frame walls

Single-swing, in interior masonry partition

Single door   Double door

Single-swing, in interior frame partition

Single door   Double door

Double-Acting doors

Single door   Double door

In and out doors

Folding door or folding partition

End hung

ACCESS DOOR

Center hung

ACCESS DOOR

Double-leaf door

Revolving door

[1] When interference occurs with 90° swing, indicate door swing at 45°.
[2] Actual material of the threshold may be indicated by abbreviation in accordance with MIL-STD-12, Abbreviations for Use on Drawings.

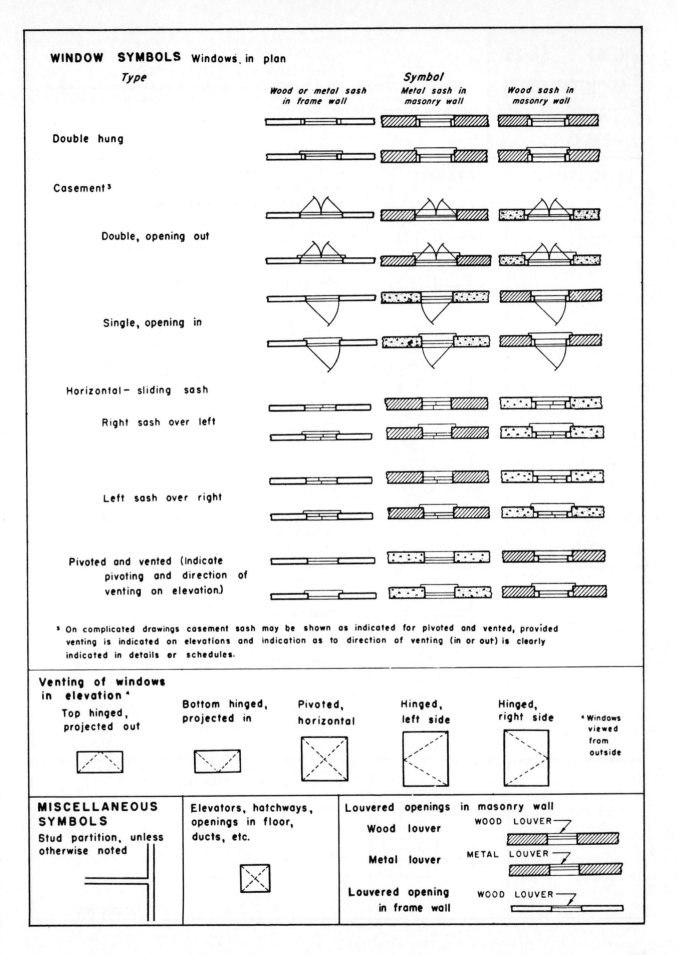

WINDOW SYMBOLS Windows, in plan

Type	Symbol
	Wood or metal sash in frame wall — *Metal sash in masonry wall* — *Wood sash in masonry wall*

Double hung

Casement³

    Double, opening out

    Single, opening in

Horizontal - sliding sash

    Right sash over left

    Left sash over right

Pivoted and vented (Indicate pivoting and direction of venting on elevation.)

³ On complicated drawings casement sash may be shown as indicated for pivoted and vented, provided venting is indicated on elevations and indication as to direction of venting (in or out) is clearly indicated in details or schedules.

Venting of windows in elevation ⁴

Top hinged, projected out — Bottom hinged, projected in — Pivoted, horizontal — Hinged, left side — Hinged, right side

⁴ Windows viewed from outside

MISCELLANEOUS SYMBOLS

Stud partition, unless otherwise noted

Elevators, hatchways, openings in floor, ducts, etc.

Louvered openings in masonry wall

    Wood louver   WOOD LOUVER

    Metal louver   METAL LOUVER

    Louvered opening in frame wall   WOOD LOUVER

Extracted from NEMA SB25-1960, Signalling Apparatus Symbols for Use on Architectural Drawings, with the permission of the National Electrical Manufacturers Association, 155 East 44 Street, New York, N.Y.

BASIC SYMBOL	EXAMPLE	
		I. Nurse Call System Devices (Any Type)
	①	Nurses' annunciator (can add a number after it as 24 to indicate number of lamps)
	②	Call station, single cord, pilot light
	③	Call station, double cord, microphone-speaker
	④	Corridor dome light, 1 lamp
	⑤	Transformer
	⑥	Any other item on same system—use numbers as required
		II. Paging System Devices (Any Type)
	◇1	Keyboard
	◇2	Flush annunciator
	◇3	2-face annunciator
	◇4	Any other item on same system—use numbers as required
		III. Fire Alarm System Devices (Any Type) Including Smoke and Sprinkler Alarm Devices
	□1	Control panel
	□2	Station

(continued)

BASIC SYMBOL	EXAMPLE	
		10-in. gong
		Presignal chime
		Any other item on same system—use numbers as required
	IV. Staff Register System Devices (Any Type)	
	1	Phone operators' register
	2	Entrance register—flush
	3	Staff room register
	4	Transformer
	5	Any other item on same system—use numbers as required
	V. Electric Clock System Devices (Any Type)	
	1	Master clock
	2	12-in. secondary—flush
	3	12-in. double dial—wall-mounted
	4	18-in. skeleton dial
	5	Any other item on same system—use numbers as required

BASIC SYMBOL	EXAMPLE	
		VI. Public Telephone System Devices
	1	Switchboard
	2	Desk phone
	3	Any other item on same system—use numbers as required
		VII. Private Telephone System Devices (Any Type)
	1	Switchboard
	2	Wall phone
	3	Any other item on same system—use numbers as required
		VIII. Watchman System Devices (Any Type)
	1	Central station
	2	Key station
	3	Any other item on same system—use numbers as required
		IX. Sound System
	1	Amplifier
	2	Microphone
	3	Interior speaker
	4	Exterior speaker
	5	Any other item on same system—use numbers as required

BASIC SYMBOL	EXAMPLE	
		X. Other Signal System Devices
	①1	Buzzer
	②2	Bell
	③3	Push button
	④4	Annunciator
	⑤5	Any other item on same system—use numbers as required

CONSTRUCTION (BRICK)

Extracted from TM5-230; TO 00-25-103, General Drafting, Construction (Brick), Department of the Army, Department of the Air Force, with the permission of the Office of the Secretary of Defense, Public Affairs Department, Washington.

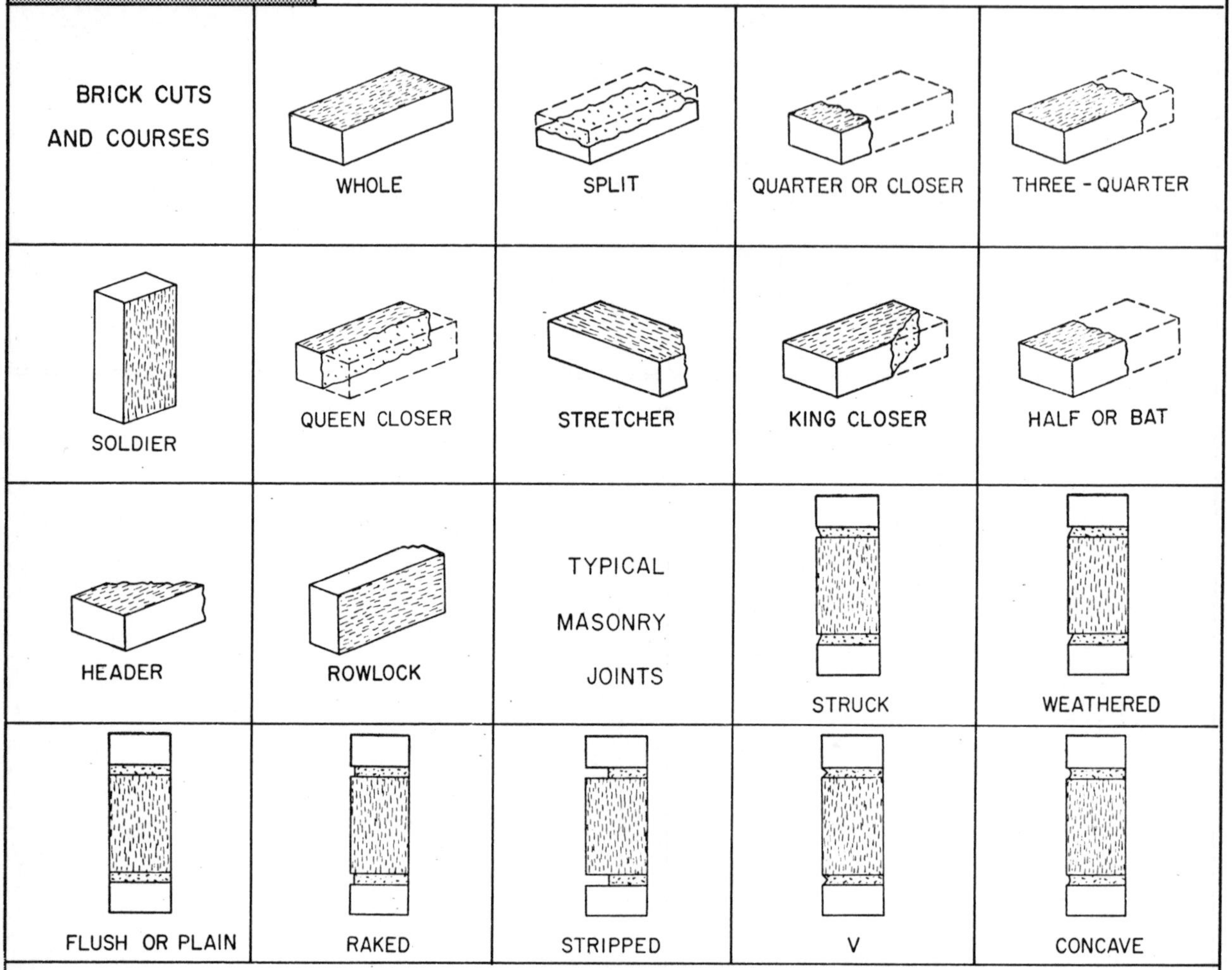

BRICK CUTS AND COURSES				
	WHOLE	SPLIT	QUARTER OR CLOSER	THREE - QUARTER
SOLDIER	QUEEN CLOSER	STRETCHER	KING CLOSER	HALF OR BAT
HEADER	ROWLOCK	TYPICAL MASONRY JOINTS	STRUCK	WEATHERED
FLUSH OR PLAIN	RAKED	STRIPPED	V	CONCAVE

Brick bonds.

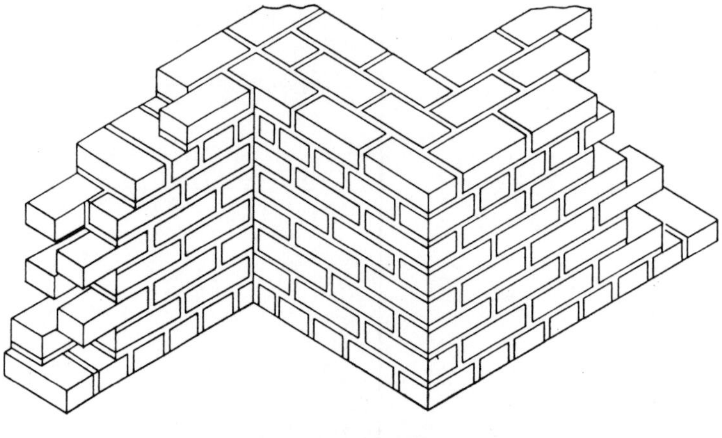

COMMON BOND

360

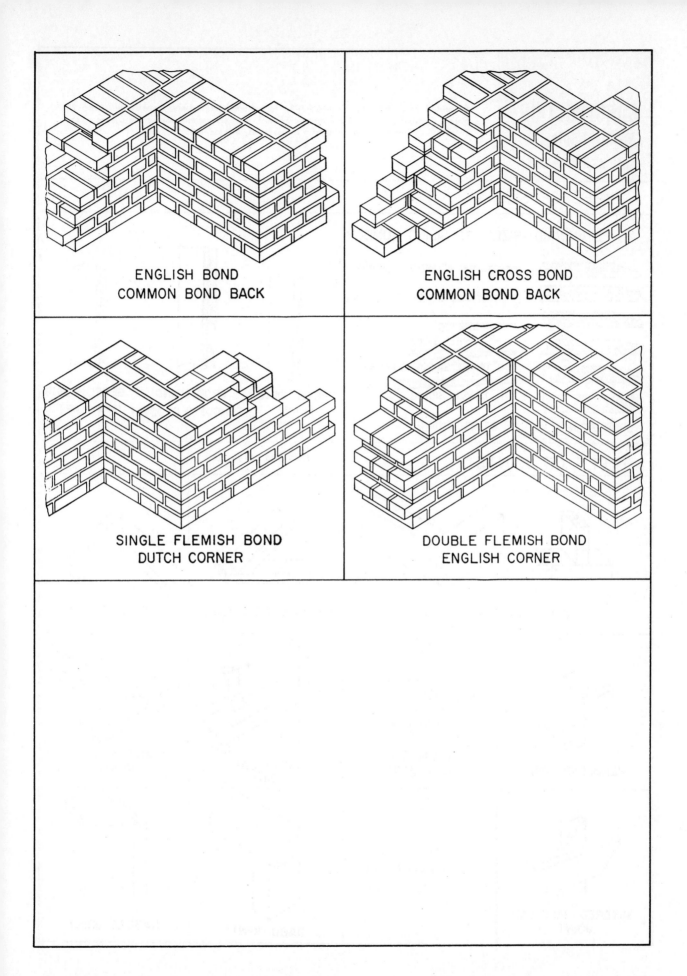

ENGLISH BOND
COMMON BOND BACK

ENGLISH CROSS BOND
COMMON BOND BACK

SINGLE FLEMISH BOND
DUTCH CORNER

DOUBLE FLEMISH BOND
ENGLISH CORNER

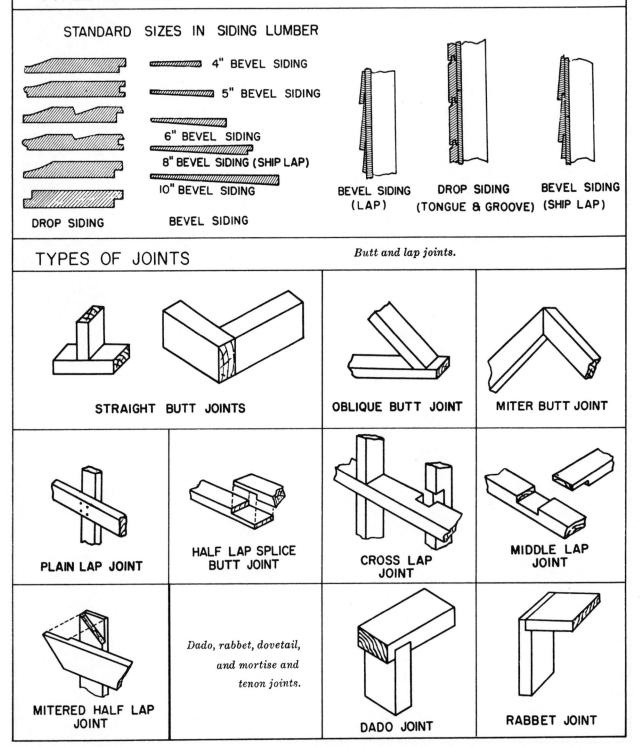

CONSTRUCTION
(WOOD· Joints, Splices, Hardware)

Extracted from TM5-230; TO 00-25-103, Department of the Army, Department of the Air Force, General Drafting, Construction (Wood), with the permission of the Office of the Secretary of Defense, Public Affairs Department, Washington.

TYPES OF SIDING

STANDARD SIZES IN SIDING LUMBER

4" BEVEL SIDING

5" BEVEL SIDING

6" BEVEL SIDING

8" BEVEL SIDING (SHIP LAP)

10" BEVEL SIDING

DROP SIDING

BEVEL SIDING

BEVEL SIDING (LAP)

DROP SIDING (TONGUE & GROOVE)

BEVEL SIDING (SHIP LAP)

TYPES OF JOINTS

Butt and lap joints.

STRAIGHT BUTT JOINTS

OBLIQUE BUTT JOINT

MITER BUTT JOINT

PLAIN LAP JOINT

HALF LAP SPLICE BUTT JOINT

CROSS LAP JOINT

MIDDLE LAP JOINT

MITERED HALF LAP JOINT

Dado, rabbet, dovetail, and mortise and tenon joints.

DADO JOINT

RABBET JOINT

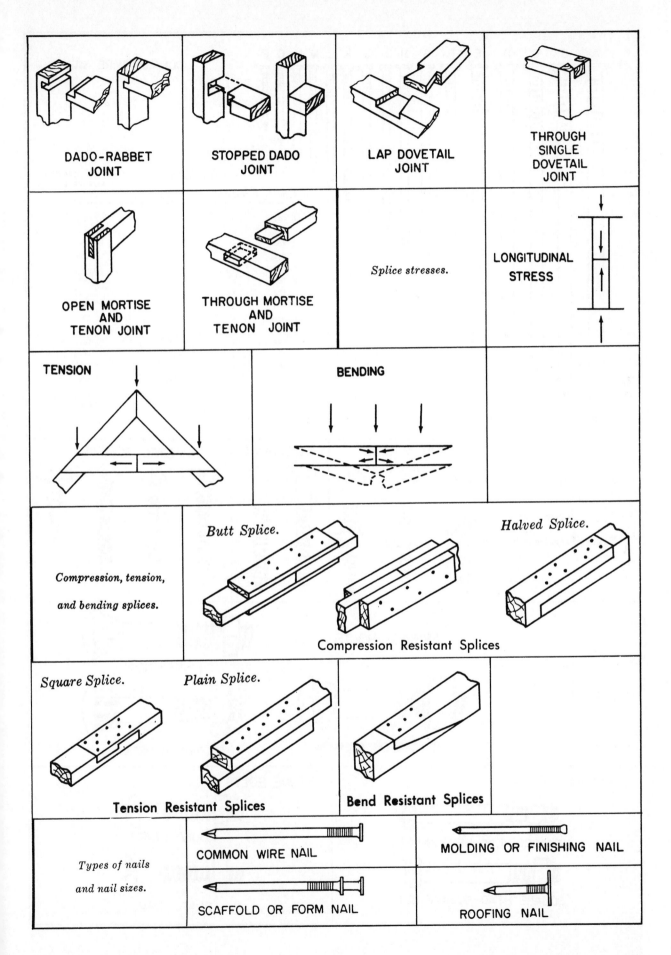

DADO-RABBET JOINT

STOPPED DADO JOINT

LAP DOVETAIL JOINT

THROUGH SINGLE DOVETAIL JOINT

OPEN MORTISE AND TENON JOINT

THROUGH MORTISE AND TENON JOINT

Splice stresses.

LONGITUDINAL STRESS

TENSION

BENDING

Compression, tension, and bending splices.

Butt Splice.

Halved Splice.

Compression Resistant Splices

Square Splice.

Plain Splice.

Tension Resistant Splices

Bend Resistant Splices

Types of nails and nail sizes.

COMMON WIRE NAIL

MOLDING OR FINISHING NAIL

SCAFFOLD OR FORM NAIL

ROOFING NAIL

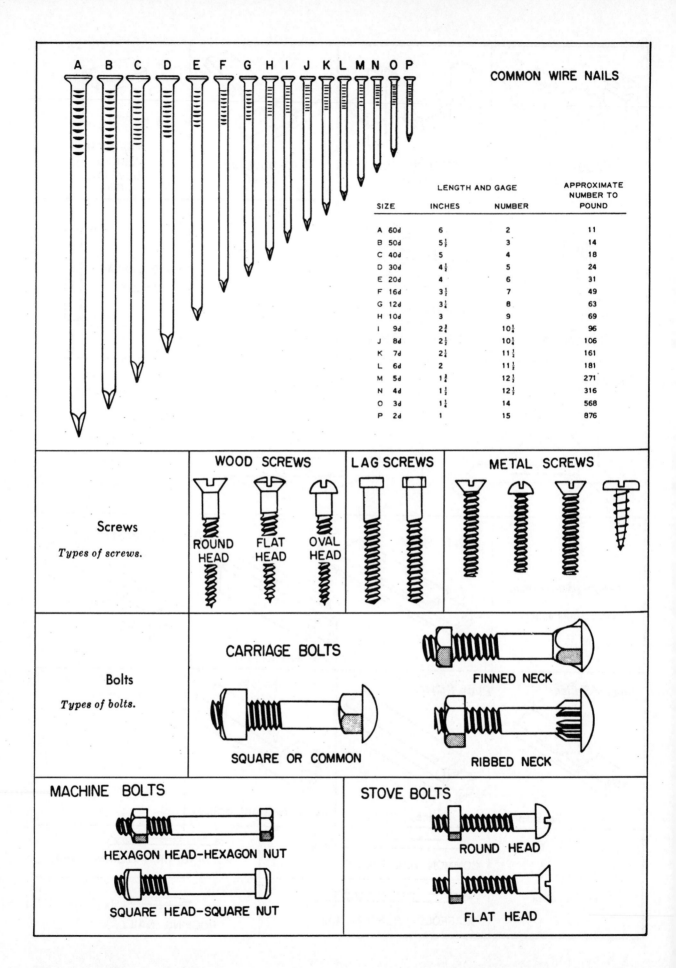

COMMON WIRE NAILS

| SIZE | LENGTH AND GAGE | | APPROXIMATE NUMBER TO POUND |
	INCHES	NUMBER	
A 60d	6	2	11
B 50d	5½	3	14
C 40d	5	4	18
D 30d	4½	5	24
E 20d	4	6	31
F 16d	3½	7	49
G 12d	3¼	8	63
H 10d	3	9	69
I 9d	2¾	10¼	96
J 8d	2½	10¼	106
K 7d	2¼	11½	161
L 6d	2	11½	181
M 5d	1¾	12½	271
N 4d	1½	12½	316
O 3d	1¼	14	568
P 2d	1	15	876

Screws

Types of screws.

WOOD SCREWS

ROUND HEAD FLAT HEAD OVAL HEAD

LAG SCREWS

METAL SCREWS

Bolts

Types of bolts.

CARRIAGE BOLTS

FINNED NECK

SQUARE OR COMMON

RIBBED NECK

MACHINE BOLTS

HEXAGON HEAD—HEXAGON NUT

SQUARE HEAD—SQUARE NUT

STOVE BOLTS

ROUND HEAD

FLAT HEAD

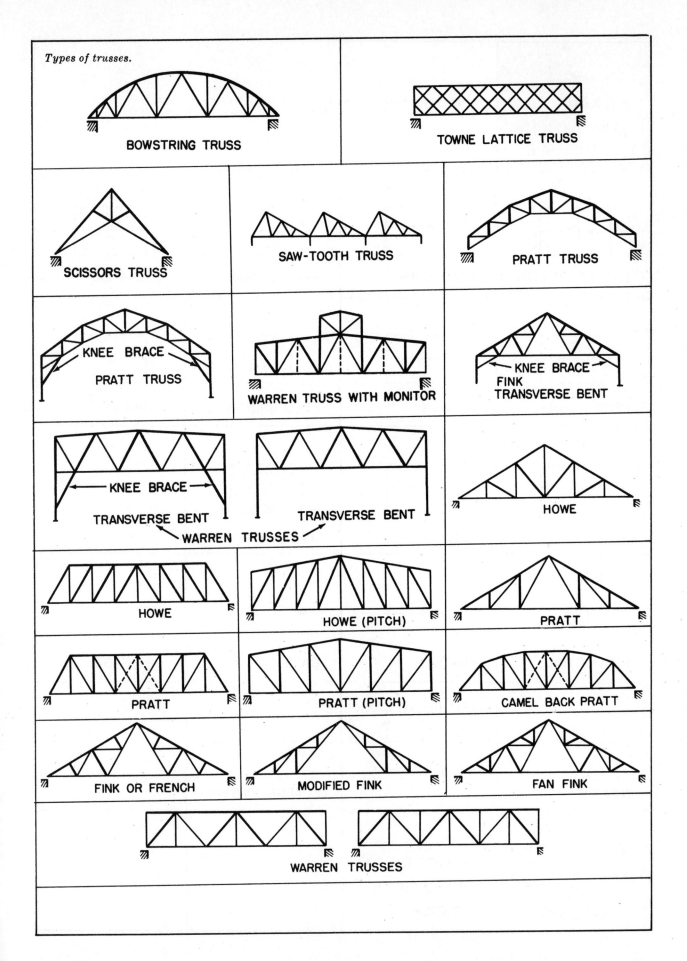

Types of trusses.

BOWSTRING TRUSS

TOWNE LATTICE TRUSS

SCISSORS TRUSS

SAW-TOOTH TRUSS

PRATT TRUSS

KNEE BRACE
PRATT TRUSS

WARREN TRUSS WITH MONITOR

KNEE BRACE
FINK
TRANSVERSE BENT

KNEE BRACE
TRANSVERSE BENT

TRANSVERSE BENT

WARREN TRUSSES

HOWE

HOWE

HOWE (PITCH)

PRATT

PRATT

PRATT (PITCH)

CAMEL BACK PRATT

FINK OR FRENCH

MODIFIED FINK

FAN FINK

WARREN TRUSSES

FARM
YARD LAYOUT

Reproduced herein through the courtesy of the Farm Equipment Institute, 608 S. Dearborn Street, Chicago, Ill. and Van Dusen & Company, Inc., Wayzata, Minn.

S **SHED OR SHELTER**	F B **FEED BUNK**	F / S **FEED STORAGE**	S / R **SILO ROOM**
F / R **FEED ROOM**	G **GRANARY**	F G **FEED GRINDER**	C **CORN CRIB**
H **HOUSE**	B **BARN**	**HARD SURFACE AREA**	
SERVICE POLE	**FENCE**	**GATE**	D **DRAINAGE**
N **NORTH**	**STEEP HILL OR BANK** ↑ ↑ ↑ ↑ ↑ **ARROW UP HILL**	**ROADS & DRIVEWAY**	
	SILO **INDICATE FILLER** **DOOR & CHUTE** **LOCATION**		

GRAPHIC REPRESENTATION AND SYMBOLS FOR DRAFTING AND MARKING

Title *Page*

Extracted from the "Tool Engineers Handbook," prepared by the American Society of Tool Engineers, Detroit, Mich., with the permission of the publisher, McGraw-Hill Book Company, Inc., New York.

3 HOLES 120°	 0.5 x R 0.866026 x R 1.732051 x R	**4 HOLES** 90°	 0.707107 x R 0.707107 x R 1.414214 x R
5 HOLES 72°	 0.951056 x R 0.309016 x R 0.809016 x R 0.587785 x R 1.175570 x R	**6 HOLES** 60°	 0.5 x R 1 x R 0.866026 x R
7 HOLES 51°-25'-43"	 0.781832 x R 0.222522 x R 0.623490 x R 0.900968 x R 0.433882 x R 0.867764 x R 0.974928 x R	**8 HOLES** 45°	 0.923880 x R 0.382684 x R 0.382684 x R 0.765366 x R 0.923880 x R
9 HOLES 40°	 0.984808 x R 0.642788 x R 0.173684 x R 0.766044 x R 0.5 x R 0.939692 x R 0.342020 x R 0.684040 x R 0.866026 x R	**10 HOLES** 36°	 0.618034 x R 0.309017 x R 0.809016 x R 0.587786 x R 0.951056 x R
11 HOLES 32°-43'-38"	 0.909632 x R 0.540640 x R 0.415416 x R 0.841254 x R 0.142316 x R 0.959492 x R 0.654860 x R 0.281733 x R 0.563466 x R 0.755750 x R 0.989822 x R	**12 HOLES** 30°	 0.258819 x R 0.965926 x R 0.707106 x R 0.258819 x R 0.517638 x R 0.707106 x R 0.965926 x R
13 HOLES 27°-41'-32"	 0.992710 x R 0.822984 x R 0.464722 x R 0.885456 x R 0.120536 x R 0.568064 x R 0.354604 x R 0.970942 x R 0.748510 x R 0.239315 x R 0.478630 x R 0.663124 x R 0.935016 x R	**14 HOLES** 25°-42'-51"	 0.445044 x R 0.433882 x R 0.781832 x R 0.974928 x R 0.222522 x R 0.623490 x R 0.900968 x R

Extracted from TM5-230; TO 00-25-103, Department of the Army, Department of the Air Force, General Drafting, Line Characteristics and Convention, with the permission of the Office of the Secretary of Defense, Public Affairs Department, Washington.

CENTERLINE		THIN
DIMENSION		THIN
LEADER		THIN
BREAK (LONG)		THIN
PHANTOM		THIN
SECTIONING AND EXTENSION LINE		THIN
HIDDEN		MEDIUM
STITCH LINE		MEDIUM
OUTLINE OR VISIBLE LINE		THICK
BREAK (SHORT)		THICK
DATUM LINE		THICK
CUTTING PLANE		EXTRA THICK
VIEWING PLANE		EXTRA THICK
CUTTING PLANE FOR COMPLEX OR OFFSET VIEWS		EXTRA THICK

Extracted from NAVPERS 10471–Draftsman 3, Navy Training Courses, U.S. Navy Training Publications Center for the Bureau of Naval Personnel, with the permission of the Office of the Secretary of Defense, Public Affairs Department, Washington. (Reproduced twice size for clarity.)

Aluminum, magnesium, and their alloys	Asphalt	Copper, brass, bronze, and their compositions
Asbestos, magnesia, filler packings and similar materials	Babbitt, lead, solder, bearing metal and white metals	Brick
Felt and leather (natural)	Cut stone	Coal
Fabric and flexible material	Cork	Cinder block

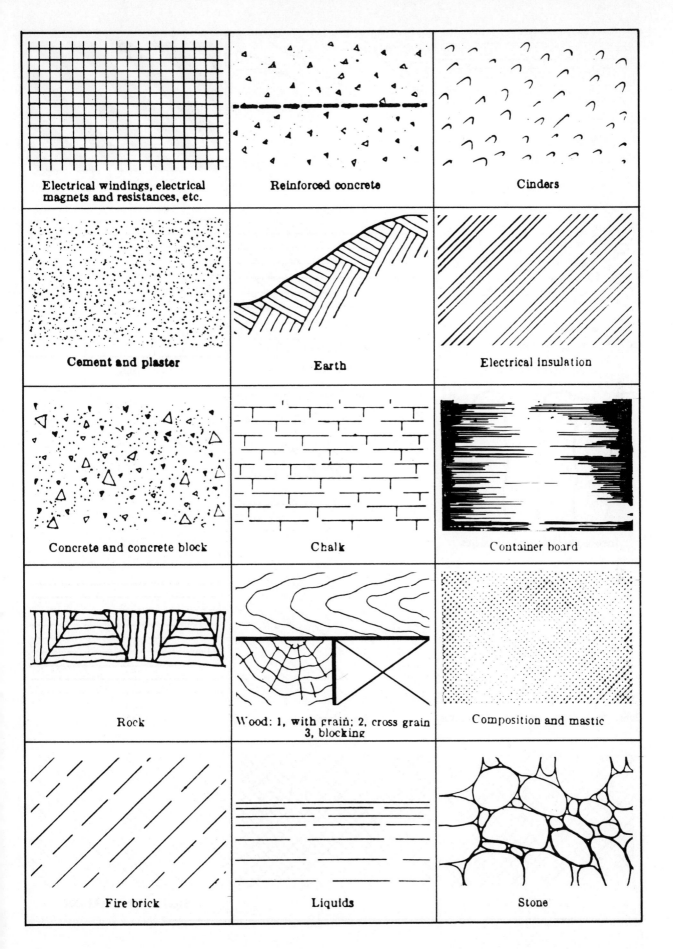

Electrical windings, electrical magnets and resistances, etc.	Reinforced concrete	Cinders
Cement and plaster	Earth	Electrical insulation
Concrete and concrete block	Chalk	Container board
Rock	Wood: 1, with grain; 2, cross grain 3, blocking	Composition and mastic
Fire brick	Liquids	Stone

371

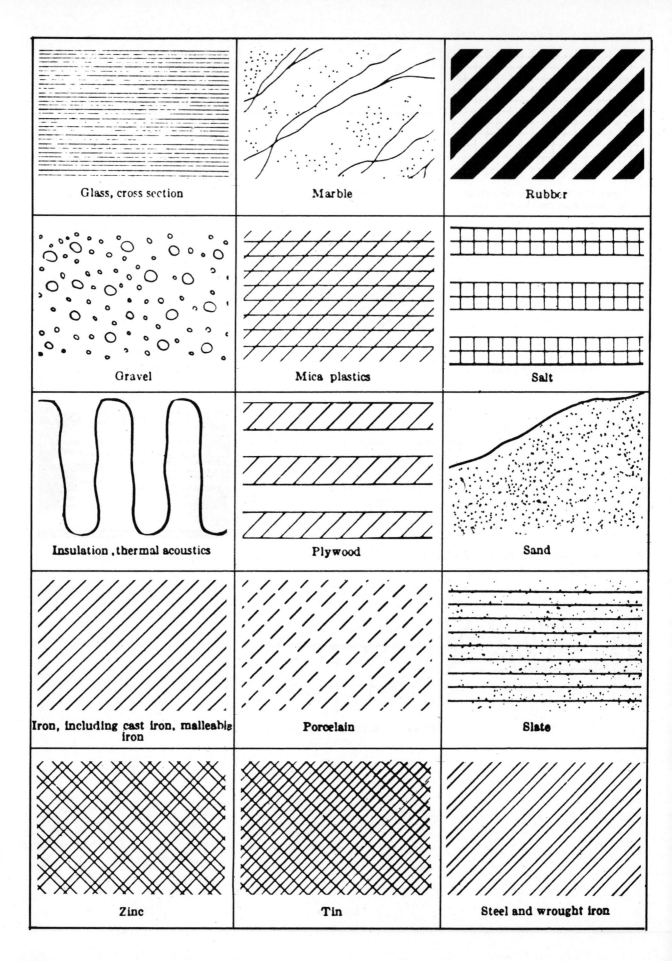

Glass, cross section

Marble

Rubber

Gravel

Mica plastics

Salt

Insulation, thermal acoustics

Plywood

Sand

Iron, including cast iron, malleable iron

Porcelain

Slate

Zinc

Tin

Steel and wrought iron

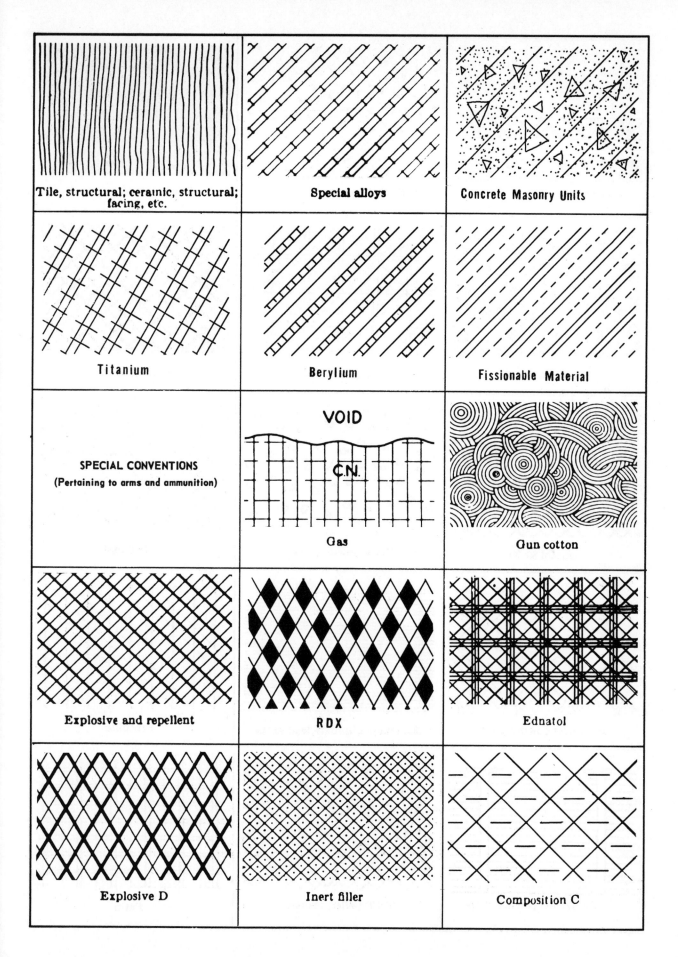

Tile, structural; ceramic, structural; facing, etc.

Special alloys

Concrete Masonry Units

Titanium

Berylium

Fissionable Material

SPECIAL CONVENTIONS
(Pertaining to arms and ammunition)

VOID

C.N.

Gas

Gun cotton

Explosive and repellent

RDX

Ednatol

Explosive D

Inert filler

Composition C

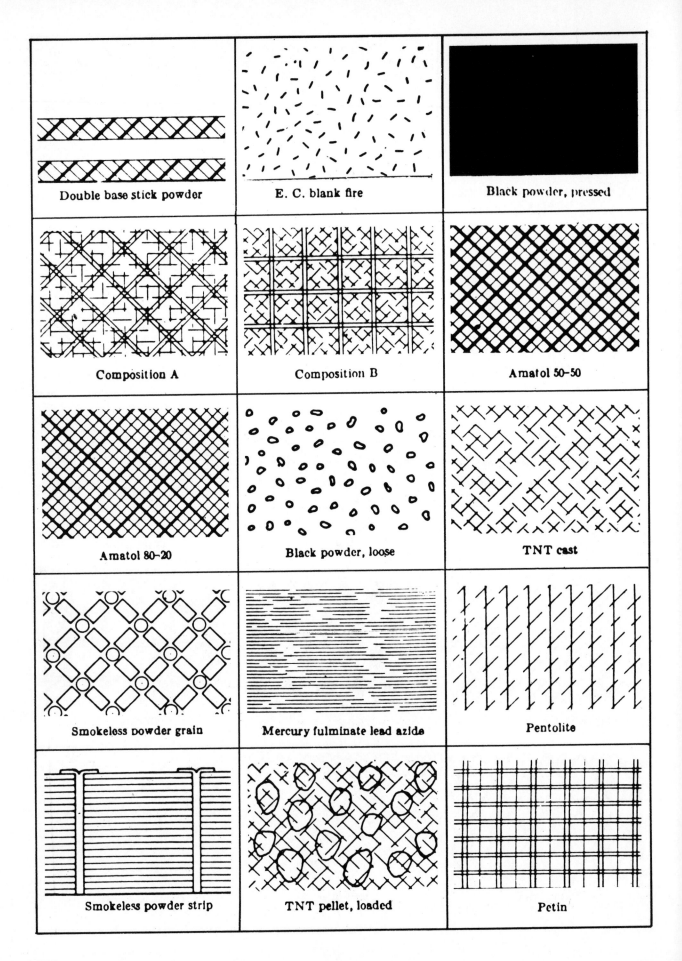

Double base stick powder

E. C. blank fire

Black powder, pressed

Composition A

Composition B

Amatol 50-50

Amatol 80-20

Black powder, loose

TNT cast

Smokeless powder grain

Mercury fulminate lead azide

Pentolite

Smokeless powder strip

TNT pellet, loaded

Petin

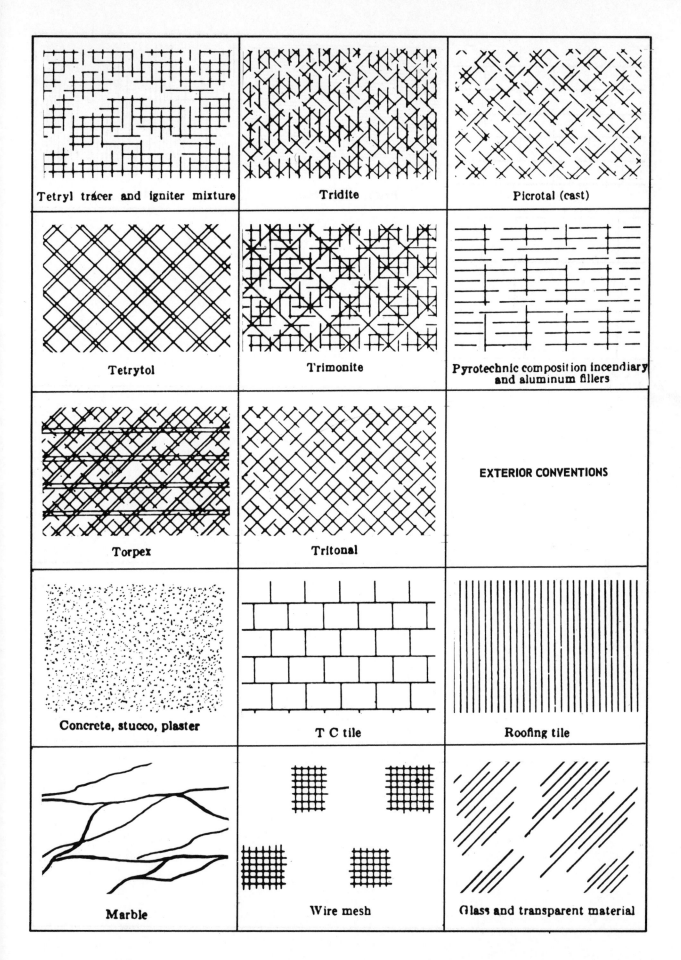

Tetryl tracer and igniter mixture

Tridite

Picrotal (cast)

Tetrytol

Trimonite

Pyrotechnic composition incendiary and aluminum fillers

Torpex

Tritonal

EXTERIOR CONVENTIONS

Concrete, stucco, plaster

T C tile

Roofing tile

Marble

Wire mesh

Glass and transparent material

375

Brick	Brick, small scale	Metal
Concrete block, cinder block		

The Code Identifies....

1. Metal gauge by drum head color & "M" color on drum sidewall.

2. Gasket material by angular symbols

    a) Number of symbols = number of bungs in drum head.

3. Type lining by circular symbols

    a) Number of symbols = number of lining coats.

Example: 18 gauge drum, two bungs in head (PE gaskets), two coats pigmented phenolic lining.

White head   ■   ■   = 2 PE gaskets in head.

White "M's"   ○   ○   = 2 coats pigmented phenolic lining.

Code Symbols

ANGULAR		GASKET MATERIAL
	Bar	Buna-N
	Triangle	Fiber
	Square	Polyethylene
	Diamond	Garlock

CIRCULAR		TYPE LINING
	Dot	Pigmented
	Ring	Phenolic
	Half Circle	Mod-phenolic
	Circle	Plastisol

MIL·STD 129 C **MARKING** **(SHIPMENT and** **STORAGE)**	*Extracted from MIL-STD-129C (superceding MIL-STD-129B), Marking for Shipment and Storage, with the permission of the Office of the Secretary of Defense, Public Affairs Department, Washington.*	

Bureau and Corps symbols.

 BUREAU OF AERONAUTICS	 BUREAU OF ORDNANCE	 BUREAU OF YARDS AND DOCKS
 BUREAU. OF SHIPS	 BUREAU OF SUPPLIES AND ACCOUNTS	 MARINE CORPS
 COAST GUARD	*Army service symbols.*  QUARTERMASTER CORPS	 ORDNANCE CORPS
 CHEMICAL CORPS	SIGNAL CORPS 	

CORPS OF ENGINEERS

TRANSPORTATION CORPS

Symbol for medical services of the Armed Forces.

Crescent symbol for subsistence items.

Radiation symbols.

TYPE I SYMBOL

TYPE II SYMBOL

Symbols for electronic equipment. Color: Green

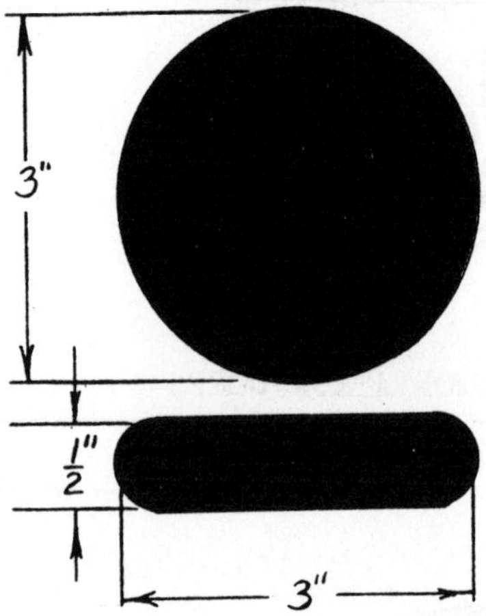

RADAR EQUIPMENT

RADIO COMMUNICATION EQUIPMENT

SHIPBOARD UNDERWATER SOUND EQUIPMENT

HARBOR DETECTION EQUIPMENT

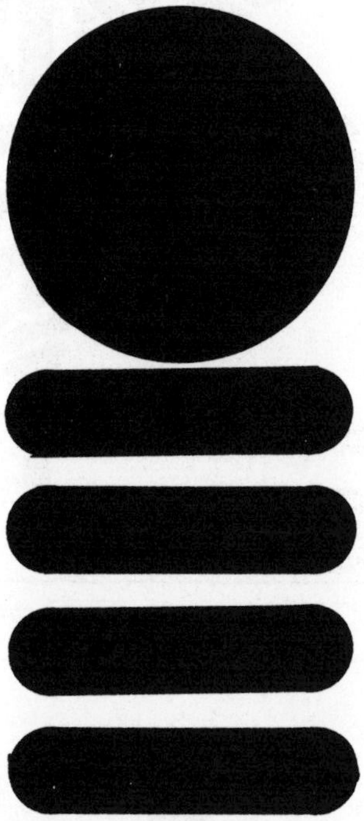

RADIOLOGICAL (RADIAC) EQUIPMENT

Radiation Hazard

USE NO HOOKS

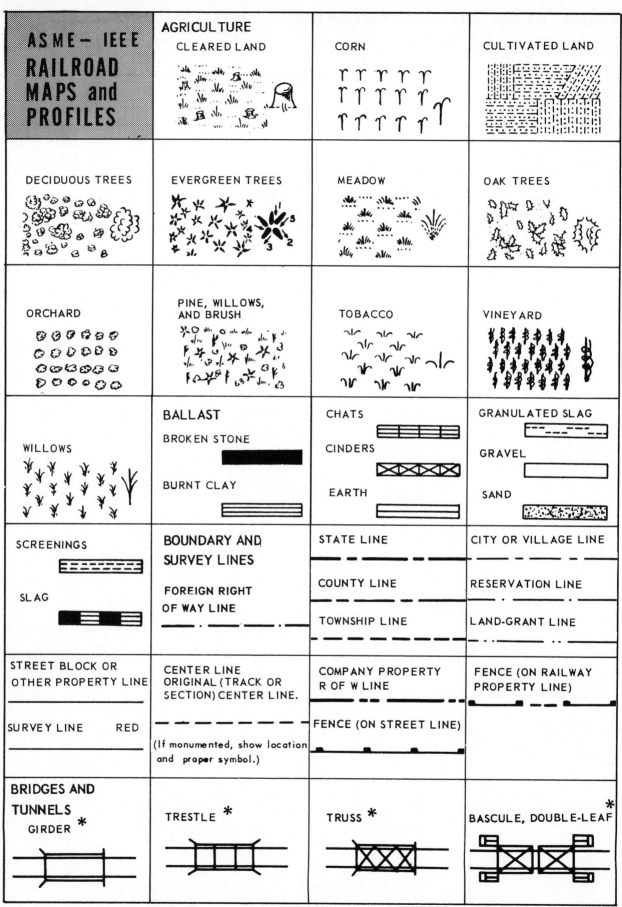

ASME — IEEE RAILROAD MAPS and PROFILES

AGRICULTURE

CLEARED LAND

CORN

CULTIVATED LAND

DECIDUOUS TREES

EVERGREEN TREES

MEADOW

OAK TREES

ORCHARD

PINE, WILLOWS, AND BRUSH

TOBACCO

VINEYARD

WILLOWS

BALLAST

BROKEN STONE

BURNT CLAY

CHATS

CINDERS

EARTH

GRANULATED SLAG

GRAVEL

SAND

SCREENINGS

SLAG

BOUNDARY AND SURVEY LINES

FOREIGN RIGHT OF WAY LINE

STATE LINE

COUNTY LINE

TOWNSHIP LINE

CITY OR VILLAGE LINE

RESERVATION LINE

LAND-GRANT LINE

STREET BLOCK OR OTHER PROPERTY LINE

SURVEY LINE   RED

CENTER LINE ORIGINAL (TRACK OR SECTION) CENTER LINE.

(If monumented, show location and proper symbol.)

COMPANY PROPERTY R OF W LINE

FENCE (ON STREET LINE)

FENCE (ON RAILWAY PROPERTY LINE)

BRIDGES AND TUNNELS
GIRDER *

TRESTLE *

TRUSS *

BASCULE, DOUBLE-LEAF *

Extracted from American Standard Graphical Symbols for Use on Railroad Maps and Profiles (ASA Y32.7-1957), with the permission of the publisher, the American Society of Mechanical Engineers, United Engineering Center, 345 East 47 Street, New York, N.Y.

BASCULE, SINGLE-LEAF*	DRAW SPAN*	LIFT SPAN*	MOVABLE BRIDGE CIRCUIT CONTROLLER
MOVABLE BRIDGE LOCK	MOVABLE BRIDGE PIPE COUPLER	MOVABLE BRIDGE RAIL LOCK	TUNNEL
(*State whether deck, half through or through bridge and use letters to describe girder and truss bridges. Give loading.)	**BUILDINGS AND STRUCTURES** BRICK ** B	CONCRETE** C	CORRUGATED IRON** CI
FRAME** F	STONE** S	** (**Indicate use and number of stories.)	CAR OR LOCOMOTIVE WASHER
CINDER PIT Cinder Hoist CP CH	COALING STATION -MECHANICAL C S	COALING STATION (TRESTLE) CS	DIESEL SHOP DS
ENGINE HOUSE (CIRCULAR)	ENGINE HOUSE (RECTANGULAR) (Indicate kind and character.)	FREIGHT STATION FS	GENERATING STATION DS
GRAIN ELEVATOR GE	INTERLOCKING OR BLOCK STATION (OPERATOR SYMBOL OPTIONAL) OPERATOR FACING TRACK OPERATOR WITH BACK TO TRACK		LIGHTNING-ARRESTER HOUSE LA

OIL COLUMN	OIL STORAGE AND DELIVERY TANKS	PASSENGER STATION	PLATFORM OR DRIVEWAY (Indicate kind and character.)
DIESEL OIL – DO FUEL OIL – FO LUBRICATING OIL – LO	DIESEL OIL – DO FUEL OIL – FO LUBRICATING OIL – LO	PS	
PRIVY	SECTION HOUSE	SECTION TOOL HOUSE	SUBSTATION
			S S
TURNTABLE (Indicate type and construction by combination of letters.)	**CARTOGRAPHY** BENCH MARK BM X 1232	CEMETERIES CEM ✝	CHURCH, SCHOOL
CITY	CITY LIMITS (*Hatch or color (transparent) red.)	COAST GUARD AND LIFE SAVING STATION C G S L S S	COKE OVENS
FIRE LIMITS	IRON MONUMENT	LIGHTHOUSE OR BEACON	MERIDIAN MAGNETIC N VARIATION ANGLE
MERIDIAN Z	MINE OR QUARRY Mine – M Quarry – Q M	MINE TUNNEL	OIL AND GAS WELLS
PROSPECT X	SECTION CENTER 17	SECTION CORNER 17 | 16 20 | 21	SHAFT

STONE MONUMENT	TANKS AND OIL RESERVOIRS	TRIANGULATION STATION OR TRANSIT POINT	VILLAGE
CULVERTS, SEWERS, ETC. (Indicates direction of flow →) CATCH BASIN	MANHOLE	MASONRY ARCH OR FLAT-TOP CULVERT	PIPE (OVER 36 IN. DIAM.) SIZE AND KIND
PIPE DRAIN OR WOOD BOX (36 IN. DIAM. AND UNDER) SIZE AND KIND	SEWER SIZE AND KIND	SUMP SUMP	**ELECTRIFIED LINES** FEEDER FEEDER → THIRD RAIL
JUMPERS RUNNING RAIL OR CENTER-LINE OF TRACK RUNNING RAIL	OVERHEAD RAIL OR WIRE STATE KIND	SWITCH	THIRD RAIL RUNNING RAIL OR CENTER-LINE OF TRACK
FENCES (Give height of fence.) BARBWIRE FENCE —X—X—X—	BOARD FENCE ELECTRIC FENCE —E—E—E—	HEDGE INTERTRACK FENCE	PICKET FENCE RAIL FENCE
SNOW FENCE	SNOW SHED	STOCK PENS	STONE FENCE WORM FENCE
WOVEN-WIRE FENCE	**FIRE PREVENTION** AUTOMATIC SPRINKLER AS	CHECK VALVE (Give size and kind.)	CHEMICAL FIRE EXTINGUISHER (Hand or wheel carriage.)

FIRE ALARM BOX (Give box number.) F A	**FIRE DEPT CONNECTION**	**FIRE HYDRANT** (Show size, number of hose and pumper connections.)	**HOSE AND HYDRANT HOUSE**
POST INDICATOR VALVE (Give size)	**WALL REEL OR HOSE RACK**	(Pipe fittings, valves, and other water-supply fixtures to be indicated and labeled by name where possible.)	**HIGHWAYS AND CROSSINGS** CATTLE GUARD
CROSSING GATE GATE ARM SIDEWALK CROSSING GATE WITH SIDEWALK ARM CROSSING GATE WITHOUT SIDEWALK ARM GATE ARM WITH LAMPS (Letters should be included within symbols or adjacent thereto to indicate characteristics such as: A - Automatic, M - Manual, A-M — Auto-Manual.)	**FARM GATE**		**PRIVATE AND SECONDARY ROADS**
PRIVATE ROAD CROSSING	**PUBLIC AND MAIN ROADS** (Show state or U.S. route number.)	**ROAD CROSSING AT GRADE**	**ROAD CROSSING UNDER GRADE**
ROAD CROSSING OVERHEAD	**SIGNALS** * -HIGHWAY CROSSING BELL	**CROSSING SIGN**	**FLASHING LIGHTS** ONE WAY BOTH WAYS
FLASHING LIGHT AND NO TURN SIGN FY = Flashing yellow NLT = No left turn NRT = No right turn	**ILLUMINATED STOP SIGN** S T O P	**NUMBER OF TRACKS SIGN** (Mounted on signal post) (Number of tracks to be shown on plan or covered by note.)	**ROTATING DISK** STOP
STOP ON RED SIGNAL SIGN S R S	**STOP WHEN SWINGING SIGN** S W S	**TRAFFIC DIRECTION**	**WIG-WAG** * (Combination of symbols may be used as required.)

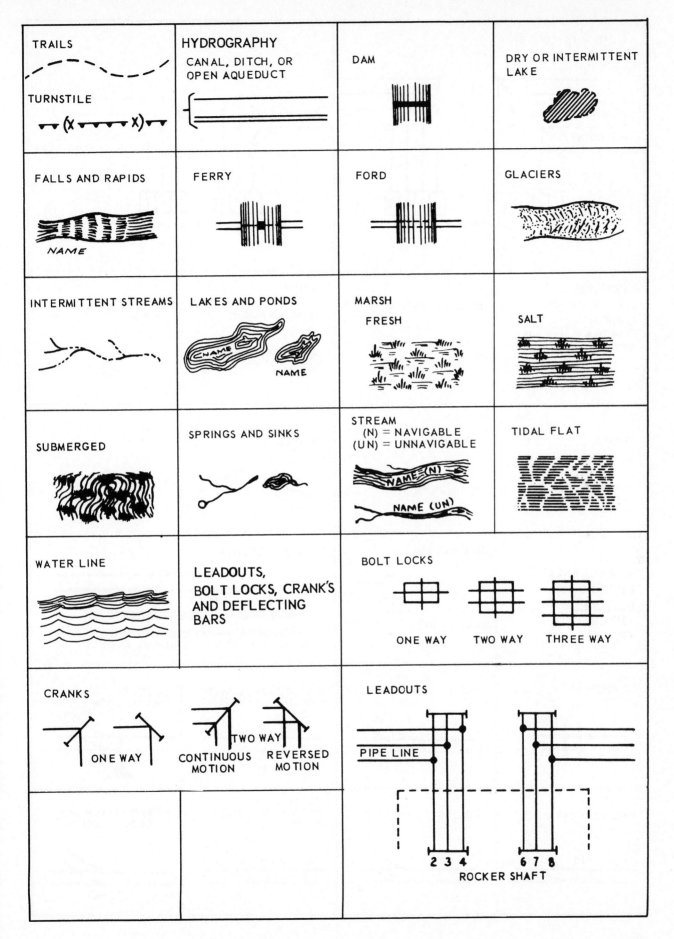

TRAILS

TURNSTILE

HYDROGRAPHY

CANAL, DITCH, OR OPEN AQUEDUCT

DAM

DRY OR INTERMITTENT LAKE

FALLS AND RAPIDS

NAME

FERRY

FORD

GLACIERS

INTERMITTENT STREAMS

LAKES AND PONDS

NAME

NAME

MARSH

FRESH

SALT

SUBMERGED

SPRINGS AND SINKS

STREAM
(N) = NAVIGABLE
(UN) = UNNAVIGABLE

NAME (N)

NAME (UN)

TIDAL FLAT

WATER LINE

LEADOUTS, BOLT LOCKS, CRANK'S AND DEFLECTING BARS

BOLT LOCKS

ONE WAY   TWO WAY   THREE WAY

CRANKS

ONE WAY

TWO WAY

CONTINUOUS MOTION

REVERSED MOTION

LEADOUTS

PIPE LINE

2 3 4   6 7 8
ROCKER SHAFT

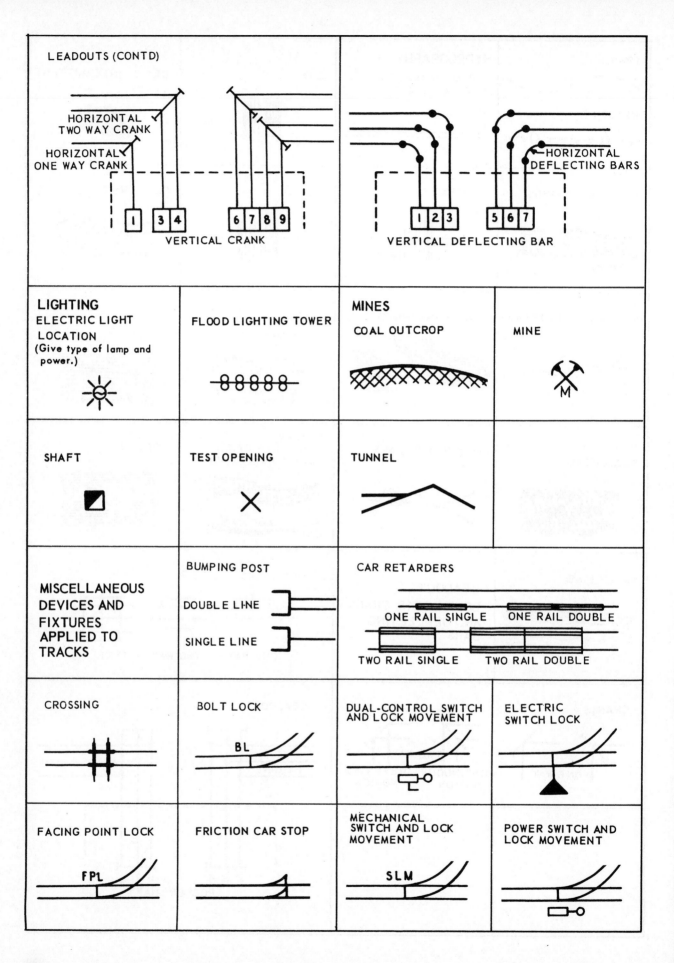

LEADOUTS (CONTD)

HORIZONTAL
TWO WAY CRANK

HORIZONTAL
ONE WAY CRANK

VERTICAL CRANK

HORIZONTAL
DEFLECTING BARS

VERTICAL DEFLECTING BAR

LIGHTING
ELECTRIC LIGHT
LOCATION
(Give type of lamp and
power.)

FLOOD LIGHTING TOWER

MINES
COAL OUTCROP

MINE

SHAFT

TEST OPENING

TUNNEL

MISCELLANEOUS
DEVICES AND
FIXTURES
APPLIED TO
TRACKS

BUMPING POST

DOUBLE LINE

SINGLE LINE

CAR RETARDERS

ONE RAIL SINGLE   ONE RAIL DOUBLE

TWO RAIL SINGLE   TWO RAIL DOUBLE

CROSSING

BOLT LOCK

BL

DUAL-CONTROL SWITCH
AND LOCK MOVEMENT

ELECTRIC
SWITCH LOCK

FACING POINT LOCK

FPL

FRICTION CAR STOP

MECHANICAL
SWITCH AND LOCK
MOVEMENT

SLM

POWER SWITCH AND
LOCK MOVEMENT

RAIL LUBRICATOR	TRACK SCALE	SWITCH CIRCUIT CONTROLLER	SPRING SWITCH
SPRING SWITCH WITH MECHANICAL LOCK	SWITCH STAND	INDUCTIVE TRAIN STOP	INSULATED RAIL JOINTS
		CLEAR	
		STOP	
		UNWOUND (STOP)	TRACK CIRCUITS IN BOTH DIRECTIONS
TRACK CIRCUIT ON LEFT NONE ON RIGHT	TRACK CIRCUIT ON RIGHT NONE ON LEFT	INSULATED SWITCH ROD	DRAGGING EQUIPMENT DETECTOR
SKATE MACHINES	TRACK INSTRUMENT	TRIP TRAIN STOP	
MANUAL			STOP
POWER			CLEAR
		NONAUTOMATIC MECHANICAL POWER	
STOP	OIL AND GAS		
CLEAR	LOCATION, RIG, OR DRILLING WELL	DRY HOLE	
SLOTTED SEMIAUTOMATIC AUTOMATIC			
DRY HOLE WITH SHOWING OF OIL	GAS WELL	GAS WELL WITH SHOWING OF OIL	OIL WELL
SMALL OIL WELL	SALT WELL	SYMBOL OF ABANDONMENT: V	NUMBER OF WELLS, THUS

		AIR PIPE AND FITTINGS	EXPANSION JOINT
SHOW DAILY PRODUCTION, THUS: ☼ 3M/7 ● 3M/3B 2 ● 30B SALT SAND 3 ☼ 1½M INJUN 6 ● 13 INJUN 5 M = 1000 Cubic Feet. B = Barrels. Injun is name of well.		COMBINATION COCK AND UNION	
MANIFOLD CONDENSER	PIPE ANCHOR	PLUG COCK (DRAIN OR BLOWOFF)	REDUCER OR BUSHING (POINT TO SMALLER PIPE)
MAIN AUXILIARY RESERVOIR	TEE	UNION	VALVE (Indicate size.)
WATER SUPPLY AND PIPE LINES For detailed plans, select symbols from other Standards	WATER (COMPANY PIPE) COLD HOT	CONDENSATE. GAS	OIL LINES REFRIGERANT
STEAM (*Give size and kind of pipe and direction of flow.)	METER (Give name and size)	RISER (Give size and kind of pipe)	TRACK PAN
WATER COLUMN GAS COLUMN (Letter in circle to designate kind of column.)	WATER TANK (Give character, diameter, height, capacity in gallons.)	SIGNAL PIPE AND WIRE LINES ARROW INDICATES DIRECTION OF MOVEMENT OF PIPE LINE NORMAL TO REVERSE →	COMPENSATOR COMPRESSED AIR
DUCT AND AIR MECHANICAL PIPE AND AIR	MECHANICAL PIPE AND DUCT MECHANICAL PIPE DUCT AND AIR	OIL ENCLOSED PIPE LINE PIPE ADJUSTING SCREW	PIPE (MECHANICAL) SPLICING CHAMBER

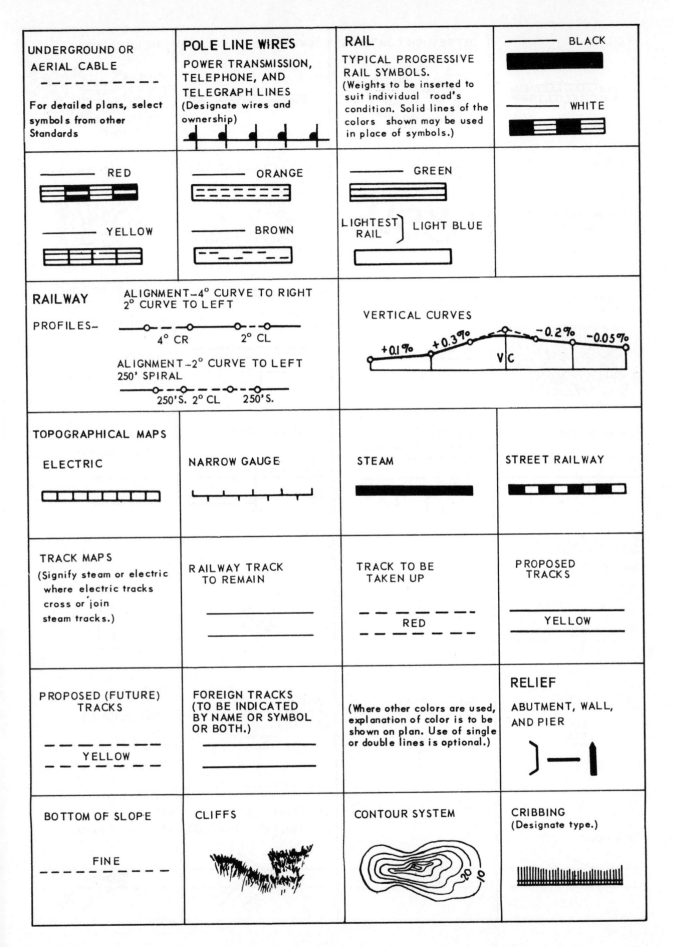

UNDERGROUND OR AERIAL CABLE - - - - - - - - - - For detailed plans, select symbols from other Standards	POLE LINE WIRES POWER TRANSMISSION, TELEPHONE, AND TELEGRAPH LINES (Designate wires and ownership)	RAIL TYPICAL PROGRESSIVE RAIL SYMBOLS. (Weights to be inserted to suit individual road's condition. Solid lines of the colors shown may be used in place of symbols.)	BLACK WHITE
RED YELLOW	ORANGE BROWN	GREEN LIGHTEST RAIL } LIGHT BLUE	
RAILWAY PROFILES—	ALIGNMENT—4° CURVE TO RIGHT 2° CURVE TO LEFT 4° CR 2° CL ALIGNMENT—2° CURVE TO LEFT 250' SPIRAL 250'S. 2° CL 250'S.	VERTICAL CURVES +0.1% +0.3% −0.2% −0.05% V C	
TOPOGRAPHICAL MAPS ELECTRIC	NARROW GAUGE	STEAM	STREET RAILWAY
TRACK MAPS (Signify steam or electric where electric tracks cross or join steam tracks.)	RAILWAY TRACK TO REMAIN	TRACK TO BE TAKEN UP - - - - - RED - - - - -	PROPOSED TRACKS YELLOW
PROPOSED (FUTURE) TRACKS - - - - - - YELLOW - - - - - -	FOREIGN TRACKS (TO BE INDICATED BY NAME OR SYMBOL OR BOTH.)	(Where other colors are used, explanation of color is to be shown on plan. Use of single or double lines is optional.)	RELIEF ABUTMENT, WALL, AND PIER
BOTTOM OF SLOPE FINE - - - - - - -	CLIFFS	CONTOUR SYSTEM 20 10	CRIBBING (Designate type.)

393

CUT	DEPRESSION CONTOURS	EMBANKMENT	HILL SHADING
LEVEES	MINE DUMPS	SAND AND SAND DUNES	SUBMARINE CONTOURS
TAILINGS OR MINING DEBRIS	TOP OF SLOPE MEDIUM	**SIGNAL SUPPORTS** BRACKET POST	CANTILEVER POST
GROUND MAST	GROUND MAST WITH BRACKET ATTACHMENT	SIGNAL BRIDGE	(Signal governs movement on solid lines.)
SIGN BOARDS AND POSTS BRIDGE AND TUNNEL WARNING	FLANGER SIGN	MILE POST	OTHER POSTS (Describe with letters.)
SECTION POST	WHISTLE POST	YARD LIMIT AND ROADWAY SIGNS, LEGEND AS REQUIRED	**SWITCHES AND DERAILS** REFER TO TRACK MAP SYMBOLS
SINGLE SWITCH SET FOR STRAIGHT TRACK	SET FOR TURNOUT	THREE-WAY SWITCH SET FOR LEFT TURNOUT	SET FOR STRAIGHT TRACK

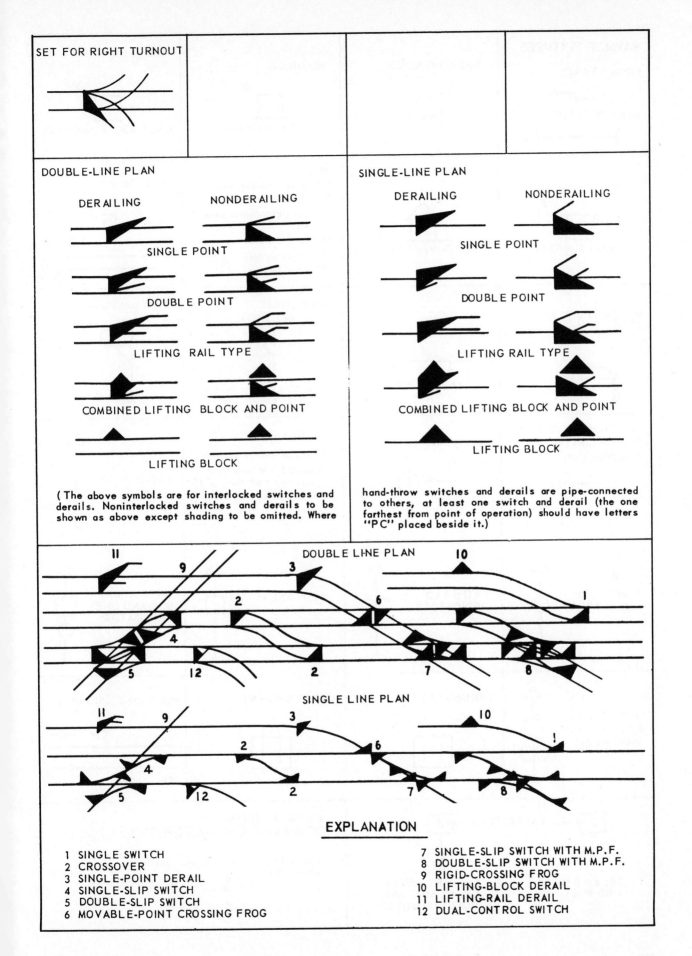

SET FOR RIGHT TURNOUT

DOUBLE-LINE PLAN

DERAILING NONDERAILING

SINGLE POINT

DOUBLE POINT

LIFTING RAIL TYPE

COMBINED LIFTING BLOCK AND POINT

LIFTING BLOCK

(The above symbols are for interlocked switches and derails. Noninterlocked switches and derails to be shown as above except shading to be omitted. Where

SINGLE-LINE PLAN

DERAILING NONDERAILING

SINGLE POINT

DOUBLE POINT

LIFTING RAIL TYPE

COMBINED LIFTING BLOCK AND POINT

LIFTING BLOCK

hand-throw switches and derails are pipe-connected to others, at least one switch and derail (the one farthest from point of operation) should have letters "PC" placed beside it.)

DOUBLE LINE PLAN

SINGLE LINE PLAN

EXPLANATION

1 SINGLE SWITCH
2 CROSSOVER
3 SINGLE-POINT DERAIL
4 SINGLE-SLIP SWITCH
5 DOUBLE-SLIP SWITCH
6 MOVABLE-POINT CROSSING FROG

7 SINGLE-SLIP SWITCH WITH M.P.F.
8 DOUBLE-SLIP SWITCH WITH M.P.F.
9 RIGID-CROSSING FROG
10 LIFTING-BLOCK DERAIL
11 LIFTING-RAIL DERAIL
12 DUAL-CONTROL SWITCH

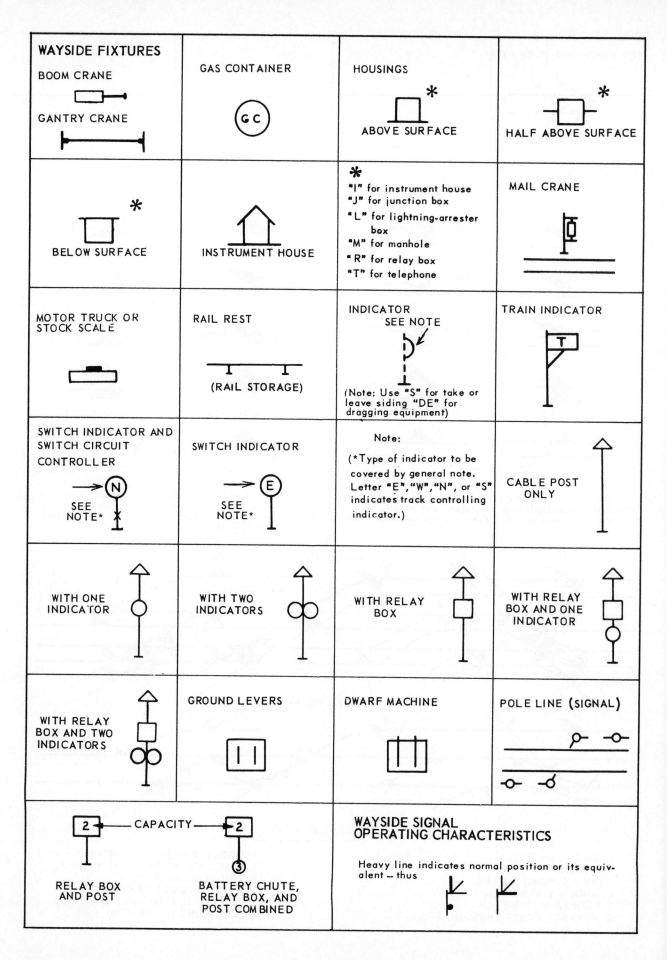

WAYSIDE FIXTURES BOOM CRANE GANTRY CRANE	GAS CONTAINER G C	HOUSINGS ABOVE SURFACE	HALF ABOVE SURFACE
BELOW SURFACE	INSTRUMENT HOUSE	* "I" for instrument house "J" for junction box "L" for lightning-arrester box "M" for manhole "R" for relay box "T" for telephone	MAIL CRANE
MOTOR TRUCK OR STOCK SCALE	RAIL REST (RAIL STORAGE)	INDICATOR SEE NOTE (Note: Use "S" for take or leave siding "DE" for dragging equipment)	TRAIN INDICATOR T
SWITCH INDICATOR AND SWITCH CIRCUIT CONTROLLER N SEE NOTE*	SWITCH INDICATOR E SEE NOTE*	Note: (*Type of indicator to be covered by general note. Letter "E","W","N", or "S" indicates track controlling indicator.)	CABLE POST ONLY
WITH ONE INDICATOR	WITH TWO INDICATORS	WITH RELAY BOX	WITH RELAY BOX AND ONE INDICATOR
WITH RELAY BOX AND TWO INDICATORS	GROUND LEVERS	DWARF MACHINE	POLE LINE (SIGNAL)
2 —CAPACITY— 2 RELAY BOX AND POST	2 3 BATTERY CHUTE, RELAY BOX, AND POST COMBINED	**WAYSIDE SIGNAL OPERATING CHARACTERISTICS** Heavy line indicates normal position or its equivalent – thus	

Prefix the letter "A" to abbreviation if used for approach lighting. Abbreviations to be used only where more than one type of signal is shown on plan.

ABBREVIATIONS

E	Electric semaphore	M	Mechanical
P	Position light	C	Color light
CP	Color position light	SL	Searchlight

EXPLANATORY DATA

THREE-POSITION SEMIAUTOMATIC STICK 45° TO 90°
SEMIAUTOMATIC NONSTICK 0° TO U.Q. 45°

FOUR POSITION
SEMIAUTOMATIC STICK 0° TO U.Q. 45° TO 90° NONAUTOMATIC 0° TO L.Q. 45°

NONOPERATING

MARKERS
NORMALLY NOT LIGHTED: NON-STICK

○

NORMALLY LIGHTED: NON-STICK

●

NORMALLY NOT LIGHTED: STICK

φ

NORMALLY LIGHTED: STICK

◆

GRADE SIGNAL

Ⓖ

SMASHBOARD SIGNALS

POWER    MECHANICAL

GRAPHICAL SYMBOLS

POSITION OR EQUIV-ALENT	NON-AUTOMATIC	SEMIAUTOMATIC		AUTOMATIC	SPECIAL REQUIRES REFERENCE TO NOTES
		STICK	NON STICK		
0° U.Q. 45°					
0° L.Q. 45°					
0° U.Q. 90°					
U.Q. 45° L.Q. 45°					
U.Q. 45° 90°					
L.Q. 45° U.Q. 90°					
0° U.Q. 45° L.Q. 45°					
0° U.Q. 45° 90°					
0° U.Q. 90° L.Q. 45°					
U.Q. 45° 90° L.Q. 45°					
0° U.Q.45° 90° L.Q. 45°					

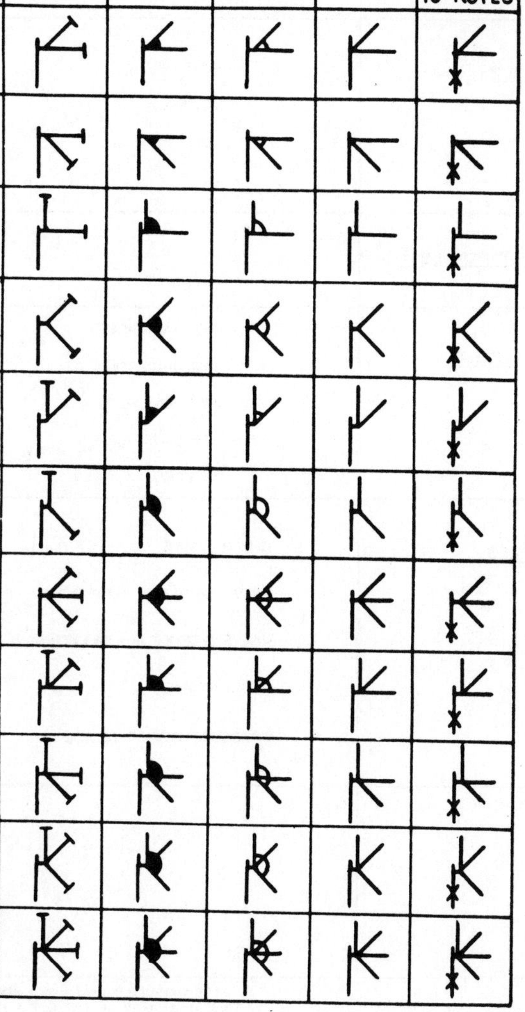

	A.G.A. MAPPING	Extracted from DMC-62-4, AGA Standard on Graphic Symbols for Piping Maps, with the permission of the publisher, the American Gas Association, 420 Lexington Avenue, New York, N.Y.	

ITEM	TYPE	SYMBOL	COMMENTS
MAINS	EXISTING	———————	*
	PROPOSED	— — — — —	
PIPE MATERIAL	STEEL	S.	
	CAST IRON	C.I.	
	DUCTILE IRON	D.I.	
	WROUGHT IRON	W.I.	
	COPPER	C.U.	
	PLASTIC	P.L.	
PRESSURE	HIGH	H.P.	PRESSURE LIMITS FOR EACH CATEGORY TO BE ESTABLISHED BY INDIVIDUAL COMPANIES. OTHER SIMILAR DESIGNATIONS MAY BE ADOPTED BY INDIVIDUAL COMPANIES TO MEET VARYING REQUIREMENTS.
	MEDIUM	M.P.	
	LOW	L.P.	
WALL THICKNESS			IF DESIRED, WALL THICKNESS MAY BE SHOWN BY DECIMAL.
TYPE JOINT	BELL & SPIGOT	B.S.	
	COMPRESSION	C.	
	MECHANICAL	M.J.	
	THREADED	T.	
	WELDED	W.	
VALVES	CHECK VALVE		ARROW INDICATES DIRECTION OF FLOW.
	VALVE (WITH BOX OR EXTENSION)		IF NECESSARY TO DISTINGUISH BETWEEN KIND OF VALVE, USE LETTER SYMBOLS. (G-GATE, P-PLUG, TC-THROUGH CONDUIT, M-MANUAL, A-AUTOMATIC OR R-REMOTE)
	VALVE (WITHOUT BOX OR EXTENSION)		
	REGULATOR		USE LETTER SYMBOL TO INDICATE TYPE. (A-ABOVE GROUND, B-BURIED OR V-VAULT OR PIT)
	PRESSURE RELIEF DEVICE		USE LETTER SYMBOL TO INDICATE TYPE. (MS-MECHANICAL RELIEF OR LS-LIQUID SEAL)
			CONTINUED

* EXPLANATION OF MAINS

IT IS SUGGESTED THAT LINES REPRESENTING GAS MAINS BE VERY HEAVY ON THE DRAWING SO THAT THEY SHOW UP DISTINCTLY. IT IS ALSO RECOMMENDED THAT LINE SIZE, OPERATING PRESSURE, MATERIAL AND TYPE OF JOINT BE DESIGNATED BY LETTERS & FIGURES. YEAR OF INSTALLATION MAY ALSO BE SHOWN.

2" PIPE
2"S-MP-T
STEEL
THREADED
MEDIUM PRESSURE

ITEM	TYPE	SYMBOL	COMMENTS
FITTINGS	ELBOW – 45°		
	ELBOW – 90°		
	TEE		
	WYE		
	CROSS		
	OFFSET		
	COMPRESSION COUPLING (NONINSULATING)		
	FLANGED JOINT (NONINSULATING)		
	UNION		
	ECCENTRIC REDUCER	8″ ▲ 6″	
	CONCENTRIC REDUCER	8″ ▶ 6″	
	ORIFICE FLANGE OR FITTING		
	LINE STOPPER FITTING (SUCH AS MUELLER OR WILLIAMSON STOPPLE)	CL	
	BELL JOINT OR LEAK CLAMP	Z Z	Z's INDICATE LIMITS OF CONTINUOUS CLAMPED LINE. FOR AN INDIVIDUAL CLAMP DELETE USE OF Z's.
MISCELLANEOUS	CROSSOVER (NO CONNECTION)		
	MAIN END (WELDED FLAT PLATE)		
	MAIN END (CAST IRON PLUG OR BLIND FLANGE)		
	MAIN (WELDING CAP, THREADED COUPLING & PLUG, THREADED CAP OR CAST IRON CAP)		
	DRIP		IF DESIRED, TO DISTINGUISH BETWEEN TYPES OF DRIPS, ADD LETTER SYMBOL IN LARGE CIRCLE. (L–LINE DRIP, S–SYPHON DRIP) OTHERS AS REQUIRED.
	BLOWDOWN OR TEST STAND	2″	
	CASING		IF DESIRED, SHOW CASING SIZE BY NUMBER.
	RIVER & OR SWAMP WEIGHT		
	REINFORCING SLEEVE (PUMPKIN)		
	PIPELINE CLEANING INSTALLATION	PIG	

CONTINUED

ITEM	TYPE	SYMBOL	COMMENTS
CORROSION PROTECTION	ANODE (WITH TEST LEAD WIRES)	(AL)	
	ANODE (WITHOUT TEST LEAD WIRES)	(A)	NUMBER OF ANODES IN BED CAN BE SHOWN BY ADDING NUMBER.
	BONDED	(B) ALSO (B)	IF DESIRED, USE "SB" FOR SOLID BOND AND "RB" FOR RESISTANCE BOND.
	LEAD WIRES	(L)	IF MORE THAN ONE WIRE, SHOW BY ADDED LINE.
	RECTIFIER & GROUND BED	(R)	
	INSULATED JOINT		USE LETTER SYMBOL TO DESIGNATE TYPE, IF DESIRED. (C-COUPLED F-FLANGED U-UNION)
	PROTECTIVE COATED PIPE (EXTERIOR)	Y (PC) Y	"Y" INDICATES LIMITS OF COATED AREA. IF AREA COVERED BY MAP IS COMPLETELY COATED IT SHOULD BE INDICATED BY A GENERAL NOTE AND THE SYMBOL WOULD NOT BE NECESSARY. TYPE OF COATING MAY BE INDICATED, IF DESIRED.
	PROTECTIVE COATED PIPE (INTERIOR)	Y (IC) Y	
	INTERNAL SEALED PIPE	Y (IS) Y	
ACCESSORIES	HOLDER STATION	H.	
	METER STATION	M.	
	ODORIZER	O.	ACCESSORIES WHERE A STATION PERFORMS MORE THAN ONE FUNCTION COMBINE LETTERS TO DESIGNATE ALL FUNCTIONS PERFORMED.
	REGULATOR PIT	R.P.	
	REGULATOR STATION (ABOVE GROUND)	R.S	
	VALVE PIT	V.P.	
COMPRESSOR STATIONS	RECIPROCATING COMP. STA.		
	GAS TURBINE DRIVEN CENTRIFUGAL COMP. STA.		
	ELECTRIC MOTOR DRIVEN CENTRIFUGAL COMP. STA.		
	GAS ENGINE DRIVEN CENTRIFUGAL COMP. STA.		
	STEAM TURBINE DRIVEN CENTRIFUGAL COMP. STA.		
PLANTS	NATURAL GAS LIQUIDS ABSORPTION PLANT		
	NATURAL GAS LIQUIDS PRODUCTS FRACTIONATION PLANT		
	GAS DEHYDRATION PLANT		
	GAS PURIFICATION & DEHYDRATION PLANT		
WELL SYMBOLS			USE SYMBOLS FROM A.P.I. STD. RP-35.

PAGE 401

Extracted from API Recommended Practice for Oil-mapping Symbols (API RP35), with the permission of the publisher, the American Petroleum Institute, Division of Production, Dallas, Tex.

Location .... ◯

Abandoned Location .... erase symbol

Dry Hole ....

Oil Well .... ●

Abandoned Oil Well ....

Gas Well ....

Abandoned Gas Well ....

Distillate Well ....

Abandoned Distillate Well ....

Dual Completion—Oil .... ◉

Dual Completion—Gas ....

Drilled Water-input Well .... ⌀W

Converted Water-input Well .... ●W

Drilled Gas-input Well .... ⌀G

Converted Gas-input Well .... ●G

Bottom-hole Location .... ◯----x
    (x indicates bottom of hole. Changes in well status
      should be indicated as in symbols above.)

Salt-water Disposal Well .... ⊕SWD

U.S. Coast & Geodetic Survey

MAPPING
(AERONAUTICAL)

Extracted from Local and Sectional Aeronautical Charts, with the permission of the Director, Coast and Geodetic Survey, Department of Commerce, Washington.

LOCAL CHARTS

The Local Aeronautical Chart series is designed to supplement the Sectional Charts by providing additional landmark information and topographic detail in the vicinity of large air terminals. The index map below indicates the coverage of published local charts.

Because of frequent changes, Local Charts are scheduled for printing every six months (Honolulu and San Juan annually) to provide the airman with the latest charted information possible, and are sold through authorized agents located at airports and principal cities throughout the United States. They may also be obtained by writing to the Director, Coast and Geodetic Survey, U. S. Department of Commerce, Washington 25, D. C.

In the lower right hand corner is printed the date of the chart. The scheduled time for the next edition is indicated under the date. After the expiration of this time from the date of the chart, users are advised to check with notices (Dates of Latest Prints) on file with authorized agents. Charts that carry older dates than those shown on this list of dates are obsolete.

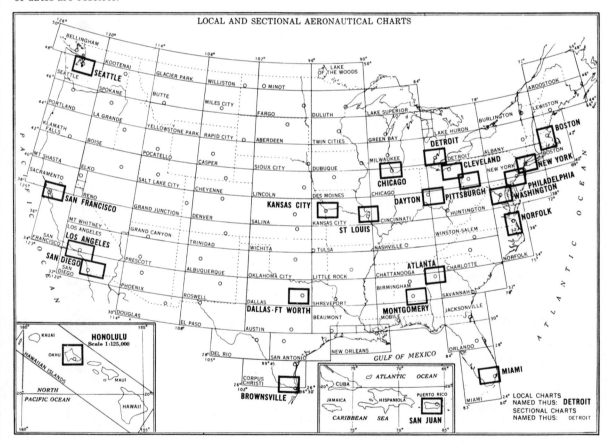

LOCAL AND SECTIONAL AERONAUTICAL CHARTS

SECTIONAL CHARTS

The Sectional Aeronautical Chart series provides complete coverage of the United States except Alaska and is designed primarily for contact flying. The charts portray detailed cultural and topographic features including important landmarks and selected aeronautical information required for visual navigation supplemented by instruments.

Because of frequent changes, most Sectional Charts are scheduled for printing every six months to provide the airman with the latest charted information possible. Others are scheduled annually. Aeronautical Charts are sold through authorized agents located at airports and principal cities throughout the United States. They may also be obtained by writing to the Director, Coast and Geodetic Survey, U. S. Department of Commerce, Washington 25, D. C.

AERONAUTICAL SYMBOLS   AERODROMES

Aerodromes with facilities	LAND	WATER	Aerodromes with emergency or no facilities	LAND	WATER
Civil	⊕	⊕	Landing Area	○	
Joint Civil and Military	◉	◉	Anchorage		⚓
Military	◎	◉	Heliport (Selected)		
Aerodromes with hard-surfaced runways at least 1500 feet long	Civil Military		Aerodromes with hard-surfaced runways at least 1500 feet long		
Aerodrome with runway length of 4000 feet or over			Landing Area with runway length 4000 feet or over		

AERODROME DATA
AND LANDING FACILITIES INFORMATION

LAND	WATER

LAND

```
PITTSBURGH
1168 L H 80
Airport of entry
GCA ILS DF
396 118.7 126.2
257.8 ,122.7G
```

1168	Elevation in feet
L	Minimum lighting
H	Hard surfaced runway
80	Length of longest runway in hundreds of feet
GCA ILS	Controlled approach systems
DF	Direction Finding Station
396 118.7 126.2 257.8 3053	Control tower transmitting frequencies.
122.7G 122.9G	Non-standard control tower guarding frequencies.

WATER

```
NAS NORFOLK
oo L S 120
3053
```

oo	Elevation in feet
L	Minimum lighting
S	Normal sheltered take-off area
120	Length of longest runway in hundreds of feet

LF/MF tower frequency shown first, followed in order by primary VHF local control, primary military VHF and UHF, and non-standard guarding frequencies.

```
MILLER
827 - - 26 U
```

U	Aeronautical advisory station licensed to operate on 122.8 mc.

When facility or information is lacking, the respective character is replaced by a dash.

AIR NAVIGATION LIGHTS

Rotating Light	_____☆	Flashing Light	____ Fl ☆
Rotating Light (With flashing code lights)	____ ···☆	Flashing Light (With code)	____ Fl ☆
Rotating Light (With course lights and site number)	____ !2 ☆	Lightship	____
Rotating Light (On top of high structure)	____ 1504 ☆	Marine Light	____ Occ W R G ●

F—Fixed	Qk Fl—Quick Flashing	Occ—Occulting	Gp—Group	W—White	B—Blue	(Sector)—Sector
Fl—Flashing	I Qk Fl—Interrupted Quick Flashing	Alt—Alternating	R—Red	G—Green	(U)—Unwatched	sec—Second

Marine lights are white unless colors are indicated; alternating lights are red and white unless otherwise indicated

CONTINUED

AERONAUTICAL SYMBOLS MISCELLANEOUS

Obstruction, less than 500 ft. above ground _ _ _ _ _ _ _ 1104 △

Obstruction, 500 feet or higher above ground _ _ _ 1490
(Numerals indicate elevation above sea level top)
(UC: Under construction, position and elevation unverified) △ UC

Prominent Transmission Line _ _ _ _ _ _ —T— — —T—

T-Line Crossing _ _ _ _ _ _ —T—— —T CAUTION

Mooring Mast _ _ _ _ _ _ _ _ _ _ _ _ _ _ _ _ _ _

Isogonic Line _ _ _ _ _ _ _ _ _ _ _ _ — — —8°E— — — —
(Values for 1960)

Reporting Point (Compulsory) _ _ _ _ _ _ _ _ _ _ _ _ _ _ _ ▲

Reporting Point (Non-compulsory) _ _ _ _ _ _ _ _ _ _ _ _ _ _ △

Abandoned Airport _ _ _ _ _ _ _ _ _ _ _ _ _ _ _ _ _ Abandoned airport ▪

Ocean Station Vessel (Normal position) _ _ _ _ _ _ _ _ _

International Boundary _ _ _ _ _ _ _ _ _
(Closed to passage of aircraft
except through air corridor)

Restricted areas are numbered and are indicated on the charts as follows:

Prohibited Area	Restricted, Warning, or Danger Area	Caution Area
P-20 OR C6P9	R-2201 W-559 OR C5D27	C-520

RADIO FACILITIES

All radio facility data are printed in blue with the exception of certain LF/MF facilities such
as tower frequencies, radio ranges and associated airways, which are printed in magenta.
Methods of indicating specific voice and CW calls are shown below   Use of the word "Radio" within the box indicates voice facilities

Radio Range _ _ _ _ _ _ _ _ _ _ _ _ ○
(With voice)   (Two letter identification assigned
when associated with VOR)
BALTIMORE RADIO
257 BL ▄▄▄

Radio Range _ _ _ _ _ _ _ _ _ _ ○
(Without voice)
EGLIN
209 VPS ▄▄
No voice

Nondirectional Radiobeacon _ _ _ ◉←
(With voice)
DOUGLAS RADIO
251 DGW ▄▄

Nondirectional Radiobeacon _ _ _ ◉←
(Without voice)
DIXIE
388 DXE ▄▄
No voice

Marine Radiobeacon _ _ _ _ _ _ _ ○
(Without voice)
RBn
ASHTABULA
314 ▄▄▄
0m-10m & 30m-40m

Outer Marker Radiobeacon _ _ ◉←
(Shown when component
of airway system)
LOM
359 EW ▄▄
No voice

Radio Communication Station _ _ _ _ ○
(With voice)
CS
GOWEN RADIO
4470

Radio Communication Station _ _ _ _ ○
(Without voice)
CS
KAZAN
5200 CKNX
No voice

Radio Broadcasting Station _ _ _ _ _ ○
BS
CFRB
1010

Radio Fan Marker Beacons _ _
100 watts
5 watts
NOTT
BATES
DIXIE

Localizer _ _ _ _ _ _ _ _ _ _ _ _ _ _ ○ LOCALIZER
(Shown when component   109.5 I BED
of airway system)

CONTINUED

AERONAUTICAL SYMBOLS RADIO FACILITIES

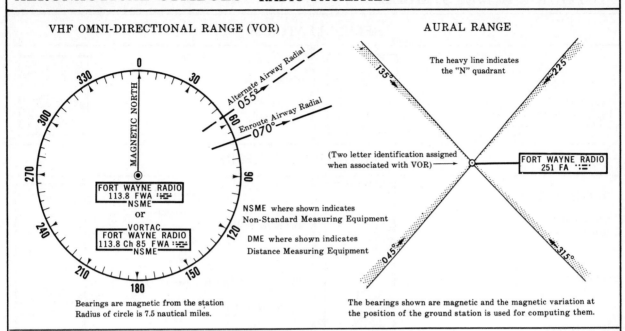

VHF OMNI-DIRECTIONAL RANGE (VOR)

MAGNETIC NORTH

Alternate Airway Radial
055°

Enroute Airway Radial
070°

FORT WAYNE RADIO
113.8 FWA
NSME

or

VORTAC
FORT WAYNE RADIO
113.8 Ch 85 FWA
NSME

NSME where shown indicates
Non-Standard Measuring Equipment

DME where shown indicates
Distance Measuring Equipment

Bearings are magnetic from the station
Radius of circle is 7.5 nautical miles.

AURAL RANGE

The heavy line indicates
the "N" quadrant

(Two letter identification assigned
when associated with VOR)→

FORT WAYNE RADIO
251 FA

The bearings shown are magnetic and the magnetic variation at
the position of the ground station is used for computing them.

AIR TRAFFIC CONTROL

Control Zone

High Density
Traffic Zone

(Within continental U.S. except Alaska all airspace at and above 14,500
feet, excluding airspace less than 1500 feet above terrain, prohibited
areas, and certain restricted areas, is included within the Continental
Control Area, and blue tint therefore indicates only controlled airspace
below 14,500 feet).

Controlled Federal Airways (normally 10 miles wide)   Uncontrolled Federal Airway

Low Altitude Federal Airways within continental U.S. except Alaska are effective only below 14,500 feet MSL.   (Effective April 6, 1961)
Canadian airways and air routes extend to 23,000 feet ASL.

TOPOGRAPHICAL SYMBOLS

CITIES AND TOWNS	HIGHWAYS AND ROADS
Metropolitan Areas_____ **NEW YORK**	Dual Lane and Super Highways_____
Large Cities_____ **RICHMOND**	Primary Roads_____
Cities_____ Arlington	Secondary Roads_____
Small Cities & Large Towns _____ Freehold ☐	Trails _____
Towns_____ Corville ○	U. S. Road Markers_____ 🛡60
Small Towns & Villages_____ Arcola ○	National, State or_____ 37 Provincial Road Markers
	Road Names_____ **ALASKA HIGHWAY**

CONTINUED

TOPOGRAPHICAL SYMBOLS

RELIEF FEATURES

Contours { Reliable ....
Approximate ....
Depression ....

Levees or Eskers ....

Peaks or Buttes, isolated ....

Bluffs, Cliffs & Escarpments ....

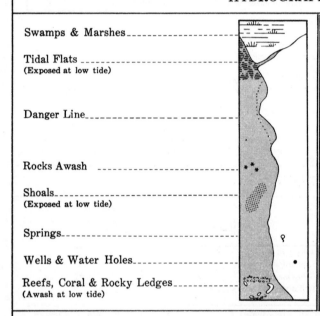

Sand { Dunes ....
Areas ....
Ridges ....

Lava Flow ....

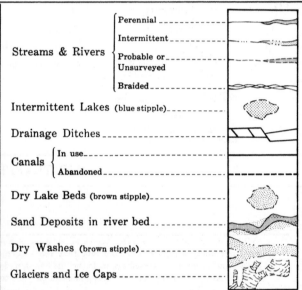

HYDROGRAPHIC FEATURES

Swamps & Marshes ....

Tidal Flats ....
(Exposed at low tide)

Danger Line ....

Rocks Awash ....

Shoals ....
(Exposed at low tide)

Springs ....

Wells & Water Holes ....

Reefs, Coral & Rocky Ledges ....
(Awash at low tide)

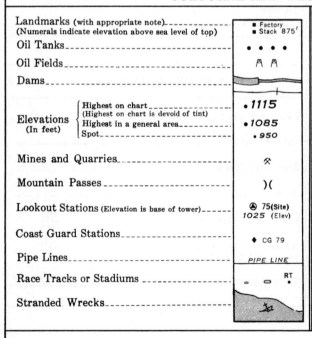

Streams & Rivers { Perennial ....
Intermittent ....
Probable or ....
Unsurveyed
Braided ....

Intermittent Lakes (blue stipple) ....

Drainage Ditches ....

Canals { In use ....
Abandoned ....

Dry Lake Beds (brown stipple) ....

Sand Deposits in river bed ....

Dry Washes (brown stipple) ....

Glaciers and Ice Caps ....

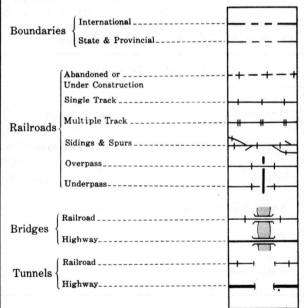

CULTURAL AND MISCELLANEOUS

Landmarks (with appropriate note) ....
(Numerals indicate elevation above sea level of top)

Oil Tanks ....

Oil Fields ....

Dams ....

Elevations { Highest on chart ....
(In feet)   (Highest on chart is devoid of tint)
Highest in a general area ....
Spot ....

Mines and Quarries ....

Mountain Passes ....

Lookout Stations (Elevation is base of tower) ......

Coast Guard Stations ....

Pipe Lines ....

Race Tracks or Stadiums ....

Stranded Wrecks ....

■ Factory
■ Stack 875'

• • • •

⚲ ⚲

•1115

•1085

•950

⚒

)(

⊕ 75(Site)
1025 (Elev)

◆ CG 79

PIPE LINE

RT

Boundaries { International ....
State & Provincial ....

Railroads { Abandoned or ....
Under Construction
Single Track ....
Multiple Track ....
Sidings & Spurs ....
Overpass ....
Underpass ....

Bridges { Railroad ....
Highway ....

Tunnels { Railroad ....
Highway ....

CONTINUED

406

SEARCH AND RESCUE

GROUND TO AIR EMERGENCY CODE DISTRESS SIGNALS

REQUIRE DOCTOR, SERIOUS INJURIES _ _ _ _ _ _ _ _	I	
REQUIRE MEDICAL SUPPLIES _ _ _ _ _	II	
UNABLE TO PROCEED _ _ _ _ _ _	X	
REQUIRE FOOD AND WATER _ _ _ _ _	F	
REQUIRE FIREARMS AND AMMUNITION _ _ _ _ _ _ _	⩔	
REQUIRE MAP AND COMPASS _ _ _ _	□	

REQUIRE SIGNAL LAMP WITH BATTERY, AND RADIO _ _ _ _ _ _ _	I	
INDICATE DIRECTION TO PROCEED _ _	K	
AM PROCEEDING IN THIS DIRECTION _ _	↑	
WILL ATTEMPT TAKE-OFF _ _ _ _ _	|>	
AIRCRAFT SERIOUSLY DAMAGED _ _	L⌐	
PROBABLY SAFE TO LAND HERE _ _ _	△	
IF IN DOUBT, USE INTERNATIONAL SYMBOL _ _ _ _ _ _ _ _ _	SOS	

REQUIRE FUEL AND OIL _ _ _ _ _ _	L
ALL WELL _ _ _ _ _ _ _ _ _ _	LL
NO _ _ _ _ _ _ _ _ _ _ _	N
YES _ _ _ _ _ _ _ _ _ _ _	Y
NOT UNDERSTOOD _ _ _ _ _	JL
REQUIRE MECHANIC _ _ _ _ _	W

INSTRUCTIONS:

1. Lay out symbols by using strips of fabric or parachutes, pieces of wood, stones, or any available material.
2. Provide as much color contrast as possible between material used for symbols and background against which symbols are exposed.
3. Symbols should be at least 10 feet high or larger, if possible. Care should be taken to lay out symbols exactly as shown to avoid confusion with other symbols.
4. In addition to using symbols, every effort is to be made to attract attention by means of radio, flares, smoke, or other available means.
5. When ground is covered with snow, signals can be made by dragging, shoveling or tramping the snow. The depressed areas forming the symbols will appear to be black from the air.
6. Pilot should acknowledge message by rocking wings from side to side.

VISUAL EMERGENCY SIGNALS

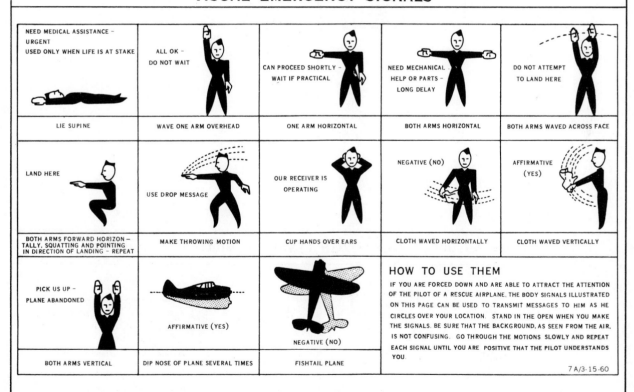

NEED MEDICAL ASSISTANCE – URGENT USED ONLY WHEN LIFE IS AT STAKE — LIE SUPINE	ALL OK – DO NOT WAIT — WAVE ONE ARM OVERHEAD
CAN PROCEED SHORTLY – WAIT IF PRACTICAL — ONE ARM HORIZONTAL	NEED MECHANICAL HELP OR PARTS – LONG DELAY — BOTH ARMS HORIZONTAL
DO NOT ATTEMPT TO LAND HERE — BOTH ARMS WAVED ACROSS FACE	

LAND HERE — BOTH ARMS FORWARD HORIZONTALLY, SQUATTING AND POINTING IN DIRECTION OF LANDING – REPEAT

USE DROP MESSAGE — MAKE THROWING MOTION

OUR RECEIVER IS OPERATING — CUP HANDS OVER EARS

NEGATIVE (NO) — CLOTH WAVED HORIZONTALLY

AFFIRMATIVE (YES) — CLOTH WAVED VERTICALLY

PICK US UP – PLANE ABANDONED — BOTH ARMS VERTICAL

AFFIRMATIVE (YES) — DIP NOSE OF PLANE SEVERAL TIMES

NEGATIVE (NO) — FISHTAIL PLANE

HOW TO USE THEM

IF YOU ARE FORCED DOWN AND ARE ABLE TO ATTRACT THE ATTENTION OF THE PILOT OF A RESCUE AIRPLANE, THE BODY SIGNALS ILLUSTRATED ON THIS PAGE CAN BE USED TO TRANSMIT MESSAGES TO HIM AS HE CIRCLES OVER YOUR LOCATION. STAND IN THE OPEN WHEN YOU MAKE THE SIGNALS. BE SURE THAT THE BACKGROUND, AS SEEN FROM THE AIR, IS NOT CONFUSING. GO THROUGH THE MOTIONS SLOWLY AND REPEAT EACH SIGNAL UNTIL YOU ARE POSITIVE THAT THE PILOT UNDERSTANDS YOU.

7 A/3-15-60

CONTINUED

MILITARY CLIMB CORRIDORS

The Military Climb Corridors illustrated below have been designated as Restricted Areas and Warning Area.

Pilots of Century Series aircraft on active air defense missions are unable to see and safely avoid other aircraft during the climb phase of a scramble. In the interest of safety, the Dept. of Defense and the FAA have agreed to establish restricted corridors to segregate such operations from other air traffic. ALL FLIGHTS through these areas must obtain prior approval from the Appropriate Authority.

The lateral and vertical limits of the Military Climb Corridors are indicated below. The relation of these corridors to the terrain and aeronautical facilities can be seen on the face of this chart, where the lateral limits are also shown.

LATERAL LIMITS OF MILITARY CLIMB CORRIDORS

VICTORVILLE, CALIF. (GEORGE AFB) RESTRICTED AREA R-2526

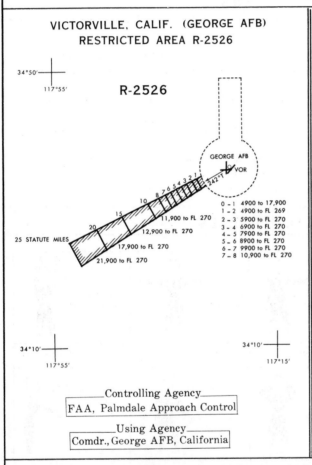

R-2526

0 – 1	4900 to 17,900
1 – 2	4900 to FL 269
2 – 3	5900 to FL 270
3 – 4	6900 to FL 270
4 – 5	7900 to FL 270
5 – 6	8900 to FL 270
6 – 7	9900 to FL 270
7 – 8	10,900 to FL 270

11,900 to FL 270
12,900 to FL 270
17,900 to FL 270
21,900 to FL 270

25 STATUTE MILES

Controlling Agency
FAA, Palmdale Approach Control

Using Agency
Comdr., George AFB, California

OXNARD, CALIF. (OXNARD AFB) RESTRICTED AREA R-2527/W-527

R-2527/W-527

0 – 1	2100 to 15,100
1 – 2	2100 to FL 240
2 – 5	2100 to FL 270
5 – 10	6100 to FL 270
10 – 15	10,100 to FL 270
15 – 20	15,100 to FL 270
20 – 27	19,100 to FL 270

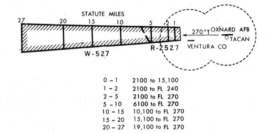

Controlling Agency
FAA, Ventura Approach Control

Using Agency
Comdr., Oxnard AFB, Calif.

PROFILE SHOWING UPPER AND LOWER LEVEL OF MILITARY CLIMB CORRIDORS

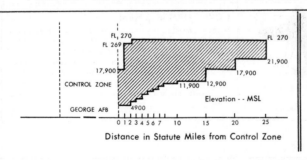

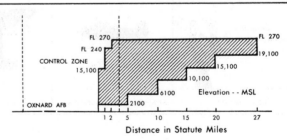

NOTE: Consult NOTAMS and Flight Information Publications for changes in data subsequent to date of chart.

CONTINUED

408

RADIOTELEGRAPH CODE AND PHONETIC ALPHABET
INTERNATIONAL (ICAO)

A— ALFA ·—	K— KILO —·—	U— UNIFORM ··—	0— ZE-RO —————
B— BRAVO —···	L— LIMA ·—··	V— VICTOR ···—	1— WUN ·————
C— CHARLIE —·—·	M— MIKE ——	W— WHISKEY ·——	2— TOO ··———
D— DELTA —··	N— NOVEMBER —·	X— XRAY —··—	3— TREE ···——
E— ECHO ·	O— OSCAR ———	Y— YANKEE —·——	4— FOW-er ····—
F— FOXTROT ··—·	P— PAPA ·——·	Z— ZULU ——··	5— FIFE ·····
G— GOLF ——·	Q— QUEBEC ——·—		6— SIX —····
H— HOTEL ····	R— ROMEO ·—·		7— SEV-en ——···
I— INDIA ··	S— SIERRA ···		8— AIT ———··
J— JULIETT ·———	T— TANGO —		9— NIN-er ————·

LIGHT SIGNAL PROCEDURES FOR AIRPORT TRAFFIC CONTROL

Signals from a portable traffic control light shall mean the following:

Color and Type of Signal	On the Ground	In Flight
STEADY GREEN	Cleared for take-off	Cleared to land
FLASHING GREEN	Cleared to taxi	Return for landing (to be followed by steady green at proper time)
STEADY RED	Stop	Give way to other aircraft and continue circling
FLASHING RED	Taxi clear of landing area (runway) in use	Airport unsafe-do not land
FLASHING WHITE	Return to starting point on airport	....
ALTERNATING RED & GREEN	General Warning Signal - Exercise Extreme Caution.	

AIRCRAFT HOLDING

The standard holding flight path of an aircraft is to follow the specified course inbound to the holding fix, make a 180 degree turn to the right, fly a parallel straight course outbound from the holding fix for two minutes, make another 180 degree turn to the right and again follow the specified course inbound.

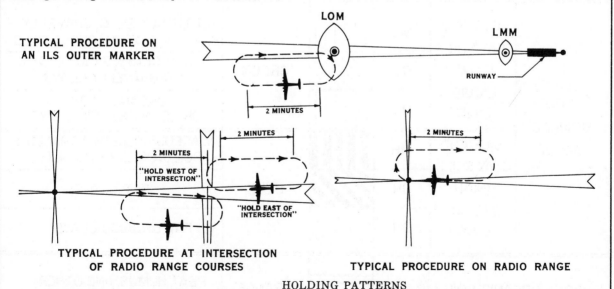

TYPICAL PROCEDURE ON AN ILS OUTER MARKER

LOM LMM RUNWAY 2 MINUTES

"HOLD WEST OF INTERSECTION" "HOLD EAST OF INTERSECTION" 2 MINUTES 2 MINUTES 2 MINUTES

TYPICAL PROCEDURE AT INTERSECTION OF RADIO RANGE COURSES

TYPICAL PROCEDURE ON RADIO RANGE

HOLDING PATTERNS

All holding patterns normally used are depicted on Coast and Geodetic Survey Terminal Area Charts.

TOPOGRAPHIC (SOIL COMPOSITION)

Extracted from TM5-230; TO 00-25-103, Department of the Army, Department of the Air Force, General Drafting, Soil Symbols, with the permission of the Office of the Secretary of ·Defense, Public Affairs Department, Washington.

MAJOR DIVISIONS		LETTER	SYMBOL		NAME
1	2	3	HATCHING 4	COLOR 5	6
COURSE GRAINED SOILS	GRAVELS AND GRAVELLY SOILS	GW		RED	GRAVEL OR SANDY GRAVEL WELL GRADED
		GP			GRAVEL OR SANDY GRAVEL POORLY GRADED
		GM		YELLOW	SILTY GRAVEL OR SILTY SANDY GRAVEL
		GC			CLAYEY GRAVEL OR CLAYEY SANDY GRAVEL
	SANDS AND SANDY SOILS	SW		RED	SAND OR GRAVELLY SAND WELL GRADED
		SP			SAND OR GRAVELLY SAND POORLY GRADED
		SM		YELLOW	SILTY SAND OR SILTY GRAVELLY SAND
		SC			CLAYEY SAND OR CLAYEY GRAVELLY SAND
FINE GRAINED SOILS	SILT AND CLAY SOILS (LOW LIQUID LIMIT)	ML		GREEN	SILTS, SANDY SILTS, GRAVELLY SILTS, OR DIATOMACEOUS SOILS
		CL			LEAN CLAYS, SANDY CLAYS, OR GRAVELLY CLAYS
		OL			ORGANIC SILTS OR LEAN ORGANIC CLAYS
	SILT AND CLAY SOILS (HIGH LIQUID LIMIT)	MH		BLUE	MICACEOUS SILTS, DIATOMACEOUS SOILS, OR ELASTIC SILTS
		CH			FAT CLAYS
		OH			FAT ORGANIC CLAYS
FIBROUS ORGANIC SOILS		Pt		ORANGE	PEAT, HUMUS, AND OTHER ORGANIC SWAMP SOILS

410

Dept. of Agriculture
U.S. Army
TOPOGRAPHY
Surveying-Mapping

Extracted from Agriculture Handbook No. 135, with the permission of the Soil Conservation Service, Department of Agriculture, Washington; also Elements of Surveying (TM5-232), with the permission of the Office of the Secretary of Defense, Public Affairs Department, Washington.

BOUNDARY LINES

Watershed or Area

Section Line

Farm Boundary No Fence

Permanent Fence

New Fence

Crop Boundary No Fence

Field Boundary No Fence

HIGHWAYS & RAILROADS

All Weather Road

Dirt Road

Private or Field Road

Bridge

Single Track Railroad

Double Track Railroad

LAND USE SYMBOLS FOR SMALL AREAS ONLY

Cultivated Land ... L

Woodland ... F

Permanent Pasture ... P

Idle Land ... X

Buildings and Lots ... H

Orchards ... O

Permanent Hay (Grass and Legume) ... N

Wildlife ... V

Unclassified ... U

DRAINAGE

Continuous Stream, Large

Continuous Stream, Small

Intermittent Stream

Stream Disappears on Flat

Stream Disappears in Sink

Large Deep Gully

Gully, Cannot Cross with Farm Implements

DRAINAGE (Continued)

Gully, Can Cross with Farm Implements

Levee

Spring

Lake or Pond ... With Dam

Intermittent Lake or Pond

Marsh

Terrace

Diversion

Grassed Watercourse ... M

Terrace Outlet

Permanent Structure

MISCELLANEOUS SYMBOLS

Mine, Quarry, Gravel Pit

Cemetery

Church

School House

Occupied Residence, Store

ADDITIONAL SYMBOLS — ENGINEERING DWGS.

North Arrow ... N

Section Center ... 3

Section Corner ... 6|5 / 7|8

Existing Tile

Proposed Tile

Break in Tile Size ... 400'-6" ... 200'-4"

Break in Grade ... 6% 1% ... 1% 2%

Relief Well

Breather

Existing Open Ditch (Less than 4' Deep)

Proposed Open Ditch (Less than 4' Deep)

Existing Open Ditch (4' Deep or Over)

Proposed Open Ditch (4' Deep or Over)

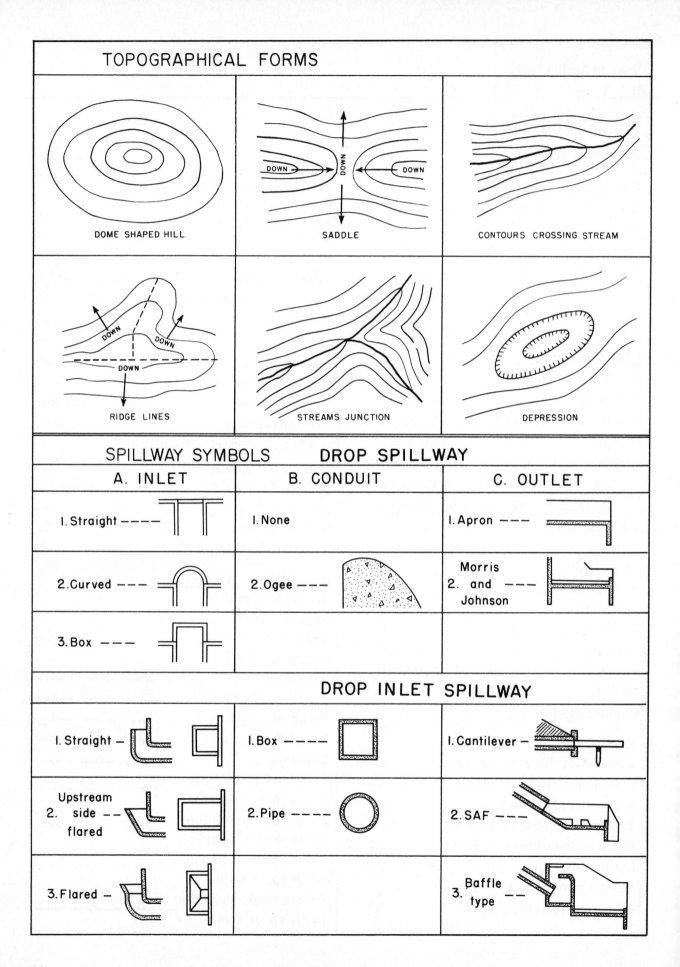

TOPOGRAPHICAL FORMS

DOME SHAPED HILL

SADDLE

CONTOURS CROSSING STREAM

RIDGE LINES

STREAMS JUNCTION

DEPRESSION

SPILLWAY SYMBOLS   DROP SPILLWAY

A. INLET	B. CONDUIT	C. OUTLET
1. Straight ————	1. None	1. Apron ———
2. Curved ———	2. Ogee ———	Morris 2. and ——— Johnson
3. Box ———		

DROP INLET SPILLWAY

1. Straight —	1. Box ————	1. Cantilever —
Upstream 2. side —— flared	2. Pipe ————	2. SAF ———
3. Flared —		3. Baffle type ——

412

CHUTE SPILLWAY

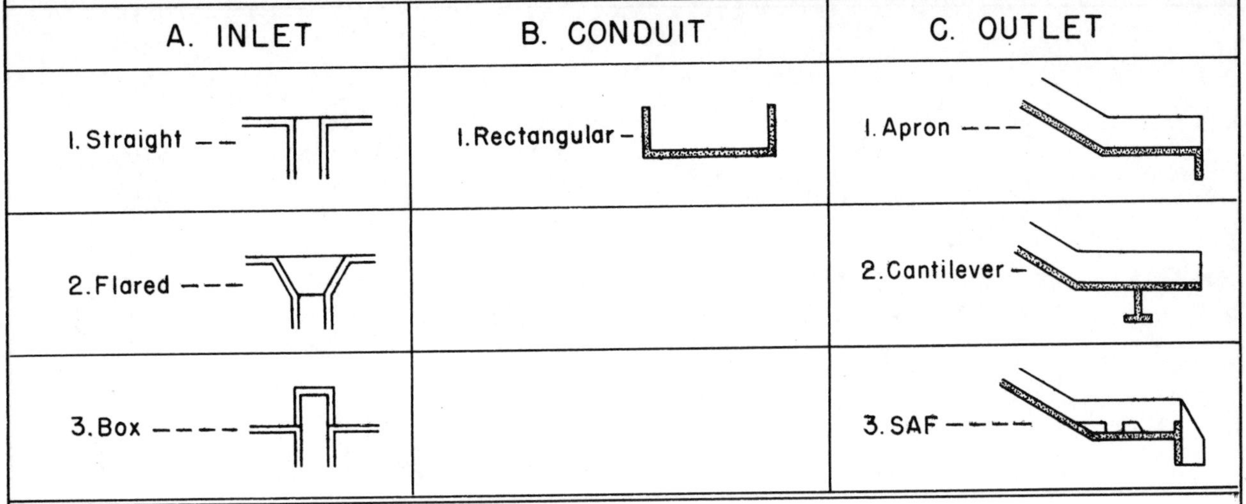

A. INLET	B. CONDUIT	C. OUTLET
1. Straight – –	1. Rectangular –	1. Apron – – –
2. Flared – – –		2. Cantilever –
3. Box – – – –		3. SAF – – – –

CODE OF SURVEYOR'S HAND SIGNALS—U.S. ARMY

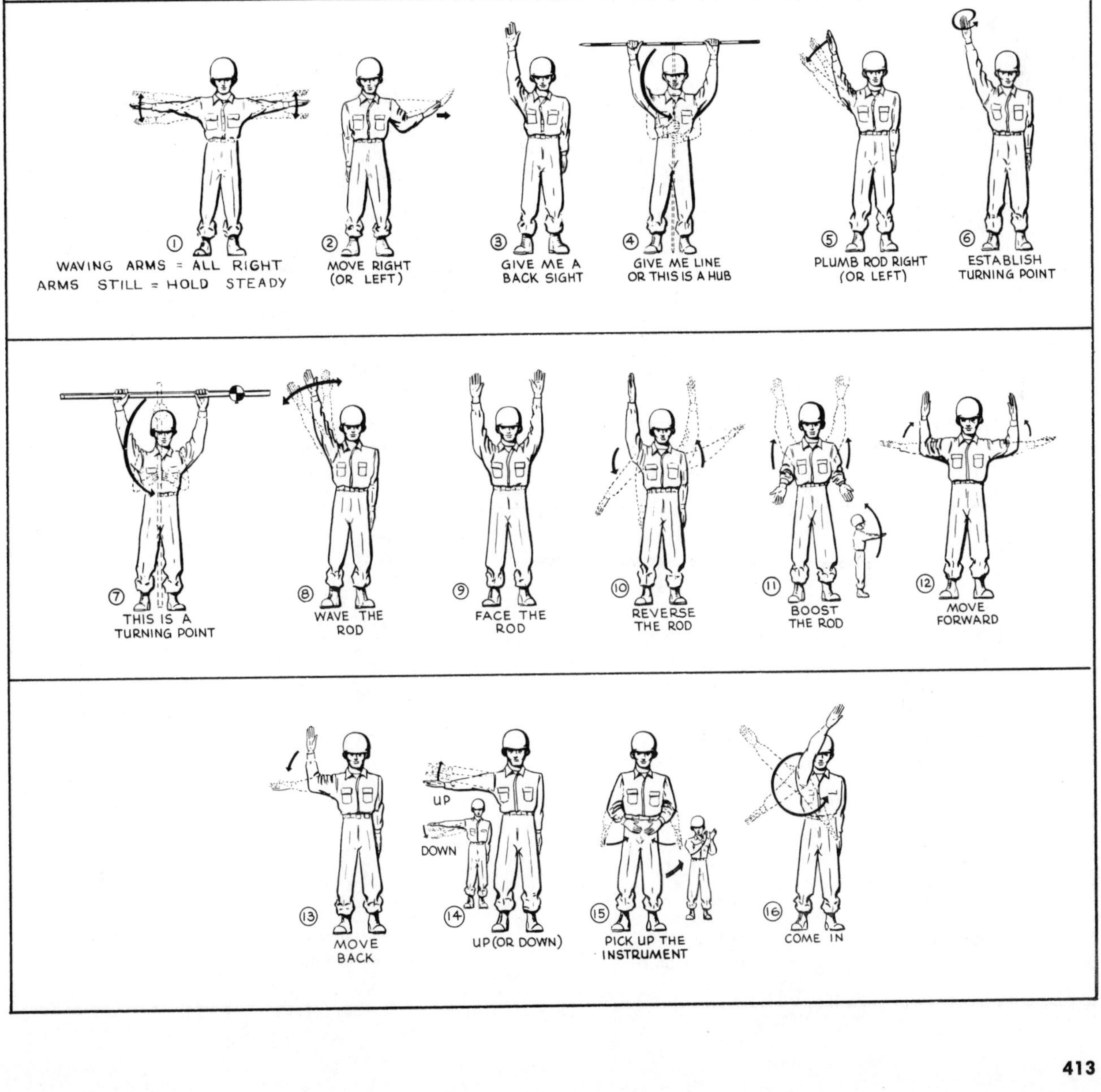

① WAVING ARMS = ALL RIGHT
ARMS STILL = HOLD STEADY

② MOVE RIGHT
(OR LEFT)

③ GIVE ME A
BACK SIGHT

④ GIVE ME LINE
OR THIS IS A HUB

⑤ PLUMB ROD RIGHT
(OR LEFT)

⑥ ESTABLISH
TURNING POINT

⑦ THIS IS A
TURNING POINT

⑧ WAVE THE
ROD

⑨ FACE THE
ROD

⑩ REVERSE
THE ROD

⑪ BOOST
THE ROD

⑫ MOVE
FORWARD

⑬ MOVE
BACK

⑭ UP (OR DOWN)

⑮ PICK UP THE
INSTRUMENT

⑯ COME IN

Move in this direction   Move in this direction   Plumb rod   Plumb rod   Turning point

Use long rod   Observation completed
or Move on
or Understood

Step
away
from
inst.

Walk
in
tight
circle

Wrong face
or Check clamp
or Rod upside down

Move down

Move up   Turning point
(by rod man)   Wave rod slowly
from side to side   Come in

Extracted from "General Cartography" by Erwin Raisz, with the permission of the publisher, McGraw-Hill Book Company, Inc., New York.

Plains

blank

undifferentiated | Tundra | Boreal forest | Wet taiga | Bush

Forest Grass Dry land Sand Gravel Hamada Savanna

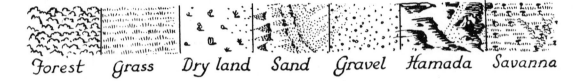

Palms Jungle Selva Rice Plowed land Corn Grain Tree crop

Dissected ~ rolling land | Cuestas & flatirons | Flood plains | Fans

Plateaus

low — high — cut-up — canyon land ~ mesas ~ badland

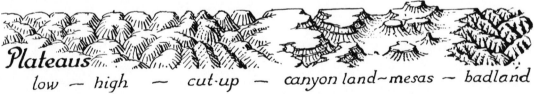

Syncline Anticline

Folded ridges — Dome — Basin ridge ~ Arched basin

Block Mts — reduced Complex mts. — glaciated

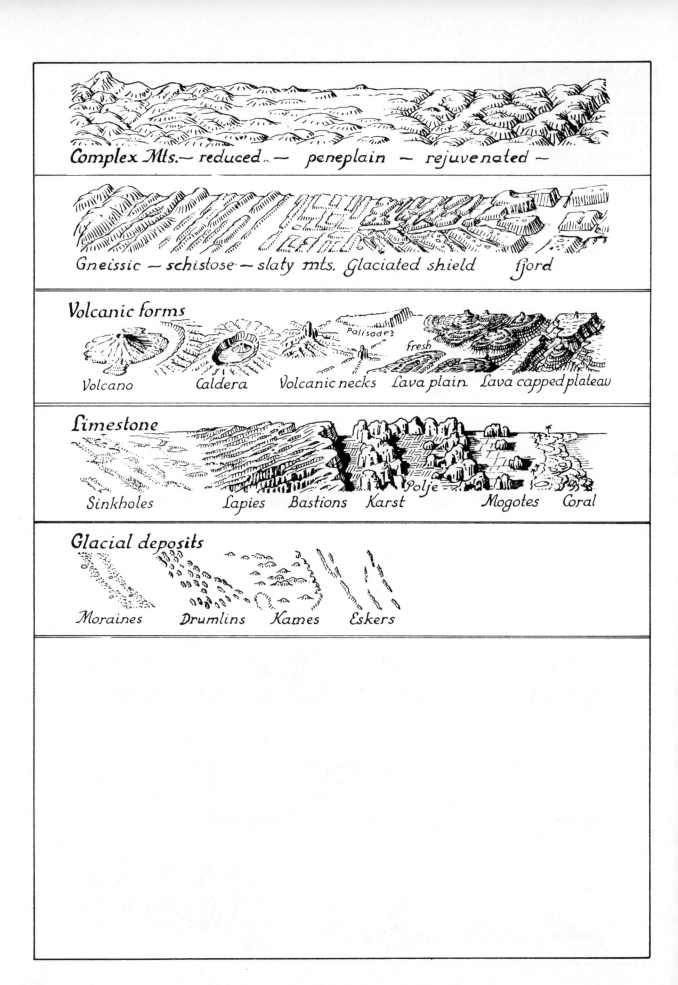

Complex Mts. - reduced - peneplain - rejuvenated -

Gneissic - schistose - slaty mts. Glaciated shield fjord

Volcanic forms

Volcano   Caldera   Volcanic necks   Lava plain   Lava capped plateau

Limestone

Sinkholes   Lapies   Bastions   Karst   Mogotes   Coral

Glacial deposits

Moraines   Drumlins   Kames   Eskers

Reproduced herein from the Coast and Geodetic Survey, Information Sheet, Station Marks, with the permission of the Director, Coast and Geodetic Survey, Department of Commerce, Washington. These standard bronze station marks of the Coast and Geodetic Survey are set in concrete or bedrock to serve as permanent marks for the stations they represent.

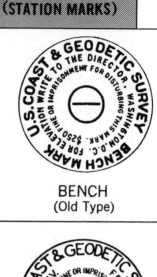

BENCH
(Old Type)

BENCH
(New Type)
Two Bench Marks Consolidated

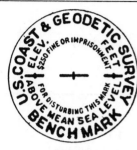

BENCH
(Old Type)

TRAVERSE

TRIANGULATION

GRAVITY
(Old Type)

GRAVITY
(New Type)

TOPOGRAPHIC

AZIMUTH

REFERENCE

MAGNETIC

AGI GEOLOGICAL (Map and Fault Symbols)

Reproduced herein from the AGI handbook, Geologic Map Symbols Section, through the courtesy of the American Geological Institute, 2101 Constitution Avenue N.W., Washington.

BEDDING	Strike and dip of beds	Approximate strike and dip	Strike and dip where upper bed can be distinguished, used only in areas of complex overturned folding
Generalized strike and dip of crumpled, plicated crenulated, or undulating beds	Horizontal beds	Strike of vertical beds	Strike and dip of overturned beds
Strike and dip of beds and plunge of slickensides	Apparent dip	**FOLIATION AND CLEAVAGE**	Strike and dip of foliation
Strike of vertical foliation	Strike of horizontal foliation	Strike and dip of cleavage	Strike of vertical cleavage
Horizontal cleavage	Alternative symbols for other planar elements	The map explanation should always specify the type of cleavage mapped	
LINEATIONS	Bearing and plunge of lineation	Horizontal lineation	Strike and dip of beds and plunge of lineation
Strike and dip of beds, showing horizontal lineation	Vertical beds, showing plunge of lineation	Vertical beds, showing horizontal lineation	Strike and dip of beds, showing rake of lineation
Vertical lineation	Double lineation	Strike and dip of foliation and plunge of lineation	Strike and dip of foliation, showing horizontal lineation

Vertical foliation, showing plunge of lineation	Vertical foliation, showing horizontal lineation	Strike and dip of foliation, showing rake of lineation	Generalized strike of folded beds, or foliation, showing plunge of fold axes
JOINTS	Strike and dip of joint	Horizontal joint	Strike of vertical joint
Strike and dips of multiple systems	**CONTACTS**	Definite contact	Inferred contact
Contact, showing dip	Approximate contact	Concealed contact	Vertical contact
FOLDS	Anticline, showing trace of axial plane and bearing and plunge of axis.	Overturned anticline, showing trace of axial plane, direction of dip of limbs, and bearing and plunge of axis	Plunge of minor anticline, showing degree of plunge
Approximate axis	Concealed axis	Syncline, showing trace of axial plane and bearing and plunge of axis.	Overturned syncline, showing trace of axial plane and direction of dip of limbs.
Plunge of minor syncline, showing degree of plunge	Inferred axis	Doubtful axis, dotted where concealed	Fold with inclined axial plane, showing dip and bearing of plane and plunge of axis
Horizontal Fold Axis	Dome	**FAULTS**	Fault, showing dip
Approximate fault	Concealed fault	Normal fault, hachures on down side	High-angle fault, movement — U, up, and D, down

Normal fault, showing bearing and plunge of relative movement of downthrown (D) block	Fault, showing bearing and plunge of grooves, striations, or slickensides	Vertical fault	Inferred fault
Doubtful fault, dotted where concealed	Fault, showing relative movement	Thrust or low-angle reverse faults, T, upper plate	Thrust or reverse fault, barbs on side of upper plate
Reverse fault, showing bearing and plunge of relative movement of downthrown (D) block	Lineaments	Fault zone or shear zone, showing dip.	Fault breccia
CROSS SECTIONS	*Overthrust* / *Underthrust*	Low-angle fault / *Normal fault*	Reverse fault
Vertical	A, movement away / T, movement toward / High-angle fault	Klippe	Fenster or window
		Horizontal movement in tear or shear fault	
OIL & GAS WELLS	Well location / Oil well	Oil well, with show of gas	Dry hole, with show of oil
Abandoned oil well	Abandoned oil well, with show of gas	Oil and gas well	Dry hole, with show of oil and gas
Abandoned oil and gas well	Shut-in well	Dry hole	Gas well
Gas well, with show of oil	Dry hole, with show of gas	Abandoned gas well	Abandoned gas well, with show of oil

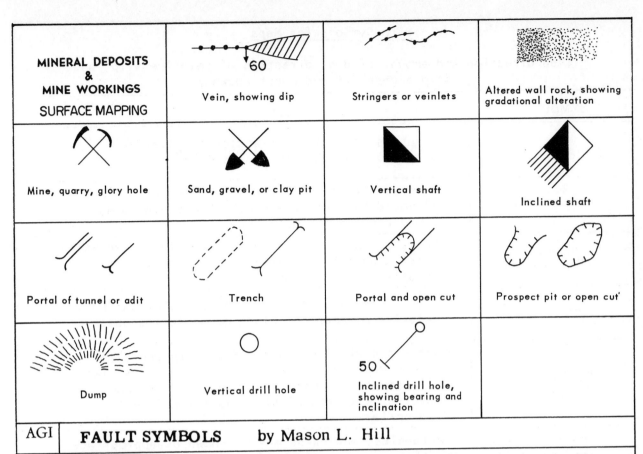

MINERAL DEPOSITS & MINE WORKINGS SURFACE MAPPING	Vein, showing dip	Stringers or veinlets	Altered wall rock, showing gradational alteration
Mine, quarry, glory hole	Sand, gravel, or clay pit	Vertical shaft	Inclined shaft
Portal of tunnel or adit	Trench	Portal and open cut	Prospect pit or open cut
Dump	Vertical drill hole	Inclined drill hole, showing bearing and inclination	

AGI   FAULT SYMBOLS   by Mason L. Hill

INTRODUCTION: The following fault symbols are designed to remove the ambiguity resulting from failure of traditional symbols to distinguish between fault _slip_ and fault _separation_. Where a linear geologic element is displaced the _actual_ relative movement (slip) can be determined (e.g., displaced intersection of dike and bed). Generally, however, where a tabular geologic element is displaced only _apparent_ relative movement (separation) can be determined. Thus, for example, these symbols provide for the important distinction between normal fault (only separation known) and normal slip fault (slip known). Refer to "Dual Classification of Faults," Mason L. Hill (1959), A.A.P.G. Bull., v. 43, p. 217-21.

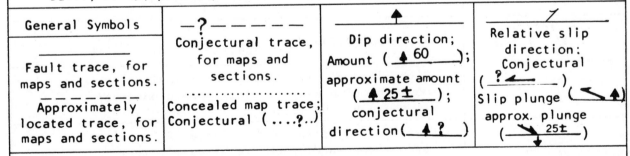

General Symbols	Conjectural trace, for maps and sections. Concealed map trace; Conjectural (....?..)	Dip direction; Amount (60); approximate amount (25±); conjectural direction (?)	Relative slip direction: Conjectural (?) Slip plunge ( ) approx. plunge (25±)
Fault trace, for maps and sections. Approximately located trace, for maps and sections.			

Note: Fault trace may be distinguished from other geologic contacts by weight or color of line, or by labeling with name or symbol, as desired. Slip plunge is vertical angle measured downward from horizontal to net slip.

Slip Symbols for Maps

(Add direction and amount of dip, direction of relative slip, and slip plunge, if and where known.)

SYMBOL	DESCRIPTION
	Thrust slip fault. Triangles on relatively overthrust block; Fault dips $< 45^\circ$
	Reverse slip fault. Rectangles on relatively elevated hanging wall block; Fault dips $> 45^\circ$ Dip direction is shown here.
 65	Normal slip fault. Barbs on relatively depressed hanging wall block; Fault dip and direction of relative slip are shown here.
	Right-lateral slip fault. Arrows shown sidewise relative movement of block opposite the observer.
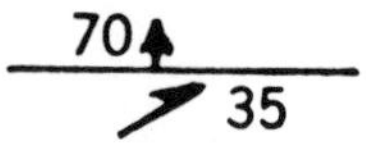 70 / 35	Left-lateral slip fault. Fault dip and slip plunge are shown here. If dip-slip and strike-slip components were nearly equal, the name reverse left-lateral slip fault would be appropriate.

Note: Triangles, rectangles, and barbs may be shown as appropriate and convenient along the map trace of the fault. However, none of these symbols should be used on maps unless some evidence of at least the approximate orientation of slip is obtained.

Slip Symbols for Sections

SYMBOL	DESCRIPTION
	Thrust slip fault. Arrow shows principal relative movement component; Fault dips $< 45^\circ$.
	Reverse slip fault. Fault dips $> 45^\circ$
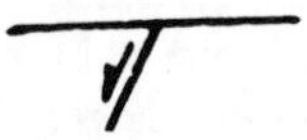	Normal slip fault.
 T	Right-lateral slip fault. Principal relative movement component of block toward observer is shown by the letter T.
 A	Left-lateral slip fault. Letter A (away) and arrow (downward) show relative movement components. If these components are nearly equal, the name normal left-lateral slip fault is used.

Note: Single barb arrows and letters (T and A) may be shown on either side of the section trace of the fault, as appropriate and convenient. However, none of these symbols should be used on sections if only separation is determined.

Separation Symbols for Maps

(Add direction and amount of dip, if and where known.)

SYMBOL	DESCRIPTION
D ——— } U ↓ 65	Dip separation-apparent relative movement in fault dip; D-downthrown or U-upthrown. Normal fault has dip toward downthrown block; Reverse fault has $>45°$ dip toward upthrown block (illustrated); Thrust fault has $<45°$ dip toward overthrown block
R ——— } L	Strike separation - apparent relative movement in fault strike of block opposite the observer. Right-lateral fault, R; Left-lateral fault, L.
L ↓ D	Dip and strike separations nearly equal. A normal left-lateral fault is illustrated.

Note: Letters indicating separation may be shown as appropriate and convenient on either side of the fault trace. The symbols (+) and (-) may be substituted for U and D but none represents any component of slip. Separation symbols are not needed for sections, and are only occasionally necessary for maps because the displacement of tabular geologic elements is usually obvious.

REMARKS: The essential function of these proposed fault symbols is to let geologists clearly indicate where information on fault slip has been determined, and not allow them to indicate slip where only separation is known. As customary, only those symbols which are used on a particular geologic illustration need be shown in the legend.

Extracted from the Preparation of Illustrations for Reports of the U.S. Geological Survey, with the permission of the U.S. Geological Survey, Department of the Interior, Washington.

DESCRIPTION	SYMBOL	DESCRIPTION	SYMBOL	DESCRIPTION	SYMBOL
Geologic boundaries		Axis of overturned anticline		Spring	
Inferred boundaries		Axis of overturned syncline		Thermal spring	
Known fault		Axis of plunging anticline showing direction of pitch		Mineral spring	
Probable or inferred fault		Axis of plunging syncline showing direction of pitch		OIL AND GAS WELLS	
Concealed fault (covered by later deposits)		Glacial striae		Site for test well	
Fault zone, shear zone		Mine shaft		Location of well	
Dip of fault plane		·Inclined shaft		Well being drilled	
Vertical fault		Tunnel opening on maps of large scale		Dry hole	
Overthrust side of thrust fault		Mine tunnels, showing direction		Dry hole, with show of oil	
Upheaved side of normal fault		Raises		Dry hole, with show of gas	
Downdropped side of normal fault		Winzes		Dry hole, with show of oil and gas	
Strike and dip of bedding		Mine workings		Oil well	
Strike of vertical strata		Mines or quarries		Oil well, with show of gas	
Horizontal beds		Abandoned mine or quarry		Abandoned oil well	
Strike and dip of overturned beds		Placer mine, surface mine		Abandoned oil well, with show of gas	
Prevailing dip of beds		Abandoned placer or surface mine		Gas well	
Strike and dip of schistosity		Prospect		Gas well, with show of oil	
Strike of vertical schistosity		Mine pits		Abandoned gas well	
Strike and dip of joint planes		Mine dump		Abandoned gas well, with show of oil	
Strike of vertical joint planes		Drill hole		Oil and gas well	
Rock exposure without observed strike and dip		Inclined drill hole, showing direction		Abandoned oil and gas well	
Rock exposure with observed strike and dip		WATER WELLS		Oil tanks	
Rock exposure with strike and dip of schistosity		Well, character not indicated			
General dip of beds having subordinate folds		Nonflowing well		COAL OUTCROP SYMBOLS (usually shown in color)	
Anticline with observed pitch		Flowing well		Coal outcrop (dotted line hypothetical)	
Syncline with observed pitch		Unsuccessful or dry well		Exposure or bloom on coal outcrop	
Axis of anticline		Nonflowing well, with pumping plant		Drift or slope on coal outcrop	
Axis of syncline		Flowing well, with pumping plant			

SECTIONS

SURFICIAL	Soil, silt, or alluvium	Sand	a b — Glacial till and moraines	a b
	Gravel and stratified drift	Loess	SEDIMENTARY — Conglomerate	Massive sandstone

CONTINUED

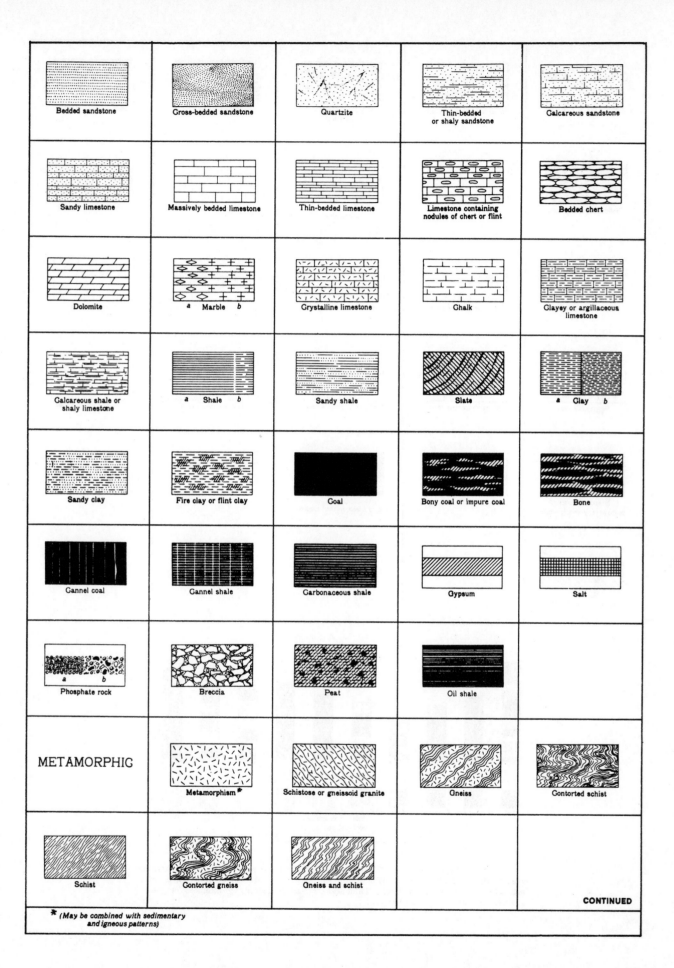

Bedded sandstone

Cross-bedded sandstone

Quartzite

Thin-bedded or shaly sandstone

Calcareous sandstone

Sandy limestone

Massively bedded limestone

Thin-bedded limestone

Limestone containing nodules of chert or flint

Bedded chert

Dolomite

a Marble b

Crystalline limestone

Chalk

Clayey or argillaceous limestone

Calcareous shale or shaly limestone

a Shale b

Sandy shale

Slate

a Clay b

Sandy clay

Fire clay or flint clay

Coal

Bony coal or impure coal

Bone

Cannel coal

Cannel shale

Carbonaceous shale

Gypsum

Salt

a b
Phosphate rock

Breccia

Peat

Oil shale

METAMORPHIC

Metamorphism *

Schistose or gneissoid granite

Gneiss

Contorted schist

Schist

Contorted gneiss

Gneiss and schist

CONTINUED

* (May be combined with sedimentary and igneous patterns)

425

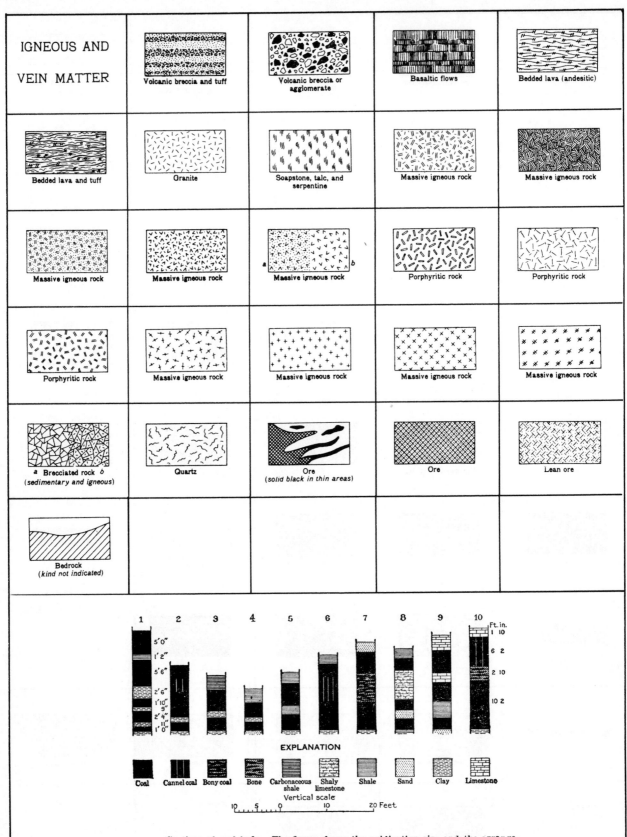

IGNEOUS AND VEIN MATTER

Volcanic breccia and tuff

Volcanic breccia or agglomerate

Basaltic flows

Bedded lava (andesitic)

Bedded lava and tuff

Granite

Soapstone, talc, and serpentine

Massive igneous rock

Massive igneous rock

Massive igneous rock

Massive igneous rock

Massive igneous rock

Porphyritic rock

Porphyritic rock

Porphyritic rock

Massive igneous rock

Massive igneous rock

Massive igneous rock

Massive igneous rock

a Brecciated rock b
(sedimentary and igneous)

Quartz

Ore
(solid black in thin areas)

Ore

Lean ore

Bedrock
(kind not indicated)

EXPLANATION

Coal   Cannel coal   Bony coal   Bone   Carbonaceous shale   Shaly limestone   Shale   Sand   Clay   Limestone

Vertical scale

10   5   0   10   20 Feet

—Sections of coal beds. The figure shows the publication size and the arrangement of the sections. Each section should be drawn three-tenths or four-tenths of an inch wide and reduced one-half. Thickness can be indicated by numbers, as shown on sections 1 and 10, or by bar scale.

TOPOGRAPHIC
FEATURES

U. S. GEOLOGICAL SURVEY

RELIEF

—Methods of expressing relief:

    (A) by contour lines,

    (B) by hachures,

    (C) by shading on
           stipple board,

    (D) by a brush drawing.

The four examples given represent the same area.

The drawings were made twice the size of the printed cuts.

A

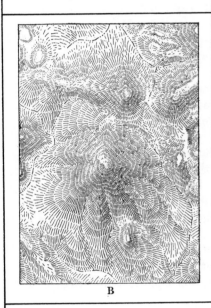

B

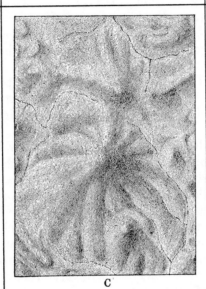

C

D

CULTURAL

The cultural features represented on a map include " the works of man "— not only cities, towns, buildings, bridges, railroads, and other roads, but State, county, and other boundary lines—in short, all that part of a three-color base map which is shown in black, the engraved plate for the black being called the culture plate. The features named in the list below are the cultural features referred to.

Aqueduct mains.	Cities.	Land-section lines.	Post offices.	Section lines.
Aqueduct tunnels.	County lines.	Levees.	Precinct lines.	Settlements.
Bench marks.	Dams.	Mains.	Prospects.	Shafts.
Boundary lines.	District lines.	Mineral monuments.	Province lines.	Streets.
Boundary monuments.	Ditches.	Mine tunnels.	Quarries.	Telegraph lines.
Breakwaters.	Electric power lines.	Mines.	Quarter-section lines.	Towns.
Bridges.	Fences.	National forests.	Railroads, steam or elec-	Township corners.
Buildings.	Ferries.	National parks.	Ranches.	Townships.
Cable lines.	Fords.	Oil tanks.	Reservation boundaries.	Trails.
Camps.	Gas wells.	Oil wells.	Reservoirs.	Tramways.
Canal locks.	Hedges.	Open cuts.	Roads.	Triangulation stations.
Canals.	Hospitals.	Park boundaries.	Ruins.	Tunnels.
Cemeteries.	Jetties.	Paths.	Schoolhouses.	Villages.
Churches.	Land-grant lines.	Pits.	Section corners.	Water mains.
				Water wells.
				Waterworks.
				Windmills.

General directions.—The drainage features of a map should be so drawn as to suggest the natural courses of the streams. Streams should not be drawn in straight, hard lines, as such lines are decidedly unnatural and produce a crude effect. The course of a river may be straight in general, but it is likely to be somewhat sinuous in detail. If the streams shown on a preliminary map are drawn in a clumsy or characterless fashion they should be redrawn with a freehand effect or made slightly wavy, in order that they may appear more natural. The gradual widening of streams from source to mouth should also be shown in the drawing. On small-scale maps, where the eye can at once see a stream through its full length, this almost imperceptible widening can be expressed by a line of almost uniform weight except for the stretch near the source, where it should grow thinner and taper off. On maps which are to be reproduced directly from drawings in black and white and which are to show both contour lines and drainage the lines representing the streams and other water bodies should generally be drawn freehand and slightly heavier than the contour lines, which should be sharper and more precise.

The names of all streams or other bodies of water should be in italic letters, those of the larger streams being lettered in capitals and those of the smaller streams in capitals and lower-case letters.

Water lining.—The use of water lining on black and white maps should be limited to maps on which the water areas are not readily distinguishable from the land areas. In rough drawings that are to serve only as copy for engravers a flat color may be used for water areas and its conversion into water lines specified. In base maps to be reproduced in three colors a light-blue tint may be used in lieu of water lining, and it can be printed either flat or in a fine ruling transferred to the stone that is to print the drainage. The engraving of water lines is expensive, and the flat blue color should generally be preferred.

Water lining usually consists of 30 to 45 lines on engraved or large maps, but on small maps and sketch maps the number may be reduced as desired. Care should be taken that the lines are as nearly parallel as they can be made freehand and of even weight or thickness. The first three to six lines outside the coast line should be somewhat closer together than those farther out and should conform closely to the coast line, but the spacing between the lines should increase and the lines should become almost imperceptibly less conformable to the coast line as they reach their outer limit, the last three to six being made with the greatest care and refinement. Water-lined maps that are to be reproduced by photographic processes should be drawn at least twice publication size. The reduction will bring the lines closer together, and the reproduction will show a more refined effect than could possibly be produced by the most skillful drawing.

Good examples of water lining, such as are shown on the topographic atlas sheets of the Survey, should be studied by draftsmen before they undertake such work.

BOUNDARY LINES AND SURVEYORS' MARKS

State or international boundary line............
County boundary line............
Township, section, and quarter-section lines............
Reservation boundary line............
Land grant boundary line............
Civil township boundary line............
City and small park boundary line............
Boundary monument............
Township and section corners recovered............
Triangulation station............
Bench mark............
U. S. mineral or locating monument............

PUBLIC WORKS

Railroad, single track............
Railroad, double track............
Juxtaposition of railroads............
Electric railroad and tramway............
Railroad in wagon road............ *Steam* *Electric*
Railroad tunnel............
Railroad station............
Electric power line............
Wagon roads, good............ *Large scale map* *Small scale map*
Wagon roads, poor or private............
Trail or route of travel............
Telegraph line............
Telegraph line in roads............
Telegraph line on trail............
Fences, of any kind............
Fence, stone............
Fence, worm............
Fence, wire............ *barbed* *smooth*
Hedge............
City or town............
City or town (large scale)............
Capital............
County seat............
Towns............
Buildings............
Ruins............
Post office............ *PO*
Cemeteries............ *CEM*
Church............
Schoolhouse............

WATER FEATURES

Streams............
Intermittent stream............
Unsurveyed streams............
Falls and rapids............
Springs............
Glaciers............
Lakes or ponds............
Intermittent lake or pond............
Marsh, fresh............
Marsh, salt............
Tidal flat............
Canal or ditch............
Bridges............
Draw bridges............
Ferry (point upstream)............
Ford............
Dams............
Locks (point upstream)............
Waterlining and breakwater............

RELIEF FEATURES

Contour lines............
Hachures............
Depression contour............
Woods............

Heavy growth   *Scattered*   *Area above timber line*

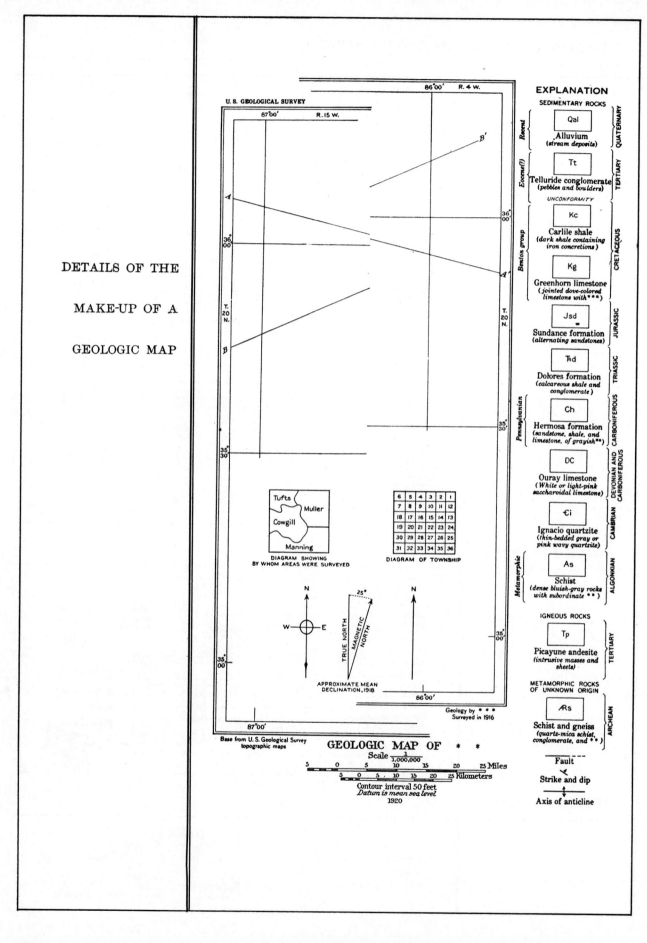

DETAILS OF THE

MAKE-UP OF A

GEOLOGIC MAP

EXPLANATION

SEDIMENTARY ROCKS

QUATERNARY — *Recent*
Qal
Alluvium
(*stream deposits*)

TERTIARY — *Eocene(?)*
Tt
Telluride conglomerate
(*pebbles and boulders*)

UNCONFORMITY

CRETACEOUS — *Benton group*
Kc
Carlile shale
(*dark shale containing iron concretions*)

Kg
Greenhorn limestone
(*jointed dove-colored limestone with * * **)

JURASSIC
Jsd
Sundance formation
(*alternating sandstones*)

TRIASSIC
Ŧrd
Dolores formation
(*calcareous shale and conglomerate*)

CARBONIFEROUS — *Pennsylvanian*
Ch
Hermosa formation
(*sandstone, shale, and limestone, of grayish***)

DEVONIAN AND CARBONIFEROUS
DC
Ouray limestone
(*White or light-pink saccharoidal limestone*)

CAMBRIAN
Ꞓi
Ignacio quartzite
(*thin-bedded gray or pink wavy quartzite*)

ALGONKIAN — *Metamorphic*
As
Schist
(*dense bluish-gray rocks with subordinate * ***)

IGNEOUS ROCKS

TERTIARY
Tp
Picayune andesite
(*intrusive masses and sheets*)

METAMORPHIC ROCKS OF UNKNOWN ORIGIN

ARCHEAN
Ꜳrs
Schist and gneiss
(*quartz-mica schist, conglomerate, and * ***)

- - - -
Fault

Strike and dip

Axis of anticline

U. S. GEOLOGICAL SURVEY

86°00′ R. 4 W.

87°00′ R. 15 W.

Tufts
Muller
Cowgill
Manning

DIAGRAM SHOWING
BY WHOM AREAS WERE SURVEYED

6	5	4	3	2	1
7	8	9	10	11	12
18	17	16	15	14	13
19	20	21	22	23	24
30	29	28	27	26	25
31	32	33	34	35	36

DIAGRAM OF TOWNSHIP

N
W — E
TRUE NORTH   MAGNETIC NORTH   25°

N

APPROXIMATE MEAN
DECLINATION, 1918

Geology by * * *
Surveyed in 1916

Base from U. S. Geological Survey
topographic maps

GEOLOGIC MAP OF   *   *

Scale $\frac{1}{1,000,000}$

5   0   5   10   15   20   25 Miles
5   0   5   10   15   20   25 Kilometers

Contour interval 50 feet
Datum is mean sea level
1920

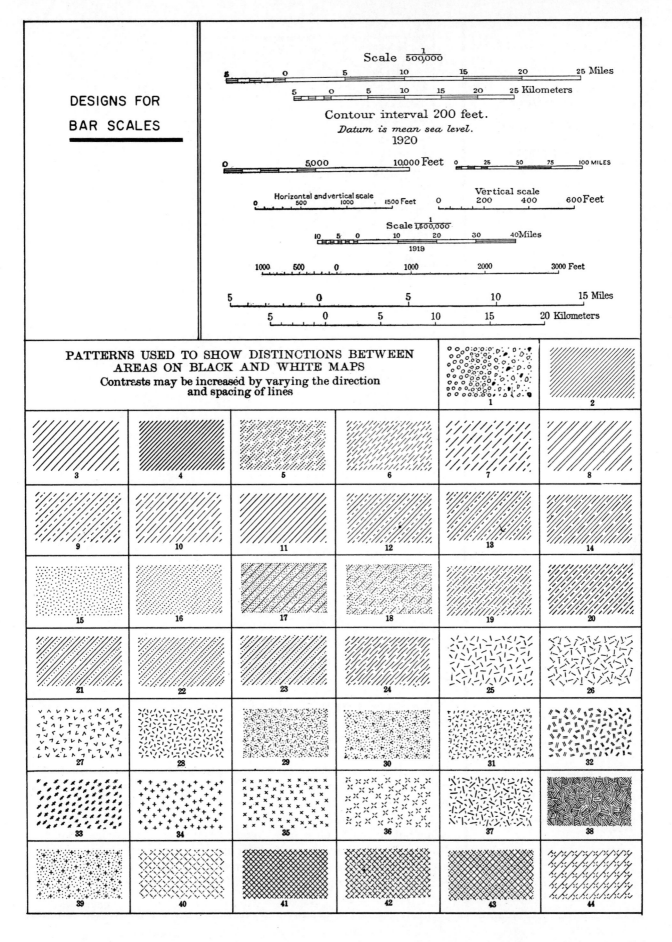

DESIGNS FOR
BAR SCALES

Scale $\frac{1}{500,000}$

5   0   5   10   15   20   25 Miles

5   0   5   10   15   20   25 Kilometers

Contour interval 200 feet.
Datum is mean sea level.
1920

0   5,000   10,000 Feet   0   25   50   75   100 MILES

Horizontal and vertical scale
0   500   1000   1500 Feet

Vertical scale
0   200   400   600 Feet

Scale $\frac{1}{1,500,000}$

10   5   0   10   20   30   40 Miles
1919

1000   500   0   1000   2000   3000 Feet

5   0   5   10   15 Miles

5   0   5   10   15   20 Kilometers

PATTERNS USED TO SHOW DISTINCTIONS BETWEEN
AREAS ON BLACK AND WHITE MAPS
Contrasts may be increased by varying the direction
and spacing of lines

1   2   3   4   5   6   7   8   9   10   11   12   13   14   15   16   17   18   19   20   21   22   23   24   25   26   27   28   29   30   31   32   33   34   35   36   37   38   39   40   41   42   43   44

431

MAP BEARING

SIX AREAL

LINE PATTERNS

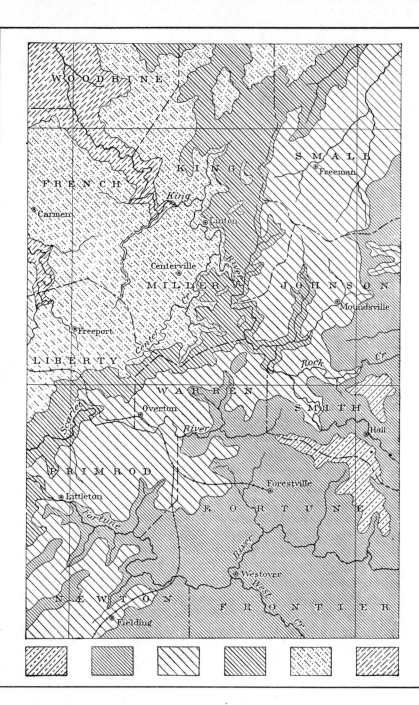

STANDARD COLORS

FOR GEOLOGIC

MAPS

The standard series of colors for systems of sedimentary rocks is shown on the maps in the Survey's geologic folios but is subject to modifications for use on maps in other Survey reports. Each system is represented by a different color, and if there are two or more formations in one system they are generally distinguished by using different patterns composed of straight parallel lines in the same color. The patterns for subaerial deposits (chiefly Quaternary) are composed of dots or circles, or combinations of both, and may be printed in any color, but the color most often used is yellow or ochraceous orange. No specific colors are prescribed for igneous rocks, but if only a few areas are shown red or pink is preferred. The colors used for igneous rocks are generally more brilliant and purer than those used for sedi-

CONTINUED

432

mentary rocks. For small areas they are used " solid "; for large areas they are reduced in tone by the use of a suitable cross-line pattern or " reticle." Metamorphic rocks are represented by short dashes irregularly placed. These dashes may be in black or in color over a ground tint or over an uncolored area, or they may be in white on a ground tint or pattern. The standard colors used for the sedimentary series covering the 12 systems recognized by the Geological Survey are: Quaternary (Q), *ochraceous orange;* Tertiary (T), *yellow ocher* and *isabella color;* Cretaceous (K), olive-green or *rainette-green;* Jurassic (J), *blue-green* or *niagara-green;* Triassic (Ṝ), light peacock-blue or *bluish gray-green;* Carboniferous (C), blue or *columbia-blue;* Devonian (D), gray-purple or *heliotrope-gray;* Silurian (S), purple or *argyle-purple;* Ordovician (O), red-purple or *rocellin-purple;* Cambrian (Ꞓ), brick-red or *etruscan red;* Algonkian (A), **terra** cotta or *onion-skin pink;* Archean (Ꞧ), gray-brown or *drab.*[10]

GENERAL
 	
GROUND-WATER
 	
FEATURES
	Area of absorption or outcrop: Flat color used on the map to show the geologic system in which the absorbing formation occurs.
	Areas showing depths to water table: Shades of purple and gray; if possible the shades showing the areas of least depth should be darkest and the shades should grade from those to lighter tints.
	Contours of water table, or contours on water-bearing formations: Gray or purple curves or lines.
	Areas of artesian flow: Blue flat tint, or fine ruling in blue. Depth to water-bearing formations: Gradation of a single color or of two related colors from dark for shallow depths to light for greater depths.
	Nonflowing artesian areas (pumped wells): Green flat tint, or fine ruling in green. Depth to water-bearing formations shown by gradation of tint if possible from dark for shallow depths to light for greater depths.
	Head of artesian water: Blue curves or lines.
	Areas that discharge ground water: Blue flat tint, or fine ruling in blue.
	Areas irrigated with ground water: Green flat tint, or fine ruling in green.
	
	O Well, character not indicated.
	O Well, nonflowing.
	   Well, flowing.
	   Well, unsuccessful or dry.
	◎ Well, nonflowing, with pumping plant.
	◉ Well, flowing, with pumping plant.
	   Springs.
	   Spring, thermal.
	   Spring, mineral.

ABBREVIATIONS	A.	Arroyo.	Is.	Islands.	Pk.	Peak.

Abbreviations:

A.	Arroyo.	Is.	Islands.	Pk.	Peak.
B. M.	Bench mark.	Jc.	Junction.	P. O.	Post office.
Bdy.	Boundary.	L.	Lake.	Pt.	Point.
Br.	Branch, bridge.	Lat.	Latitude.	R.	Range, river.
C.	Cape.	Ldg.	Landing.	Res.	Reservation, reservoir.
Can.	Canal, canyon.	L. S. S.	Life-saving station.		
Cem.	Cemetery.			R. H.	Road house.
Co.	County.	L. H.	Lighthouse.	S.	South.
Cr.	Creek.	Long.	Longitude.	Sd.	Sound.
E.	East.	M. P.	Milepost.	S. H.	Schoolhouse.
El.	Elevation.	M. M.	Mineral monument.	Sta.	Station.
Est.	Estuary.			Str.	Stream.
Fk.	Fork.	Mt.	Mount.	T.	Township.
Ft.	Fort, foot.	Mtn.	Mountain.	Tel.	Telegraph.
Gl.	Gulch, glacier.	Mts.	Mountains.	W.	West.
Hbr.	Harbor.	N.	North.		
I.	Island.	Pen.	Peninsula.		

CONTINUED

Words like mount, river, point should not be abbreviated where they form a part of the name of a city or town, as Rocky Mount, Fall River, West Point. Neither the word nor the abbreviation for railroad or railway should be placed on a map; the chartered name (or initials of the name) and the road symbol are sufficient.

Names of States and Territories should be abbreviated, where abbreviation is necessary, as follows:

Ala.	Ga.	Minn.	N. J.	Tenn.
Ariz.	Ill.	Miss.	N. Mex.	Tex.
Ark.	Ind.	Mo.	N. Y.	Va.
Calif.	Kans.	Mont.	Okla.	Vt.
Colo.	Ky.	Nebr.	Oreg.	Wash.
Conn.	La.	Nev.	Pa.	W. Va.
D. C.	Mass.	N. C.	R. I.	Wis.
Del.	Md.	N. Dak.	S. C.	Wyo.
Fla.	Mich.	N. H.	S. Dak.	

Alaska, Guam, Hawaii, Idaho, Iowa, Maine, Ohio, Samoa, and Utah should be written in full.

The abbreviations used on the margins of maps for subdivisions of land should be as follows (note punctuation): T. 2 N., R. 3 W. On large-scale plats the marginal lettering should be as follows: N. $\frac{1}{2}$ NE. $\frac{1}{4}$ sec. 1, T. 7 N., R. 2 W.; fractional secs. 2 and 35, Tps. 7 and 8 N., R. 2 W.; NW. $\frac{1}{4}$ sec. 20, T. 7 N., R. 2 W. In spelling fractions use half and quarter, not one-half and one-quarter.

The abbreviated forms of such names as North Fork and South Fork should be N. Fork and S. Fork, not North Fk. and South Fk.

Additional abbreviations used on illustrations are as follows:

N. for north, NE. for northeast, NNE. for north-northeast, etc. Capitalize directions affixed to street names, as NW., SE. (1800 F St. NW.).

Sec. and secs. for section and sections before a number. Capitalize only at the beginning of a line or sentence.

a. m. and p. m. for antemeridian and postmeridian, as 4.30 p. m. Lower-case unless in line of caps.

& in names of corporations or companies. On Survey miscellaneous maps "and" is spelled out in railroad names.

B. t. u. for British thermal units.

bbl., bbls. for barrel, barrels.

bu. for bushel or bushels.

c. c. for cubic centimeter.

cm. for centimeter.

cwt. for hundredweight.

dwt. or pwt. for pennyweight.

oz. for ounce or ounces.

etc. (not &c.) for et cetera.

ft. for foot or feet.

H. m. s. for hours, minutes, and seconds. (Use capital H.)

in. for inch or inches.

kw. for kilowatt or kilowatts.

£ s. d. for pounds, shillings, and pence.

per cent (omitting period) for per centum. Spell out percentage.

ser. for series.

St. for Saint or street.

U. S. Army for United States Army, as distinguished from United States of America (U. S. A.).

yd., yds. for yard, yards.

CONTINUED

The names of certain months may in some places be abbreviated; those of others should invariably be spelled out. The following are the correct forms:

Jan.	Apr.	July	Oct.
Feb.	May	Aug.	**Nov.**
Mar.	June	Sept.	Dec.

The abbreviations for number. and numbers before figures are No. and Nos. The o should never be raised, as in N°. The abbreviation for Mac is Mc, not M^c.

All periods should be omitted from abbreviations used in the body of a map unless their omission would cause misunderstanding. They are generally unnecessary, and if used on some maps they are likely to be mistaken for symbols representing certain features, such as houses or flowing wells, if either are shown. Periods used on drawings that are to be reproduced " direct " or photomechanically should always be slightly exaggerated.

LETTERING

The cultural features are named on maps by letters of two distinct styles—slanting gothic for public works and roman for habitations and civil divisions. The size of the letters used should indicate in a general way the relative importance of the feature or group to which they are applied, but on some maps the county seats, State capitals, and large cities may be distinguished by different symbols. The names of civil divisions are lettered in sizes depending on their relative grade and the size of the area or space in which the names are to appear.

The features shown on a topographic map may be broadly separated into four groups and are lettered as follows:

Civil divisions (countries, States, counties, townships, land grants, reservations, cities, towns, villages, settlements, schools, lodges, ranches, etc.), roman capitals or capitals and lower case.

Public works (railroads, tunnels, roads, canals, ferries, bridges, fords, dams, mains, mines, forts, trails, etc.), slanting gothic capitals (light) or capitals and lower case.

Hydrographic features (oceans, seas, gulfs, bays, lakes, ponds, rivers, creeks, brooks, springs, wells, falls, rapids, marshes, glaciers, etc.), italic capitals or capitals and lower case.

Hypsographic features (mountains, ranges, peaks, plateaus, cliffs, buttes, canyons, valleys, peninsulas, islands, capes, etc.), upright gothic capitals (light) or capitals and lower case.

GRAPHICAL SYMBOLS FOR METEOROLOGY

Extracted from C.A.A. Technical Manual No. 104, Pilots Weather Handbook and reproduced herein through the courtesy of the Civil Aeronautics Administration, Department of Commerce, Washington. Other sections herein contained are established standards of the U.S. Weather Bureau, Department of Commerce, Washington.

Station Model Construction

Symbol showing type of middle cloud.*

Figures showing barometric pressure at sea level (1024.7 millibars).

Figures showing net amount of barometric change in past 3 hours. (in tenths of millibars - 2.8 millibars).

Symbol showing barometric tendency in past 3 hours.

+ or - sign showing pressure higher or lower than 3 hours ago.

Code figure showing time precipitation began or ended (in this case ended since present and past weather are of different types).

Past weather during 6 hours preceding observation.*

Figures showing amount precipitation in last 6 hours (.45").*

Arrow showing direction of middle cloud.*

** Figures showing force of wind in knots (each 1/2 barb=5kts.) Circle around station circle and no wind shaft indicate a calm wind.

Arrow shaft showing direction of wind (from northwest).

Figures showing temperature in degrees Fahrenheit.

Symbol showing amount of total sky covered by clouds.

Visibility in miles and fractions.

Symbol showing present state of weather.*

Figures showing dew point in degrees Fahrenheit.

Symbol showing type of low cloud.

** Height of base of clouds in hundreds of feet.

** Coverage of lower clouds in tenths.

* Omitted when data not observed or not recorded. "M" is used in place of missing elements.

** This data is actually in code. However, this interpretation is accurate enough for practical purposes.

Dept. of Commerce **METEOROLOGY** (Present and Past States)				

00	**0**	**1**	**2**	**3**	**4**
0	Cloud development NOT observed or NOT observable during past hour.	Clouds generally dissolving or becoming less developed during past hour.	State of sky on the whole unchanged during past hour.	Clouds generally forming or developing during past hour.	Visibility reduced by smoke.
10	Light fog.	Patches of shallow fog at station NOT deeper than 6 feet on land.	More or less continuous shallow fog at station, NOT deeper than 6 feet on land.	Lightning visible, no thunder heard.	Precipitation within sight, but NOT reaching the ground at station.
20	Drizzle (NOT freezing and NOT falling as showers) during past hour, but NOT at time of observation.	Rain (NOT freezing and NOT falling as showers) during past hour, but NOT at time of observation.	Snow (NOT falling as showers) during past hour, but NOT at time of observation.	Rain and snow (NOT falling as showers) during past hour, but NOT at time of ob.	Freezing drizzle or freezing rain (NOT falling as showers) during past hour, but NOT at time of ob.
30	Slight or moderate duststorm or sandstorm, has decreased during past hour.	Slight or moderate duststorm or sandstorm, no appreciable change during past hr.	Slight or moderate duststorm or sandstorm, has increased during past hour.	Severe duststorm or sandstorm, has decreased during past hr.	Severe duststorm or sandstorm, no appreciable change during past hour.
40	Fog at distance at time of ob., but NOT at station during past hour.	Fog in patches.	Fog, sky discernible, has become thinner during past hour.	Fog, sky NOT discernible, has become thinner during past hour.	Fog, sky discernible, no appreciable change during past hr.
50	Intermittent drizzle (NOT freezing) slight at time of observation.	Continuous drizzle (NOT freezing) slight at time of observation.	Intermittent drizzle (NOT freezing) moderate at time of ob.	Continuous drizzle (NOT freezing), mod. at time of observation.	Intermittent drizzle (NOT freezing), thick at time of observation.
60	Intermittent rain (NOT freezing), slight at time of observation.	Continuous rain (NOT freezing slight at time of ob.	Intermittent rain (NOT freezing), moderate at time of ob.	Continuous rain (NOT freezing), moderate at time of ob.	Intermittent rain (NOT freezing), heavy at time of observation.
70	Intermittent fall of snowflakes, slight at time of observation.	Continuous fall of snowflakes, slight at time of observation.	Intermittent fall of snowflakes, moderate at time of observation.	Continuous fall of snowflakes, moderate at time of observation.	Intermittent fall of snowflakes, heavy at time of observation.
80	Slight rain shower(s).	Moderate or heavy rain shower(s).	Violent rain shower(s).	Slight shower(s) of rain and snow mixed.	Moderate or heavy shower(s) of rain and snow mixed.
90	Moderate or heavy shower(s) of hail, with or without rain, or rain and snow mixed, NOT associated with thunder.	Slight rain at time of observation; thunderstorm during past hr., but NOT at time of observation.	Moderate or heavy rain at time of ob.; thunderstorm during past hour, but NOT at time of observation.	Slight snow or rain and snow mixed or hail at time of observa.; thunderstorm during past hour, but NOT at time of observation.	Mod. or heavy snow, or rain and snow mixed or hail at time of ob.;thunderstorm during past hour, but NOT at time of ob.

	5	6	7	8	9
0	Dry haze.	Widespread dust in suspension in the air, NOT raised by wind, at time of observation.	Dust or sand raised by wind, at time of ob.	Well developed dust devil(s) within past hr.	Duststorm or sandstorm within sight of or at station during past hour.
10	Precipitation within sight, reaching the ground, but distant from station.	Precipitation within sight, reaching the ground, near to but NOT at station.	Thunder heard, but no precipitation at the station.	Squall(s) within sight during past hour.	Funnel cloud(s) within sight during past hour.
20	Showers of rain during past hour, but NOT at time of observation.	Showers of snow, or of rain and snow, during past hour, but NOT at time of observation.	Showers of hail, or of hail and rain, during past hour, but NOT at time of observation.	Fog during past hour, but NOT at time of observation.	Thunderstorm (with or without precipitation) during past hour, but NOT at time of ob.
30	Severe duststorm or sandstorm, has increased during past hour.	Slight or moderate drifting snow, generally low.	Heavy drifting snow, generally low.	Slight or moderate drifting snow, generally high.	Heavy drifting snow, generally high.
40	Fog, sky NOT discernible, no appreciable change during past hour.	Fog, sky discernible, has begun or become thicker during past hour.	Fog, sky NOT discernible, has begun or become thicker during past hour.	Fog, depositing rime, sky discernible.	Fog, depositing rime, sky NOT discernible.
50	Continuous drizzle (NOT freezing) thick at time of observation.	Slight freezing drizzle.	Moderate or heavy freezing rain.	Drizzle and rain, slight.	Drizzle and rain, moderate or heavy.
60	Continuous rain (NOT freezing), heavy at time of observation.	Slight freezing rain.	Moderate or heavy freezing rain.	Rain or drizzle and snow, slight.	Rain or drizzle and snow, mod'te or heavy.
70	Continuous fall of snowflakes, heavy at time of observation.	Ice needles (with or without fog).	Granular snow (with or without fog).	Isolated starlike snow crystals (with or without fog).	Ice pellets (sleet, U. S. definition).
80	Slight snow shower(s).	Moderate or heavy snow shower(s).	Slight shower(s) of soft or small hail with or without rain or rain and snow mixed.	Moderate or heavy shower(s) of soft or small hail with or without rain or rain and snow mixed.	Slight shower(s) of hail, with or without rain or rain and snow mixed, not associated with thunder.
90	Slight or mod. thunderstorm without hail, but with rain and/or snow at time of ob.	Slight or mod. thunderstorm, with hail at time of observation.	Heavy thunderstorm, without hail, but with rain and/or snow at time of observation.	Thunderstorm combined with duststorm or sandstorm at time of ob.	Heavy thunderstorm with hail, at time of ob.

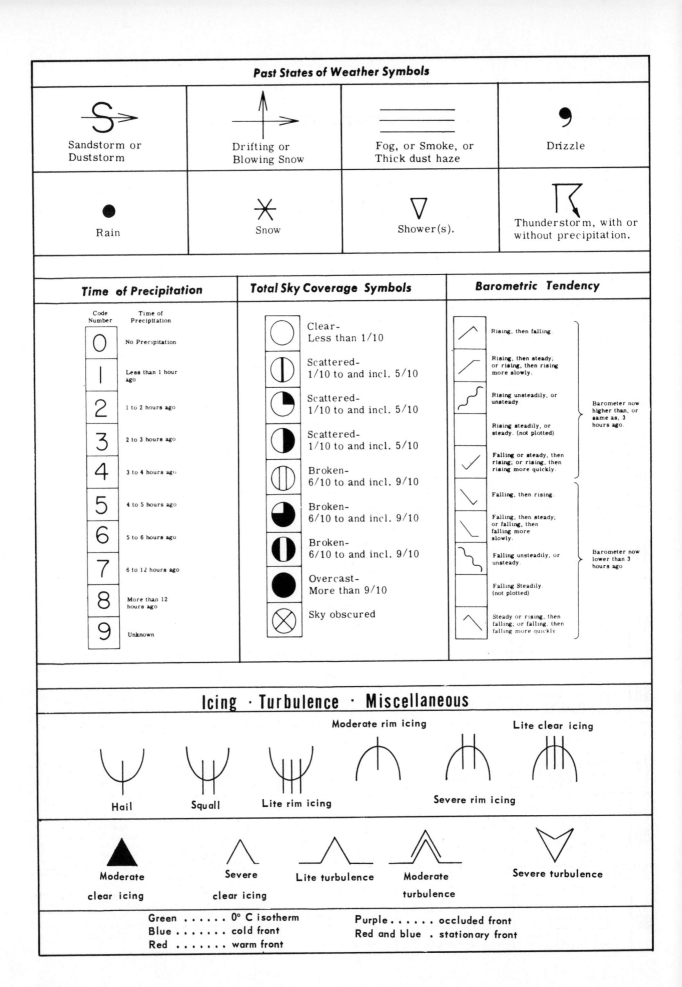

Past States of Weather Symbols

Sandstorm or Duststorm	Drifting or Blowing Snow	Fog, or Smoke, or Thick dust haze	Drizzle
Rain	Snow	Shower(s).	Thunderstorm, with or without precipitation.

Time of Precipitation

Code Number	Time of Precipitation
0	No Precipitation
1	Less than 1 hour ago
2	1 to 2 hours ago
3	2 to 3 hours ago
4	3 to 4 hours ago
5	4 to 5 hours ago
6	5 to 6 hours ago
7	6 to 12 hours ago
8	More than 12 hours ago
9	Unknown

Total Sky Coverage Symbols

Clear- Less than 1/10

Scattered- 1/10 to and incl. 5/10

Scattered- 1/10 to and incl. 5/10

Scattered- 1/10 to and incl. 5/10

Broken- 6/10 to and incl. 9/10

Broken- 6/10 to and incl. 9/10

Broken- 6/10 to and incl. 9/10

Overcast- More than 9/10

Sky obscured

Barometric Tendency

Rising, then falling.

Rising, then steady; or rising, then rising more slowly.

Rising unsteadily, or unsteady

Rising steadily, or steady. (not plotted)

Falling or steady, then rising; or rising, then rising more quickly.

} Barometer now higher than, or same as, 3 hours ago.

Falling, then rising.

Falling, then steady; or falling, then falling more slowly.

Falling unsteadily, or unsteady.

Falling Steadily. (not plotted)

Steady or rising, then falling, or falling, then falling more quickly

} Barometer now lower than 3 hours ago

Icing · Turbulence · Miscellaneous

Hail   Squall   Lite rim icing   Moderate rim icing   Severe rim icing   Lite clear icing

Moderate clear icing   Severe clear icing   Lite turbulence   Moderate turbulence   Severe turbulence

Green . . . . . . 0° C isotherm   Purple . . . . . . occluded front
Blue . . . . cold front   Red and blue . stationary front
Red . . . . warm front

U.S. Dept. of Commerce
METEOROLOGY
(Wind Speeds on Surface Maps)

Extracted from Daily Weather Maps of the Weather Bureau, and reproduced herein through the courtesy of the U.S. Weather Bureau, Department of Commerce, Washington. These data and symbology also appear in NAVAER 00-80U-24, Meteorology for Naval Aviators.

PLOTTED	Miles(Statute)PerHour		Knots	
◎	Calm		Calm	
	1 -	4	1 -	2
	5 -	8	3 -	7
	9 -	14	8 -	12
	15 -	20	13 -	17
	21 -	25	18 -	22
	26 -	31	23	27
	32 -	37	28 -	32
	38 -	43	33 -	37
	44 -	49	38 -	42
	50 -	54	43 -	47
	55 -	60	48 -	52
	61 -	66	53 -	57
	67 -	71	58 -	62
	72 -	77	63 -	67
	78 -	83	68 -	72
	84 -	89	73 -	77
	119 -	123	103 -	107

441

Dept. of Commerce
METEOROLOGY
(Weather Map Analysis)

1. In symbols 1-12 inclusive, Column III, barbs may be separated more than shown, but a continuous line will always be drawn through the bases of the barbs.

2. In symbols 13-18 inclusive, Column III, the barbs will always be separated and will always be drawn without a connecting line.

3. In symbols 19-26 inclusive, Column III, the barbs may be spaced a greater distance than shown here, but the length of the dash between barbs should equal the space between the dash and each adjacent barb.

4. In symbol 35, Columns II and III, the spacing between the continuous lines will normally be about 1/8 inch, but may be greated when the intertropical convergence zone is broad.

(I) ANALYSIS FEATURE	(II) SYMBOL ON COLORED MAPS	(III) SYMBOL ON BLACK AND WHITE MAPS
1. Cold front -- surface*	——————————— Blue	▲▲▲▲▲
2. Cold front aloft*	— — — — — Blue	△△△△△
3. Cold front aloft -- becoming surface		△▲△▲△
4. Cold front -- surface -- going aloft		▲△▲△▲
5. Warm front -- surface*	——————————— Red	●●●●●
6. Warm front aloft*	— — — — — Red	⌒⌒⌒⌒⌒
7. Warm front aloft -- becoming surface		⌒●⌒●⌒
8. Warm front -- surface -- becoming aloft		●⌒●⌒●
9. Quasi-stationary front -- surface	Red | Blue | Red | Blue | Red Red and Blue	▲●▲●▲
10. Quasi-stationary front aloft	Red Blue Red Blue Red and Blue	△⌒△⌒△
11. Occluded front -- surface*	——————————— Purple	▲●▲●▲
12. Occluded front aloft*	— — — — — Purple	△⌒△⌒△
13. Frontogenesis, resulting in the formation of a cold front at the surface	● ● ● ● ● ● ● ● Blue	▲ ▲ ▲ ▲ ▲
14. Frontogenesis, resulting in the formation of a warm front at the surface	● ● ● ● ● ● ● ● Red	● ● ● ● ●
15. Frontogenesis, resulting in the formation of a quasi-stationary front at the surface	Red Blue Red Blue Red Blue Red Blue Red and Blue ● ● ● ● ● ● ● ●	● ▲ ● ▲ ●
16. Frontogenesis, resulting in the formation of a cold front aloft	O O O O O O O O Blue	△ △ △ △ △
17. Frontogenesis, resulting in the formation of a warm front aloft	O O O O O O O O Red	⌒ ⌒ ⌒ ⌒ ⌒
18. Frontogenesis, resulting in the formation of a quasi-stationary front aloft	R B R B R B R B Red (R) and O O O O O O O O Blue (B)	Red Blue Red Blue Red ⌒ △ ⌒ △ ⌒
19. Cold front at the surface under-going frontolysis	///////////////// Blue	▲ - ▲ - ▲ - ▲
20. Warm front at the surface under-going frontolysis	///////////////// Red	● - ● - ● - ●

(I) ANALYSIS FEATURE	(II) SYMBOL ON COLORED MAPS	(III) SYMBOL ON BLACK AND WHITE MAPS
21. Quasi-stationary front at the surface, undergoing frontolysis	R B R B R B R B R B R B R B R B R Red (R) and Blue (B)	◖ – ▲ – ◖ – ▲ – ◖
22. Occluded front at the surface, undergoing frontolysis	/ / / / / / / / / / / / / / / / Purple	◖ – ▲ – ◖ – ▲ – ◖
23. Cold front aloft, undergoing frontolysis	/ / / / / / / / / / / / Blue	△ – △ – △ – △ – △
24. Warm front aloft, undergoing frontolysis	/ / / / / / / / / / / / Red	◠ – ◠ – ◠ – ◠ – ◠
25. Quasi-stationary front aloft, undergoing frontolysis	R B R B R B R B R B R B R B / / / / / / / / / / / / / / R B R B R B R B R B R B R B Red (R) and Blue (B)	◡ – △ – ◡ – △ – ◡
26. Occluded front aloft, undergoing frontolysis	/ / / / / / / / / / / / / Purple	◠ – △ – ◠ – △ – ◠
27. Instability line (non-frontal line along which squalls or other evidences of marked instability exist)	▬▬▬ • • ▬▬ • • Purple	▬▬▬ • • ▬▬ • •
28. Trough line	▬▬ — ▬▬ — ▬▬ — ▬▬ Brown	▬▬ — ▬▬ — ▬▬ — ▬▬
29. Ridge line	⋀⋁⋀⋁⋀⋁⋀⋁ Brown	⋀⋁⋀⋁⋀⋁⋀⋁
30. Shear line or surge line (tropical analysis)	▬▬ • ▬ • ▬ • ▬ Blue	▬▬ • ▬ • ▬ • ▬
31. Line of convergence (tropical analysis)	⊕ ⊕ ⊕ ⊕ ⊕ ⊕ Brown	⊕ ⊕ ⊕ ⊕ ⊕ ⊕
32. Line of divergence (tropical analysis)	+ + + + + + Brown	+ + + + + +
33. Center of tropical cyclonic circulation (strongest wind Beaufort Force 5 to 11 inclusive)	၅ Red	၅
34. Tropical hurricane center (strongest wind Beaufort Force 12 or greater)	၅ Red	၅
35. Intertropical convergence zone	▱▱▱▱▱ Red	▱▱▱▱▱

Weather map

* I.M.O. Standard

443

CLOUDS OF GENERA Sc, St, Cu, Cb.

1. Cumulus humilis. **L 1**

2. Cumulus congestus. **L 2**

3. Cumulus congestus. **L 2**

4. Cumulonimbus calvus. **L 3**

5. Stratocumulus cumulogenitus. **L 4**

6. Stratocumulus. **L 5**

444

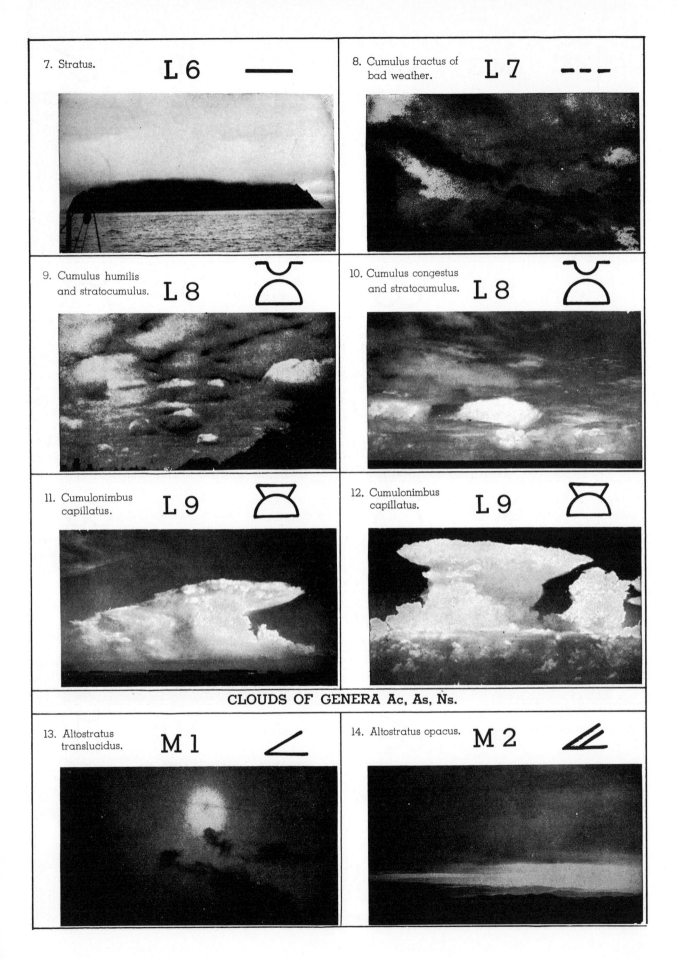

7. Stratus.   **L 6**   —

8. Cumulus fractus of bad weather.   **L 7**   - - -

9. Cumulus humilis and stratocumulus.   **L 8**

10. Cumulus congestus and stratocumulus.   **L 8**

11. Cumulonimbus capillatus.   **L 9**

12. Cumulonimbus capillatus.   **L 9**

CLOUDS OF GENERA Ac, As, Ns.

13. Altostratus translucidus.   **M 1**

14. Altostratus opacus.   **M 2**

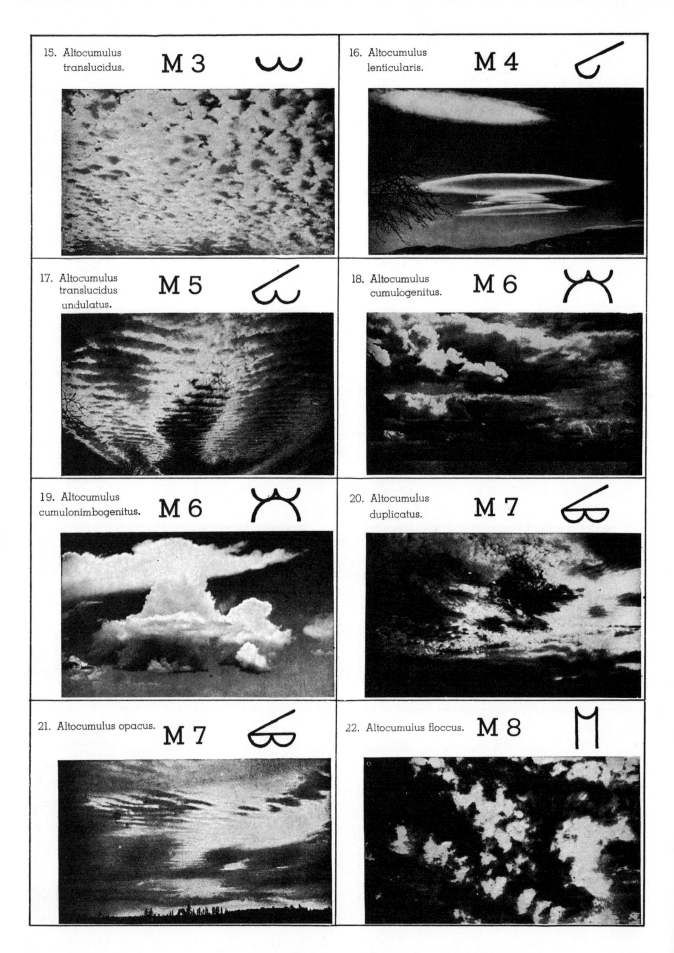

15. Altocumulus translucidus. **M 3**

16. Altocumulus lenticularis. **M 4**

17. Altocumulus translucidus undulatus. **M 5**

18. Altocumulus cumulogenitus. **M 6**

19. Altocumulus cumulonimbogenitus. **M 6**

20. Altocumulus duplicatus. **M 7**

21. Altocumulus opacus. **M 7**

22. Altocumulus floccus. **M 8**

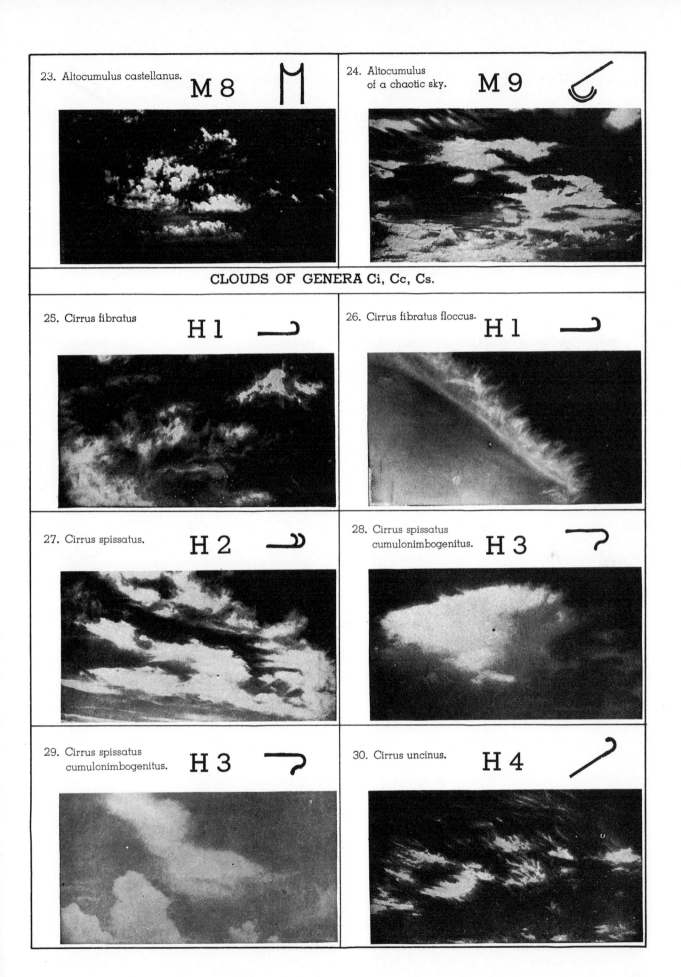

23. Altocumulus castellanus. **M 8**

24. Altocumulus of a chaotic sky. **M 9**

CLOUDS OF GENERA Ci, Cc, Cs.

25. Cirrus fibratus **H 1**

26. Cirrus fibratus floccus. **H 1**

27. Cirrus spissatus. **H 2**

28. Cirrus spissatus cumulonimbogenitus. **H 3**

29. Cirrus spissatus cumulonimbogenitus. **H 3**

30. Cirrus uncinus. **H 4**

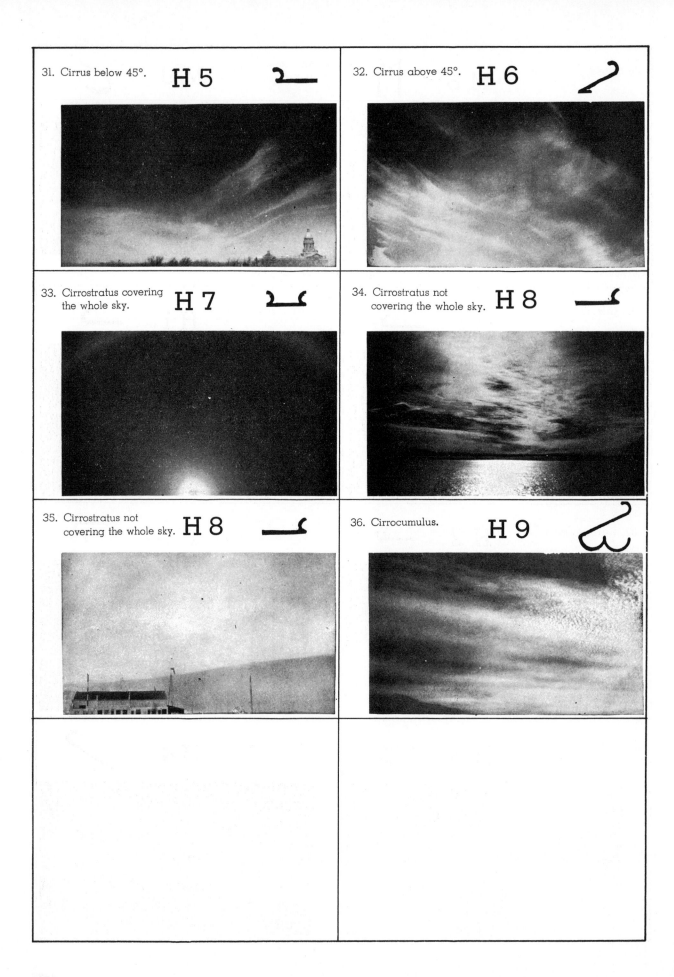

31. Cirrus below 45°. **H 5**

32. Cirrus above 45°. **H 6**

33. Cirrostratus covering the whole sky. **H 7**

34. Cirrostratus not covering the whole sky. **H 8**

35. Cirrostratus not covering the whole sky. **H 8**

36. Cirrocumulus. **H 9**

Cloud Symbols

Cloud Symbols

LOW CLOUDS

C_L	Description (Abridged From I.M.O. Code)
*	Cu with little vertical development and seemingly flattened.
*	Cu of considerable development, generally towering, with or without other Cu or Sc bases all at same level.
*	Cb with tops lacking clear-cut outlines, but distinctly not cirriform or anvil-shaped; with or without Cu, Sc, or St.
	Sc formed by spreading out of Cu; Cu often present also.
*	Sc not formed by spreading out of Cu.
*	St or Fs or both, but not Fs of bad weather.
- - -	Fs and/or Fc of bad weather (scud) usually under As and Ns
*	Cu and Sc (not formed by spreading out of Cu) with bases at different levels
*	Cb having a clearly fibrous (cirriform) top, often anvil-shaped with or without Cu, Sc, St, or scud.

MIDDLE CLOUDS

C_M	Description (Abridged From I.M.O. Code)
*	Thin As (entire cloud layer semitransparent).
*	Thick As, or Ns.
*	Thin Ac; cloud elements not changing much and at a single level.
	Thin Ac in patches; cloud elements continually changing and/or occurring at more than one level.
*	Thin Ac in bands or in a layer gradually spreading over sky and usually thickening as a whole.
	Ac formed by the spreading out of Cu.
*	Double-layered Ac or a thick layer of Ac, not increasing; or As and Ac both present at same or different levels.
	Ac in the form of Cu-shaped tufts or Ac with turrets.
	Ac of a chaotic sky, usually at different levels; patches of dense Ci are usually present also.

HIGH CLOUDS

C_H	Description (Abridged From I.M.O. Code)
*	Filaments of Ci, scattered and not increasing.
	Dense Ci in patches or twisted sheaves, usually not increasing.
*	Ci, often anvil-shaped, derived from or associated with Cb.
	Ci, often hook-shaped, gradually spreading over the sky and usually thickening as a whole.
	Ci and Cs, often in converging bands, or Cs alone; the continuous layer not reaching 45° altitude.
	Ci and Cs, often in converging bands, or Cs alone, the continuous layer exceeding 45° altitude.
*	Cs covering the entire sky.
	Cs not increasing and not covering entire sky; Ci and Cc may be present.
*	Cc alone or Cc with some Ci or Cs, but the Cc being the main cirriform cloud present.

Cloud Abbreviation

St or Fs-Stratus or Fractostratus
Ci-Cirrus
Cs-Cirrostratus
Cc-Cirrocumulus
Ac-Altocumulus
As-Altostratus
Sc-Stratocumulus
Ns-Nimbostratus
Cu or Fc-Cumulus or Fractocumulus
Cb-Cumulonimbus

* MOST COMMON

COMMON CONTRACTIONS Following is a list of some of the abbreviations for words or groups of words for use in transmission of weather information, including forecasts and the remarks to be found at the end of teletyped reports.　　　　**NAVAER 00–80U–24**

Words	Abbreviations	Words	Abbreviations
about	ABT	deepen	DPN
above	ABV	delayed	DLAD
accompany	ACPY	delayed weather	PDW
across	ACRS	dense	DNS
advance	ADVN	develop	DVLP
after	AFT	dewpoint	DWPNT
after dark	AFDK	diminish	DMSH
afternoon	AFTN	dissipate	DSIPT
aircraft	ACFT	dissipating	DSIPTG
airmass	AMS	distant	DSNT
airport	ARPT	divide	DVD
airway	AWY	drift	DRFT
aloft	ALF	drizzle	DRZL
along	ALG	during	DURG
altimeter setting	ALSTG	early	ERY
amount	AMT	ending	ENDG
around	ARND	entire	ENTR
barometer	BRM	estimate	EST
become	BCM	evening	EVE
becoming	BCMG	extend	XTD
before	BFR	extreme	XTRM
begin	BGN	falling	FLG
behind	BHND	field	FLD
below	BLO	flurry	FLRY
between	BTN	follow	FLW
broken	BRKN	forecast	FCST
ceiling	CIG	forming	FRMG
center	CNTR	freeze	FRZ
central	CNTRL	frequent	FQT
change	CHG	from	FM
clear	CLR	front	FNT
clearing	CLRG	frontal passage	FROPA
cloud	CLD	frost	FRST
coastal	CSTL	forenoon	FORNN
commence	CMNC	generally	GENLY
condition	CND	gradual	GRDL
continuing	CONTG	ground	GND
correction	CQN	ground fog	GNDFG
cumulonimbus	CB	group	GRP
daybreak	DABRK	hailstone	HLSTO
daylight	DALGT	hard freeze	HDFRZ
decrease	DCR	hazy	HZY
decreasing	DCRG	heavy	HVY

Words	Abbreviations	Words	Abbreviations
heavier	HVYR	moderate	MDT
high	HI	morning	MRNG
higher	HIER	mostly	MSTLY
high broken	HBRKN	mountain	MTN
high overcast	HOVC	move	MOV
high scattered	HSCTD	nautical miles	NLM
horizon	HRZN	night	NGT
hundred	HND	northern	NRN
hurricane	HURCN	numerous	NMRS
hurricane report	HUREP	obscure	OBSC
icing	ICG	observe	OBS
icing in precipitation	ICGIP	occasion	OCN
icing in clouds	ICGIC	occasional	OCNL
ice on runways	IR	occasionally	OCNLY
improve	IPV	occluded front	OCFNT
increase	INCR	occlusion	OCLN
indefinite	INDFT	outlook	OTLK
inoperative	INOPV	over	OVR
instrument	INST	overcast	OVC
intense	INTS	overhead	OVHD
intermittent	INTMT	on top	OTP
in vicinity of	INVOF	partly	PTLY
knollsman	KOL	pilot balloon	PIBAL
knots	KTS	observation	
latitude	LATD	not observed, because	PICO
layer	LYR	of clouds	
level	LVL	not observed, no	PIHE
lift	LFT	helium	
light	LGT	not observed, because	PIRA
lightning	LTNG	of rain	
likely	LKLY	period	PRD
little	LTL	persisting	PRSTG
little change	LTLCG	possible	PSBL
local	LCL	portion	PTN
locally	LCLY	precipitation	PCPN
longitude	LONG	pressure	PRES
lower	LWR	prevail	PVL
lower broken	LWRBRKN	quadrant	QUAD
lower overcast	LWROVC	radiosonde data	RADAT
lower scattered	LWSCTD	radar winds aloft	RAWIN
mean sea level	MSL	ragged	RGD
middle	MID	range	RNG
midnight	MIDN	rapid	RPD
mild	MLD	rapidly	RPDLY
mile (statute)	MI	reach	RCH
miles per hour	MPH	redeveloping	REDVLPG
millibars	MBS	reforming	REFRMG
missing	MISG	region	RGN
mixed	MXD	remain	RMN

Words	Abbreviations	Words	Abbreviations
remark	RMRK	unlimited	UNL
ridge	RDG	unsteady	UNSTDY
river	RVR	until	TIL
runway	RNWY	upper	UPR
scattered	SCTD	upward	UPWD
schedule	SKD	valley	VLY
sections	SXNS	variable	VRBL
several	SVRL	vicinity	VCNTY
severe	SVR	visibility	VSBY
shallow	SHLW	visible	VSB
shift	SHFT	warm	WRM
shower	SHWR	weak	WK
sleet	SLT	weaken	WKN
slightly	SLGTLY	weather	WX
smoke	SMK	western	WRN
snow	SNW	westerly	WLY
somewhat	SMWHAT	westward	WWD
spreading	SPRDG	widely	WL
sprinkle	SPKL	will	WL
squall	SQAL	wind	WND
squall lines	SQLNS		

WORD ENDINGS

Words	Abbreviations	Words	Abbreviations
station	STN	able	BL
storm	STM	al	L
surface	SFC	ally, erly, ly	LY
sunrise	SUNRS	ary, ery, ory	RY
synopsis	SYNS	ance, ence	NC
telephone	TLFO	der	DR
temperature	TMP	ed, ied	D
terminal	TRML	ening	NG
thick	THK	er, ier, or	RN
thin	THN	ern	RN
thousand	THSD	ically	CLY
threaten	THTN	iest, est	ST
throughout	THRUT	iness, ness	NS
thunder	THDR	ing	G
thunderhead	THD	ity	TY
thundershower	TSHWR	ive	V
thunderstorm	TSTM	ment	MT
tonight	TNGT	our	US
topping	TPG	s, es, ies	S
toward	TWD	tion, ation	N
trough	TROF	ward	WD
turbulence	TURBC		
unknown	UNK		

Dept. of Commerce

PATENT

Extracted from Guide for Patent Draftsmen (May, 1961), and reproduced herein through the courtesy of the U.S. Patent Office, Department of Commerce, Washington.

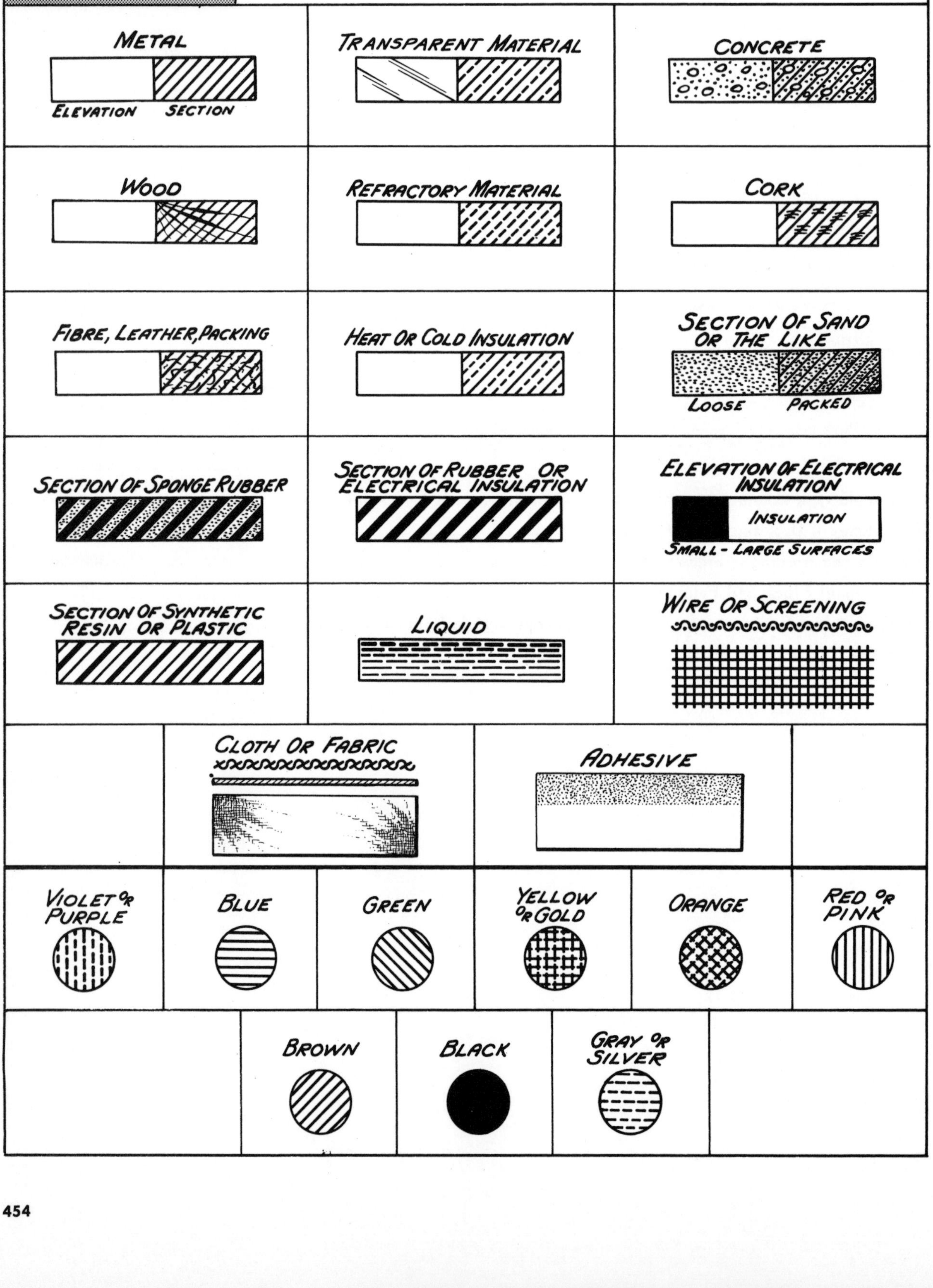

METAL
ELEVATION
SECTION
TRANSPARENT MATERIAL
CONCRETE
WOOD
REFRACTORY MATERIAL
CORK
FIBRE, LEATHER, PACKING
HEAT OR COLD INSULATION
SECTION OF SAND OR THE LIKE
LOOSE
PACKED
SECTION OF SPONGE RUBBER
SECTION OF RUBBER OR ELECTRICAL INSULATION
ELEVATION OF ELECTRICAL INSULATION
INSULATION
SMALL - LARGE SURFACES
SECTION OF SYNTHETIC RESIN OR PLASTIC
LIQUID
WIRE OR SCREENING
CLOTH OR FABRIC
ADHESIVE
VIOLET OR PURPLE
BLUE
GREEN
YELLOW OR GOLD
ORANGE
RED OR PINK
BROWN
BLACK
GRAY OR SILVER

	RESISTOR	VARIABLE RESISTOR	POTENTIOMETER	RHEOSTATS	CONDENSERS
Electrical Symbols	1	2	3	4	5
GANGED VARIABLE CONDENSERS 6	INDUCTORS 7	INDUCTOR ADJUSTABLE CORE 8	INDUCTOR OR REACTOR POWDERED MAGNETIC CORE 9	TRANSFORMER SATURABLE CORE 10	TRANSFORMER AIR CORE 11
VARIABLE TRANSFORMER 12	TRANSFORMER MAGNETIC CORE 13	AUTO-TRANSFORMER ADJUSTABLE 14	CROSSED AND JOINED WIRES 15	MAIN CIRCUITS / SHUNT OR CONTROL CIRCUITS 16	FUSE 17
COAXIAL CABLES 18	SHIELDING 19	BATTERY 20	THERMOELEMENT 21	BELL 22	AMMETER 23
MILLIAMMETER 24	VOLTMETER 25	GALVANOMETER 26	WATTMETER 27	SWITCH 28	DOUBLE POLE SWITCH 29
DOUBLE POLE DOUBLE THROW SWITCH 30	PUSH BUTTON TWO POINT MAKE 31	SELECTOR OR CONNECTOR OR FINDER SWITCH 32	CIRCUIT BREAKER OVERLOAD 33	RELAY 34	POLARIZED RELAY 35
DIFFERENTIAL RELAY 36	ANNUNCIATORS SIDE FRONT 37	DROP ANNUNCIATOR 38	DRUM TYPE SWITCH OR CONTROL 39	COMMUTATOR MOTOR OR GENERATOR 40	REPULSION MOTOR 41
INDUCTION MOTOR THREE PHASE SQUIRREL CAGE 42	INDUCTION MOTOR PHASE WOUND SECONDARY 43	SYNCHRONOUS MOTOR OR GEN. THREE PHASE 44	MOTOR GENERATOR 45	ROTARY CONVERTER THREE PHASE 46	FREQUENCY CHANGER THREE PHASE 47
TROLLEYS 48	THIRD RAIL SHOE 49	RECEIVERS 50	TRANSMITTER OR MICROPHONE 51	TELEPHONE HOOK 52	TELEGRAPH KEY 53

Electrical Symbols – continued	SWITCH BOARD PLUG AND JACK 54	PHONOGRAPH PICKUP 55	DYNAMIC SPEAKER 56	ANTENNA 57	LOOP ANTENNA 58
GROUND 59	SPARK GAP 60	LIGHTNING ARRESTER 61	DETECTOR OR RECTIFIER ANODE CATHODE GENERIC 62	DETECTOR OR RECTIFIER ANODE CATHODE CRYSTAL 63	PIEZOELECTRIC CRYSTAL 64
INCANDESCENT LAMP 65	MERCURY ARC RECTIFIER 66	ENVELOPE GAS FILLED 67	DIODE 68	TRIODE 69	PENTODE INDIRECTLY HEATED CATHODE 70
TRANSISTOR EMITTER COLLECTOR BASE 71	TRANSISTOR EMITTER COLLECTOR BASE 72	TRANSISTOR N P N JUNCTION TYPE 73	TRANSISTOR P N P JUNCTION TYPE 74	AMPLIFIER A 75	THERMIONIC FULL WAVE RECTIFIER 76
FULL WAVE RECTIFIER GAS FILLED 77	PHOTOELECTRIC CELL 78	GLOW DISCHARGE TUBE 79	X-RAY TUBE 80	CATHODE RAY TUBE 81	SPOT WELDING 82
DEPOSIT WELDING 83				Mechanical Symbols	CONDUIT CROSSING AND INTERSECTING 1
SECTIONS LARGE ENDS ROD PIPE 2	SCREW THREAD 3	CLUTCH 4	FRICTION CLUTCH 5	BRAKE 6	FLEXIBLE COUPLING 7
FLUID COUPLING 8	SPROCKET AND CHAIN 9		SPUR GEARS 10	BEVEL GEARS 11	WORM GEAR 12
SPUR GEARS SIDE VIEW 13	WELDS PLAN SECTION 14	SPOT WELD 15	INJECTOR NOZZLE 16	FIXED RESISTANCE 17	VARIABLE RESISTANCE 18

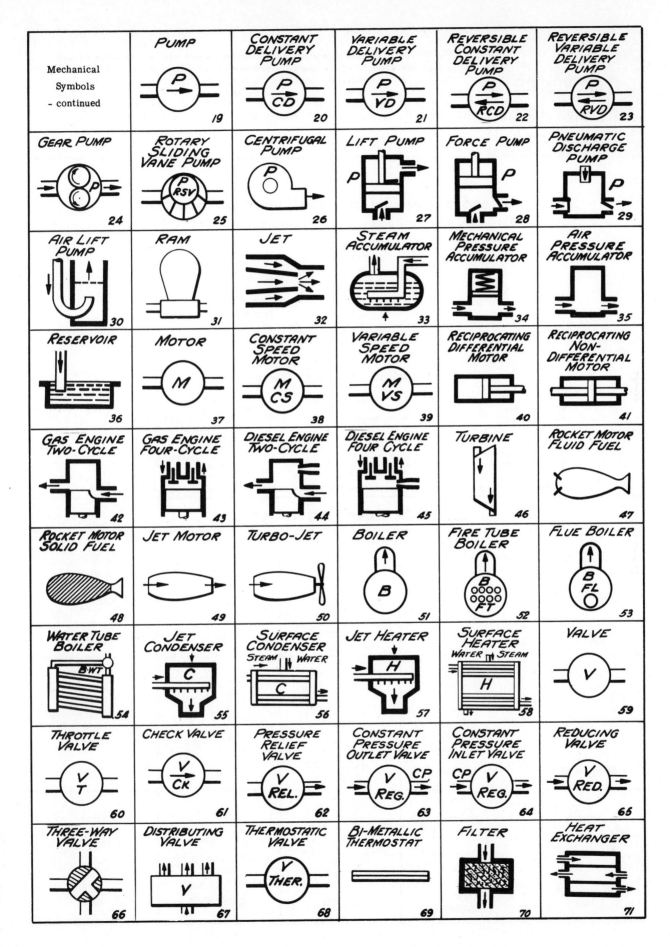

	PUMP	CONSTANT DELIVERY PUMP	VARIABLE DELIVERY PUMP	REVERSIBLE CONSTANT DELIVERY PUMP	REVERSIBLE VARIABLE DELIVERY PUMP
Mechanical Symbols – continued	P **19**	P CD **20**	P VD **21**	P RCD **22**	P RVD **23**
GEAR PUMP	ROTARY SLIDING VANE PUMP	CENTRIFUGAL PUMP	LIFT PUMP	FORCE PUMP	PNEUMATIC DISCHARGE PUMP
P **24**	P RSV **25**	P **26**	P **27**	P **28**	P **29**
AIR LIFT PUMP **30**	RAM **31**	JET **32**	STEAM ACCUMULATOR **33**	MECHANICAL PRESSURE ACCUMULATOR **34**	AIR PRESSURE ACCUMULATOR **35**
RESERVOIR **36**	MOTOR M **37**	CONSTANT SPEED MOTOR M CS **38**	VARIABLE SPEED MOTOR M VS **39**	RECIPROCATING DIFFERENTIAL MOTOR **40**	RECIPROCATING NON-DIFFERENTIAL MOTOR **41**
GAS ENGINE TWO-CYCLE **42**	GAS ENGINE FOUR-CYCLE **43**	DIESEL ENGINE TWO-CYCLE **44**	DIESEL ENGINE FOUR CYCLE **45**	TURBINE **46**	ROCKET MOTOR FLUID FUEL **47**
ROCKET MOTOR SOLID FUEL **48**	JET MOTOR **49**	TURBO-JET **50**	BOILER B **51**	FIRE TUBE BOILER B FT **52**	FLUE BOILER B FL **53**
WATER TUBE BOILER B·WT **54**	JET CONDENSER C **55**	SURFACE CONDENSER STEAM WATER C **56**	JET HEATER H **57**	SURFACE HEATER WATER STEAM H **58**	VALVE V **59**
THROTTLE VALVE V T **60**	CHECK VALVE V CK **61**	PRESSURE RELIEF VALVE V REL. **62**	CONSTANT PRESSURE OUTLET VALVE V REG. CP **63**	CONSTANT PRESSURE INLET VALVE CP V REG. **64**	REDUCING VALVE V RED. **65**
THREE-WAY VALVE **66**	DISTRIBUTING VALVE V **67**	THERMOSTATIC VALVE V THER. **68**	BI-METALLIC THERMOSTAT **69**	FILTER **70**	HEAT EXCHANGER **71**

The electron tube basing diagrams herein were extracted from the following manuals, through the courtesy of the Radio Corporation of America, Electron Tube Division, Harrison, N.J. Receiving Tubes and Picture Tubes (1275-J); Transmitting Tubes (TT-4); Receiving-type Tubes for Industry and Communication (RIT-104B); Photosensitive Devices and Cathode-ray Tubes (CRPD-105A). This section in no way illustrates every type available through all manufacturers, but represents the most common electron tubes used today.

Legend for Base and Envelope Connection Diagrams

Diagrams show terminals viewed from base or filament end of tube

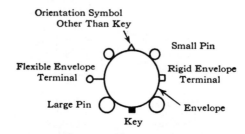

KEY: BASING DIAGRAMS (Bottom Views)

● = Gas-Type Tube	F+ = Filament (positive only)	IS = Internal Shield
BC = Base Sleeve	F− = Filament (negative only)	K = Cathode
BS = Base Shell	FM = Filament Tap	LC = Limited Connection—Do Not Use,
C = External Conductive Coating	G = Grid	Except As Specified in Data
CL = Collector	H = Heater	NC = No Internal Connection
DJ = Deflecting Electrode	HL = Heater Tap for Panel Lamp	P = Plate (Anode)
ES = External Shield	HM = Heater Tap	RC = Ray-Control Electrode
F = Filament	IC = Internal Connection—	S = Shell
	Do Not Use	TA = Target

Subscripts for multi-unit types: B, beam unit; D, diode unit; HP, heptode unit; HX, hexode unit; P. pentode unit; T, triode unit; TR, tetrode unit.

RCA Receiving Tubes

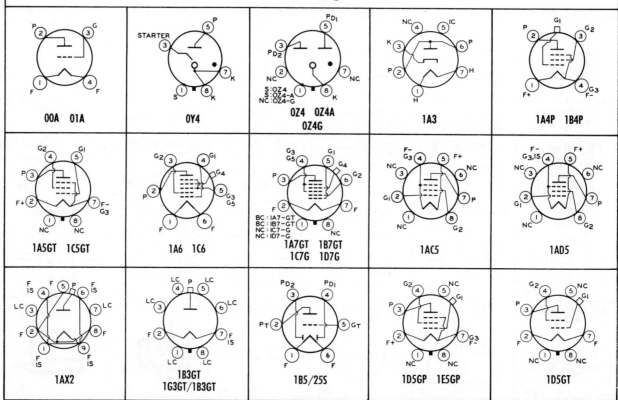

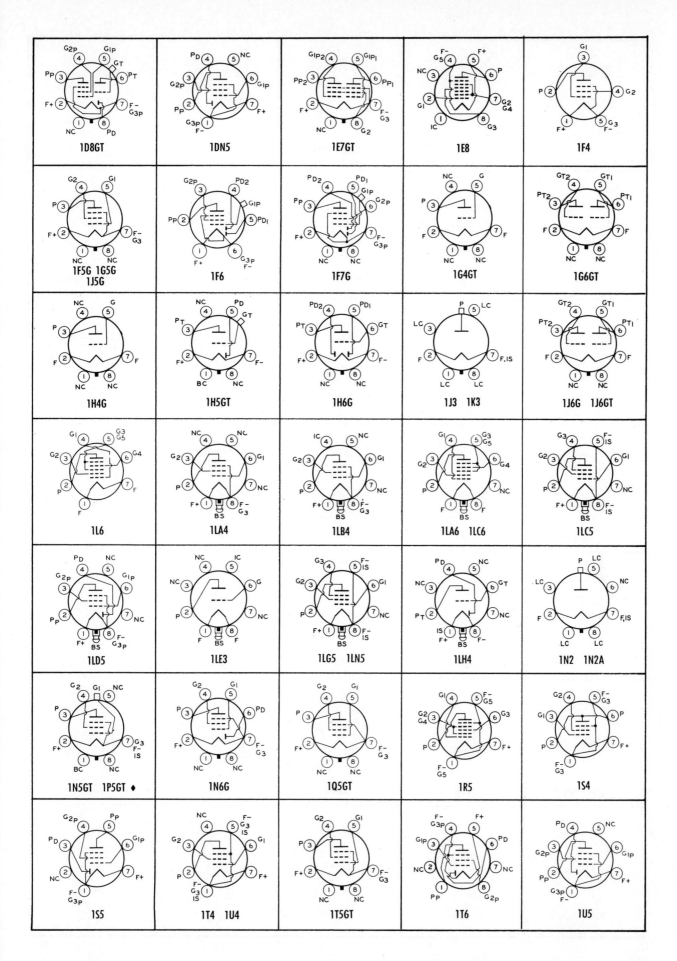

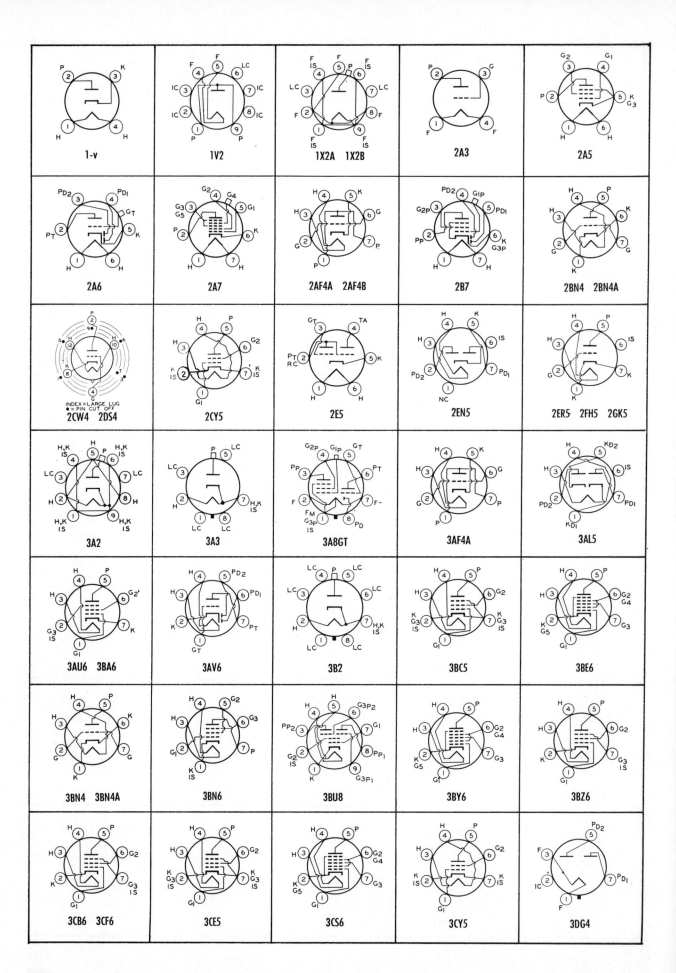

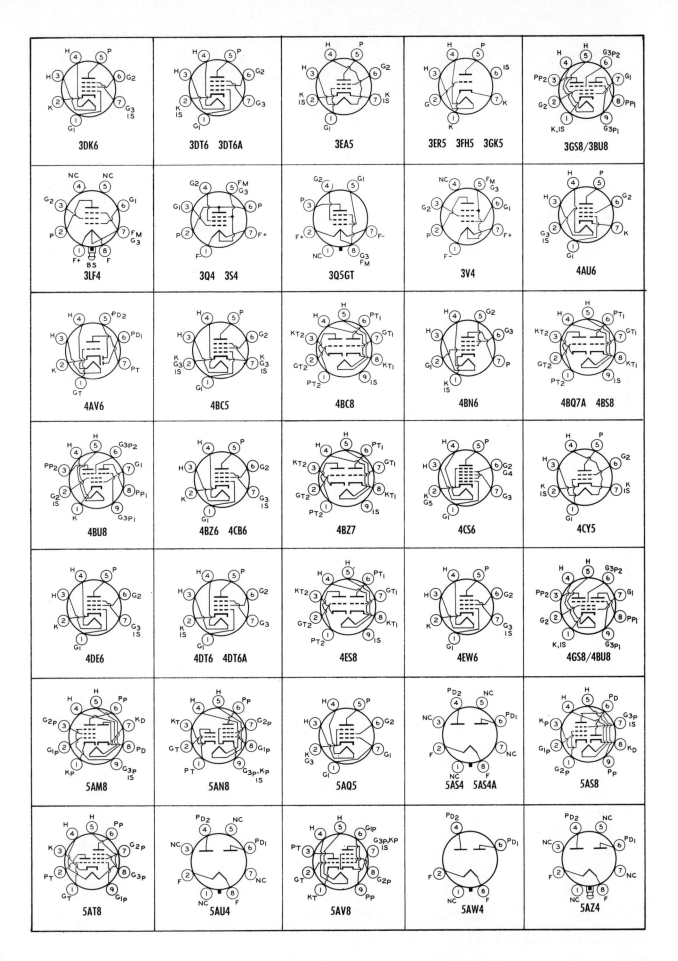

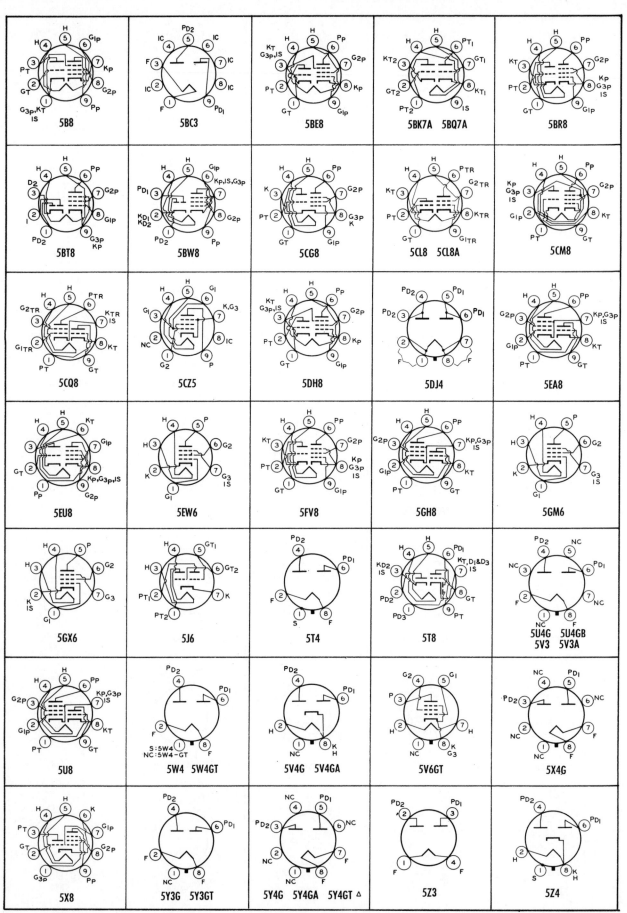

△ Pins 4 and 6 are omitted.

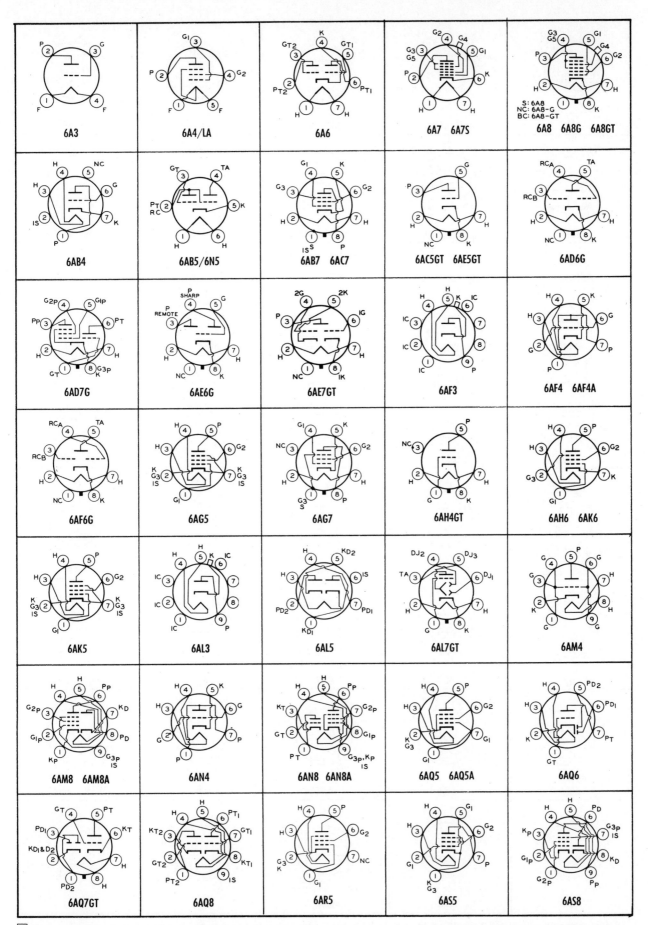

Socket terminals 1, 2, 4, and 6 should not be used as tie points.

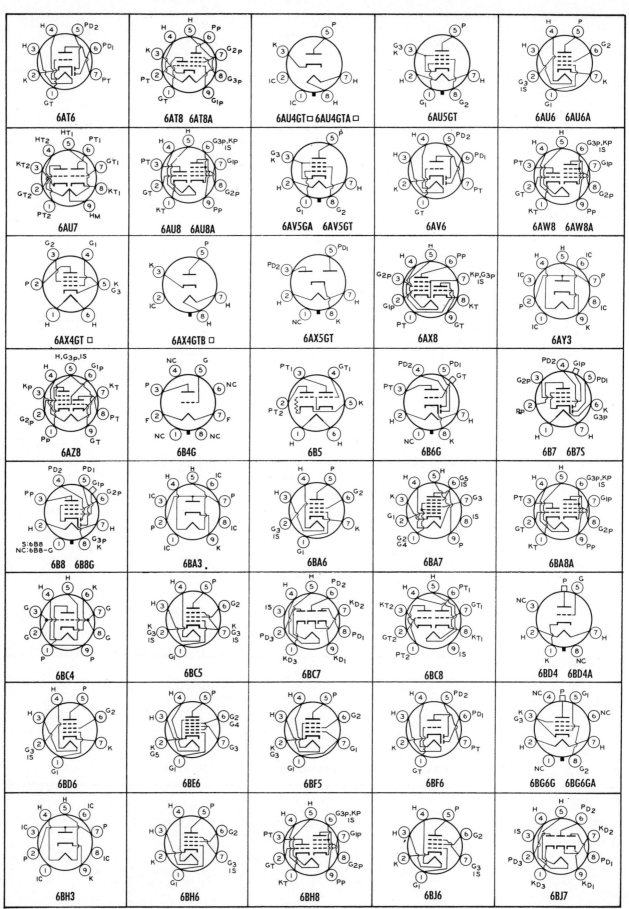

☐ Socket terminals 1, 2, 4, and 6 should not be used as tie points.

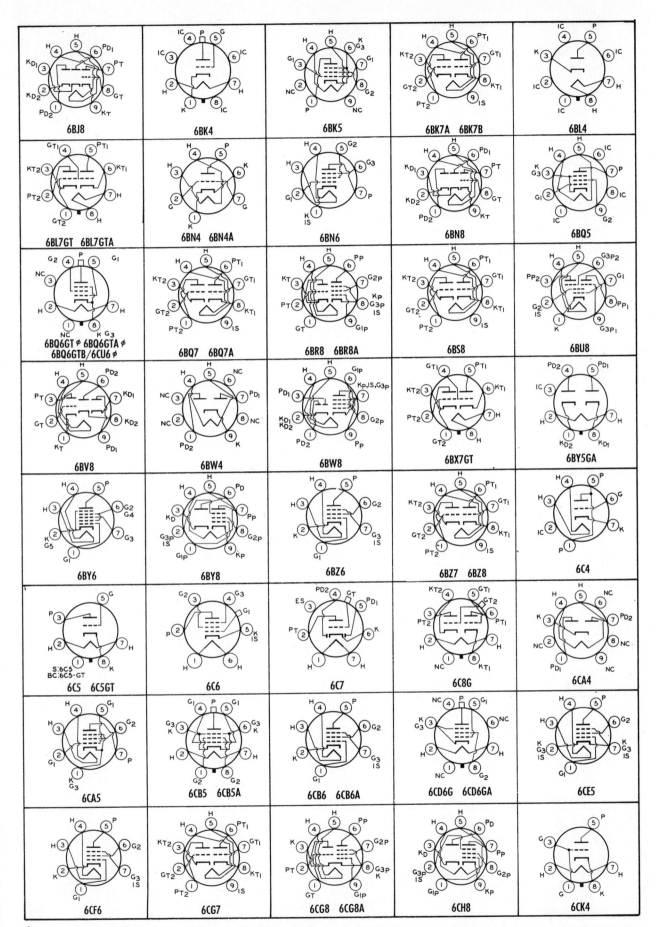

ϕ On the 6-pin bases pin No. 1 as well as pin No. 6 is omitted.

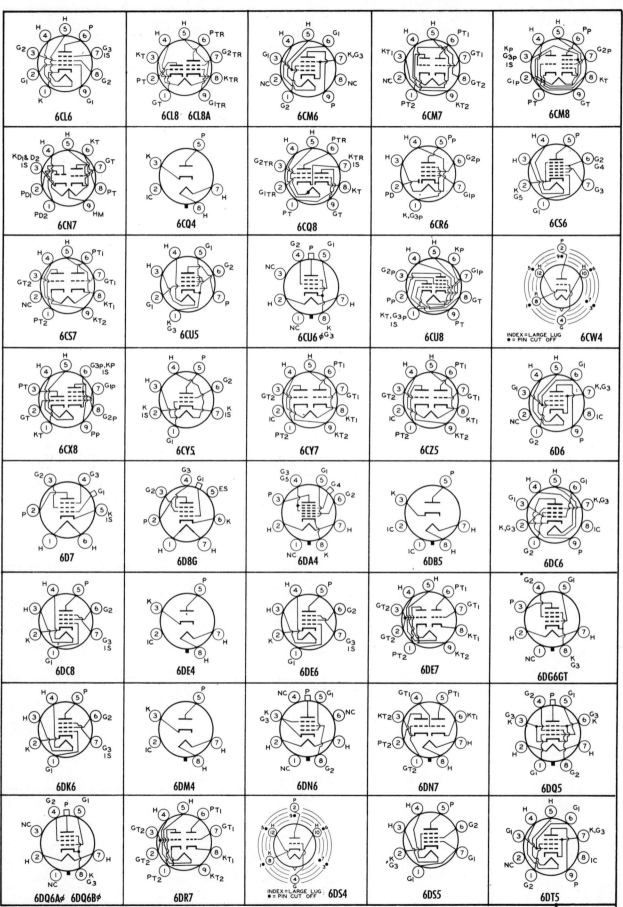

φ On the 6-pin bases pin No. 1 as well as pin No. 6 is omitted.

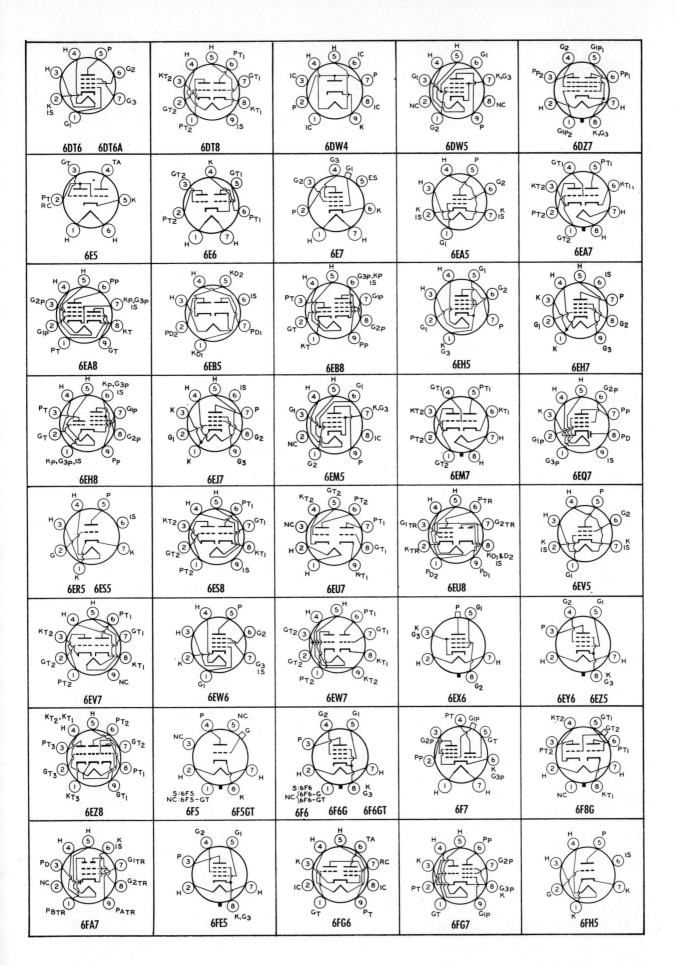

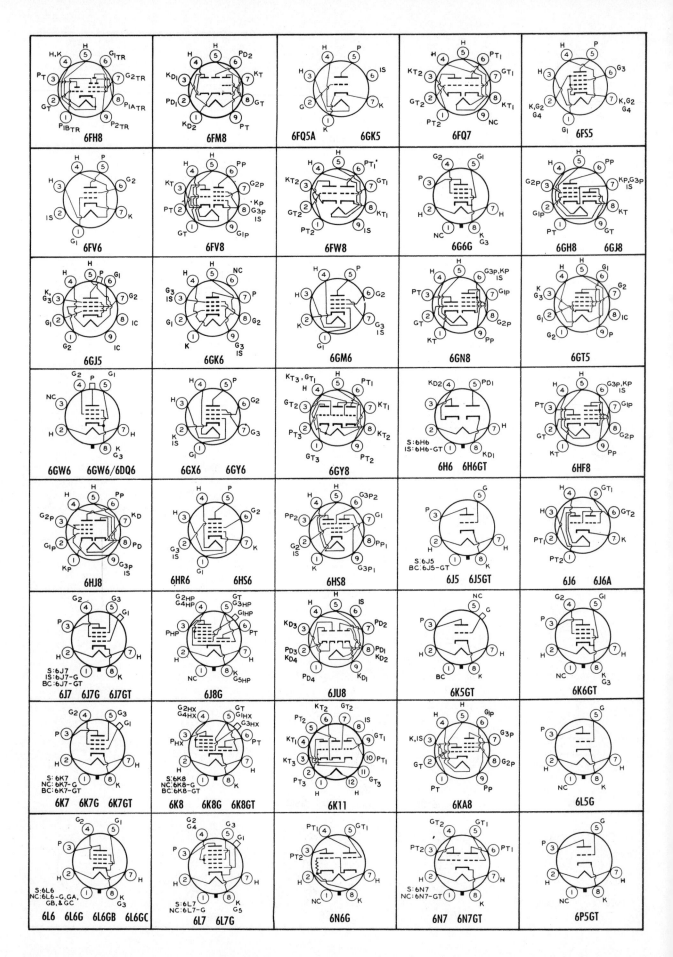

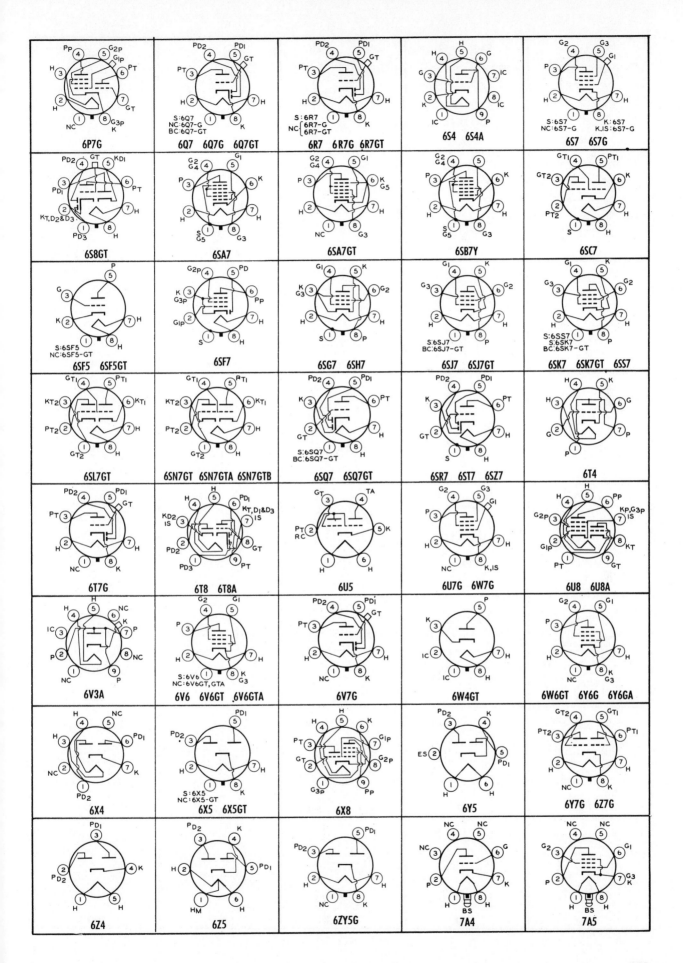

469

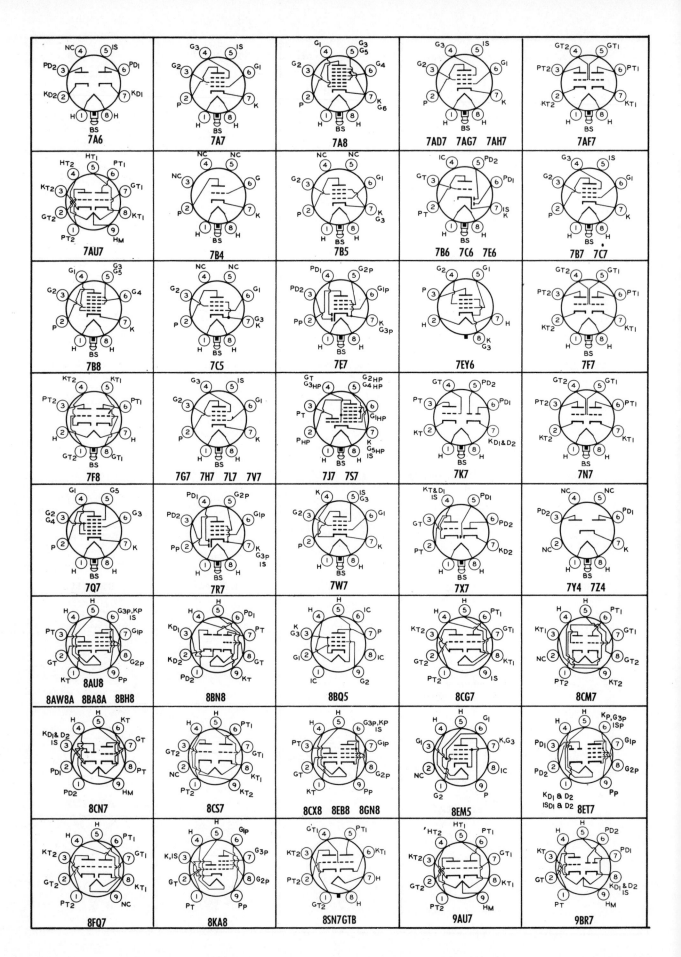

470

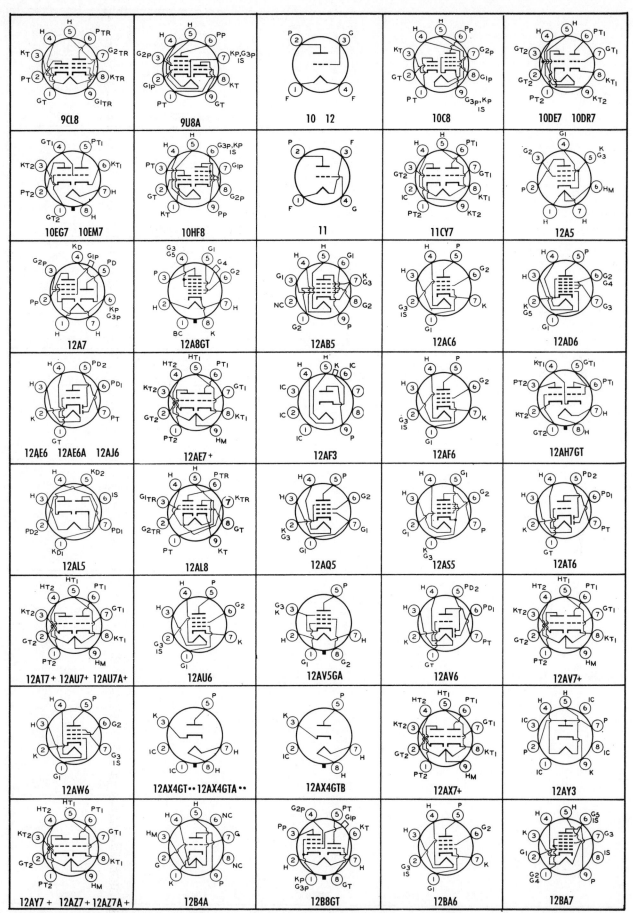

9CL8	9U8A	10 12	10C8	10DE7 10DR7
10EG7 10EM7	10HF8	11	11CY7	12A5
12A7	12A8GT	12AB5	12AC6	12AD6
12AE6 12AE6A 12AJ6	12AE7 +	12AF3	12AF6	12AH7GT
12AL5	12AL8	12AQ5	12AS5	12AT6
12AT7+ 12AU7+ 12AU7A+	12AU6	12AV5GA	12AV6	12AV7+
12AW6	12AX4GT•• 12AX4GTA••	12AX4GTB	12AX7+	12AY3
12AY7+ 12AZ7+12AZ7A+	12B4A	12B8GT	12BA6	12BA7

+ Heater for section 2 between pins 4 and 9; for section 1 between pins 5 and 9.
•• On the 5-pin bases pin 1 as well as pins 4 and 6 is omitted.

471

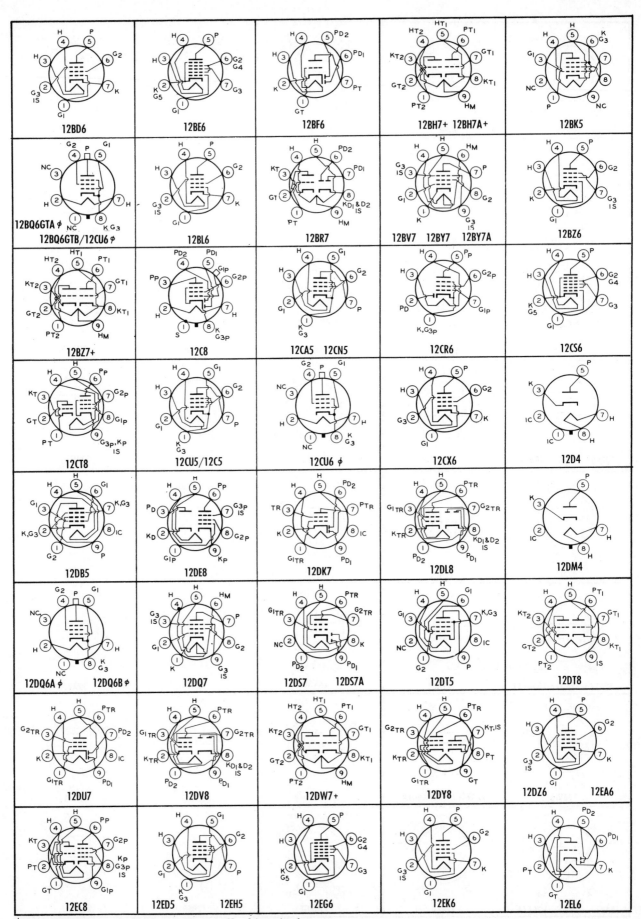

12BD6 12BE6 12BF6 12BH7+ 12BH7A+ 12BK5

12BQ6GTA φ
12BQ6GTB/12CU6 φ 12BL6 12BR7 12BV7 12BY7 12BY7A 12BZ6

12BZ7+ 12C8 12CA5 12CN5 12CR6 12CS6

12CT8 12CU5/12C5 12CU6 φ 12CX6 12D4

12DB5 12DE8 12DK7 12DL8 12DM4

12DQ6A φ   12DQ6B φ 12DQ7 12DS7 12DS7A 12DT5 12DT8

12DU7 12DV8 12DW7+ 12DY8 12DZ6   12EA6

12EC8 12ED5 12EH5 12EG6 12EK6 12EL6

φ On the 6-pin bases pin No. 1 as well as pin No. 6 is omitted.
+ Heater for section 2 between pins 4 and 9; for section 1 between pins 5 and 9.

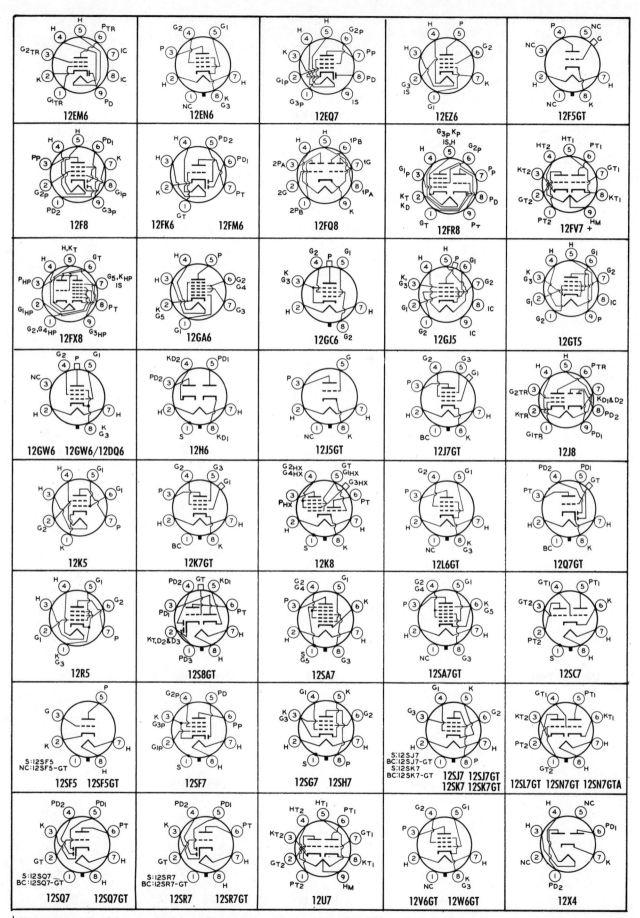

+ Heater for section 2 between pins 4 and 9; for section 1 between pins 5 and 9.

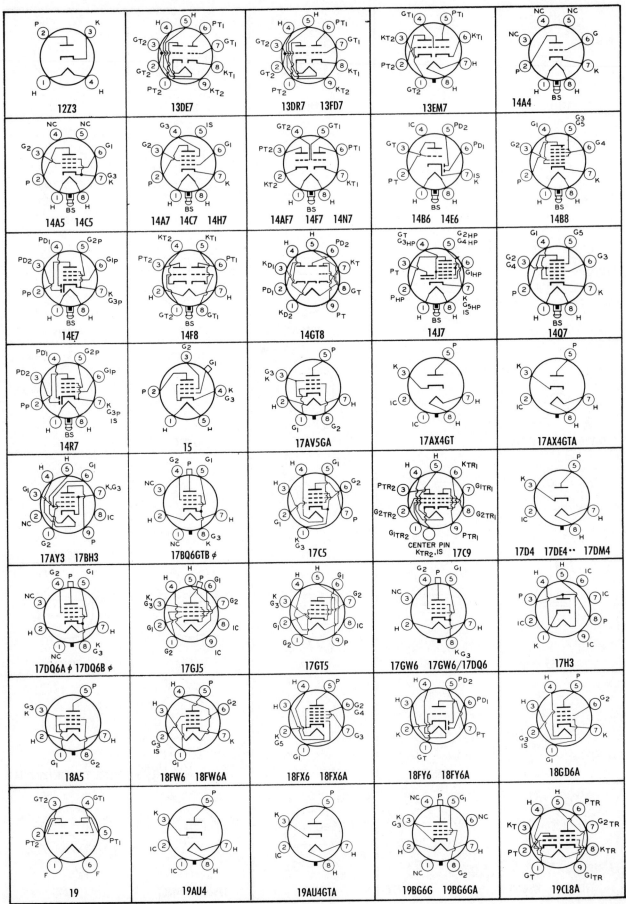

φ On the 6-pin bases pin No. 1 as well as pin No. 6 is omitted.

•• On the 5-pin bases pin 1 as well as pins 4 and 6 is omitted.

474

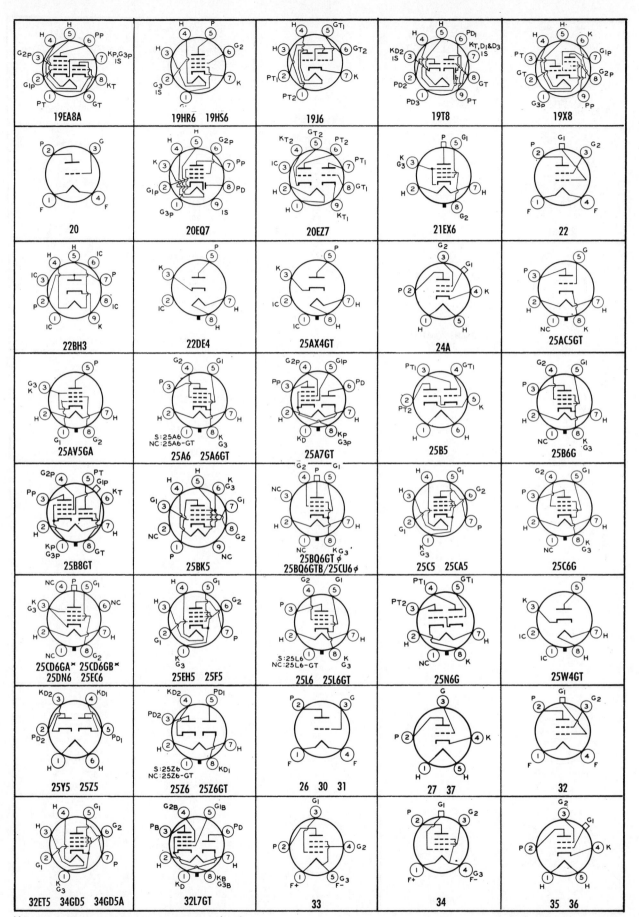

X On the 5-pin bases pins 1, 4, and 6 are omitted.

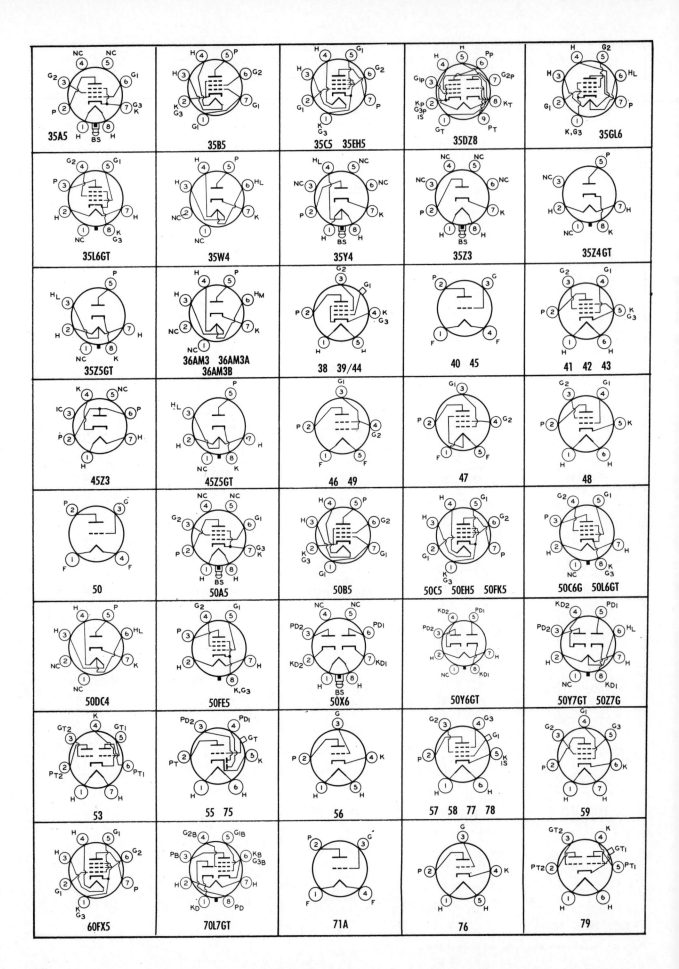

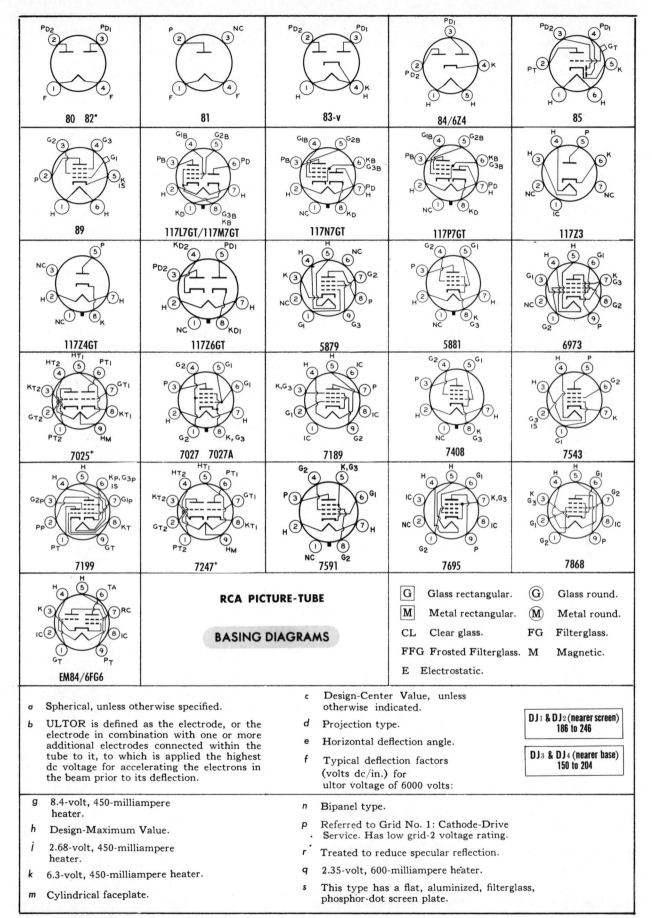

RCA PICTURE-TUBE

BASING DIAGRAMS

G	Glass rectangular.	Ⓖ	Glass round.
Ⓜ	Metal rectangular.	Ⓜ	Metal round.
CL	Clear glass.	FG	Filterglass.
FFG	Frosted Filterglass.	M	Magnetic.
E	Electrostatic.		

Tube types shown: 80 82*, 81, 83-v, 84/6Z4, 85, 89, 117L7GT/117M7GT, 117N7GT, 117P7GT, 117Z3, 117Z4GT, 117Z6GT, 5879, 5881, 6973, 7025+, 7027 7027A, 7189, 7408, 7543, 7199, 7247+, 7591, 7695, 7868, EM84/6FG6

a Spherical, unless otherwise specified.

b ULTOR is defined as the electrode, or the electrode in combination with one or more additional electrodes connected within the tube to it, to which is applied the highest dc voltage for accelerating the electrons in the beam prior to its deflection.

c Design-Center Value, unless otherwise indicated.

d Projection type.

e Horizontal deflection angle.

f Typical deflection factors (volts dc/in.) for ultor voltage of 6000 volts:

DJ1 & DJ2 (nearer screen) 186 to 246

DJ3 & DJ4 (nearer base) 150 to 204

g 8.4-volt, 450-milliampere heater.

h Design-Maximum Value.

i 2.68-volt, 450-milliampere heater.

k 6.3-volt, 450-milliampere heater.

m Cylindrical faceplate.

n Bipanel type.

p Referred to Grid No. 1: Cathode-Drive Service. Has low grid-2 voltage rating.

r Treated to reduce specular reflection.

q 2.35-volt, 600-milliampere heater.

s This type has a flat, aluminized, filterglass, phosphor-dot screen plate.

+ Heater for section 2 between pins 4 and 9; for section 1 between pins 5 and 9.

● 82 is a mercury-vapor type.

† 6.3-volt, 1.8-ampere heater (three heaters paralleled internally).

u 6.3-volt, 1.6-ampere heater (three heaters paralleled internally).

v This type has an integral protective window.

✠ Active RCA Picture-Tube Types shown here can replace more than 300 different types of industry picture tubes. The RCA Picture Tube Replacement and Interchangeability Chart is available on request.

Unless otherwise noted, all picture tubes listed have 6.3-volt, 600-milliampere heaters.

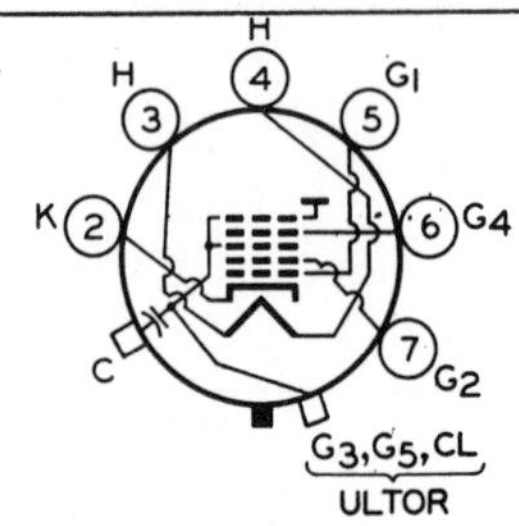

7FA
FOCUSING ELECTRODE = G₄

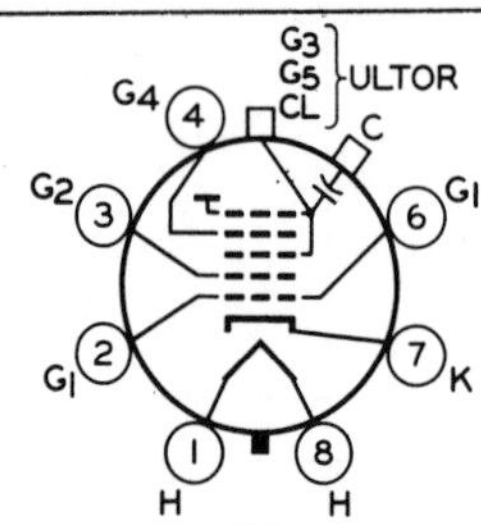

8HR
FOCUSING ELECTRODE = G₄

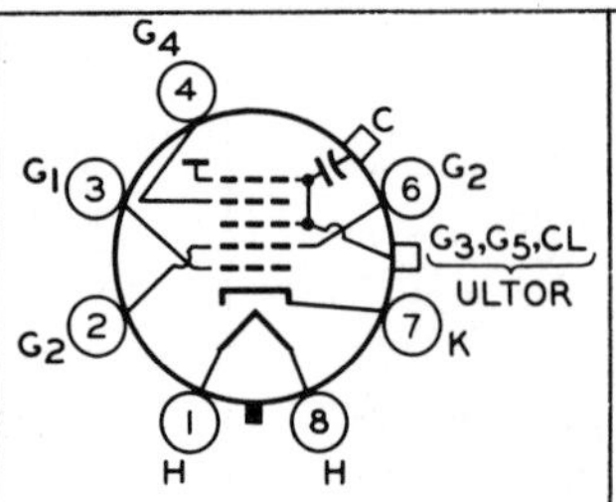

8JK
FOCUSING ELECTRODE = G₄

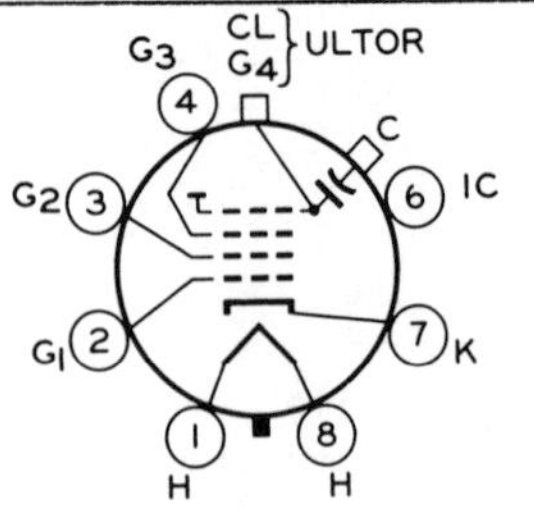

8JR
FOCUSING ELECTRODE = G₃

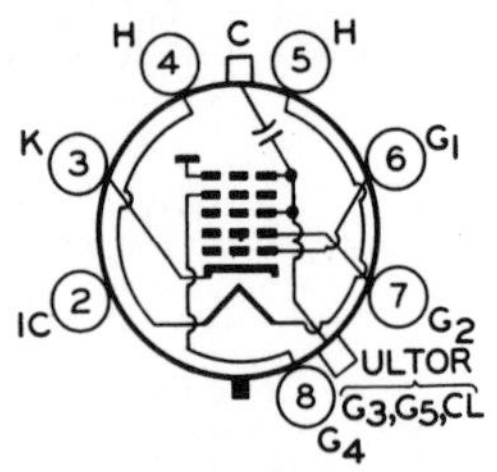

8KP
FOCUSING ELECTRODE = G₄

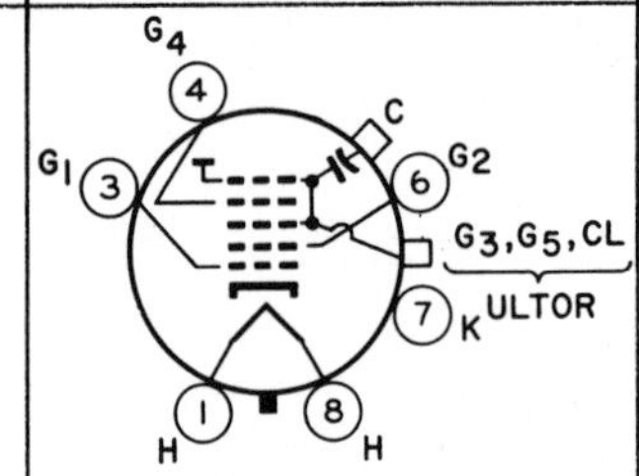

8KW
FOCUSING ELECTRODE = G₄

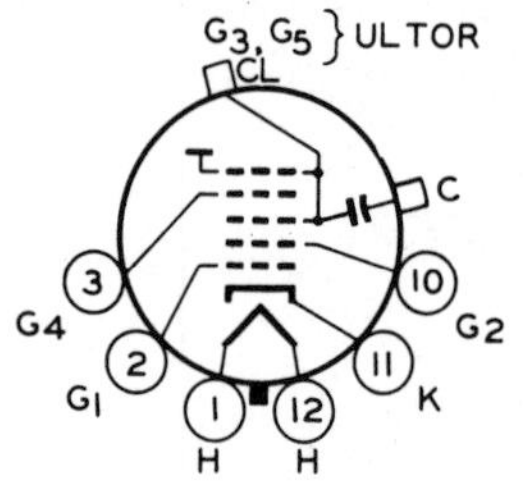

12AB
FOCUSING ELECTRODE = G₄

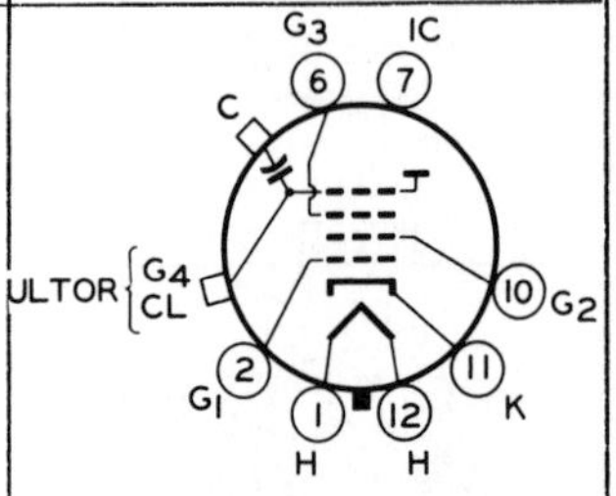

12C
FOCUSING ELECTRODE = G₃

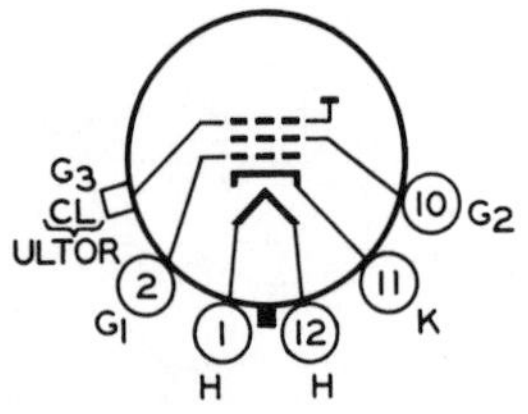

12D

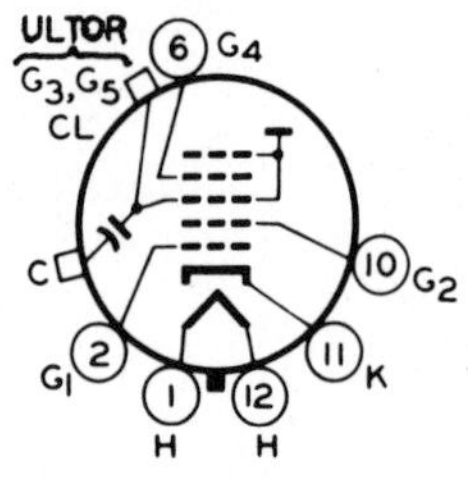

12L
FOCUSING ELECTRODE = G₄

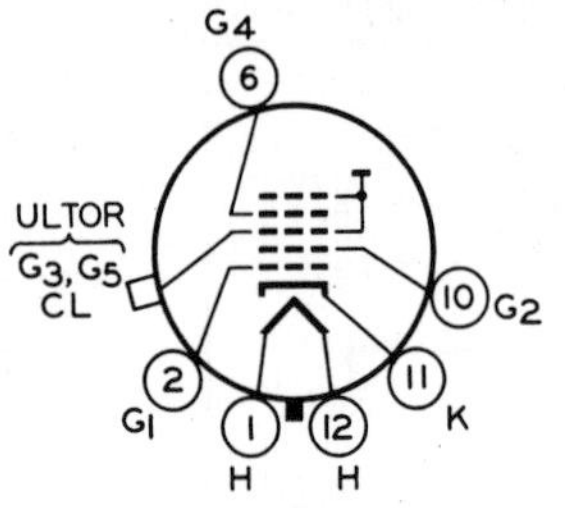

12M
FOCUSING ELECTRODE = G₄

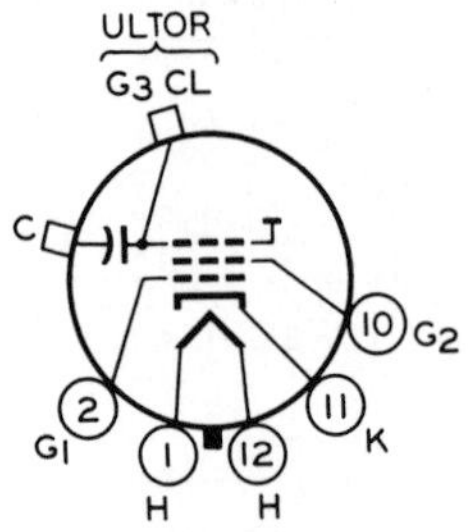

12N

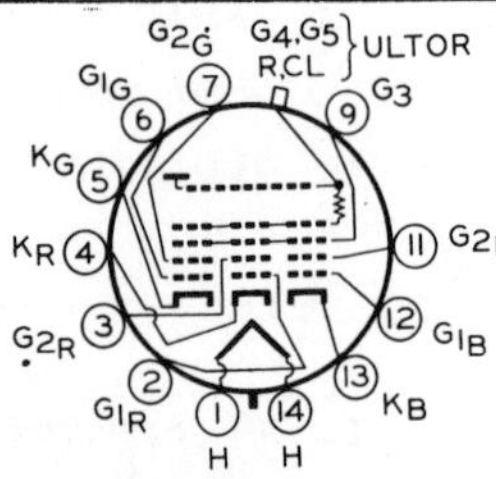

14AH
FOCUSING ELECTRODE = G₃

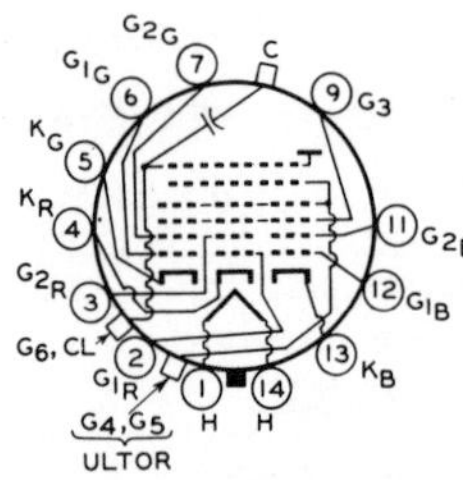

14AL

14AL
CAP OVER PIN NO. 1:
CAP OVER PIN NO. 2:
G₆ + CL & HIGH-VOLTAGE TERMINAL. Connect High-Voltage Supply to this Cap and also connect 50,000-ohm resistor between this Cap and the Cap over Pin No. 1 (Ultor Cap).
FOCUSING ELECTRODE = G₃

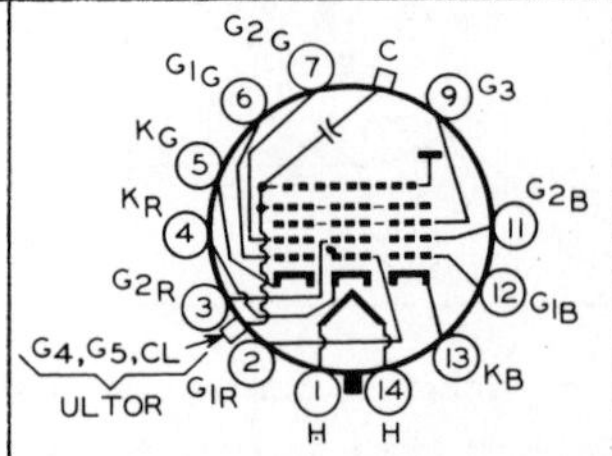

14AU
FOCUSING ELECTRODE = G₃

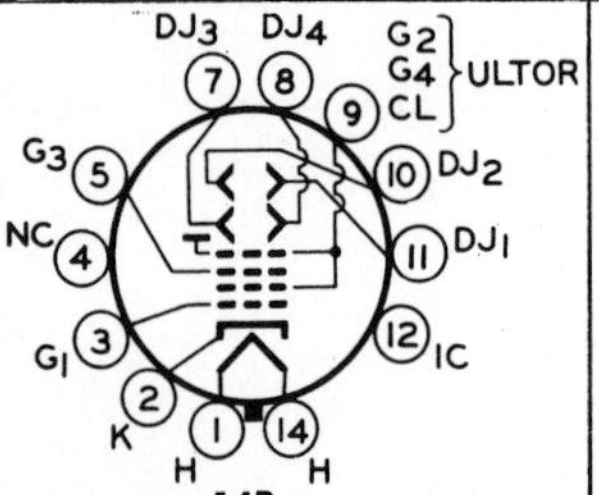

14R
FOCUSING ELECTRODE = G₃

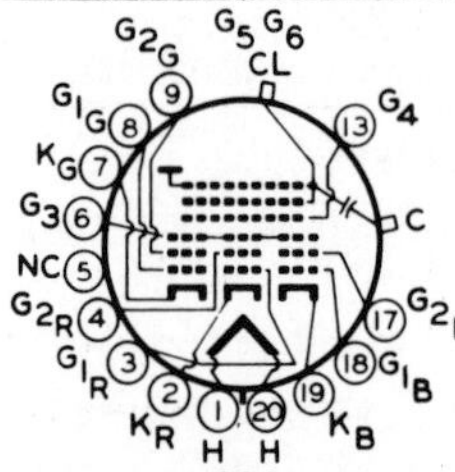

20A
FOCUSING ELECTRODE = G₃

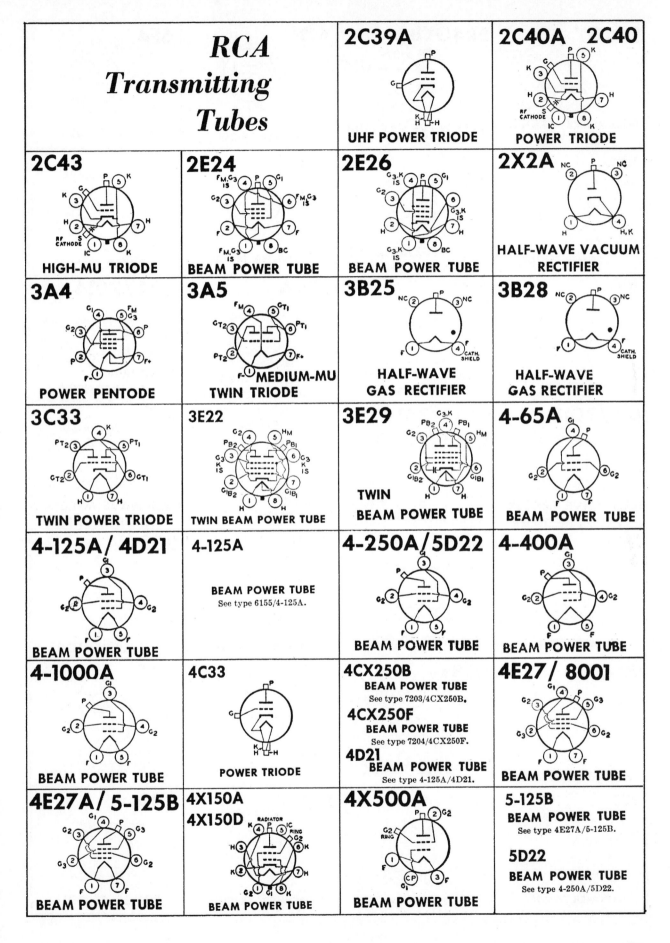

RCA *Transmitting Tubes*

2C39A
UHF POWER TRIODE

2C40A   2C40
POWER TRIODE

2C43
HIGH-MU TRIODE

2E24
BEAM POWER TUBE

2E26
BEAM POWER TUBE

2X2A
HALF-WAVE VACUUM RECTIFIER

3A4
POWER PENTODE

3A5
MEDIUM-MU TWIN TRIODE

3B25
HALF-WAVE GAS RECTIFIER

3B28
HALF-WAVE GAS RECTIFIER

3C33
TWIN POWER TRIODE

3E22
TWIN BEAM POWER TUBE

3E29
TWIN BEAM POWER TUBE

4-65A
BEAM POWER TUBE

4-125A/ 4D21
BEAM POWER TUBE

4-125A
BEAM POWER TUBE
See type 6155/4-125A.

4-250A/5D22
BEAM POWER TUBE

4-400A
BEAM POWER TUBE

4-1000A
BEAM POWER TUBE

4C33
POWER TRIODE

4CX250B
BEAM POWER TUBE
See type 7203/4CX250B.
4CX250F
BEAM POWER TUBE
See type 7204/4CX250F.
4D21
BEAM POWER TUBE
See type 4-125A/4D21.

4E27/ 8001
BEAM POWER TUBE

4E27A/ 5-125B
BEAM POWER TUBE

4X150A
4X150D
BEAM POWER TUBE

4X500A
BEAM POWER TUBE

5-125B
BEAM POWER TUBE
See type 4E27A/5-125B.

5D22
BEAM POWER TUBE
See type 4-250A/5D22.

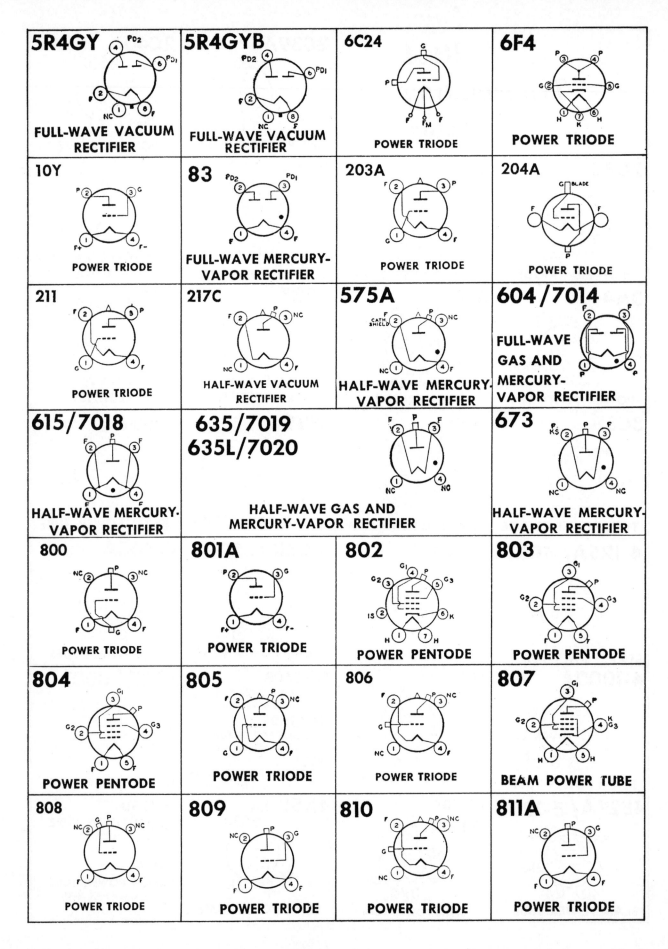

5R4GY
FULL-WAVE VACUUM RECTIFIER

5R4GYB
FULL-WAVE VACUUM RECTIFIER

6C24
POWER TRIODE

6F4
POWER TRIODE

10Y
POWER TRIODE

83
FULL-WAVE MERCURY-VAPOR RECTIFIER

203A
POWER TRIODE

204A
POWER TRIODE

211
POWER TRIODE

217C
HALF-WAVE VACUUM RECTIFIER

575A
HALF-WAVE MERCURY-VAPOR RECTIFIER

604/7014
FULL-WAVE GAS AND MERCURY-VAPOR RECTIFIER

615/7018
HALF-WAVE MERCURY-VAPOR RECTIFIER

635/7019
635L/7020
HALF-WAVE GAS AND MERCURY-VAPOR RECTIFIER

673
HALF-WAVE MERCURY-VAPOR RECTIFIER

800
POWER TRIODE

801A
POWER TRIODE

802
POWER PENTODE

803
POWER PENTODE

804
POWER PENTODE

805
POWER TRIODE

806
POWER TRIODE

807
BEAM POWER TUBE

808
POWER TRIODE

809
POWER TRIODE

810
POWER TRIODE

811A
POWER TRIODE

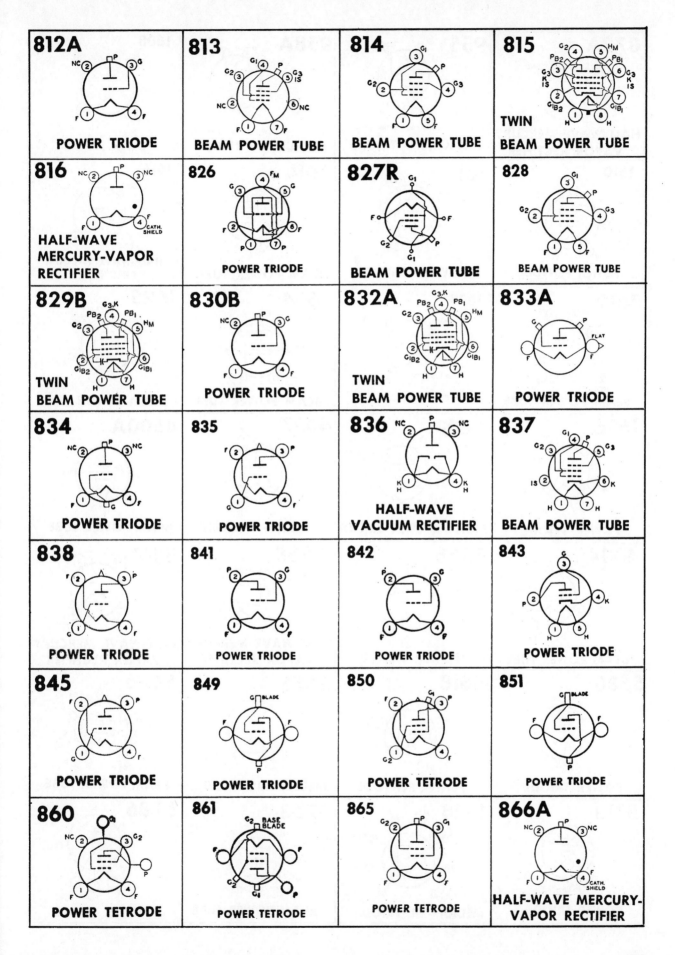

812A POWER TRIODE

813 BEAM POWER TUBE

814 BEAM POWER TUBE

815 TWIN BEAM POWER TUBE

816 HALF-WAVE MERCURY-VAPOR RECTIFIER

826 POWER TRIODE

827R BEAM POWER TUBE

828 BEAM POWER TUBE

829B TWIN BEAM POWER TUBE

830B POWER TRIODE

832A TWIN BEAM POWER TUBE

833A POWER TRIODE

834 POWER TRIODE

835 POWER TRIODE

836 HALF-WAVE VACUUM RECTIFIER

837 BEAM POWER TUBE

838 POWER TRIODE

841 POWER TRIODE

842 POWER TRIODE

843 POWER TRIODE

845 POWER TRIODE

849 POWER TRIODE

850 POWER TETRODE

851 POWER TRIODE

860 POWER TETRODE

861 POWER TETRODE

865 POWER TETRODE

866A HALF-WAVE MERCURY-VAPOR RECTIFIER

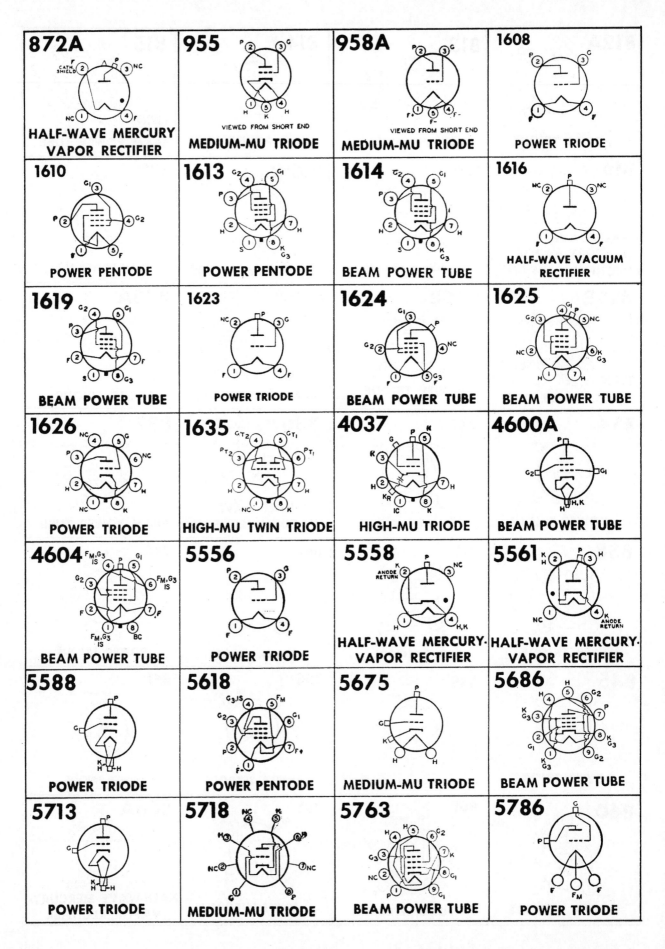

872A — HALF-WAVE MERCURY VAPOR RECTIFIER

955 — MEDIUM-MU TRIODE — VIEWED FROM SHORT END

958A — MEDIUM-MU TRIODE — VIEWED FROM SHORT END

1608 — POWER TRIODE

1610 — POWER PENTODE

1613 — POWER PENTODE

1614 — BEAM POWER TUBE

1616 — HALF-WAVE VACUUM RECTIFIER

1619 — BEAM POWER TUBE

1623 — POWER TRIODE

1624 — BEAM POWER TUBE

1625 — BEAM POWER TUBE

1626 — POWER TRIODE

1635 — HIGH-MU TWIN TRIODE

4037 — HIGH-MU TRIODE

4600A — BEAM POWER TUBE

4604 — BEAM POWER TUBE

5556 — POWER TRIODE

5558 — HALF-WAVE MERCURY-VAPOR RECTIFIER

5561 — HALF-WAVE MERCURY-VAPOR RECTIFIER

5588 — POWER TRIODE

5618 — POWER PENTODE

5675 — MEDIUM-MU TRIODE

5686 — BEAM POWER TUBE

5713 — POWER TRIODE

5718 — MEDIUM-MU TRIODE

5763 — BEAM POWER TUBE

5786 — POWER TRIODE

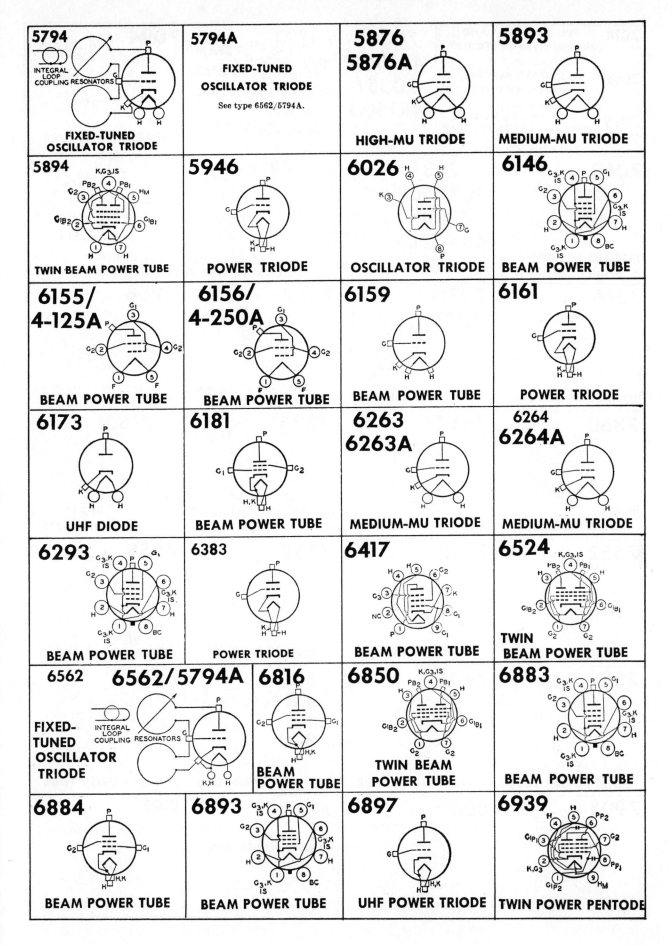

5794
INTEGRAL LOOP COUPLING RESONATORS
FIXED-TUNED OSCILLATOR TRIODE

5794A
FIXED-TUNED OSCILLATOR TRIODE
See type 6562/5794A.

5876 5876A
HIGH-MU TRIODE

5893
MEDIUM-MU TRIODE

5894
TWIN BEAM POWER TUBE

5946
POWER TRIODE

6026
OSCILLATOR TRIODE

6146
BEAM POWER TUBE

6155/ 4-125A
BEAM POWER TUBE

6156/ 4-250A
BEAM POWER TUBE

6159
BEAM POWER TUBE

6161
POWER TRIODE

6173
UHF DIODE

6181
BEAM POWER TUBE

6263 6263A
MEDIUM-MU TRIODE

6264 6264A
MEDIUM-MU TRIODE

6293
BEAM POWER TUBE

6383
POWER TRIODE

6417
BEAM POWER TUBE

6524
TWIN BEAM POWER TUBE

6562 6562/5794A
FIXED-TUNED OSCILLATOR TRIODE
INTEGRAL LOOP COUPLING RESONATORS

6816
BEAM POWER TUBE

6850
TWIN BEAM POWER TUBE

6883
BEAM POWER TUBE

6884
BEAM POWER TUBE

6893
BEAM POWER TUBE

6897
UHF POWER TRIODE

6939
TWIN POWER PENTODE

7014 FULL-WAVE GAS AND MERCURY-VAPOR RECTIFIER *See type 604/7014.* **7018** HALF-WAVE MERCURY-VAPOR RECTIFIER *See type 615/7018.* **7019** HALF-WAVE GAS AND MERCURY-VAPOR RECTIFIER *See type 635/7019.* **7020** *See type 635L/7020.*	**7034/ 4X150A 7035/ 4X150D** **BEAM POWER TUBE** **7054** POWER PENTODE *See type 8077/7054.*		**7094** **BEAM POWER TUBE**
7060 MEDIUM-MU TRIODE—POWER PENTODE	**7203/ 4CX250B 7204/ 4CX250F** BEAM POWER TUBE	**7212** AA'=PLANE OF ELECTRODES BEAM POWER TUBE	**7213** BEAM POWER TUBE
7214 BEAM POWER TUBE	**7270 7271** BEAM POWER TUBE	**7357** AA'=PLANE OF ELECTRODES BEAM POWER TUBE	**7358** AA'=PLANE OF ELECTRODES BEAM POWER TUBE
7360 BEAM-DEFLECTION TUBE	**7457** BEAM POWER TUBE	**7533** COAXIAL OUTPUT TERMINAL RESONATORS TUNABLE OSCILLATOR TRIODE	**7551** BEAM POWER TUBE
7552 HIGH-MU TRIODE	**7553** HIGH-MU TRIODE	**7554** HIGH-MU TRIODE	**7558** BEAM POWER TUBE
7580 BEAM POWER TUBE	**7649** BEAM POWER TUBE	**7650 7651 7801 7870** BEAM POWER TUBE	**7842 7843 7844** BEAM POWER TUBE
7905 BEAM POWER TUBE	**8000** POWER TRIODE	**8001** BEAM POWER TUBE *See type 4E27/8001.*	**8003** POWER TRIODE

8005

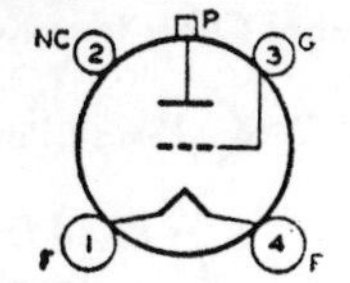

NC ② P ③ G

f ① ④ F

POWER TRIODE

8008

CATH. SHIELD ② F P F ③

NC ① ④ NC

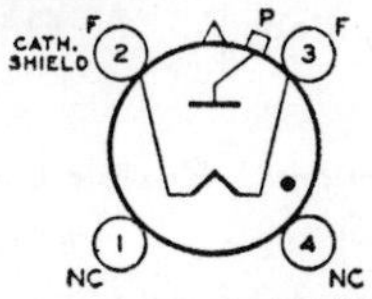

HALF-WAVE MERCURY-VAPOR RECTIFIER

8012A

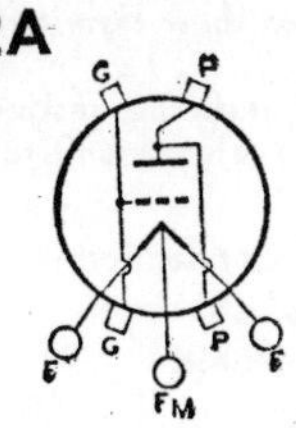

G P

G G

P

F_M

POWER TRIODE

8025A

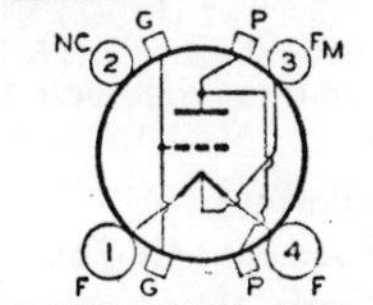

NC ② P ③ F_M

G G P

① ④

G CAPS NEARER BASE
P CAPS NEARER BULB TIP

POWER TRIODE

8072

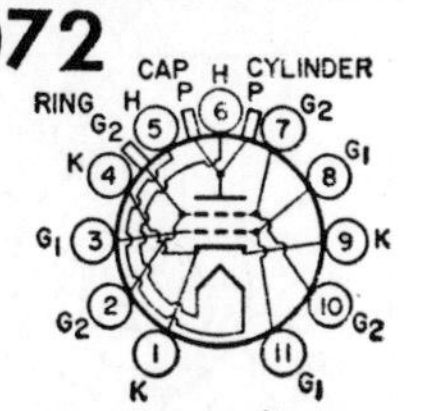

CAP H CYLINDER
RING H P ⑤ ⑥ ⑦ G2
K ④ ⑧ G1
G1 ③ ⑨ K
G2 ② ⑩ G2
① ⑪
K G1

BEAM POWER TUBE

8077/7054

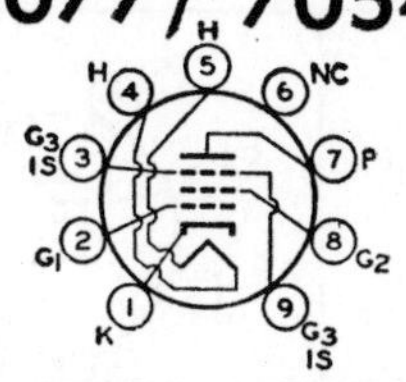

H ⑤ ⑥ NC
G3 IS ③ ⑦ P
G1 ② ⑧ G2
① ⑨ G3
K IS

POWER PENTODE

8121

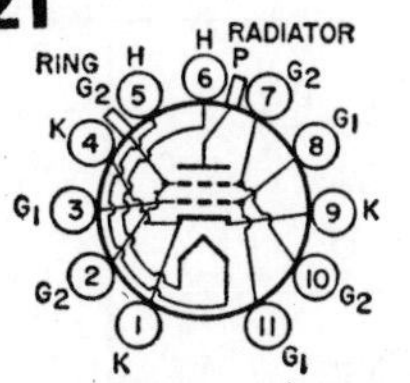

H RADIATOR
RING H P ⑤ ⑥ ⑦ G2
K ④ ⑧ G1
G1 ③ ⑨ K
G2 ② ⑩ G2
① ⑪
K G1

BEAM POWER TUBE

8122

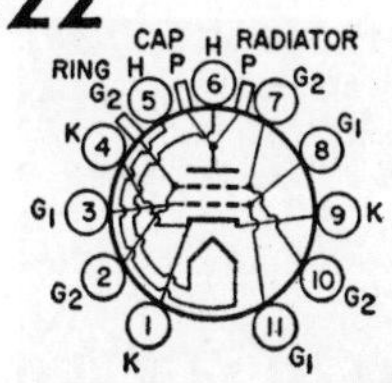

CAP H RADIATOR
RING H P ⑤ ⑥ ⑦ G2
K ④ ⑧ G1
G1 ③ ⑨ K
G2 ② ⑩ G2
① ⑪
K G1

BEAM POWER TUBE

9002

H ④ ⑤ P
H ③ ⑥ G
K ② ⑦ K
①
P

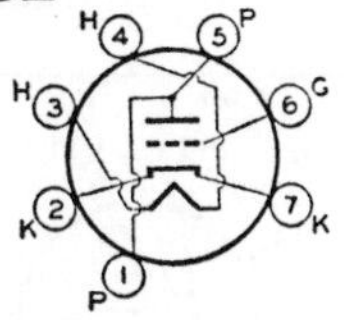

MEDIUM-MU TRIODE

Diagrams show terminals veiwed from base or filament end of tube.

Alphabetical subscripts B, D, P, T, and TR, indicate, respectively, beam unit, diode unit, pentode unit, triode unit, and tetrode unit in multi-unit types.

F = Filament
FM = Filament Mid-Tap
G = Grid
H = Heater
HM = Heater Tap

IC = Internal Connection— Do Not Use.
IS = Internal Shield
K = Cathode
• = Gas-Type Tube

NC = No Connection
P = Plate (Anode)
S = Shell
TA = Target
TC = Thermocouple

Orientation Symbol Other than Key
Flexible Envelope Terminal
Small Pin
Rigid Envelope Terminal
Large Pin
Key
Envelope

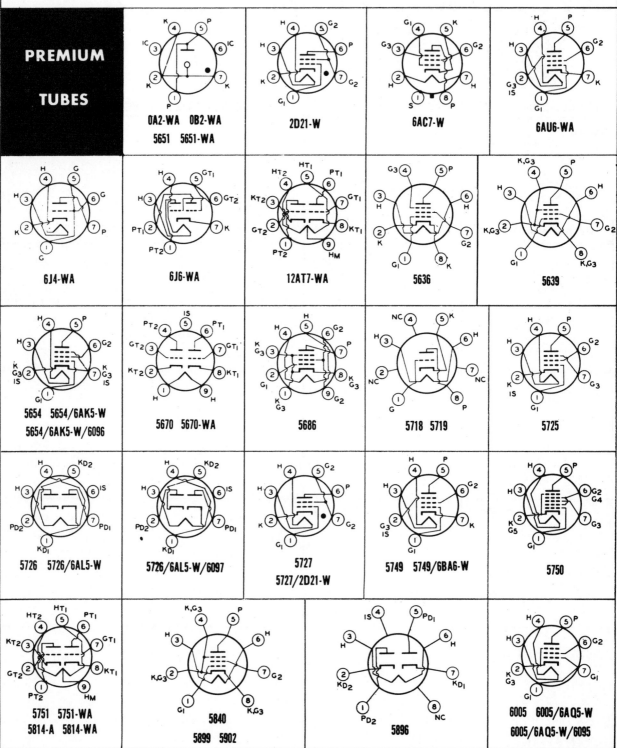

PREMIUM TUBES

0A2-WA   0B2-WA
5651   5651-WA

2D21-W

6AC7-W

6AU6-WA

6J4-WA

6J6-WA

12AT7-WA

5636

5639

5654   5654/6AK5-W
5654/6AK5-W/6096

5670   5670-WA

5686

5718   5719

5725

5726   5726/6AL5-W

5726/6AL5-W/6097

5727
5727/2D21-W

5749   5749/6BA6-W

5750

5751   5751-WA
5814-A   5814-WA

5840
5899   5902

5896

6005   6005/6AQ5-W
6005/6AQ5-W/6095

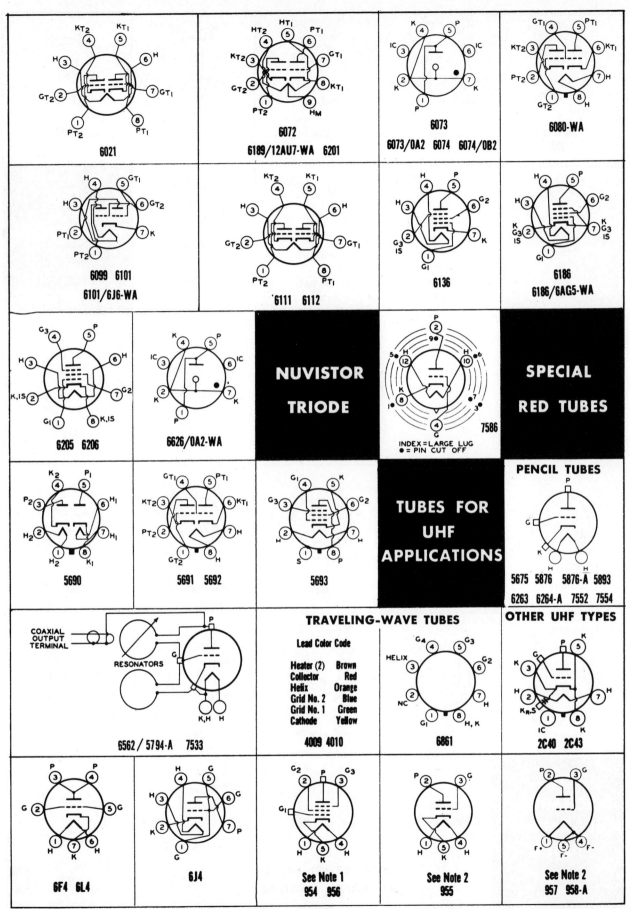

6021

6072
6189/12AU7-WA 6201

6073
6073/0A2 6074 6074/0B2

6080-WA

6099 6101
6101/6J6-WA

6111 6112

6136

6186
6186/6AG5-WA

6205 6206

6626/0A2-WA

NUVISTOR TRIODE

7586

INDEX=LARGE LUG
● = PIN CUT OFF

SPECIAL RED TUBES

5690

5691 5692

5693

TUBES FOR UHF APPLICATIONS

PENCIL TUBES

5675 5876 5876-A 5893
6263 6264-A 7552 7554

COAXIAL OUTPUT TERMINAL

RESONATORS

6562 / 5794-A 7533

TRAVELING-WAVE TUBES

Lead Color Code

Heater (2)	Brown
Collector	Red
Helix	Orange
Grid No. 2	Blue
Grid No. 1	Green
Cathode	Yellow

4009 4010

HELIX

6861

OTHER UHF TYPES

2C40 2C43

6F4 6L4

6J4

See Note 1
954 956

See Note 2
955

See Note 2
957 958-A

Note 1: P is on long part of bulb (top); G is on short part of bulb.
Note 2: Long part of bulb is top.

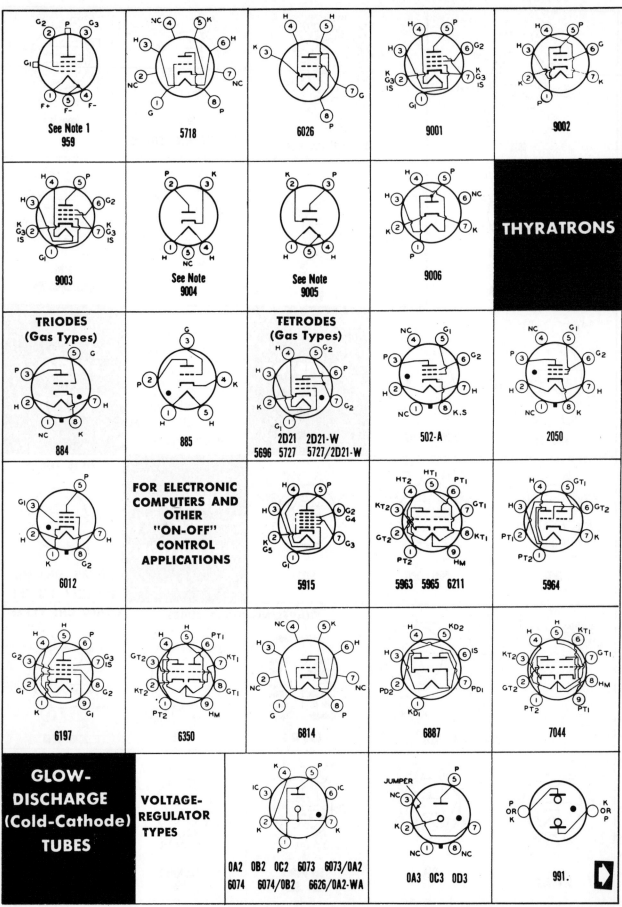

See Note 1
959

5718

6026

9001

9002

9003

See Note
9004

See Note
9005

9006

THYRATRONS

**TRIODES
(Gas Types)**

884

885

**TETRODES
(Gas Types)**

2D21   2D21-W
5696   5727   5727/2D21-W

502-A

2050

6012

**FOR ELECTRONIC
COMPUTERS AND
OTHER
"ON-OFF"
CONTROL
APPLICATIONS**

5915

5963   5965   6211

5964

6197

6350

6814

6887

7044

**GLOW-
DISCHARGE
(Cold-Cathode)
TUBES**

**VOLTAGE-
REGULATOR
TYPES**

0A2   0B2   0C2   6073   6073/0A2
6074   6074/0B2   6626/0A2-WA

0A3   0C3   0D3

991.

Note : Long part of bulb is top.

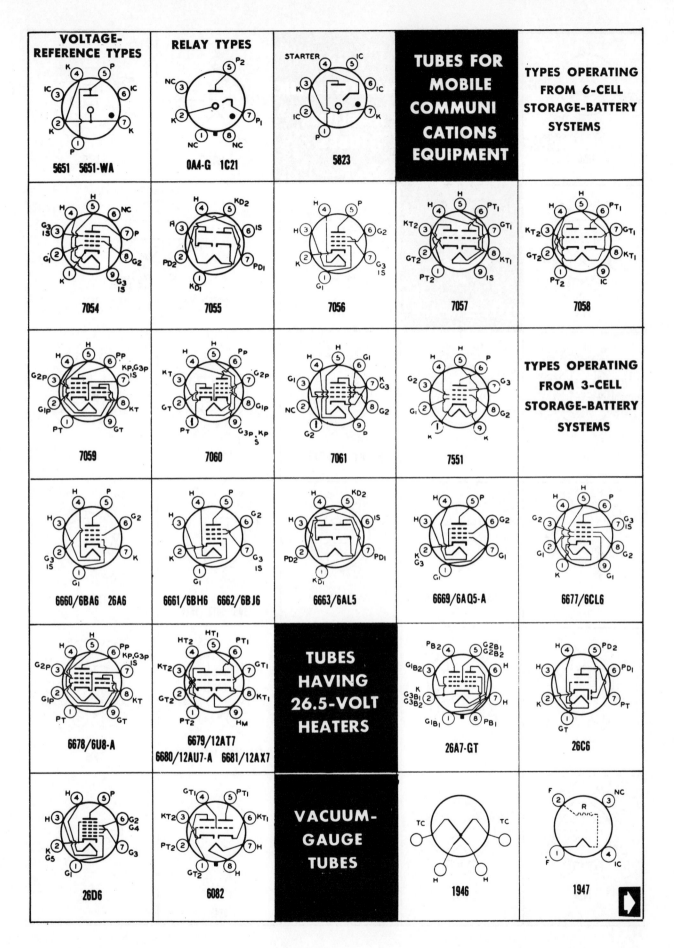

VOLTAGE-REFERENCE TYPES	RELAY TYPES		TUBES FOR MOBILE COMMUNICATIONS EQUIPMENT	TYPES OPERATING FROM 6-CELL STORAGE-BATTERY SYSTEMS
5651 5651-WA	0A4-G 1C21	5823		
7054	7055	7056	7057	7058
7059	7060	7061	7551	TYPES OPERATING FROM 3-CELL STORAGE-BATTERY SYSTEMS
6660/6BA6 26A6	6661/6BH6 6662/6BJ6	6663/6AL5	6669/6AQ5-A	6677/6CL6
6678/6U8-A	6679/12AT7 6680/12AU7-A 6681/12AX7	TUBES HAVING 26.5-VOLT HEATERS	26A7-GT	26C6
26D6	6082	VACUUM-GAUGE TUBES	1946	1947

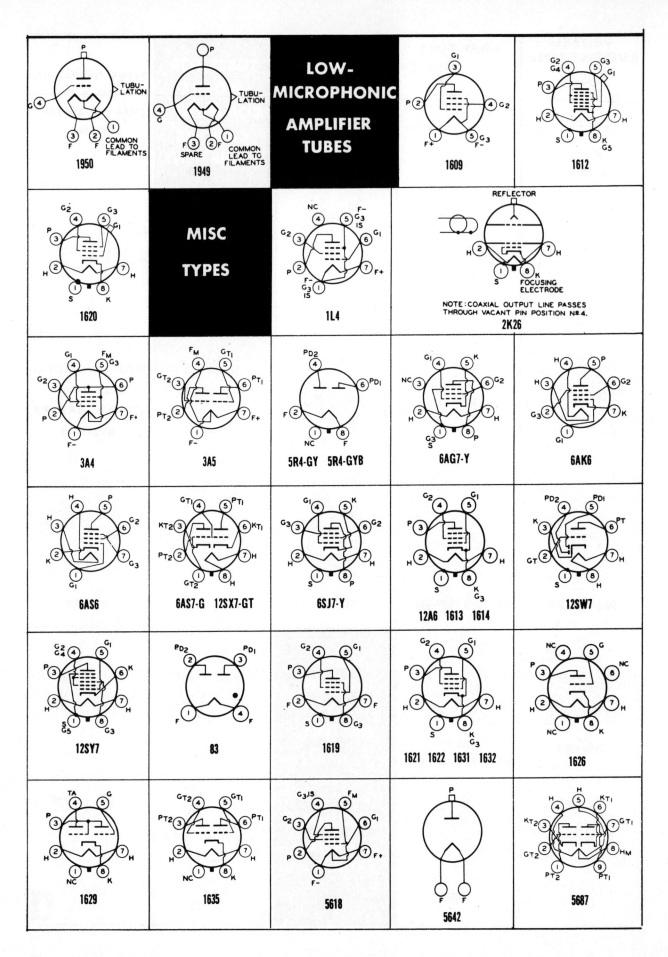

490

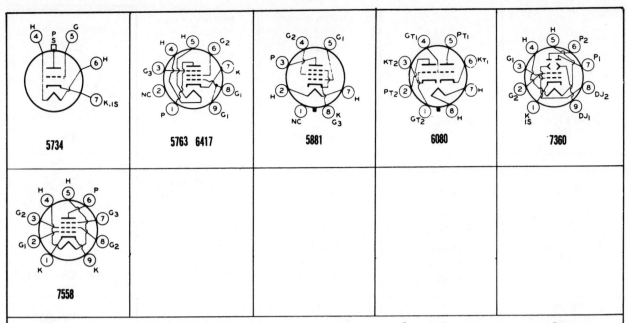

5734   5763 6417   5881   6080   7360

7558

Photosensitive Devices and Cathode-Ray Tubes

KEY TO BASE AND ENVELOPE CONNECTION DIAGRAMS

Diagrams show terminals viewed from the base end of the type

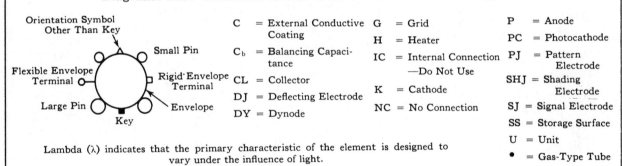

C = External Conductive Coating	G = Grid	P = Anode
	H = Heater	PC = Photocathode
C_b = Balancing Capacitance	IC = Internal Connection —Do Not Use	PJ = Pattern Electrode
CL = Collector		SHJ = Shading Electrode
DJ = Deflecting Electrode	K = Cathode	SJ = Signal Electrode
DY = Dynode	NC = No Connection	SS = Storage Surface
		U = Unit
		• = Gas-Type Tube

Lambda (λ) indicates that the primary characteristic of the element is designed to vary under the influence of light.

Note 1: Direction of radiation is into end of bulb.

Note 2: Direction of light is into end of bulb.

Note 3: Direction of light is perpendicular to axis of photocathode.

Note 4: Direction of light is into dormer window.

Note 5: Direction of light is into concave side of photocathode.

Note 6: Direction of light is into face of cell.

PHOTOTUBES   Single-Unit and Twin-Unit Types

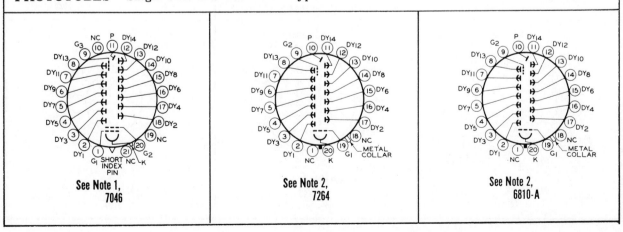

See Note 1, 7046   See Note 2, 7264   See Note 2, 6810-A

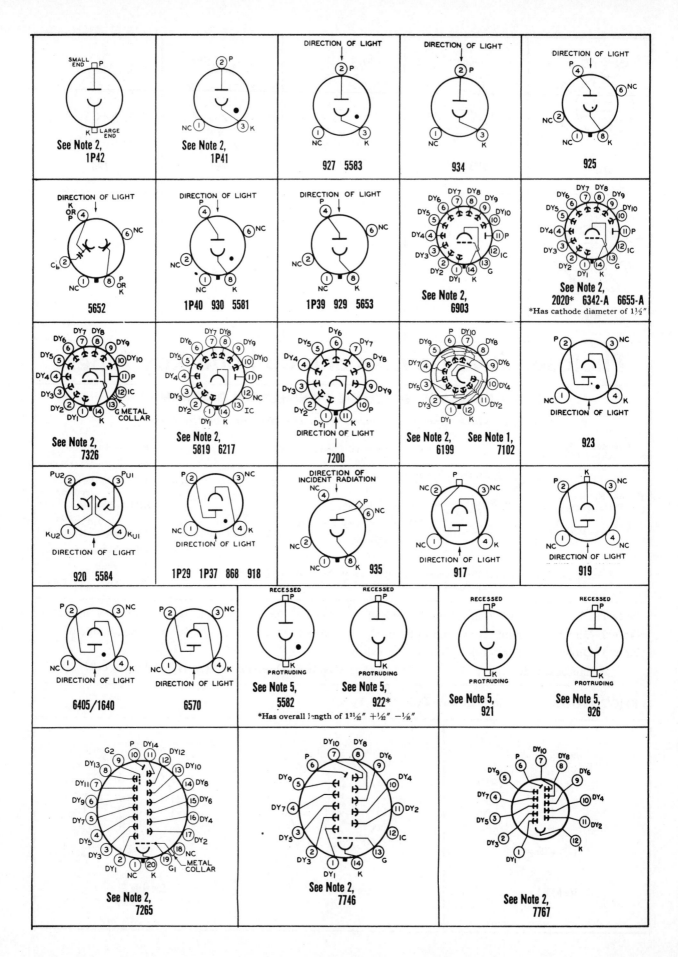

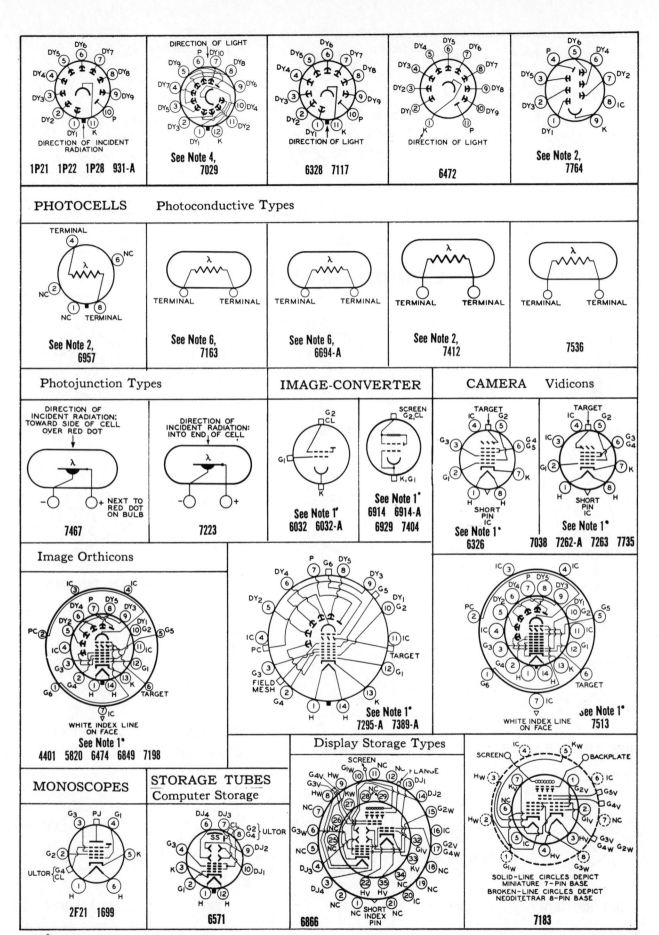

PHOTOCELLS   Photoconductive Types

See Note 2,
6957

See Note 6,
7163

See Note 6,
6694-A

See Note 2,
7412

7536

Photojunction Types

IMAGE-CONVERTER

CAMERA   Vidicons

7467

7223

See Note 1*
6032   6032-A

See Note 1*
6914   6914-A
6929   7404

See Note 1*
6326

See Note 1*
7038   7262-A   7263   7735

Image Orthicons

See Note 1*
4401   5820   6474   6849   7198

See Note 1*
7295-A   7389-A

See Note 1*
7513

MONOSCOPES

STORAGE TUBES
Computer Storage

Display Storage Types

2F21   1699

6571

6866

7183

1P21   1P22   1P28   931-A

See Note 4,
7029

6328   7117

6472

See Note 2,
7764

Note 1*: Direction of radiation is perpendicular to photocathode end of tube.

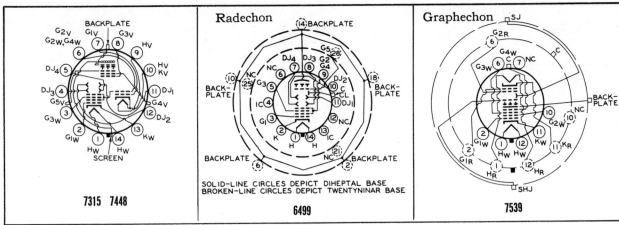

7315 7448

Radechon

SOLID-LINE CIRCLES DEPICT DIHEPTAL BASE
BROKEN-LINE CIRCLES DEPICT TWENTYNINAR BASE

6499

Graphechon

7539

OSCILLOGRAPH TYPES

Cathode-Ray Tubes

1EP1 1EP2 1EP11

2AP1-A

2BP1 2BP11

3AP1-A

3AQP1

3BP1-A

3JP1 3JP7

3KP1 3KP4 3KP7 3KP11

3RP1 3RP1-A

3WP1 3WP2 3WP11

5ABP1 5ABP7 5ABP11 5ADP1

5AHP7 5AHP7-A

5BP1-A

5CP1-A 5CP7-A
5CP11-A 5CP12

5FP7-A 5FP14-A
5FP15-A 7BP7-A

5UP1 5UP7 5UP11

7MP7

7VP1

10KP7

5FP4-A 12DP7-A

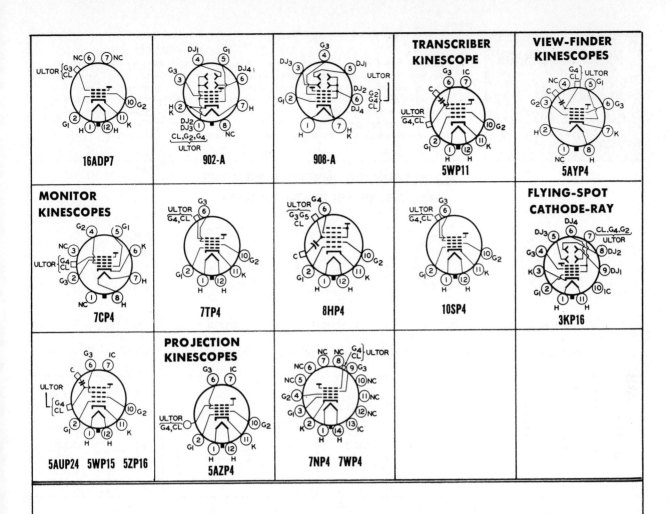

16ADP7

902-A

908-A

TRANSCRIBER KINESCOPE

5WP11

VIEW-FINDER KINESCOPES

5AYP4

MONITOR KINESCOPES

7CP4

7TP4

8HP4

10SP4

FLYING-SPOT CATHODE-RAY

3KP16

5AUP24 5WP15 5ZP16

PROJECTION KINESCOPES

5AZP4

7NP4 7WP4

Extracted from Catalog MS-15 (February, 1963), Standard Circular Plugs and Variations Designed to MIL-C-5015, MS and MS Type Connectors, reprinted herein through the courtesy and permission of the Cannon Electric Company, 3208 Humboldt Street, Los Angeles, Calif. The diagrams herein represent only a portion of the great variety of connectors available. The Cannon Plug Guide (Catalog CPG-5) describes this variety by specific grouping. MS connectors were selected for incorporation because of their wide and diversified use in industry and military equipment.

MS ALTERNATE INSERT POSITIONS
FACE VIEW OF PIN CONTACT INSERTS

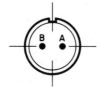

| NORMAL POSITION | POSITION W | POSITION X | POSITION Y | POSITION Z |

The above diagrams indicate the current alternate insert positions of MS Cannon Plugs designed to MIL-C-5015.

1 CONTACT

8S-1	10S-2	12S-4	12-5	14-3	14S-4	16-2	16S-3
1-#16	1-#16	1-#16	1-#12	1-#8	1-#16	1-#12	1-#16
A	A	D	D	A	D	E	B

16-12	18-6	18-7	18-16	20-2	22-7	28-2009-33	AVAILABLE IN TEFLON ONLY
1-#4	1-#4	1-#8	1-#12 HIGH VOLTAGE	1-#0	1-#0	1-#12	HIGH VOLTAGE
A	D	B	C	D	E		

CONTACTS — SERVICE

2 CONTACTS

10SL-4	12S-1	12S-2	12S-3	14S-9	16S-4	16-11	16-13
2-#16	POS. NO. 12 OF 12S-3	POS. NO. 13 OF 12S-3	2-#16	2-#16	2-#16	2-#12	2-#12 (A-IRON) (B-CONSTANTAN)
A	FOR SPEC. USE 12S-3	FOR SPEC. USE 12S-3	A	A FOR SPEC. USE 12S-3	D	A	A

16S-15	16S-16	18-3	18-14	18-25	18-26	20-5	
POS. NO. 12 OF 16S-4	POS. NO. 13 OF 16S-4	2-#12	1-#4 (A) 1-#16 (B)	POS. NO. 12 OF 18-3	POS. NO. 13 OF 18-3	2-#16	
FOR SPEC. USE 16S-4	FOR SPEC. USE 16S-4	D FOR SPEC. USE 18-5	A	FOR SPEC. USE 18-5	FOR SPEC. USE 18-5	E	

CONTACTS — SERVICE

IDENTIFICATION OF SYMBOLS

▲ Inserts available in resilient (polychloroprene) to MIL-R-3065 and/or Silcan.

* Inserts available in standard MIL-M-14 plastic.

☐ Inserts available in one piece——molded in——pressurized pin inserts.

● Total tooling not yet complete consult Cannon Field Office for availability.

⬤ Authorized insert arrangements to latest revision of MIL-C-5015 Specifications.

Note: Pin front view is shown in all layouts. Layouts approximately half scale.

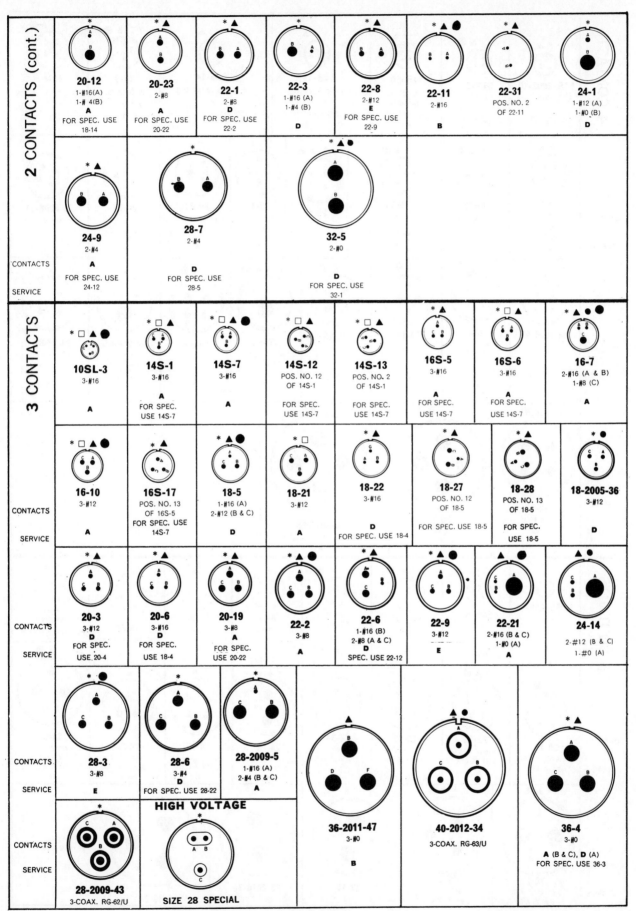

2 CONTACTS (cont.)

20-12	20-23	22-1	22-3	22-8	22-11	22-31	24-1
1-#16(A) 1-#4(B) A FOR SPEC. USE 18-14	2-#8 A FOR SPEC. USE 20-22	2-#8 D FOR SPEC. USE 22-2	1-#16 (A) 1-#4 (B) D	2-#12 E FOR SPEC. USE 22-9	2-#16 B	POS. NO. 2 OF 22-11	1-#12 (A) 1-#0 (B) D

24-9	28-7	32-5
2-#4 A FOR SPEC. USE 24-12	2-#4 D FOR SPEC. USE 28-5	2-#0 D FOR SPEC. USE 32-1

CONTACTS

SERVICE

3 CONTACTS

10SL-3	14S-1	14S-7	14S-12	14S-13	16S-5	16S-6	16-7
3-#16 A	3-#16 FOR SPEC. USE 14S-7	3-#16 A	POS. NO. 12 OF 14S-1 FOR SPEC. USE 14S-7	POS. NO. 2 OF 14S-1 FOR SPEC. USE 14S-7	3-#16 A FOR SPEC. USE 14S-7	3-#16 A FOR SPEC. USE 14S-7	2-#16 (A & B) 1-#8 (C) A

16-10	16S-17	18-5	18-21	18-22	18-27	18-28	18-2005-36
3-#12 A	POS. NO. 13 OF 16S-5 FOR SPEC. USE 14S-7	1-#16 (A) 2-#12 (B & C) D	3-#12 A	3-#16 D FOR SPEC. USE 18-4	POS. NO. 12 OF 18-5 FOR SPEC. USE 18-5	POS. NO. 13 OF 18-5 FOR SPEC. USE 18-5	3-#12 D

CONTACTS

SERVICE

20-3	20-6	20-19	22-2	22-6	22-9	22-21	24-14
3-#12 D FOR SPEC. USE 20-4	3-#16 D FOR SPEC. USE 18-4	3-#8 A FOR SPEC. USE 20-22	3-#8 A	1-#16 (B) 2-#8 (A & C) D FOR SPEC. USE 22-12	3-#12 E	2-#16 (B & C) 1-#0 (A) A	2-#12 (B & C) 1-#0 (A)

CONTACTS

SERVICE

28-3	28-6	28-2009-5	36-2011-47	40-2012-34	36-4
3-#8 E	3-#4 FOR SPEC. USE 28-22	1-#16 (A) 2-#4 (B & C) A	3-#0 B	3-COAX. RG-63/U	3-#0 A (B & C), D (A) FOR SPEC. USE 36-3

CONTACTS

SERVICE

HIGH VOLTAGE

28-2009-43	SIZE 28 SPECIAL
3-COAX. RG-62/U	

CONTACTS

SERVICE

Note: Pin front view is shown in all layouts. Layouts approximately half scale.

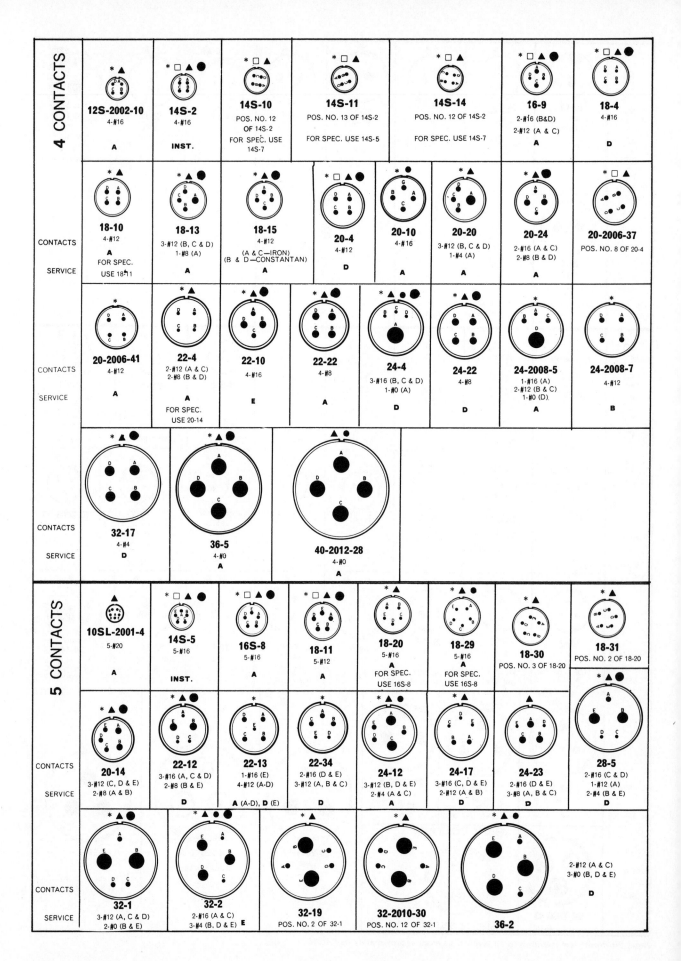

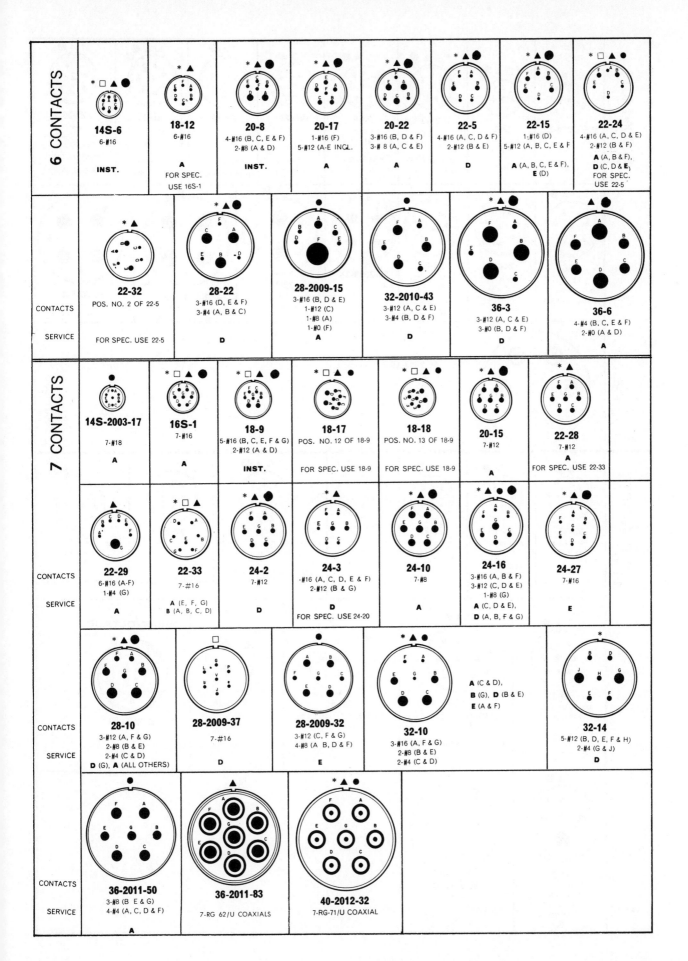

6 CONTACTS

14S-6
6-#16
INST.

18-12
6-#16
*
▲
A
FOR SPEC.
USE 16S-1

20-8
4-#16 (B, C, E & F)
2-#8 (A & D)
INST.

20-17
1-#16 (F)
5-#12 (A-E INCL.)
A

20-22
3-#16 (B, D & F)
3-#8 (A, C & E)
A

22-5
4-#16 (A, C, D & F)
2-#12 (B & E)
D

22-15
1-#16 (D)
5-#12 (A, B, C, E & F)
A (A, B, C, E & F),
E (D)

22-24
4-#16 (A, C, D & E)
2-#12 (B & F)
A (A, B & F),
D (C, D & E)
FOR SPEC.
USE 22-5

22-32
POS. NO. 2 OF 22-5
FOR SPEC. USE 22-5

28-22
3-#16 (D, E & F)
3-#4 (A, B & C)
D

28-2009-15
3-#16 (B, D & E)
1-#12 (C)
1-#8 (A)
1-#0 (F)
A

32-2010-43
3-#12 (A, C & E)
3-#4 (B, D & F)
D

36-3
3-#12 (A, C & E)
3-#0 (B, D & F)
D

36-6
4-#4 (B, C, E & F)
2-#0 (A & D)
A

CONTACTS
SERVICE

7 CONTACTS

14S-2003-17
7-#18
A

16S-1
7-#16
A

18-9
5-#16 (B, C, E, F & G)
2-#12 (A & D)
INST.

18-17
POS. NO. 12 OF 18-9
FOR SPEC. USE 18-9

18-18
POS. NO. 13 OF 18-9
FOR SPEC. USE 18-9

20-15
7-#12
A

22-28
7-#12
A
FOR SPEC. USE 22-33

22-29
6-#16 (A-F)
1-#4 (G)
A

22-33
7-#16
A (E, F, G)
B (A, B, C, D)

24-2
7-#12
D

24-3
-#16 (A, C, D, E & F)
2-#12 (B & G)
D
FOR SPEC. USE 24-20

24-10
7-#8
A

24-16
3-#16 (A, B & F)
3-#12 (C, D & E)
1-#8 (G)
A (C, D & E),
D (A, B, F & G)

24-27
7-#16
E

CONTACTS
SERVICE

28-10
3-#12 (A, F & G)
2-#8 (B & E)
2-#4 (C & D)
D (G), A (ALL OTHERS)

28-2009-37
7-#16
D

28-2009-32
3-#12 (C, F & G)
4-#8 (A, B, D & F)
E

32-10
3-#16 (A, F & G)
2-#8 (B & E)
2-#4 (C & D)
A (C & D),
B (G), D (B & E)
E (A & F)

32-14
5-#12 (B, D, E, F & H)
2-#4 (G & J)
D

CONTACTS
SERVICE

36-2011-50
3-#8 (B E & G)
4-#4 (A, C, D & F)
A

36-2011-83
7-RG 62/U COAXIALS

40-2012-32
7-RG-71/U COAXIAL

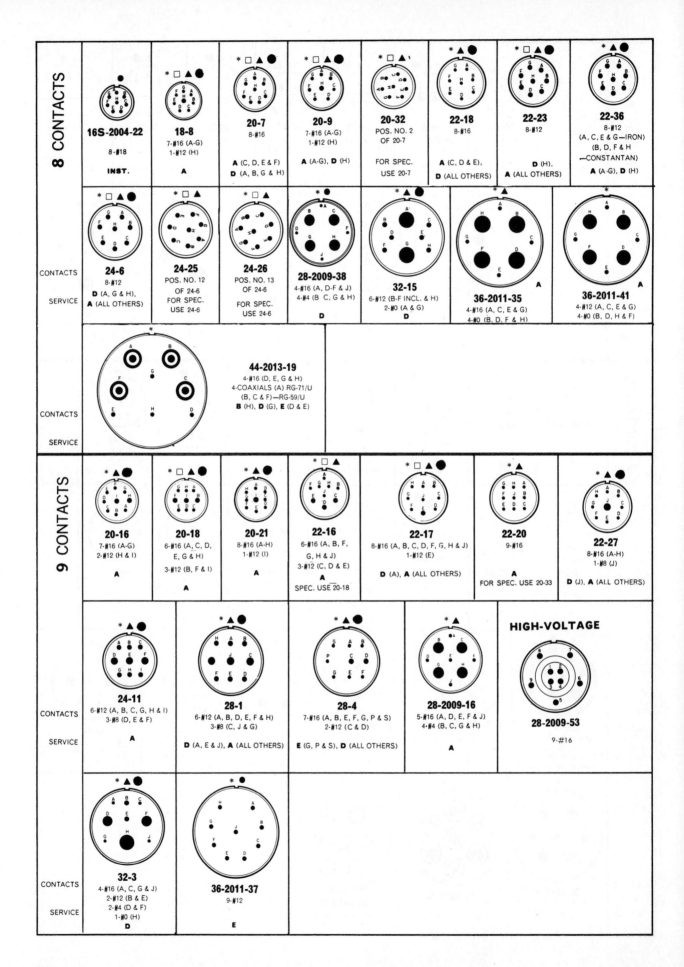

8 CONTACTS

16S-2004-22
8-#18
INST.

18-8
7-#16 (A-G)
1-#12 (H)
A

20-7
8-#16
A (C, D, E & F)
D (A, B, G & H)

20-9
7-#16 (A-G)
1-#12 (H)
A (A-G), D (H)

20-32
POS. NO. 2
OF 20-7
FOR SPEC.
USE 20-7

22-18
8-#16
A (C, D & E),
D (ALL OTHERS)

22-23
8-#12
D (H),
A (ALL OTHERS)

22-36
(A, C, E & G—IRON)
(B, D, F & H
—CONSTANTAN)
A (A-G), D (H)

CONTACTS

SERVICE

24-6
8-#12
D (A, G & H),
A (ALL OTHERS)

24-25
POS. NO. 12
OF 24-6
FOR SPEC.
USE 24-6

24-26
POS. NO. 13
OF 24-6
FOR SPEC.
USE 24-6

28-2009-38
4-#16 (A, D-F & J)
4-#4 (B, C, G & H)
D

32-15
6-#12 (B-F INCL. & H)
2-#0 (A & G)
D

36-2011-35
4-#16 (A, C, E & G)
4-#0 (B, D, F & H)

36-2011-41
4-#12 (A, C, E & G)
4-#0 (B, D, H & F)

CONTACTS

SERVICE

44-2013-19
4-#16 (D, E, G & H)
4-COAXIALS (A) RG-71/U
(B, C & F)—RG-59/U
B (H), D (G), E (D & E)

9 CONTACTS

20-16
7-#16 (A-G)
2-#12 (H & I)
A

20-18
6-#16 (A, C, D,
E, G & H)
3-#12 (B, F & I)
A

20-21
8-#16 (A-H)
1-#12 (I)
A

22-16
6-#16 (A, B, F,
G, H & J)
3-#12 (C, D & E)
A
SPEC. USE 20-18

22-17
8-#16 (A, B, C, D, F, G, H & J)
1-#12 (E)
D (A), A (ALL OTHERS)

22-20
9-#16
A
FOR SPEC. USE 20-33

22-27
8-#16 (A-H)
1-#8 (J)
D (J), A (ALL OTHERS)

CONTACTS

SERVICE

24-11
6-#12 (A, B, C, G, H & I)
3-#8 (D, E & F)
A

28-1
6-#12 (A, B, D, E, F & H)
3-#8 (C, J & G)
D (A, E & J), A (ALL OTHERS)

28-4
7-#16 (A, B, E, F, G, P & S)
2-#12 (C & D)
E (G, P & S), D (ALL OTHERS)

28-2009-16
5-#16 (A, D, E, F & J)
4-#4 (B, C, G & H)
A

HIGH-VOLTAGE

28-2009-53
9-#16

CONTACTS

SERVICE

32-3
4-#16 (A, C, G & J)
2-#12 (B & E)
2-#4 (D & F)
1-#0 (H)
D

36-2011-37
9-#12
E

CONTACTS

SERVICE

500

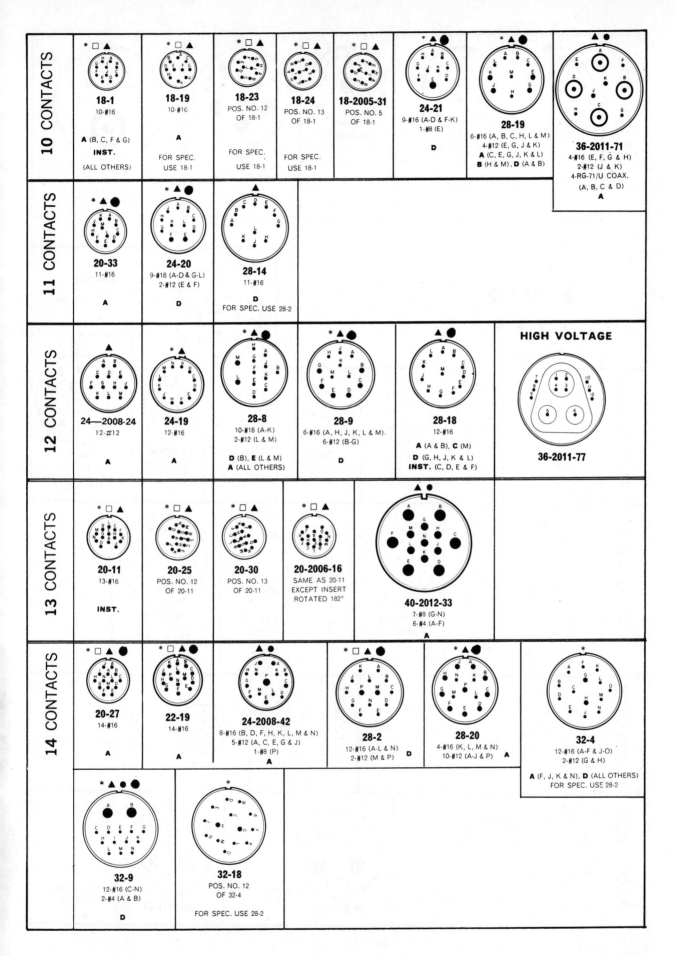

10 CONTACTS

18-1
10-#16

A (B, C, F & G)
INST.
(ALL OTHERS)

18-19
10-#16

A

FOR SPEC.
USE 18-1

18-23
POS. NO. 12
OF 18-1

FOR SPEC.
USE 18-1

18-24
POS. NO. 13
OF 18-1

FOR SPEC.
USE 18-1

18-2005-31
POS. NO. 5
OF 18-1

24-21
9-#16 (A-D & F-K)
1-#8 (E)

D

28-19
6-#16 (A, B, C, H, L & M)
4-#12 (E, G, J & K)
A (C, E, G, J, K & L)
B (H & M), D (A & B)

36-2011-71
4-#16 (E, F, G & H)
2-#12 (J & K)
4-RG-71/U COAX.
(A, B, C & D)

A

11 CONTACTS

20-33
11-#16

A

24-20
9-#16 (A-D & G-L)
2-#12 (E & F)

D

28-14
11-#16

D
FOR SPEC. USE 28-2

12 CONTACTS

24—2008-24
12-#12

A

24-19
12-#16

A

28-8
10-#16 (A-K)
2-#12 (L & M)

D (B), E (L & M)
A (ALL OTHERS)

28-9
6-#16 (A, H, J, K, L & M).
6-#12 (B-G)

D

28-18
12-#16

A (A & B), C (M)
D (G, H, J, K & L)
INST. (C, D, E & F)

HIGH VOLTAGE

36-2011-77

13 CONTACTS

20-11
13-#16

INST.

20-25
POS. NO. 12
OF 20-11

20-30
POS. NO. 13
OF 20-11

20-2006-16
SAME AS 20-11
EXCEPT INSERT
ROTATED 182°

40-2012-33
7-#8 (G-N)
6-#4 (A-F)

A

14 CONTACTS

20-27
14-#16

A

22-19
14-#16

A

24-2008-42
8-#16 (B, D, F, H, K, L, M & N)
5-#12 (A, C, E, G & J)
1-#8 (P)

A

28-2
12-#16 (A-L & N)
2-#12 (M & P)

D

28-20
4-#16 (K, L, M & N)
10-#12 (A-J & P)

A

32-4
12-#16 (A-F & J-O)
2-#12 (G & H)

A (F, J, K & N), D (ALL OTHERS)
FOR SPEC. USE 28-2

32-9
12-#16 (C-N)
2-#4 (A & B)

D

32-18
POS. NO. 12
OF 32-4

FOR SPEC. USE 28-2

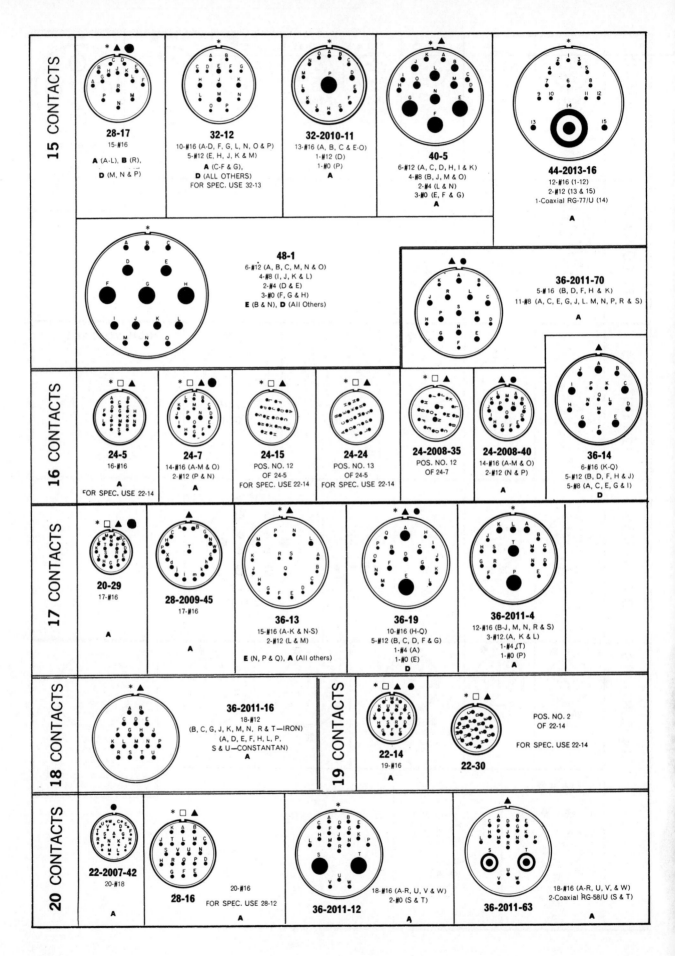

15 CONTACTS

28-17
15-#16

A (A-L), B (R),
D (M, N & P)

32-12
10-#16 (A-D, F, G, L, N, O & P)
5-#12 (E, H, J, K & M)
A (C-F & G),
D (ALL OTHERS)
FOR SPEC. USE 32-13

32-2010-11
13-#16 (A, B, C, D & E-O)
1-#12 (D)
1-#0 (P)
A

40-5
6-#12 (A, C, D, H, I & K)
4-#8 (B, J, M & O)
2-#4 (L & N)
3-#0 (E, F & G)
A

44-2013-16
12-#16 (1-12)
2-#12 (13 & 15)
1-Coaxial RG-77/U (14)
A

48-1
6-#12 (A, B, C, M, N & O)
4-#8 (I, J, K & L)
2-#4 (D & E)
3-#0 (F, G & H)
E (B & N), D (All Others)

36-2011-70
5-#16 (B, D, F, H & K)
11-#8 (A, C, E, G, J, L, M, N, P, R & S)
A

16 CONTACTS

24-5
16-#16

A
FOR SPEC. USE 22-14

24-7
14-#16 (A-M & O)
2-#12 (P & N)
A

24-15
POS. NO. 12
OF 24-5
FOR SPEC. USE 22-14

24-24
POS. NO. 13
OF 24-5
FOR SPEC. USE 22-14

24-2008-35
POS. NO. 12
OF 24-7

24-2008-40
14-#16 (A-M & O)
2-#12 (N & P)
A

36-14
6-#16 (K-Q)
5-#12 (B, D, F, H & J)
5-#8 (A, C, E, G & I)
D

17 CONTACTS

20-29
17-#16
A

28-2009-45
17-#16
A

36-13
15-#16 (A-K & N-S)
2-#12 (L & M)
E (N, P & Q), A (All others)

36-19
10-#16 (H-Q)
5-#12 (B, C, D, F & G)
1-#4 (A)
1-#0 (E)
D

36-2011-4
12-#16 (B-J, M, N, R & S)
3-#12 (A, K & L)
1-#4 (T)
1-#0 (P)
A

18 CONTACTS

36-2011-16
18-#12
(B, C, G, J, K, M, N, R & T—IRON)
(A, D, E, F, H, L, P,
S & U—CONSTANTAN)
A

19 CONTACTS

22-14
19-#16
A

22-30
POS. NO. 2
OF 22-14
FOR SPEC. USE 22-14

20 CONTACTS

22-2007-42
20-#18
A

28-16
20-#16
FOR SPEC. USE 28-12
A

36-2011-12
18-#16 (A-R, U, V & W)
2-#0 (S & T)
A

36-2011-63
18-#16 (A-R, U, V, & W)
2-Coaxial RG-58/U (S & T)
A

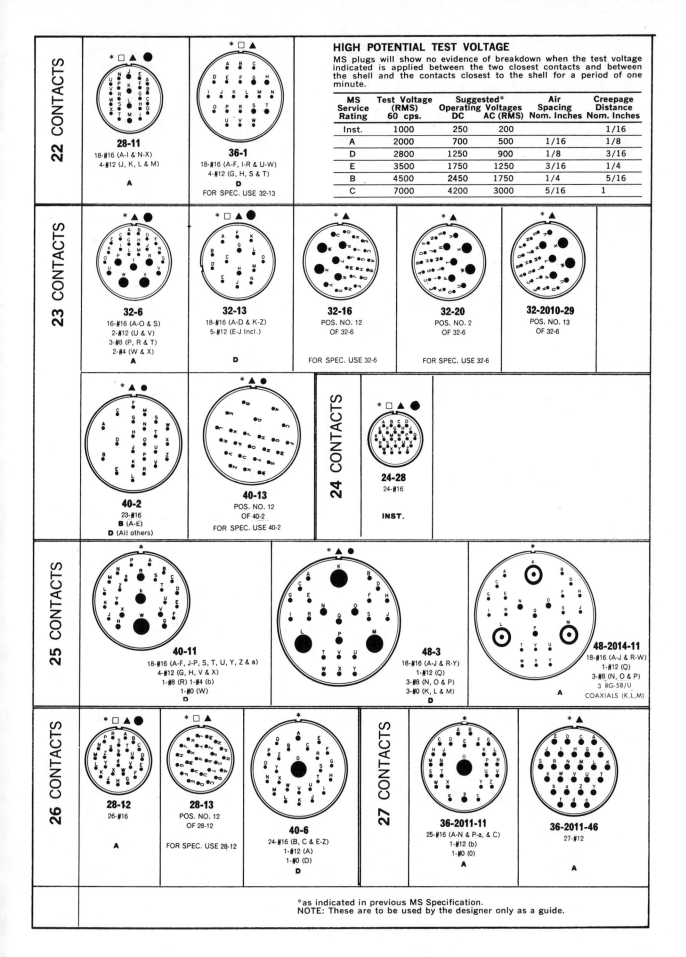

22 CONTACTS

28-11
18-#16 (A-I & N-X)
4-#12 (J, K, L & M)
A

36-1
18-#16 (A-F, I-R & U-W)
4-#12 (G, H, S & T)
D
FOR SPEC. USE 32-13

HIGH POTENTIAL TEST VOLTAGE

MS plugs will show no evidence of breakdown when the test voltage indicated is applied between the two closest contacts and between the shell and the contacts closest to the shell for a period of one minute.

MS Service Rating	Test Voltage (RMS) 60 cps.	Suggested* Operating Voltages DC	AC (RMS)	Air Spacing Nom. Inches	Creepage Distance Nom. Inches
Inst.	1000	250	200		1/16
A	2000	700	500	1/16	1/8
D	2800	1250	900	1/8	3/16
E	3500	1750	1250	3/16	1/4
B	4500	2450	1750	1/4	5/16
C	7000	4200	3000	5/16	1

23 CONTACTS

32-6
16-#16 (A-O & S)
2-#12 (U & V)
3-#8 (P, R & T)
2-#4 (W & X)
A

32-13
18-#16 (A-D & K-Z)
5-#12 (E-J Incl.)
D

32-16
POS. NO. 12
OF 32-6
FOR SPEC. USE 32-6

32-20
POS. NO. 2
OF 32-6
FOR SPEC. USE 32-6

32-2010-29
POS. NO. 13
OF 32-6

40-2
23-#16
B (A-E)
D (All others)

40-13
POS. NO. 12
OF 40-2
FOR SPEC. USE 40-2

24 CONTACTS

24-28
24-#16
INST.

25 CONTACTS

40-11
18-#16 (A-F, J-P, S, T, U, Y, Z & a)
4-#12 (G, H, V & X)
1-#8 (R) 1-#4 (b)
1-#0 (W)
D

48-3
18-#16 (A-J & R-Y)
1-#12 (Q)
3-#8 (N, O & P)
3-#0 (K, L & M)
D

48-2014-11
18-#16 (A-J & R-W)
1-#12 (Q)
3-#8 (N, O & P)
3 RG-58/U
COAXIALS (K, L, M)
A

26 CONTACTS

28-12
26-#16
A

28-13
POS. NO. 12
OF 28-12
FOR SPEC. USE 28-12

40-6
24-#16 (B, C & E-Z)
1-#12 (A)
1-#0 (D)
D

27 CONTACTS

36-2011-11
25-#16 (A-N & P-a, & C)
1-#12 (b)
1-#0 (0)
A

36-2011-46
27-#12
A

*as indicated in previous MS Specification.
NOTE: These are to be used by the designer only as a guide.

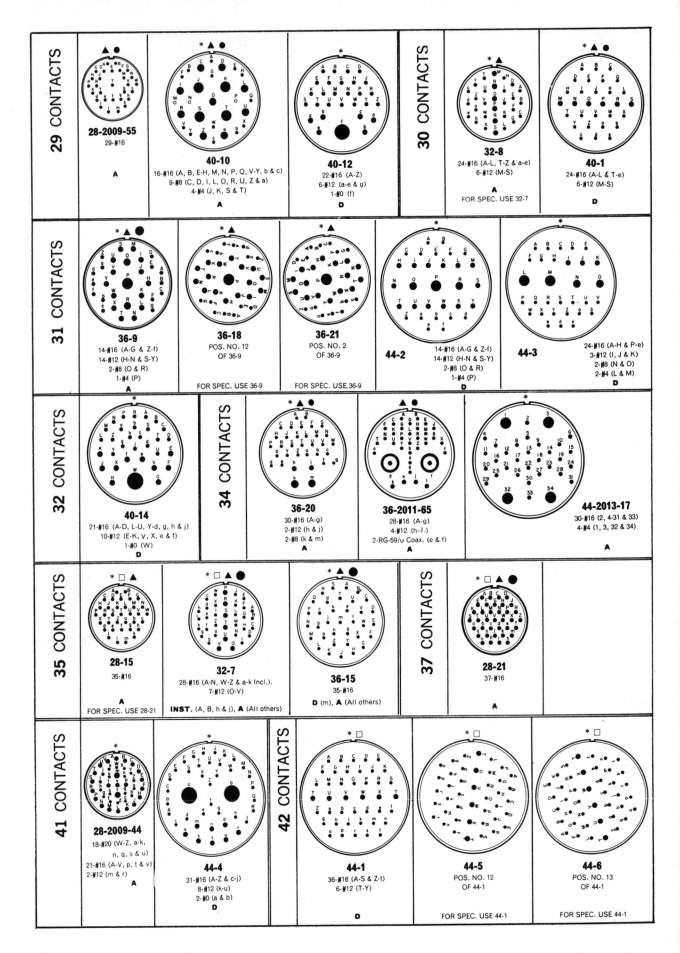

29 CONTACTS

28-2009-55
29-#16

A

40-10
16-#16 (A, B, E-H, M, N, P, Q, V-Y, b & c)
9-#8 (C, D, I, L, O, R, U, Z & a)
4-#4 (J, K, S & T)
A

40-12
22-#16 (A-Z)
6-#12 (a-e & g)
1-#0 (f)
D

30 CONTACTS

32-8
24-#16 (A-L, T-Z & a-e)
6-#12 (M-S)
A
FOR SPEC. USE 32-7

40-1
24-#16 (A-L & T-e)
6-#12 (M-S)
D

31 CONTACTS

36-9
14-#16 (A-G & Z-f)
14-#12 (H-N & S-Y)
2-#8 (O & R)
1-#4 (P)
A

36-18
POS. NO. 12
OF 36-9
FOR SPEC. USE 36-9

36-21
POS. NO. 2
OF 36-9
FOR SPEC. USE 36-9

44-2
14-#16 (A-G & Z-f)
14-#12 (H-N & S-Y)
2-#8 (O & R)
1-#4 (P)
D

44-3
24-#16 (A-H & P-e)
3-#12 (I, J & K)
2-#8 (N & O)
2-#4 (L & M)
D

32 CONTACTS

40-14
21-#16 (A-D, L-U, Y-d, g, h & j)
10-#12 (E-K, V, X, e & f)
1-#0 (W)
D

34 CONTACTS

36-20
30-#16 (A-g)
2-#12 (h & j)
2-#8 (k & m)
A

36-2011-65
28-#16 (A-g)
4-#12 (h-l)
2-RG-59/u Coax. (e & f)
A

44-2013-17
30-#16 (2, 4-31 & 33)
4-#4 (1, 3, 32 & 34)
A

35 CONTACTS

28-15
35-#16
A
FOR SPEC. USE 28-21

32-7
28-#16 (A-N, W-Z & a-k Incl.).
7-#12 (O-V)
INST. (A, B, h & j), A (All others)

36-15
35-#16
D (m), A (All others)

37 CONTACTS

28-21
37-#16
A

41 CONTACTS

28-2009-44
18-#20 (W-Z, a-k,
n, q, s & u)
21-#16 (A-V, p, t & v)
2-#12 (m & r)
A

44-4
31-#16 (A-Z & c-j)
8-#12 (k-u)
2-#0 (a & b)
D

42 CONTACTS

44-1
36-#16 (A-S & Z-t)
6-#12 (T-Y)
D

44-5
POS. NO. 12
OF 44-1
FOR SPEC. USE 44-1

44-6
POS. NO. 13
OF 44-1
FOR SPEC. USE 44-1

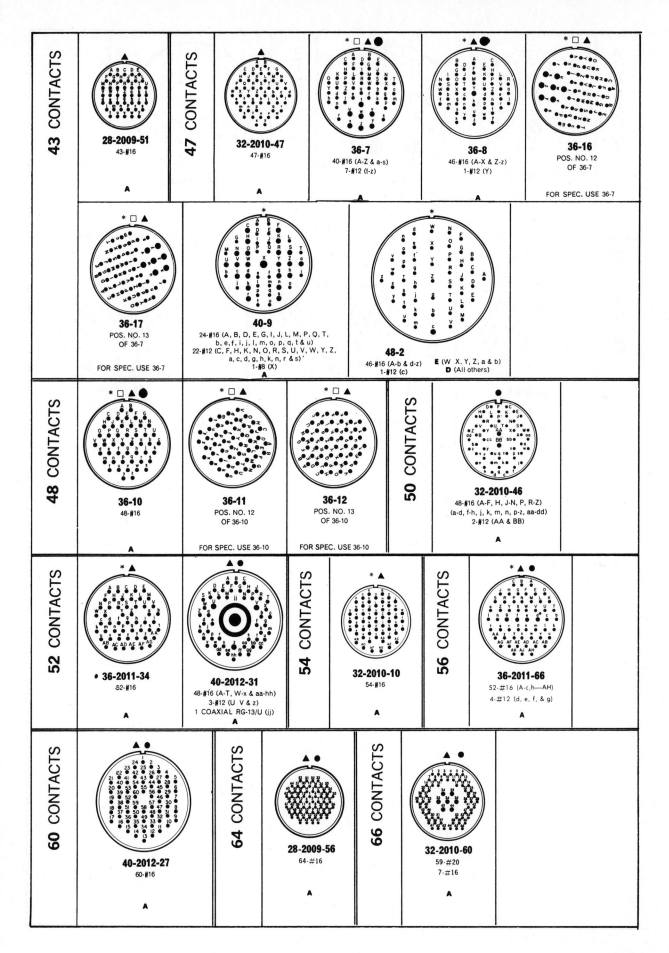

43 CONTACTS

28-2009-51
43-#16

A

47 CONTACTS

32-2010-47
47-#16

A

36-7
40-#16 (A-Z & a-s)
7-#12 (t-z)

A

36-8
46-#16 (A-X & Z-z)
1-#12 (Y)

A

36-16
POS. NO. 12
OF 36-7

FOR SPEC. USE 36-7

36-17
POS. NO. 13
OF 36-7

FOR SPEC. USE 36-7

40-9
24-#16 (A, B, D, E, G, I, J, L, M, P, Q, T,
b, e, f, i, j, l, m, o, p, q, t & u)
22-#12 (C, F, H, K, N, O, R, S, U, V, W, Y, Z,
a, c, d, g, h, k, n, r & s)'
1-#8 (X)

A

48-2
46-#16 (A-b & d-z)
1-#12 (c)

E (W, X, Y, Z, a & b)
D (All others)

48 CONTACTS

36-10
48-#16

A

36-11
POS. NO. 12
OF 36-10

FOR SPEC. USE 36-10

36-12
POS. NO. 13
OF 36-10

FOR SPEC. USE 36-10

50 CONTACTS

32-2010-46
48-#16 (A-F, H, J-N, P, R-Z)
(a-d, f-h, j, k, m, n, p-z, aa-dd)
2-#12 (AA & BB)

A

52 CONTACTS

36-2011-34
-52-#16

A

40-2012-31
48-#16 (A-T, W-x & aa-hh)
3-#12 (U, V & z)
1 COAXIAL RG-13/U (jj)

A

54 CONTACTS

32-2010-10
54-#16

A

56 CONTACTS

36-2011-66
52-#16 (A-c, h—AH)
4-#12 (d, e, f, & g)

A

60 CONTACTS

40-2012-27
60-#16

A

64 CONTACTS

28-2009-56
64-#16

A

66 CONTACTS

32-2010-60
59-#20
7-#16

A

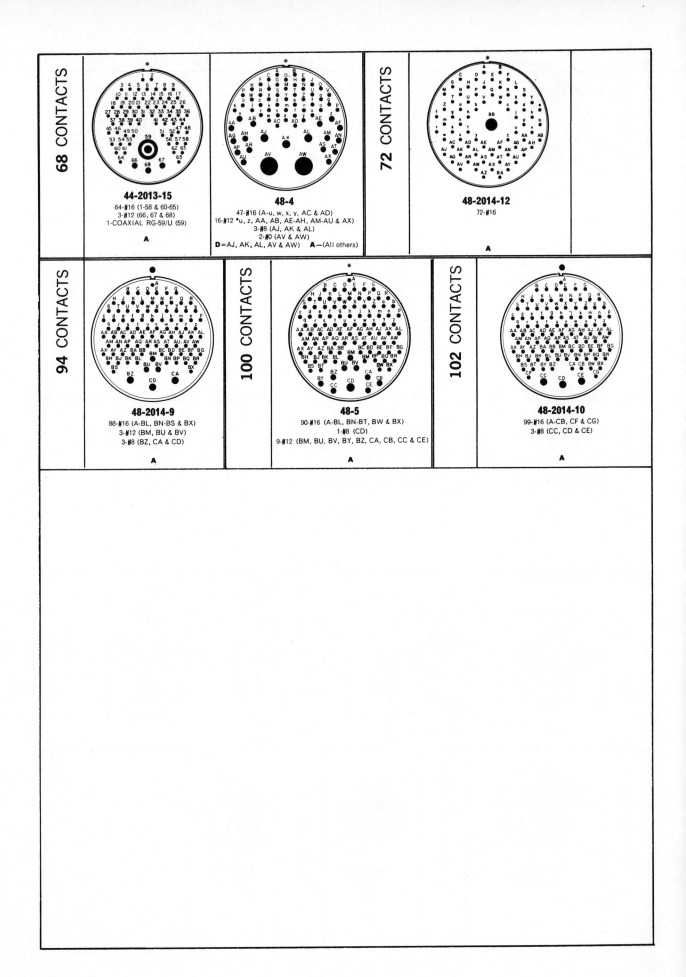

68 CONTACTS

44-2013-15
64-#16 (1-58 & 60-65)
3-#12 (66, 67 & 68)
1-COAXIAL RG-59/U (59)

A

48-4
47-#16 (A-u, w, x, y, AC & AD)
16-#12 *u, z, AA, AB, AE-AH, AM-AU & AX)
3-#8 (AJ, AK & AL)
2-#0 (AV & AW)
D=AJ, AK, AL, AV & AW)   **A**—(All others)

72 CONTACTS

48-2014-12
72-#16

A

94 CONTACTS

48-2014-9
88-#16 (A-BL, BN-BS & BX)
3-#12 (BM, BU & BV)
3-#8 (BZ, CA & CD)

A

100 CONTACTS

48-5
90-#16 (A-BL, BN-BT, BW & BX)
1-#8 (CD)
9-#12 (BM, BU, BV, BY, BZ, CA, CB, CC & CE)

A

102 CONTACTS

48-2014-10
99-#16 (A-CB, CF & CG)
3-#8 (CC, CD & CE)

A

Extracted from Gem Stones (Bulletin 585), Principle Forms of Crystalline Gem Stone Cuts, through the courtesy of the Bureau of Mines, Department of the Interior, Washington.

Principal Forms of Crystalline Gem-stone Cuts.

BRILLIANT

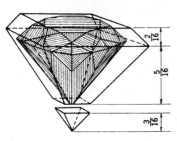
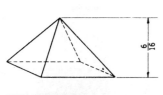

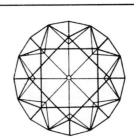
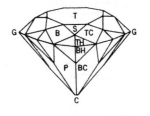

Common brilliant cuts

	Facets
Brilliant	58
Split	42
Half	16
Lisbon	74
Twentieth century	80 to 88
Multifacet	Up to 104

Facets

	Names	Number
T	Table	1
S	Star	8
B	Bezel	4
TC	Top corner	4
TH	Top half	16
BH	Bottom half	16
BC	Bottom corner	4
P	Pravilion	4
C	Culet	1
	Total	58
G	Girdle	

EMERALD

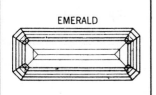

MARQUISE

PEAR SHAPE

HEART SHAPE

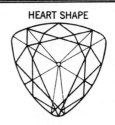

BEADS

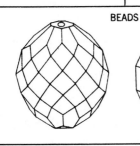

BRIOLETTE

UNCOMMON CUTS

Triangle	Shield	Keystone	Kite	Square	Trapeze

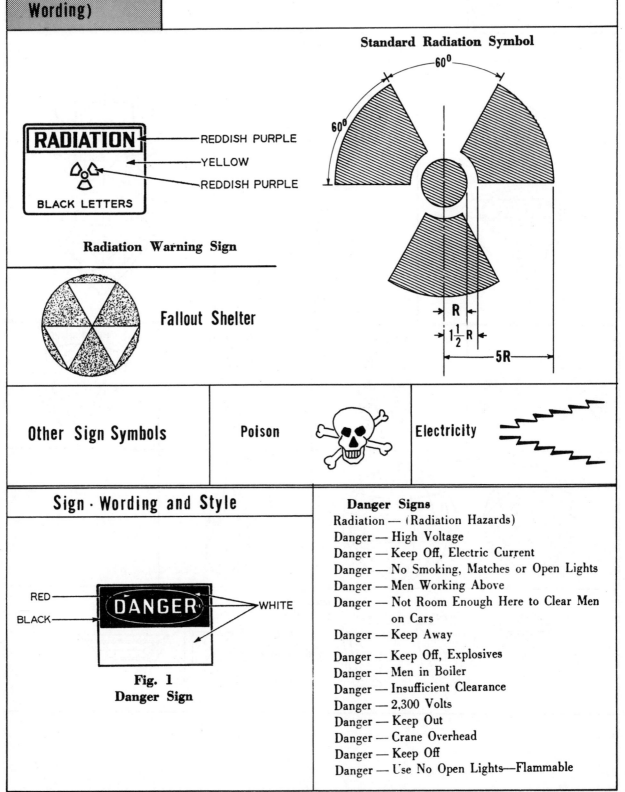

ASA   Z35.1

SIGNS
(Symbols and Wording)

Extracted from American Standard Specifications for Industrial Accident Prevention Signs (Z35.1-1951), Symbols and Wording, and reproduced herein through the courtesy of the American Standards Association, 10 East 40 Street, New York, N.Y.

Standard Radiation Symbol

60°

60°

R

$1\frac{1}{2}$ R

5R

RADIATION — REDDISH PURPLE

— YELLOW

— REDDISH PURPLE

BLACK LETTERS

Radiation Warning Sign

Fallout Shelter

Other Sign Symbols

Poison

Electricity

Sign · Wording and Style

RED

BLACK

DANGER

WHITE

**Fig. 1
Danger Sign**

Danger Signs

Radiation — (Radiation Hazards)
Danger — High Voltage
Danger — Keep Off, Electric Current
Danger — No Smoking, Matches or Open Lights
Danger — Men Working Above
Danger — Not Room Enough Here to Clear Men
          on Cars
Danger — Keep Away

Danger — Keep Off, Explosives
Danger — Men in Boiler
Danger — Insufficient Clearance
Danger — 2,300 Volts
Danger — Keep Out
Danger — Crane Overhead
Danger — Keep Off
Danger — Use No Open Lights—Flammable

**Fig. 4
Caution Sign**

Caution — Do Not Operate, Men Working on Repairs
Caution — Hands Off Switch, Men Working on Line
Caution — Working on Machines, Do Not Start
Caution — Goggles Must Be Worn When Operating This Machine
Caution — This Door Must Be Kept Closed
Caution — Electric Trucks, Go Slow
Caution — This Space Must Be Kept Clear at All Times
Caution — Stop Machinery to Clean, Oil or Repair
Caution — Keep Aisles Clear
Caution — Operators of This Machine Shall Wear Snug Fitting Clothing—No Gloves
Caution — Close Clearance
Caution — Watch Your Step
Caution — Electric Fence

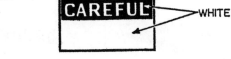

Safety Instruction Signs

Report All Injuries to the First-Aid Room at Once
Walk—Don't Run
Report All Injuries No Matter How Slight
Think, if Safe Go Ahead
Make Your Work Place Safe Before Starting the Job
Report All Unsafe Conditions to Your Foreman
Help Keep This Plant Safe and Clean

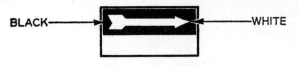

Directional Signs

This Way Out (below arrow panel)
This Way (inside arrow) Out (below arrow panel)
Fire Exit (below arrow panel)
Fire (inside arrow) Extinguisher (below arrow panel)
To the (inside arrow) Fire Escape (below arrow panel)
To the (inside arrow) First Aid (below arrow panel)
Manway (below arrow panel)
This Way to (inside arrow) First-Aid Room (below arrow panel)

Informational Signs

Blue shall be the standard color for informational signs. It may be used as the background color for the complete sign or as a panel at the top of such types as "Notice" signs, which have a white background.

No Trespassing Under Penalty of the Law
This Elevataor Is for Freight Only, Not for Passengers
No Admittance Except to Employees on Duty
No Admittance
No Admittance, Apply at Office
No Trespassing
Men
Women
For Employees Only
Office

Height of Letters (INCHES)	Distance Visible* (FEET)
3½	200-210
3	170-180
2½	140-150
2	110-120
1¾	95-105
1½	80-90
1¼	70-80
1,	60-65
⅞	50-55
¾	40-45
⅝	30-35
½	20-30
⅜	20-25
¼	15-20

*Distances specified do not include any allowance for various color combinations.

International Flags and Pennants

Published at Washington, D.C.,
by the U.S. NAVY HYDROGRAPHIC OFFICE
under the authority of the SECRETARY OF THE NAVY

ALPHABET FLAGS

NUMERAL PENNANTS

Alfa — *BLUE* — Speed Trial	**K**ilo — *YEL / BL* — Stop Instantly	**U**niform — *RED* — Standing into danger
Bravo — *RED* — Explosives	**L**ima — *YEL-BLACK / YEL* — Stop, Something to Communicate	**V**ictor — *RED* — Require Assistance
Charlie — *BLUE / RD / BLUE* — Yes	**M**ike — *BLUE* — Doctor on Board	**W**his-key — *BL / RD* — Require Medical Assistance
Delta — *BL / YEL / YEL* — Keep Clear	**N**ovember — *BLUE* — No	**X**ray — *BLUE* — Stop Your Intention
Echo — *BL / RD* — Altering Course to Starboard	**O**scar — *RD / YEL* — Man Overboard	**Y**ankee — *YEL & RED* — Carrying Mails
Foxtrot — *RED* — Disabled	**P**apa — *BLUE* — About to Sail (Lights out)	**Z**ulu — *YEL / BLA / BL / RD* — Shore Stations

NUMERAL PENNANTS	
1 — *RED*	2 — *BLUE*
3 — *RED ... BLUE*	4 — *RED*
5 — *YEL / BLUE*	6 — *BLACK*

REPEATERS

1st Repeat — *YEL / BLUE*	7 — *YEL / RED*
2nd Repeat — *BLUE*	8 — *RED*
3rd Repeat — *BLACK*	9 — *WHITE / BLACK / YEL / RED*
CODE — *RED* — Code and Answering Pennant (Decimal Point)	0 — *YEL / YEL / RED*

Golf — *YEL & BLUE* — Want a Pilot	**Q**uebec — *YEL* — Request Pratique
Hotel — *RED* — Pilot on Board	**R**omeo — *YEL / RED* — Way is off my ship
India — *YEL / BLACK* — Altering Course to Port	**S**ierra — *BLUE* — Going full speed astern
Juliet — *BLUE* — Semaphore	**T**ango — *RD / BL* — Do not pass ahead of me

Extracted from Manual on Uniform Traffic Control Devices for Streets and Highways, and reproduced herein through the courtesy of the Bureau of Public Roads, Department of Commerce, Washington. These standards are approved by American Association of State Highway Officials, Institute of Traffic Engineers, National Committee on Uniform Traffic Laws and Ordinances.

Stop Sign	Yield Sign	Speed Limit Sign		Night Speed Sign
30" x 30"	36" x 36" x 36"	24" x 30"	24" x 24"	24" x 24"
STOP RED	**YIELD** YELLOW	**SPEED LIMIT 50**	**TRUCKS 40**	**NIGHT 45**

Minimum Speed	Speed Zone Ahead Sign	End (35) Mile Speed Sign	Turn Prohibition	
24" x 30"	24" x 30"	24" x 30"	24" x 30"	
MINIMUM SPEED 40	**SPEED ZONE AHEAD**	**END 35 MILE SPEED**	**NO RIGHT TURN**	**NO U TURN**

	Lane-Use Control			30" x 30"
24" x 24"		30" x 36"		
NO TURNS	**ONLY**		**LEFT LANE MUST TURN LEFT**	**ONLY**

Do Not Pass Sign		Slower Traffic Keep Right Sign		24" x 30"
24" x 30"				
DO NOT PASS	**PASS WITH CARE**	**SLOWER TRAFFIC KEEP RIGHT**	**TRUCKS USE RIGHT LANE**	**TRUCK LANE 500 FEET**

Keep Right Sign	Do Not Enter Sign		24" x 12"	One Way Sign
24" x 30"		24" x 24"		36" x 12"
KEEP → RIGHT	**DO NOT ENTER**	**NO TRUCKS**	**PEDESTRIANS PROHIBITED**	**ONE WAY ▶**

18" x 24"	Reversible Flow and Periodic One-Way Signs		Parking and Stopping Signs	
			12" x 18"	12" x 6"
ONE WAY →	**TWO WAY TRAFFIC AHEAD**	24" x 30" **END ONE WAY**	**NO PARKING ANY TIME** RED **ONE HOUR PARKING 9AM-7PM** GREEN **NO PARKING BUS STOP** RED **2 HR PARKING 8:30AM TO 5:30PM** GREEN	**TOW-AWAY ZONE** RED

Parking Signs in Rural Districts	Walk on Left Sign	Pedestrian Crossing Signs	
24" x 30" **NO PARKING ON PAVEMENT**	18" x 24" **WALK ON LEFT FACING TRAFFIC**	12" x 18" **CROSS ON WALK SIGNAL ONLY**	CROSS ON GREEN LIGHT ONLY CROSS ON WALK SIGNAL ONLY CROSS ONLY AT CROSS WALKS NO PEDESTRIAN CROSSING 12 inches by 18 inches.

Pedestrian-Actuated Signal Sign	Keep Off Median	Road Closed Sign	Local Traffic Only Sign
9" x 12" **PUSH BUTTON FOR GREEN LIGHT**	24" x 30" **KEEP OFF MEDIAN**	48" x 30" **ROAD CLOSED**	60" x 30" **ROAD CLOSED 10 MILES AHEAD LOCAL TRAFFIC ONLY**

Weight Limit Sign	**WARNING SIGNS** 30" x 30"	
18" x 24" **WEIGHT LIMIT 10 TONS**	1. Changes in horizontal alinement 2. Intersections 3. Advance warning of control devices 4. Converging traffic lanes 5. Narrow roadways	6. Changes in highway design 7. Grades 8. Roadway surface conditions 9. Schools 10. Railroad crossings 11 Entrances and crossings *ALL YELLOW BACKGROUND*

Turn Sign	Curve Sign	Reverse Turn Sign	Reverse Curve Sign	Winding Road

Large Arrow Sign	48" x 24"	Cross Road Sign	Side Road Sign	

T Symbol Sign	Y Symbol Sign	Stop Ahead Sign	Yield Ahead Sign	Signal Ahead Sign
		STOP AHEAD	**YIELD AHEAD**	**SIGNAL AHEAD**

Merging Traffic	Pavement-Width Transition Sign	Road Narrows Sign	Narrow Bridge	One Lane Bridge
MERGING TRAFFIC		**ROAD NARROWS**	**NARROW BRIDGE**	**ONE LANE BRIDGE**

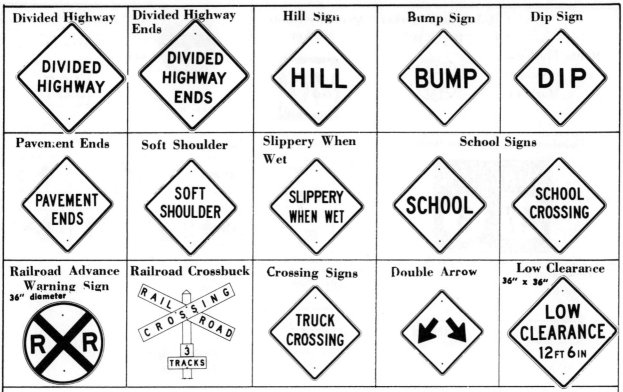

Divided Highway	Divided Highway Ends	Hill Sign	Bump Sign	Dip Sign
DIVIDED HIGHWAY	DIVIDED HIGHWAY ENDS	HILL	BUMP	DIP
Pavement Ends	Soft Shoulder	Slippery When Wet	School Signs	
PAVEMENT ENDS	SOFT SHOULDER	SLIPPERY WHEN WET	SCHOOL	SCHOOL CROSSING
Railroad Advance Warning Sign 36" diameter	Railroad Crossbuck	Crossing Signs	Double Arrow	Low Clearance 36" x 36"
R X R	RAIL ROAD CROSSING 3 TRACKS	TRUCK CROSSING		LOW CLEARANCE 12 FT 6 IN

Advisory Speed Plate

The Advisory Speed plate shall be a square plate of a standard size of 18 inches by 18 inches. When used with a warning sign larger than 36 inches by 36 inches, it shall be 24 inches square.

The plate shall carry the message (35) M.P.H. in black on a yellow background. The speed shown shall be a multiple of 5 miles per hour.

35 M.P.H.

Traffic Signal Speed
12" x 18"

SIGNALS SET FOR 25 M.P.H.

Other Warning Signs

Typical miscellaneous warning signs are PLAYGROUND, BRIDLE PATH, TUNNEL, DRAW BRIDGE, UNEVEN TRACKS, ROUGH ROAD, HIGH WATER, LOOSE GRAVEL, LOW SHOULDER, RANGE CATTLE, (FACTORY) ENTRANCE, EXIT, and FALLING ROCK. The applications of such signs are sufficiently apparent as to require no detailed specifications.

GUIDE SIGNS

Guide signs are essential to guide the motorist along established routes, to inform him of intersecting routes, to direct him to cities, villages, or other important destinations, to identify nearby rivers and streams, parks, forests, and historical sites, and generally to give him such information as will help him along his way in the most simple, direct method possible.

Guide signs are here considered in three major groups:

1. Route markers and auxiliary markers
2. Destination and distance signs
3. Information signs

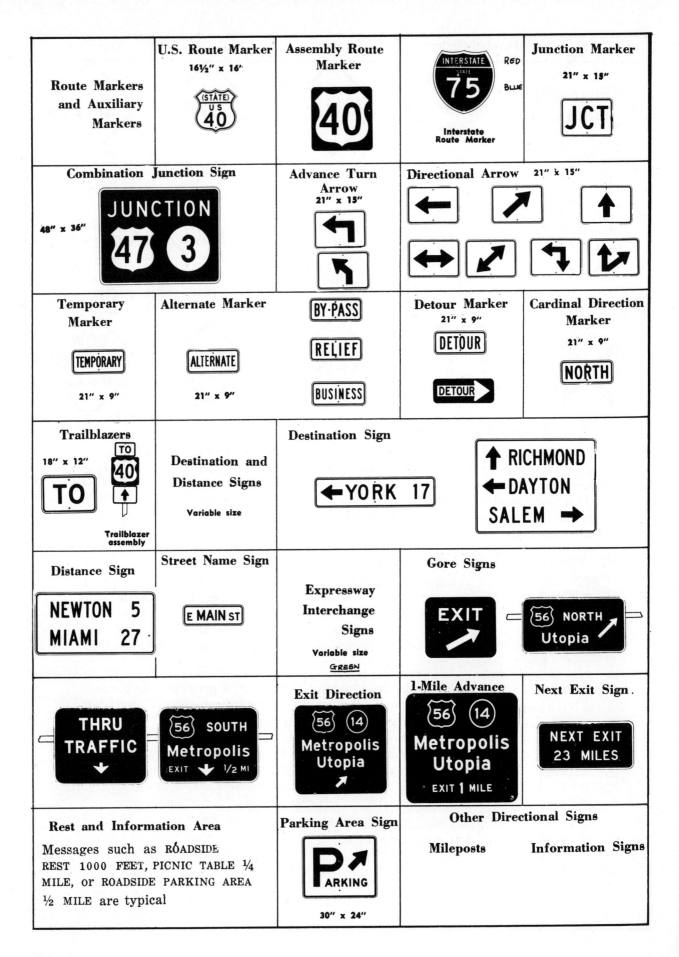

| Route Markers and Auxiliary Markers | U.S. Route Marker 16½" x 16" (STATE) US 40 | Assembly Route Marker 40 | INTERSTATE STATE 75 RED BLUE Interstate Route Marker | Junction Marker 21" x 15" JCT |

Combination Junction Sign
48" x 36"
JUNCTION 47 3

Advance Turn Arrow 21" x 15"

Directional Arrow 21" x 15"

| Temporary Marker TEMPORARY 21" x 9" | Alternate Marker ALTERNATE 21" x 9" | BY-PASS RELIEF BUSINESS | Detour Marker 21" x 9" DETOUR DETOUR | Cardinal Direction Marker 21" x 9" NORTH |

Trailblazers 18" x 12" TO TO 40 Trailblazer assembly

Destination and Distance Signs Variable size

Destination Sign
←YORK 17

↑ RICHMOND ←DAYTON SALEM →

Distance Sign
NEWTON 5 MIAMI 27

Street Name Sign
E MAIN ST

Expressway Interchange Signs Variable size GREEN

Gore Signs
EXIT ↗
56 NORTH Utopia ↗

THRU TRAFFIC ↓
56 SOUTH Metropolis EXIT ↓ ½ MI

Exit Direction
56 14 Metropolis Utopia ↗

1-Mile Advance
56 14 Metropolis Utopia EXIT 1 MILE

Next Exit Sign
NEXT EXIT 23 MILES

Rest and Information Area
Messages such as ROADSIDE REST 1000 FEET, PICNIC TABLE ¼ MILE, or ROADSIDE PARKING AREA ½ MILE are typical

Parking Area Sign
P ARKING ↗
30" x 24"

Other Directional Signs

Mileposts   Information Signs

LINOTYPE TYPOGRAPHY (Symbols Available From Typographers)

Extracted from "Linotype One-line Specimens Book," through the courtesy and permission of the publisher, Merganthaler Linotype Company, 29 Ryerson Street, Brooklyn, N.Y.

NO.	CHARACTER		POINT SIZE

Astronomical · △ 332

NO.	CHARACTER	POINT SIZE
1	♈ Aries	5½, 6, 8, 10, 11, 12, 14
2	♉ Taurus	5½, 6, 8, 10, 11, 12, 14
3	♊ Gemini	5½, 6, 8, 10, 11, 12, 14
4	♋ Cancer	5½, 6, 8, 10, 11, 12, 14
5	♌ Leo	5½, 6, 8, 10, 11, 12, 14
6	♍ Virgo	5½, 6, 8, 10, 11, 12, 14
7	♎ Libra	5½, 6, 8, 10, 11, 12, 14
8	♏ Scorpio	5½, 6, 8, 10, 11, 12, 14
9	♐ Sagittarius	5½, 6, 8, 10, 11, 12, 14
10	♑ Capricornus	5½, 6, 8, 10, 11, 12, 14
11	♒ Aquarius	5½, 6, 8, 10, 11, 12, 14
12	♓ Pisces	5½, 6, 8, 10, 11, 12, 14
13	Aries	8, 10
14	Taurus	8, 10
15	Gemini	8, 10
16	Cancer	8, 10
17	Leo	8, 10
18	Virgo	8, 10
19	Libra	8, 10
20	Scorpio	8, 10
21	Sagittarius	8, 10
22	Capricornus	8, 10
23	Aquarius	8, 10
24	Pisces	8, 10
25	Moon	5½, 6, 7, 8, 10, 12, 14, 18
26	New moon	5½, 6, 7, 8, 9, 10, 12, 14, 18
27	First quarter	5½, 6, 7, 8, 9, 10, 12, 14, 18
28	Full moon	5½, 6, 7, 8, 9, 10, 12, 14, 18
29	Last quarter	5½, 6, 7, 8, 9, 10, 12, 14, 18
30	New moon	5½, 6, 7, 8, 9, 10, 12
31	First quarter	5½, 6, 7, 8, 10, 12
32	Last quarter	5½, 6, 7, 8, 10, 12
33	First quarter	5½, 6, 7, 8, 10, 11, 12
34	Last quarter	5½, 6, 7, 8, 10, 11, 12
36	⊙ Sun	5, 5½, 6, 7, 8, 9, 10, 11, 12, 14
37	☿ Mercury	5½, 6, 7, 8, 10, 11, 12
38	♀ Venus	4, 5½, 6, 7, 8, 9, 10, 11, 12
35	⊖ Earth	5½, 6, 8, 10, 11, 12
39	⊕ Earth	5½, 6, 7, 8, 10, 11, 12, 14
45	Earth	6, 7, 8, 10, 12
40	♂ Mars	4, 5½, 6, 7, 8, 9, 10, 11, 12, 14
41	♃ Jupiter	5½, 6, 7, 8, 10, 11, 12
42	♄ Saturn	5½, 6, 7, 8, 10, 11, 12
43	Uranus	5½, 6, 7, 8, 10, 12

NO.	CHARACTER	POINT SIZE
66	♅ Uranus	6, 8, 10, 12
67	Uranus	6, 8, 10, 12
44	♆ Neptune	5½, 6, 7, 8, 10, 11, 12
62	♇ Pluto	6, 8, 10, 12
70	♀ Pluto	6, 8, 10, 12
46	☌ Conjunction	5½, 6, 8, 10, 11, 12
47	☍ Opposition	5½, 6, 8, 10, 11, 12
48	△ Trine	5½, 6, 7, 8, 10, 12
49	□ Quadrature	5½, 6, 8, 10, 12
50	⚹ Sextile	5½, 6, 8, 10, 11, 12
63	Semi sextile	6, 8, 10, 12
64	Sesquiquadrate	6, 8, 10, 12
65	Quincunx	6, 8, 10, 12
51	∝ Variation	6, 8, 10, 12
52	☊ Ascending node	5½, 6, 8, 10, 12
53	☋ Descending node	5½, 6, 8, 10, 12
54	⊠ Station mark	6, 8, 10, 11, 12
55	☉ Sun's upper limb	6, 8, 10, 11, 12
56	☉ Sun's lower limb	6, 8, 10, 11
57	⊖ Sun's center	6, 8, 10, 12
58	⌢ Runs highest	5½, 6, 8, 10
59	⌣ Runs lowest	5½, 6, 8, 10
68	Partly cloudy	6, 8, 10
69	Ⅱ Gemini	6, 8, 10, 11, 12, 14
81	Fair weather	14, 30
82	Rain or snow	14, 30
83	Local rain or snow	14, 30
84	Temperature	14, 30
85	Cold wave	14, 30

Chemical · △ 536

NO.	CHARACTER	POINT SIZE
1	/ Single bond	6, 8
2	| Single bond	6, 8
7	\ Single bond	6, 8
8	| Single bond	6, 8
20	| Single bond (Punched to right)	8

NO.	CHARACTER	POINT SIZE
3	Double bond	6, 8
4	Double bond	6, 8
5	Double bond	6, 8
6	Double bond	6, 8
21	Triple bond	8, 10
9	Reaction goes both right and left	6, 8, 9, 10, 12
10	Reaction goes both up and down	6, 7, 8, 9, 10, 11, 12
11	Equilibrium reaction beginning at right	5½, 6, 7, 8, 9, 10, 11, 12
12	Equilibrium reaction beginning at left	5½, 6, 7, 8, 9, 10, 11, 12
13	Reversible reaction beginning at left	6, 8, 9, 10, 12
14	Reaction begins at right and is completed to left	8, 10
15	Reaction begins at right and is completed to right	8, 10
16	Reaction begins at left and is completed to right	6, 8, 10
17	Reaction begins at left and is completed to left	6, 8, 10
18	Reversible reaction beginning at right	6, 8, 10
19	Reversible	8, 10
23	Elimination	8
24	Absorption	8
25	Exchange	8
26	Electrolysis	8
27	Ring opening	8
28	Repositioning	8
29	Ring Cycle	8
45	Reversible reaction	8, 10
46	Reversible reaction	8, 10

Mathematical · △ 330

NO.	CHARACTER	POINT SIZE
1	Plus	4, 5, 5½, 6, 7, 8, 9, 10, 11, 12, 14, 18, 20, 24, 30, 36
2	Minus	4, 5, 5½, 6, 7, 8, 9, 10, 11, 12, 14, 18, 20, 24, 30, 36
3	Multiplied by	4, 5, 5½, 6, 7, 8, 9, 10, 11, 12, 14, 18, 20, 24, 30, 36
4	Divided by	4, 5, 5½, 6, 7, 8, 9, 10, 11, 12, 14, 18, 20, 24, 30, 36
5	Equal to	4, 5, 5½, 6, 7, 8, 9, 10, 11, 12, 14, 18, 20, 24, 30, 36
6	Plus or minus	5, 5½, 6, 7, 8, 9, 10, 11, 12, 14, 18
7	Minus or plus	5, 5½, 6, 7, 8, 9, 10, 11, 12, 14
56	Plus or equal	5½, 6, 7, 8, 9, 10, 11, 12
73	Double plus	6, 7, 8, 9, 10, 11, 12
12	Difference between	6, 7, 8, 9, 10, 11, 12
60	Difference excess	6, 8, 9, 10, 12

NO.	CHARACTER	POINT SIZE
13	Identical with, congruent	6, 7, 8, 9, 10, 11, 12
87	Not identical with	6, 7, 8, 9, 10, 11, 12
14	Not equal to	6, 7, 8, 9, 10, 11, 12
15	Nearly equal to	6, 7, 8, 9, 10, 11, 12
61	Equals approximately	6, 7, 8, 9, 10, 11, 12
93	Equals approximately	6, 8, 9, 10
16	Equal to or greater than	6, 8, 9, 10, 11, 12
120	Equal to or less than	6, 8, 9, 10, 11, 12
21	Less than	6, 7, 8, 9, 10, 11, 12
58	Less than	6, 8, 9, 10, 12
22	Greater than	5, 6, 7, 8, 9, 10, 11, 12
57	Greater than	6, 8, 9, 10
125	Greater than or less than	6, 8, 9, 10, 12
23	Not less than	6, 7, 8, 9, 10, 11, 12
24	Not greater than	6, 7, 8, 9, 10, 11, 12
88	Less than or equal to	6, 7, 8, 9, 10, 11, 12
81	Less than or equal to	5½, 6, 7, 8, 9, 10, 11, 12
17	Less than or equal to	5½, 6, 7, 8, 9, 10, 11, 12
126	Less than or equal to	6, 8, 9, 10
124	Less than or greater than	6, 7, 8, 9, 10
91	Greater than or equal to	6, 7, 8, 9, 10, 11, 12
77	Greater than or equal to	5½, 6, 7, 8, 9, 10, 11, 12
84	Greater than or equal to	5½, 6, 7, 8, 9, 10, 11, 12
127	Greater than or equal to	6, 8, 9, 10
25	Equivalent to	6, 8, 9, 10
106	Not equivalent	6, 7, 8, 9, 10, 12
107	Not equivalent	6, 8, 9, 10, 12
136	Included in	10
137	Excluded from	8, 10
11	Difference	5½, 6, 7, 8, 9, 10, 11, 12, 14
112	Difference	6, 8, 9, 10, 12
38	Equal and parallel	6, 8, 9, 10, 12, 18
39	Approaches a limit	6, 7, 8, 9, 10, 11, 12
96	Is measured by	6, 8, 9, 10, 12
36	Perpendicular to	5½, 6, 7, 8, 9, 10, 11, 12
68	Perpendiculars	6, 8, 9, 10, 12
37	Parallel	6, 7, 8, 9, 10, 11, 12
78	Parallels	6, 8, 9, 10, 12
121	Not parallels	6, 8, 9, 10, 12
28	Angle	6, 7, 8, 9, 10, 11, 12
72	Angle	6, 7, 8, 9, 10, 12
135	Angle	8, 9, 10
76	Angles	6, 7, 8, 9, 10, 12
35	Right angle	6, 7, 8, 9, 10, 11, 12
111	Equal angles	6, 8, 9, 10, 12
29	Triangle	4, 5, 6, 7, 8, 9, 10, 11, 12, 14, 18, 20, 30

NO.	CHARACTER		POINT SIZE

Mathematical · △ 330, *continued*

NO.	CHARACTER		POINT SIZE
74	▲	Triangles 6, 8, 9, 10, 12
55	/	Rising diagonal 5½, 6, 7, 8, 9, 10, 11, 12, 14, 18, 24, 36
54	\	Falling diagonal 5½, 6, 7, 8, 9, 10, 11, 12, 14, 18, 24, 36
69	//	Parallel rising diagonal 6, 7, 8, 9, 10, 11, 12, 24, 36
70	\\	Parallel falling diagonal 6, 7, 8, 9, 10, 11, 12, 24, 36
102	///	Rising parallels 6, 7, 8, 9, 10, 12
103	\\\	Falling parallels 6, 7, 8, 9, 10, 12
104	‖‖	Triple vertical. 6, 7, 8, 9, 10, 12
108	≣	Quadruple parallels 6, 7, 8, 9, 10, 12
89	⌢	Arc 6, 7, 8, 9, 10, 11, 12
90	⌣	Arc 6, 7, 8, 9, 10, 11, 12
40	▽	Sector 6, 7, 8, 9, 10, 12
79	⌓	Segment 6, 8, 9, 10, 12
26	○	Circle 5, 6, 7, 8, 9, 10, 11, 12, 14
75	ⓢ	Circles 6, 8, 9, 10, 12
101	○	Ellipse 6, 8, 9, 10, 12
83	⌀	Diameter 6, 7, 8, 9, 10, 12
27	☐	Square 4, 5, 5½, 6, 7, 8, 9, 10, 11, 12, 14, 18, 20, 30, 36
94	⊡	Squares 6, 8, 9, 10, 12
41	▭	Rectangle 6, 7, 8, 9, 10, 11, 12, 14
95	▱	Rectangles 6, 8, 9, 10, 12
43	⊞	Cube 6, 7, 8, 9, 10, 12
42	▱	Rhomboid 6, 8, 9, 10, 12
62	▱	Rhomboids 6, 8, 9, 10, 12
100	⬠	Pentagon 6, 8, 9, 10, 12
131	⬡	Hexagon 8, 10, 12
30	∴	Hence, therefore 5, 5½, 6, 7, 8, 9, 10, 11, 12, 14, 18, 24
31	∵	Because 5, 5½, 6, 7, 8, 9, 10, 12, 14
80	·	Multiplied by . .5½, 6, 7, 7½, 8, 9, 10, 11, 12
18	:	Ratio 6, 7, 8, 9, 10, 11, 12, 14
19	::	Proportion 6, 7, 8, 9, 10, 11, 12
20	÷	Geometrical proportion . . . 6, 7, 8, 9, 10, 12
32	′	Minute 4, 5, 5½, 6, 7, 8, 9, 10, 11, 12, 14, 18, 24, 30, 36, 42
33	″	Second 4, 5, 5½, 6, 7, 8, 9, 10, 11, 12, 14, 18, 24, 30, 36, 42
34	°	Degree 4, 5, 5½, 6, 7, 8, 9, 10, 11, 12, 14, 18, 24, 30, 36, 42
67	′	Dotted minute . . . . . . ·. 6, 8, 9, 10, 11
64	″	Dotted second. 6, 8, 9, 10
65	°	Dotted degree. 6, 8, 9, 10
71	″	Cancelled second. 6, 8, 9, 10
82	‴	Triple Prime 6, 7, 8, 9, 10, 11, 12
122	√	Radical . .6, 7, 8, 9, 10, 11, 12, 14, 18, 20, 24
44	√	Root 4, 5, 5½, 6, 7, 8, 9, 10, 11, 12, 14, 18, 24, 30, 36, 48
45	¹√	Root 5½, 6, 7, 8, 9, 10, 12
46	²√	Square root 6, 7, 8, 9, 10, 12, 14
47	³√	Cube root 5, 6, 7, 8, 9, 10, 11, 12, 14
48	⁴√	Fourth root 6, 7, 8, 9, 10, 12, 14
49	⁵√	Fifth root 6, 7, 8, 9, 10, 12
50	⁶√	Sixth root 6, 7, 8, 9, 10, 12
51	⁷√	Seventh root 6, 7, 8, 9, 10, 12
52	⁸√	Eighth root 6, 7, 8, 9, 10, 12
53	⁹√	Ninth root 6, 7, 8, 10, 12
109	ⁿ√	Nth root. 6, 7, 8, 9, 10, 12
110	²ⁿ√	2nth root 6, 7, 8, 9, 10, 12
66	∠	Horizontal radical . . 6, 7, 8, 9, 10, 11, 12, 14
129	α	Alpha 6, 8, 9, 10, 11, 12
97	Σ	Summation of 7, 9, 12, 14, 18, 24
98	π	Pi (3.1416) 7, 9, 11, 12, 14
99	ε	Base (2.718) of natural system of logarithms . . 7, 9, 12
113	θ	Theta 6, 7, 8, 9, 10, 11, 12
114	φ	Phi 6, 8, 9, 10, 12, 14
115	⊿	Delta 6, 8, 9, 10, 12
8	∝	Variation 6, 7, 8, 9, 10, 11, 12
9	∞	Infinity . . . 5, 5½, 6, 7, 8, 9, 10, 11, 12, 14
130	𝓂	Mills 6, 8, 10, 12
63	⊢	Assertion sign. 6, 8, 9, 10
85	≪	. . . . 6, 7, 8, 9, 10, 12
86	≫	. . . . 6, 7, 8, 9, 10, 12
117	c̄	Mean value of c 6, 8, 10
92	∂	Differential. 6, 7, 8, 9, 10, 12
128	∂	Differential. 6, 8, 9, 10
10	∫	Integral . .6, 7, 8, 9, 10, 11, 12, 14, 18, 22, 24
59	⌣	Horizontal Integral . 6, 7, 8, 9, 10, 12, 14, 18
147	˘	Mathmodifier 10
148	˓	Mathmodifier 10
250	∿	Cycle sine 8, 10
253	ⵔ	Quantic 8
10 U	⌠	10
10 M	⎮	Piece integral 10
10 L	⌡	10
44 U	/	. . . . .6, 8, 10

NO.	CHARACTER		POINT SIZE
44 M	/	Piece root	6, 8, 10
44 L	√		6, 8, 10
133 U	⌈		8, 10
133 M	|	Piece bracket	8, 10
133 L	⌊		8, 10
134 U	⌉		8, 10
134 M	|	Piece bracket	8, 10
134 L	⌋		8, 10

10 to 134 when assembled: 10 44 133 134

6 point intended for 18 point
8 point intended for 24 point
10 point intended for 30 point

∫ √ [ ]

NO.	CHARACTER		POINT SIZE
149 U	⎛		8, 10
149 M	⎜	Sectional Parentheses	8, 10
149 L	⎝		8, 10
150 U	⎞		8, 10
150 M	⎟	Sectional Parentheses	8, 10
150 L	⎠		8, 10

When assembled: 149 150

( ) 8 point intended for 24 point
10 point intended for 30 point

(HEAVY with LIGHT, for Two-Letter Display Mold)

NO.	CHARACTER		POINT SIZE
1 H-L	+ +	Plus	18, 24
2 H-L	− −	Minus	18, 24
3 H-L	× ×	Multiplied by	18, 24
4 H-L	÷ ÷	Divided by	18, 24
5 H-L	= =	Equal to	18, 24
32 H-L	′ ′	Minute	18, 24
33 H-L	″ ″	Second	18, 24
34 H-L	° °	Degree	18, 24

Mathematical No. 2 · △ 526

NO.	CHARACTER		POINT SIZE
1	+	Plus	8, 10, 12
2	−	Minus	8, 10, 12
3	×	Multiplied by	8, 10, 12
4	÷	Divided by	8, 10, 12
5	=	Equal to	8, 10, 12
11	∼	Difference	12
12	≏	Difference between	12
13	≡	Identical with, congruent	12
14	≠	Not equal to	12
61	≅	Equals approximately	12
21	<	Less than	12
22	>	Greater than	12
36	⊥	Perpendicular to	12
37	∥	Parallel	12
96	m̲	Is measured by	12
68	⊥s	Perpendiculars	12
28	∠	Angle	12
76	∠s	Angles	12
29	△	Triangle	12
74	△s	Triangles	12
26	○	Circle	12
75	Ⓢ	Circles	12
27	□	Square	8, 10, 12
94	[S]	Squares	12
42	▱	Rhomboid	12
62	▱S	Rhomboids	12
30	∴	Hence, therefore	12

Mathematical Greek · 10 △ 670

(Approved by the American Standards Association. Available in 10 point, designed to work with Bodoni Book and similar faces. In ordering, please specify both character number and triangle number as shown.)

3	Γ	Gamma	28	δ	delta	43	ς	sigma
4	Δ	Delta	29	ϵ	epsilon	44	τ	tau
8	Θ	Theta	30	ζ	zeta	45	υ	upsilon
11	Λ	Lambda	31	η	eta	46	ϕ	phi
14	Ξ	Xi	32	θ	theta	46 S	φ	open phi
16	Π	Pi	32 S	ϑ	open theta	47	χ	chi
18	Σ	Sigma	33	ι	iota	48	ψ	psi
20	Υ	Upsilon	34	κ	kappa	49	ω	omega
21	Φ	Phi	35	λ	lambda	Supplemental:		
23	Ψ	Psi	36	μ	mu	50	ϝ	digamma
24	Ω	Omega	37	ν	nu	330	∂	partial derivative
25	α	alpha	38	ξ	xi	469	∇	nabla
26	β	beta	39	ο	omicron			
26 S	ϐ	open beta	40	π	pi			
27	γ	gamma	41	ρ	rho			
			42	σ	sigma			

NO.	CHARACTER		POINT SIZE

Medical · △ 334

NO.	CHARACTER		POINT SIZE
1	℞	Recipe, take 5, 5½,	
		6, 7, 8, 9, 10, 11, 12, 14, 18, 24, 30, 36	
2	℥	Ounce. . 5½, 6, 7, 8, 9, 10, 11, 12, 14, 18, 24	
3	ℨ	Dram 5½, 6, 7, 8, 9, 10, 11, 12, 14	
4	℈	Scruple 5½, 6, 7, 8, 9, 10, 11, 12, 14	
5	℔	Drop 5½, 6, 8, 9, 10, 11, 12, 14	
6	M	Mix 6, 8, 9, 10, 12	

Meteorological Signs · △ 566

NO.	CHARACTER		POINT SIZE
1	◯	Absolutely no clouds 10, 12	
2	◔	1/10 covered 10, 12	
3	◫	Broken clouds 10, 12	
4	⊕	Overcast 10, 12	
5	❟	Drizzle 10, 12	
6	●	Rain 10, 12	
7	✳	Snow 10, 12	
8	▽	Light and moderate rain showers . . . 10, 12	
9	≡	Light fog 10, 12	
10	≣	Fog, sky not discernible 10, 12	
11	S	Dust 10, 12	
12	⇆	Dust storm 10, 12	
13	/	High 10, 12	
24	⌐	Lightning 10, 12	
25	⌐	Thunderstorm 10, 12	
26	↑	South 10, 12	
27	↓	North 10, 12	
28	→	West 10, 12	
29	←	East 10, 12	
30	↗	Southwest 10, 12	
31	↖	Southeast 10, 12	
32	↘	Northwest 10, 12	
33	↙	Northeast 10, 12	
34	◔	Sky less than 1/10 covered 12	
35	◔	Sky 2/10 to 3/10 covered 12	
36	◑	Sky 4/10, 5/10, 6/10 covered 12	
37	◕	Sky 7/10 to 8/10 covered 12	
38	◗	Sky 9/10 covered 12	
39	◗	Sky more than 9/10 but with openings 12	
40	⊗	Sky obscured 12	
41	●	Sky 10/10 or completely covered 12	
42	▽	Showers 12	
43	∞	Haze 12	
44	⌐	Distant Lightning 12	
45	⬯	Smoke 12	

NO.	CHARACTER		POINT SIZE
46	⚟	Snow in last hour but not at time of observ. .12	
47	❟❟	Continuous moderate drizzle 12	
48	⚡	Thunderstorm with rain 12	
49	≡	Rain and Fog 12	
50	⌐	Rain in last hour but not at time of observ. . .12	
51	⊶	(Wind direction and velocity) Beaufort scale .12	
52	⊶		

SIGNS USED IN CORRECTING PROOFS

ℓ	Delete; take out	⌐	Raise
⌣	Close up	⌊	Lower
∧	Insert	[	Move to left
#	Insert space	]	Move to right

‖ Straighten type line at side of page

∥ Straighten lines

¶ Paragraph

center Put in middle of page or line

⌣ Transpose

Tr Transpose

⌐ Turn inverted letter right side up

✗ Change broken letter

Stet Let it stand as set

······ Let it stand as set

w.f. Wrong font, size or style

l.c. Lower case, not capitals

rom. Use Roman letter

bf. Use black type letters

⊙	Period	=/	Hyphen
⋀	Comma	s.c.	Use small capitals
⋁	Apostrophe	caps	Use capitals
⋁	Superior figure	ital.	Use italics
⋀	Inferior figure		

MIL-STD-12B ABBREVIATIONS for use on drawings & technical publications

Extracted from ASA Z32.13-1950, Abbreviations for Use on Drawings, with the permission of the publisher, the American Society of Mechanical Engineers, United Engineering Center, 345 East 47 Street, New York, N.Y. This standard is exactly the same as MIL-STD-12B, Abbreviations for Use on Drawings and Technical Publications.

A

Abbreviate	ABBR
Above Water	AW
Absolute	ABS
Accelerate	ACCEL
Acceleration Due to Gravity	G
Access Panel	AP
Accessory	ACCESS.
Account	ACCT
Accumulate	ACCUM
Accumulator	ACST
Acoustic	ACST
Actual	ACT.
Actuate—Actuating	ACTG
Adapter	ADPT
Adapter Booster	AB
Addendum	ADD.
Addition	ADD.
Adhesive	ADH
Adjust	ADJ
Advance	ADV
Aerodynamic	AERODYN
Aeronautic	AERO
Aeronautical Material Specifications	AMS
Aeronautical Recommended Practice	ARP
Aeronautical Standards	AS
After	AFT.
After Engine Room	AER
After Perpendicular	AP
Aggregate	AGGR
Aileron	AIL
Air Blast	AB
Air Blast Circuit Breaker	ABCB
Air Blast Transformer	ABT
Air Break Switch	ABS
Air Circuit Breaker	ACB
Air Condition	AIR COND
Air Escape	AE
Airport	AP
Airborne	ABN
Aircraft	ACFT
Airplane	APL
Airtight	AT
Alarm	ALM
Alcohol	ALC
Alkaline	ALK
Allowance	ALLOW
Alloy	ALY
Alteration	ALT
Alternate	ALT
Alternating Current	AC
Alternator	ALT
Altimeter	ALTM
Altitude	ALT
Aluminum	*AL
Amber	AMB
Ambient	AMB
American National Thread Series	†
American Standard	AMER STD
American Standard Elevator Codes	ASEC
American War Standard	AWS
American Wire Gage	AWG
Ammeter	AM
Ammonium Nitrate	AM. NIT
Ammunition	AMM
Amount	AMT
Ampere	AMP
Ampere Hour	AMP HR
Ampere Turn	AT.
Amphibian—Amphibious	AMPH
Amplitude	AM.
Amplitude Modulation	AM.
Amplifier	AMPL
Anchor Bolt	AB
Anhydrous	ANHYD
Anneal	ANL
Annunciator	ANN
Anode	A
Antenna	ANT.
Anti-Aircraft	AA
Anti-Aircraft Artillery	AAA
Anti-Aircraft Cannon	AAC
Anti-Friction Bearing	AFB
Anti-Friction Metal	AFM
Anti-Motor Boat	AMB
Anti-Motor Torpedo Boat	AMTB
Antipersonnel	APERS
Anti-Submarine	AS.
Anti-Tank	AT.
Apartment	APT.
Apparatus	APP

(continued)

Appendix	APPX
Approved	APPD
Approximate	APPROX
Arc Weld	ARC/W
Area	A
Armament	ARMT
Armature	ARM.
Arming Wire	AW
Armor Piercing	AP
Armor Piercing Capped	APC
Armor Piercing Capped Incendiary	APCI
Armor Piercing Capped Incendiary with Tracer	APCI-T
Armor Piercing Capped with Tracer	APC-T
Armor Piercing Incendiary with Tracer	API-T
Armor Piercing with Tracer	AP-T
Armor Plate	ARM-PL
Armored	ARMD
Army Air Forces	AAF
Army Ground Forces	AGF
Army Navy	AN
Army Navy Aeronautical	ANA
Army Navy Design	AND
Army Service Forces	ASF
Arrange	ARR.
Arrester	ARR.
Artificial	ART.
Artillery	ARTY
Asbestos	ASB
Asphalt	ASPH
Assemble	ASSEM
Assembly	ASSY
Assistant	ASST
Associate	ASSOC
Association	ASSN
Assort	ASST
Astronomical Time Switch	ATS
Atmosphere	ATM
Atomic	AT
Atomic Hydrogen Weld	AT/W
Attach	ATT
Attenuator	ATTEN
Audible	AUD
Audio Frequency	AF
Authorized	AUTH
Automatic	AUTO
Automatic Brightness Control	ABC
Automatic Door Seal	ADS
Automatic Frequency Control	AFC
Automatic Gain Control	AGC
Automatic Noise Limiter	ANL
Automatic Reclosing	AUTO RECL
Automatic Sensitivity Control	ASC
Automatic Volume Control	AVC
Automatic Volume Expansion	AVE
Auto-Transformer	AUTO TR
Auxiliary	AUX
Avenue	AVE
Average	AVG
Aviation	AVI
Aviation Gas Turbine	AGT
Avoirdupois	AVDP
Azimuth	AZ

B

Babbitt	BAB
Back Connected	BC
Back Feed	BF
Back Pressure	BP
Back Pressure Control	BPC
Back to Back	B to B
Backface	BF
Back-gear	BG
Bacteriological	BACT
Baffle	BAF
Bakery	BAK
Balance	BAL
Ball Bearing	BB
Ballast	BALL.
Bandolier	BAND.
Bandwidth	B
Barbette	BARB.
Barometer	BAR
Barracks	BKS
Barrel	BBL
Barrels per Day	BPD
Barrels per Hour	BPH
Base Detonating	BD

(continued)

Base Detonation Fuse	BDF
Base Ejection	BE
Base Ignition	BI
Base and Increment	B&I
Base Line	BL
Base Percussion	BP
Base Plate	BP
Basic Network	BAS NET.
Basket	BSKT
Bastard	BSTD
Battalion	BN
Batten	BATT
Battery	BAT.
Battery Commanders	BC
Battle	BAT.
Baumé	BE
Bayonette Candelabra, Double Contact	BAY. CAND DC
Beacon	BCN
Beam	BM
Bearing	BRG
Beat-Frequency Oscillator	BFO
Bell Alarm Switch	BA SW
Bell and Bell	B&B
Bell and Flange	B&F
Bell and Spigot	B&S
Bell End	BE
Benchboard	BNCHBD
Bench Mark	BM
Bending Moment	M
Bent	BT
Berthing	BERTH.
Bessemer	BESS
Between	BET.
Between Centers	BC
Between Perpendiculars	BP
Bevel	BEV
Bi Parting Doors	BIPD
Bill of Material	B/M
Billet Steel	BT ST
Birmingham Wire Gage	BWG
Blank	BLK
Blasting Powder	BLSTG PWD
Block	BLK
Blower	BLO
Blow-Off	BO
Blowout Coil	BOC
Blueprint	BP
Board	BD
Boatswain	BOSN
Bobbin	BOB.
Body Bound Bolts	BB/B
Boiler	BLR
Boiler Feed	BF
Boiler Feed Pump	BFP
Boiler Feed Water	BFW
Boiler Horsepower	BHP
Boiler House	BH
Boiler Maker	BMKR
Boiling Point	BP
Bolster	BOLS
Bolt Circle	BC
Bombardment (Projectile)	BBT
Booster	BSTR
Borrowed Light	BLT
Both Faces	BF
Both Sides	BS
Both Ways	BW
Bottom	BOT
Bottom Chord	BC
Bottom Face	BF
Boundary	BDY
Bracket	BRKT
Braid	BRD
Brake	BK
Brake Horsepower	BHP
Brake Mean Effective Pressure	BMEP
Brass	BRS
Brazing	BRZG
Breadth or Beam of Ship	B
Break	BRK
Breaker	BKR
Breech Loading	BL
Bridge	BRDG
Brightness	BRT
Brinnell Hardness	BH
British Standard	BR STD
British Thermal Units	BTU
Broach	BRO
Bronze	BRZ

(continued)

Brown & Sharp (Wire Gage, same as AWG)	B&S
Brush	BR
Building	BLDG
Building Line	BL
Bulkhead	BHD
Bullet-Proof	BPRF
Bundle	BDL
Bureau	BU
Bureau of Standards	BU STD
Burlap	BRLP
Burnish	BNH
Bus Tie	BT
Bushel	BU
Bushing	BUSH.
Bushing Current Transformer	BCT
Button	BUT.
Buzzer	BUZ
By-Pass	BYP

C

Cabinet	CAB.
Cable*	CA
Cab Over Engine	COE
Cadmium Plate	CD PL
Calculate	CALC
Caliber	CAL
Calibrate	CAL
Calked Joint	CAJ
Calking	CLKG
Calorie	CAL
Candle	C
Candelabra	CAND
Candlepower	CP
Canister	CSTR
Capacitor	CAP
Capacity	CAP
Capital	CAP.
Cap Screw	CAP. SCR
Carat	K
Carbon*	C
Carburetor	CARB
Carburize	CARB
Cargo	CAR.
Carload	CL
Carriage	CRG
Carrier	CARR
Carton	CTN
Cartridge	CTG
Cartridge Storage Case	CSC
Case Harden	CH
Casing	CSG
Cast (Used with Other Materials)	C
Cast Iron	CI
Cast Iron Pipe	CIP
Cast Steel	CS
Casting	CSTG
Castle Nut	CAS NUT
Catalogue	CAT.
Catalyst	CAT.
Catapult	CAT.
Catch Basin	CB
Cathode-Ray	CR
Cathode-Ray Tube	CRT
Cavity	CAV
Ceiling	CLG
Cement	CEM
Center	CTR
Center Line	CL
Center of Buoyancy	CB
Center of Floatation	CF
Center of Gravity	CG
Center of Pressure	CP
Center Punch	CP
Center Tap	CT
Center to Center	C to C
Centering	CTR
Centigrade	C
Centigram	CG
Centiliter	CL
Centimeter	CM
Centimeter-Gram-Second System	CGS
Centrifugal	CENT.
Centrifugal Force	CF
Ceramic	CER
Cesspool	CP
Chain	CH

Chain Grate	CG
Chamfer	CHAM
Change	CHG
Change Notice	CN
Change Order	CO
Channel	CHAN
Charge	CHG
Check	CHK
Check Valve	CV
Chemical	CHEM
Chemical Warfare Service	CWS
Chemically Pure	CP
Choke	CH
Choke Coil	CHC
Chord	CHD
Chrome Molybdenum	CR MOLY
Chrome Tanned Leather	Cr TAN. LTHR
Chromium Plate	Cr. PL
Chrome Vanadium	CR VAN
Circle	CIR
Circuit	CKT
Circular	CIR
Circular Mil	CM
Circular Mils, Thousands	MCM
Circular Pitch	CP
Circulate	CIRC
Circulating Water Pump	CWP
Circumference	CIRC
Clamp	CLP
Class	CL
Cleanout	CO
Cleanout Flush with Finished Floor	FCO
Clear	CLR
Clearance	CL
Clevis	CLV
Clockwise	CW
Closet	CLO
Closing	CL
Closing Coil	CC
Clutch	CL
Coaming	COAM
Coat Hook	CH
Coated	CTD
Coaxial	COAX
Coefficient	COEF
Coils per Slot	CPS
Cold Drawn	CD
Cold Drawn Steel	CDS
Cold Finish	CF
Cold Punched	CP
Cold Rolled	CR
Cold Rolled Steel	CRS
Cold Water	CW
Collector	COLL
Column	COL
Combat Information Center	CIC
Combination	COMB.
Combustion	COMB
Command	COM
Commanding	COM
Commanding Officer	CO
Commercial	COML
Commercial Quality	CQ
Common	COM
Common Battery	CB
Communication	COMM
Commutator	COMM
Commutator End	CE
Companion	COMP
Company	CO
Compartment	COMPT
Compensate	COMP
Complete	COMPL
Complete Round	CR
Composite	CX
Composition	COMP
Compound	COMP
Compress	COMP
Compressor	COMPR
Concentrate	CONC
Concentric	CONC
Concrete	CONC
Condensate	CNDS
Condenser	COND
Condition	COND
Conduct	COND
Conductor	COND
Conductor Head	CH
Conductor, Multiple (Number Indicated), Example	3/C
Conduit	CND
Connect	CONN
Connector	CONN
Constant	CONST
Constant Current Transformer	CCT
Construction	CONST
Contact	CONT
Contact-Making Voltmeter	CMVM
Container	CNTR
Contaminated	CONTAM
Continue	CONT
Continuous Wave	CW
Contract	CONT
Contracting Officer	CONTR O
Contractor	CONTR

Contractor Furnished Equipment	CFE
Contrast	CTRS
Control	CONT
Control Relay	CR
Control Switch	CS
Controller	CONT
Convert	CONV
Conveyor	CNVR
Cooled	CLD
Copper Oxide	CUO
Copper Plate	COP. PL
Coppersmith	CSMITH
Cord	CD
Corner	COR
Corporation	CORP
Correct	CORR
Corrosion Resistant	CRE
Corrosion Resistant Steel	CRES
Corrugate	CORR
Cotter	COT
Cotton	COT.
Cotton Webbing	COT. WEB.
Counter	CTR
Counter Clockwise	CCW
Counter Electromotive Force	CEMF
Counterbalance	CBAL
Counterbore	CBORE
Counterdrill	CDRILL
Counterpunch	CPUNCH
Countersink	CSK
Countersink Other Side	CSK-O
Counterweight	CTWT
Coupling	CPLG
Courses	C
Cover	COV
Cowling	COWL
Crank	CRK
Crankcase	CRKC
Crew (as Spaces)	CR
Cross Arm	XARM
Cross Connection	XCONN
Cross Section	XSECT
Crossbar	XBAR
Cruising	CRUIS
Crystal	XTAL
Cubic	CU
Cubic Centimeter	CC
Cubic Feet per Minute	CFM
Cubic Feet per Second	CFS
Cubic Foot	CU FT
Cubic Inch	CU IN.
Cubic Meter	CU M
Cubic Micron	CU MU
Cubic Yard	CU YD
Current	CUR
Current Directional Relay	CDR
Current Transformer	CT
Curve Drawing	CRV DWG
Customer	CUST
Cut Out	CO
Cyanide	CYN
Cycle	CY
Cycles per Minute	CPM
Cycles per Second	CPS
Cylinder	CYL
Cylinder Lock	CYL L

D

Damage Control	DC
Damper	DMPR
Dash Pot	DP
De-areating Feed Tank	DFT
Deadload	DL
Deadweight	DWT
Decalcomania	DECAL
Decibel	DB
Decibels Referred to 1 Milliwatt in 600 Ohms	DBM
Decimal	DEC
Decimeter	DM
Deck	DK
Deck Drain Valve	DDV
Deck Piercing	DP
Decontamination	DECONTN
Dedendum	DED
Deep Drawn	DD
Definite Time	DEF T
Definite Time Relay	DTR
Deflect	DEFL
Degree	(°) DEG
Delayed Automatic Volume Control	DAVC
Delineation	DEL
Demand Indicator	DI
Demand Meter	DM
Demodulator	DEM
Demolition	DML
Density	D
Dentist	DENT.
Department	DEPT
Describe	DESCR

Design	DSGN
Designation	DESIG
Designed Water Line	DWL
Detail	DET
Detector	DET
Detonator	DET
Develop	DEV
Dew Point	DP
Diagonal	DIAG
Diagram	DIAG
Diameter	DIA
Diametrical Pitch	DP
Diaphragm	DIAPH
Diesel Oil	D.O.
Differential	DIFF
Differential Time Relay	DIFF TR
Dimension	DIM.
Diode	DIO
Direct Connected	DIR CONN
Direct Current	DC
Direction Finder	DF
Directional	DIR
Discharge	DISCH
Disconnect	DISC.
Discriminator	DISCR
Dispatcher	DISP
Dispensary	DISP
Dissolved Oxygen	DO.
Distance	DIST
Distill	DSTL
Distilled Water	DW
Distribute	DISTR
District	DIST
District Engineer	DE
Ditto	DO.
Diverter	DIV
Division	DIV
Double	DBL
Double Feeder	DF
Double Glass	DG
Double Groove (Insulators)	DG
Double Groove, Double Petticoat (Insulators)	DGDP
Doubler	DBLR
Dovetail	DVTL
Dowel	DWL
Down	DN
Downspout	DS
Dozen	DOZ
Drafting	DFTG
Draftsman	DFTSMN
Drain	DR
Draw Out	DO
Drawing	DWG
Drawing List	DL
Dressed (Lumber)	DRS
Drill	DR
Drill Rod	DR
Drinking Fountain	DF
Drip Proof	DP
Drive	DR
Drive Fit	DF
Drop	D
Drop Forge	DF
Drop Man-Hole	DMH
Dry Bulb	DB
Dry Pipe Valve	DPV
Dumbwaiter	DW
Duplex	DX
Duplicate	DUP
Dynamic	DYN
Dynamo	DYN
Dynamotor	DYNM

E

Each	EA
Each Face	EF
East	E
Ebony Asbestos	EB ASB
Eccentric	ECC
Echelon	ECH
Economizer	ECON
Eductor	EDUC
Effective	EFF
Effective Horsepower	EHP
Efficiency	EFF
Ejector	EJECT.
Elastic Limit	EL
Elbow	ELL
Electric	ELEC
Electrolyte	ELECT.
Electrolytic	ELECT.
Electromotive Force	EMF
Electrostatic	ES
Elementary	ELEM
Elevate	ELEV
Elevation	EL
Elongation	ELONG
Emergency	EMER
Enamel	ENAM

Enclose	ENCL
End Cell Switch	EC SW
End to End	E to E
Engine	ENG
Engineer	ENGR
Engineering	ENGRG
Engineering Change Order	ECO
Enlisted Men	EM
Entrance	ENT
Envelope	ENV
Equal	EQ
Equalizer	EQ
Equation	EQ
Equipment	EQUIP.
Equipment & Spare Parts	E&SP
Equivalent	EQUIV
Equivalent Direct Radiation	EDR
Escape	ESC
Escutcheon	ESC
Estimate	EST
Evaporate	EVAP
Evaporator	EVAP
Excavate	EXC
Exchange	EXCH
Excitation	EXC
Exciter	EXC
Exclusive	EXCL
Executive	EXEC
Exhaust	EXH
Existing	EXIST.
Expand	EXP
Expansion (Joint)	EXP
Experiment	EXP
Explosion Proof	EP
Expulsion	EXP
Extension	EXT
Exterior	EXT
External	EXT
Extinguish	EXT
Extra Heavy	X HVY
Extra Strong	X STR
Extreme High Water	EHW
Extreme Low Water	ELW
Extrude	EXTR

F

Fabricate	FAB
Face to Face	F to F
Fahrenheit	F
Fairing	FAIR.
Farad	F
Far Side	FS
Federal	FED.
Federal Specifications	FS
Federal Stock Number	FSN
Feed	FD
Feed Water	FW
Feeder	FDR
Feet	(') FT
Feet Board Measure	FBM
Feet per Minute	FPM
Feet per Second	FPS
Female	FEM
Fiber	FBR
Field	FLD
Field Manual	FM
Field Service	FS
Field Service Modification Work Order	FSMWO
Figure	FIG.
Filament	FIL
Filament Center Tap	FCT
Fillet	FIL
Filling	FILL.
Fillister	FIL
Filter	FLT
Finger	FGR
Finish	FIN.
Finish All Over	FAO
Fire	F
Fire and Bilge	F&B
Fire & Flushing	F&F
Fire Control	FC
Fire Department Connection	FDC
Fire Door	F DR
Fire Hose	FH
Fire Hose Cabinet	FHC
Fire Hose Rack	FHR
Fire Hydrant	FHY
Fire Main	FM
Fireproof	FPRF
Fitting	FTG
Fixed Transom	FTR
Fixture	FIX.
Flame Proof	FP
Flame Tight	MT
Flange	FLG
Flashing	FL
Flashless	FLHLS
Flashless Non-Hygroscope	FNH
Flat	F
Flat Head	FH
Flat Nose (Projectile)	FN

Flexible	FLEX.
Float	FLT
Floor	FL
Floor Drain	FD
Floor Line	FL
Flooring	FLG
Fluid	FL
Fluorescent	FLUOR
Flush	FL
Focus	FOC
Foot	(') FT
Foot Candle	FC
Foot-Lambert	FL
Foot Pounds	FT LB
Footing	FTG
Force	F
Forced Draft	FD
Forced Draft Blower	FDB
Forecastle	FCSLE
Foresight	FS
Forged Steel	FST
Forging	FORG
Forward	FWD
Forward Engine Room	FER
Forward Perpendicular	FP
Foundation	FDN
Foundry	FDRY
Fractional	FRAC
Fractional Horsepower	FHP
Fragmentation	FRAG
Frame	FR
Framework	FRWK
Freeboard	FREEBD
Freezing Point	FP
Freight	FRT
Frequency	FREQ
Frequency, High	HF
Frequency, Low	LF
Frequency, Medium	MF
Frequency Modulation	FM
Frequency, Super High	SHF
Frequency, Ultra High	UHF
Frequency, Very High	VHF
Frequency, Very Low	VLF
Fresh Water	FW
Friction Horsepower	FHP
From Below	FR BEL
Front	FR
Front Connected	FC
Fuel	F
Fuel-Air Ratio	F/A RATIO
Fuel Oil	FO
Fume Tight	FT
Furnish	FURN
Fuse Block	FB
Fuselage	FUS
Fusible	FSBL
Fusion Point	FNP

G

Gage or Gauge	GA
Gallery	GALL
Gallon	GAL
Gallons per Acre per Day	GPAD
Gallons per Hour	GPH
Gallons per Minute	GPM
Gallons per Second	GPS
Galvanize	GALV
Galvanized Iron	GI
Galvanized Steel	GS
Galvanized Steel Wire Rope	GSWR
Galvanometer	GALV
Garboard	GARBD
Gas	FOC
Gas Ejection	GE
Gasket	GSKT
Gasoline	GASO
General	GEN
General Purpose (Bomb)	GP
Generator	GEN
Girder	G
Glass	GL
Glaze	GL
Government	GOVT
Government Furnished Equipment	GFE
Governor	GOV
Grade	GR
Grade Line	GL
Graduation	GRAD
Grains per Gallon	GPG
Gram	GR
Gram-Calorie	G-CAL
Gram-Meter	G-METER
Graphic	GRAPH.
Graphite	GPH
Grating	GRTG
Gravel	GVL
Gravity	G
Grease Trap	GT
Grid	G
Grind	GRD

Grommet	GROM
Groove	GRV
Gross Tons	GT
Gross Weight	GRWT
Ground	GRD
Group	GR
Guard	GD
Gunnery	GUN.
Gypsum	GYP
Gyroscope	GYRO

H

Half-Hard	½H
Half-Round	½RD
Hand Control	HC
Hand Generator	HG
Hand Reset	HR
Hand Wheel	HD WHL
Handhole	HH
Handle	HDL
Hanger	HGR
Harbor Defense	HD
Hard	H
Hard-Drawn	HD
Harden	HDN
Hardware	HDW
Hatch	H
Head	HD
Headless	HDLS
Headquarters	HQ
Heat	HT
Heat Treat	HT TR
Heater	HTR
Heavy	HVY
Heavy Machine Gun	HMG
Height	HGT
Henry	H
Hexagon	HEX
High	H
High Capacity (Projectile)	HC
High Explosive	HE
High-Explosive Incendiary	HE I
High-Explosive Incendiary with Tracer	HEI T
High Explosive with Tracer	HE T
High Frequency	HF
High Point	H PT
High Potential Test	HIPOT
High-Pressure	HP
High-Speed	HS
High-Speed Steel	HSS
High-Tensile Cast Iron	HTCI
High-Tensile Steel	HTS
High Tension	HT
High Voltage	HV
High-Water Line	HWL
Highway	HWY
Hogshead	HHD
Holder	HLR
Holding Coil	HC
Hollow	HOL
Horizontal	HOR
Horsepower	HP
Hospital	HOSP
Hot Rolled	HR
Hot Rolled Steel	HRS
Hot Water	HW
Hot Water, Circulating	HWC
Hour	HR
House	HSE
Housing	HSG
Howitzer	HOW.
Hundredweight	CWT
Hydraulic	HYD
Hypervelocity, Armor Piercing	HVAP
Hypervelocity, Target Practice	HVTP
Hydrostatic	HYDRO

I

Identify	IDENT
Ignition	IGN
Illuminate	ILLUM
Illuminating (Projectiles)	SS
Illustrate	ILLUS
Impact	IMP
Impedance	IMP.
Imperial	IMP
Impregnate	IMPG
Impulse	IMP
Inboard	INBD
Incandescent	INCAND
Incendiary	INC
Inch	(") IN.
Inches per Second	IPS
Incinerator	INCIN
Inclosure	INCL
Include	INCL
Incoming	INC
Incorporated	INC
Increase	INCR

Independent	INDEP
Indicate	IND
Indicated Air Speed	IAS
Indicated Horsepower	IHP
Induced Draft	ID
Inductance or Induction	IND
Industrial	IND
Inflammable	INFL
Information	INFO
Injection	INJ
Inlet	IN
Inlet Manhole	IMH
Inside Diameter	ID
Inspect	INSP
Install	INSTL
Instantaneous	INST
Instantaneous Automatic Volume Control	IAVC
Instantaneous Relay	IR
Instruct	INST
Instruction Book	IB
Instrument	INST
Insulate	INS
Insulating Transformer	IT
Integrating	INT
Intercept	INCPT
Interchangeable	INTCHG
Intercommunication	INTERCOM
Intercooler	INCOLR
Interior	INT
Interior Communication	IC
Interlock	INTLK
Intermediate	INTER
Intermediate Distributing Frame	IDF
Intermediate Frequency	IF
Intermediate Power Amplifier	IPA
Intermediate Pressure	IP
Intermittent	INTMT
Internal	INT
International Annealed Copper Standard	IACS
International Pipe Standard	IPS
Interphone Control Station	ICS
Interrupt	INTER
Interrupted Continuous Wave	ICW
Interruptions per Minute	IPM
Interruptions per Second	IPS
Intersect	INT
Inverse	INV
Inverse Time Relay	ITR
Invert	INV
Iron*	I
Iron Body Bronze Mounted	IBBM
Iron-Pipe Size	IPS
Irregular	IRREG
Issue	ISS

J

Jack	J
Jacket Water	JW
Japan	JAP
Job Order	JO
Joint	JT
Joint Army-Navy	JAN
Joule	J
Journal	JNL
Junction	JCT
Junction Box	JB
Junior	JR

K

Keel	K
Kelvin	K
Key	K
Keyseat	KST
Keyway	KWY
Kick Plate	KP
Kick Plate & Drip	KP&D
Kiln-Dried	KD
Kilo	K
Kilocycle	KC
Kilocycles per Second	KC
Kilogram	KG
Kiloliter	KL
Kilometer	KM
Kilovar	KVAR
Kilovolt	KV
Kilovolt-Ampere	KVA
Kilovolt-Ampere Hour	KVAH
Kilowatt	KW
Kilowatt Hour	KWH
Kinescope	KIN.
Kip (1000 lb)	K
Knocked Down	KD
Knockout	KO
Knots	KN

L

Laboratory	LAB
Lacquer	LAQ
Ladder	LAD.
Lambert	L
Laminate	LAM
Lamp	L
Lamp, Green Indicating	GIL
Lamp, Red Indicating	RIL
Lamp, Yellow Indicating	YIL
Lamp, White Indicating	WIL
Landing	LDG
Landing Gear	LG
Lateral	LAT
Latitude	LAT
Laundry	LAU
Lavatory	LAV
Lead Coated Metal	LCM
Lead Covered	LC
Leading Edge	LE
Leather	LTHR
Left	L
Left Hand	LH
Length	LG
Length Between Perpendiculars	LBP
Length Over All	LOA
Letter	LTR
License	LIC
Light	LT
Lighting	LTG
Lightning Arrester	LA
Limit	LIM
Limit Switch	LS
Limited	LTD
Limiter	LIM
Line	L
Linear	LIN
Link	LK
Liquid	LIQ
Liter	L
Lithograph	LITHO
Litter Hook	LH
Live Load	LL
Load Factor (Tabular Only)	LF
Load Limiting Resistor	LLR
Load Ratio	LR
Load Ratio Control	LRC
Load Shifting Resistor	LSR
Load Water Line	LWL
Local Oscillator	LO
Local Battery	LB
Locate	LOC
Locker	LKR
Logarithm	LOG.
Long	LG
Longeron	LONGN
Longitude	LONG.
Longitudinal Expansion Joint	LEJ
Low Explosive	LE
Low Frequency	LF
Low Pressure	LP
Low Tension	LT
Low Voltage	LV
Low-Voltage Release	LVR
Low-Speed	LS
Low-Torque	LT
Lubricate	LUB
Lubricating Oil	LO
Lumber	LBR
Lumen	L
Lumens per Watt	LPW

M

Machine	MACH
Machine Gun	MG
Machine Rifle	MR
Machine Steel	MS
Magazine	MAG
Magnaflux	M
Magnet	MAG
Magneto	MAG
Magnetomotive Force	MMF
Main	MN
Main Distributing Frame	MDF
Maintenance	MAINT
Male & Female	M&F
Malleable	MALL
Malleable Iron	MI
Manhole	MH
Manifold	MANF
Maneuvering	MANUV
Manual	MAN.
Manual Volume Control	MVC
Manufacture	MFR
Manufactured	MFD
Manufacturing	MFG
Marble	MR
Marine	MAR
Mark	MK

* See also Chemical Symbols,

Master	MA
Master Oscillator	MO
Material	MATL
Material List	ML
Maximum	MAX
Maximum Working Pressure	MWP
Mean Aerodynamic Chord	MAC
Mean Effective Pressure	MEP
Mean High Tide	MHT
Mean High Water	MHW
Mean Higher High Water	MHHW
Mean Low Tide	MLT
Mean Low Water	MLW
Mean Lower Low Water	MLLW
Mean Sea Level	MSL
Mean Spherical Candlepower	MSCP
Mean Tide	MT
Mean Width Ratio	MWR
Mechanical	MECH
Mechanical Time Fuse	MTF
Mechanism	MECH
Median	MED
Medical	MED
Medium	MED
Mega	M
Megacycles	MC
Megawatt	MW
Megawatt-Hour	MWH
Megohm	MEG
Melting Point	MP
Membrane	MEMB
Memorandum	MEMO
Metal	MET.
Meteorological	MET.
Meter (Instrument or Measure of Length)	M
Meter-Kilogram	M-KG
Mezzanine	MEZZ
Micro	μ or U
Microampere	μA or UA
Microfarad	μF or UF
Microhenry	μH or UH
Micro-Inch-Root-Mean Square	μ-IN-RMS or U-IN-RMS
Micrometer	MIC
Micromho	μMHO or UMHO
Micro-Micro	μ-μ or U-U
Micromicrofarad	$\mu\mu$F or UUF
Micromicron	$\mu\mu$ or U U
Micron	μ or U
Microphone	MIKE
Microvolt	μV or UV
Microvolts per Meter	μV/M or UV/M
Microwatt	μW or UW
Miles	MI
Miles per Gallon	MPG
Miles per Hour	MPH
Miles per Hour per Second	MPHPS
Military	MIL
Milli	M
Milliampere	MA.
Milligram	MG
Millihenry	MH
Millilambert	ML
Millimeter	MM
Million Gallons per Day	MGD
Milliseconds	MS
Millivolt	MV
Milliwatt	MW
Minimum	MIN
Minute	(') MIN
Miscellaneous	MISC
Mixture	MIX.
Model	MOD
Modify	MOD
Modulated Continuous Wave	MCW
Modulator	MOD
Mold Line	ML
Molded	MLD
Molding	MLDG
Molecular Weight	MOL WT
Momentary Contact	MC
Monitor	MON
Month	MO
Monument	MON
Morse Taper	MOR T
Motor	MOT
Motor Boat	MB
Motor Field	MF
Motor Generator	MG
Mounted	MTD
Mounting	MTG
Multiple	MULT
Multiple Contact	MC
Music Wire Gage	MWG
Muzzle Velocity	MV

N

Nacelle	NAC
Name Plate	NP
National	NATL
National Aircraft Standards	NAS
National Electrical Code	NEC
National Emergency Steel	NS
Natural	NAT
Naval Aircraft Factory	NAF
Naval Architect	NA
Navigate	NAV
Navy Yard	NYD
Near Face	NF
Near Side	NS
Negative	NEG
Network	NET
Neuropsychiatric	NP
Neutral	NEUT
New British Standard (Imperial Wire Gage)	NBS
Nickel-Silver	NI-SIL
Nipple	NIP.
Nitrostarch	NITROS
No Voltage Release	NVR
Nominal	NOM
Non-Tight	NT
Noon	M
Normal	NOR
Normally Closed	NC
Normally Open	NO
North	N
Nose Fuse	NF
Not to Scale	NTS
Number	NO.

O

Obscure	OB
Observe	OBS
Obsolete	OBS
Octagon	OCT
Office	OFF.
Officer	OFF.
Ohm	Ω
Oil Circuit Breaker	OCB
Oil Immersed Water-Cooler	OIWC
Oil Insulated	OI
Oil Insulated Self-Cooled	OISC
Oil Insulated Fan-Cooled	OIFC
Oil Switch	OS
Oil Tight	OT
Olive Drab	OD
On Center	OC
One Pole	1 P
Opening	OPNG
Operate	OPR
Opposite	OPP
Opposite Commutator End	OPP CE
Opposite Pulley End	OPP PE
Optical	OPT
Ordnance	ORD
Orifice	ORF
Original	ORIG
Ornament	ORN
Oscillate	OSC
Ounce	OZ
Out to Out	O to O
Outboard	OUTBD
Outgoing	OUT.
Outgoing Repeater	OGR
Outgoing Trunk	OGT
Outlet	OUT.
Output	OUT.
Outside Diameter	OD
Outside Face	OF
Outside Radius	OR
Outside Screw & Yoke	OS&Y
Outstanding Leg	OSL
Overall	OA
Overboard	OVBD
Overcurrent	OC
Overflow	OVFL
Overhead	OVHD
Overload	OVLD
Overvoltage	OVV
Oxidized	OXD

P

Pack	PK
Packing	PKG
Page	P
Painted	PTD
Paints and Oils	P&O
Pair	PR
Panel	PNL
Pantograph	PANT.
Pantry	PAN.
Paragraph	PAR.
Parallel	PAR.
Paravane	PARV
Parkway	PKWY
Part	PT
Parts per Million	PPM
Partition	PTN
Party	PTY
Passage	PASS.
Passenger	PASS.
Patent	PAT.
Pattern	PATT
Peck	PK
Pedestal	PED
Penny (Nails, etc)	d
Pennyweight	dWT
Pentode	PENT
Percussion	PERC
Perforate	PERF
Permanent	PERM
Permanent Magnet	PM
Perpendicular	PERP
Phase	PH
Phenolic	PHEN
Phonograph	PHONO
Phosphor Bronze	PH BRZ
Photograph	PHOTO
Physical	PHYS
Pick Up	PU
Picture	PIX
Piece	PC
Piece Mark	PC MK
Pierce	PRC
Pile	PL
Pilot	PLT
Pint	PT
Pipe Sleeve	P SL
Pipe Tap	PT
Pipe Thread*	P
Pitch	P
Pitch Circle	PC
Pitch Diameter	PD
Plan or Plane Position Indicator	PPI
Plaster	PLAS
Plastic	PLSTC
Plate	PL
Plate (Electron Tube)	P
Platform	PLATF
Plotting	PLOT.
Plumbing	PLMB
Pneumatic	PNEU
Point	PT
Point Detonating	PD
Point Detonating Fuse	PDF
Point of Compound Curve	PCC
Point of Curve	PC
Point of Frog	PF
Point of Intersection	PI
Point of Reverse Curve	PRC
Point of Spiral Tangent	PST
Point of Switch	PS
Point of Tangent	PT
Polar	POL
Polarized	POL
Pole	P
Polish	POL
Polyphase	PYPH
Porcelain	PORC
Port	P
Port and Starboard	P&S
Port of Embarkation	POE
Portable	PORT.
Position	POS
Positive	POS
Post Exchange	PX
Post Office	PO
Potable Water	POT. W
Potential	POT.
Potential Transformer	PT
Potentiometer	POT.
Pound	LB
Pounder	PDR
Pounds per Cubic Foot	PCF
Pounds per Square Foot	PSF
Pounds per Square Inch	PSI
Pounds per Square Inch Absolute	PSIA
Powder	PWD
Power	PWR
Power Amplifier	PA
Power Directional Relay	PDR
Power Factor	PF
Power Factor Meter	PFM
Power House	PH
Preamplifier	PREAMP
Precast	PRCST
Prefabricated	PREFAB
Preferred	PFD
Premolded	PRMLD
Prepare	PREP
Press	PRS
Pressure	PRESS.
Pressure Angle	PA.
Primary	PRI
Printer	PTR
Private Automatic Exchange	PAX
Private Branch Exchange	PBX
Process	PROC
Production	PROD
Production Order	PO
Profile	PF
Project	PROJ
Projectile	PROJ
Proof	PRF
Propeller	PROP
Proposed	PROP
Protection	PROT
Provision	PROV
Public Address	PA
Publication	PUB
Pull Box	PB
Pull Button Switch	PULL B SW
Pulley End	PE
Pulsating Current	PC
Pulses per Second	PPS
Pulverizer	PULV
Punch	PCH
Purchase	PUR
Push Button	PB
Push Button Station	PB STA
Push-Pull	P-P
Pyrometer	PYR
Pyrotechnic	PYRO

Q

Quadrangle	QUAD
Quadrant	QUAD
Quality	QUAL
Quantity	QTY
Quarry	QRY
Quart	QT
Quarter	QTR
Quarter-Hard	¼ H
Quarter-Round	¼ RD
Quartz	QTZ
Quartermaster Corps	QMC
Quarters	QTRS
Quick Firing	QF

R

Radial	RAD
Radiator	RAD
Radio Direction Finding	RDF
Radio Frequency	RF
Radius	R
Railing	RLG
Railroad	RR
Railway	RY
Raised Face	RF
Rapid Rectilinear	RR
Raw Water	RW
Reactive	REAC
Reactive Factor Meter	RFM
Reactive Kilovolt Ampere	KVAR
Reactive Volt Ampere	VAR
Reactive Voltmeter	RVM
Reactor	REAC
Ream	RM
Reassemble	REASM
Rankine	R
Received	RECD
Receiver	REC
Receptacle	RECP
Reciprocate	RECIP
Recirculate	RECIRC
Reclosing	RECL
Recognition	RECOG
Recommend	RECM
Record	REC
Rectangle	RECT
Rectifier	RECT
Reduce	RED.
Reduced Charge	R CHG
Reducer	RED.
Reference	REF
Reference Line	REF L
Refinery	REF
Reflector	REFL
Refractory	REFR
Refrigerate	REFR
Regenerative	REGEN
Register	REG
Regulator	REG
Reheater	RHR
Reinforce	REINF
Relative Humidity	RH
Relay	REL
Release	REL
Relief	REL
Relief Valve	RV
Remote Control	RC
Remove	REM
Renewable	REN
Repair	REP
Replace	REPL
Reproduce	REPRO
Repulsion	REP
Require	REQ
Required	REQD
Requisition	REQ
Reserve	RES
Residual	RESID
Resistance	RES
Resistor	RES

* See Screw Threads

Retainer	RET.
Retard	RET.
Retractable	RETR
Return	RET.
Reverse	REV
Revise	REV
Revolution	REV
Revolutions per Minute	RPM
Revolutions per Second	RPS
Rheostat	RHEO
Right	R
Right Hand	RH
Right of Way	R/W
Righting Arm	GZ
Ring	RING.
Ringing	RING.
Rivet	RIV
Road	RD
Rocket Launcher	RL
Rockwell Hardness	RH
Roller Bearing	RB
Roof	RF
Room	RM
Root Diameter	RD
Root Mean Square	RMS
Rotary	ROT.
Rotate	ROT.
Rough	RGH
Round	RD
Rubber	RUB.
Rudder	RUD

S

Saddle	SDL
Safe Working Pressure	SWP
Safety	SAF
Sail Area	SA
Salinometer	SAL
Salt Water	SW
Salvage	SALV
Sampling	SAMP
Sand Blast	SD BL
Sanitary	SAN
Saturate	SAT.
Saybolt Seconds Furol (Oil Viscosity)	SSF
Saybolt Seconds Universal (Oil Viscosity)	SSU
Scavange	SCAV
Schedule	SCH
Schematic	SCHEM
Scleroscope Hardness	SH
Screen	SCRN
Screening Smoke	HC
Screw	SCR
Scupper	SCUP
Scuttle	S
Sea Flood	SF
Sea Level	SL
Seamless	SMLS
Searchlight	SL
Second	SEC
Secondary	SEC
Section	SECT
Segment	SEG
Select	SEL
Selsyn	SELS
Semi-Armor Piercing	SAP
Semi-Finished	SF
Semi-Fixed	SFXD
Semi-Steel	SS
Sender	SDR
Separate	SEP
Sequence	SEQ
Serial	SER
Series	SER
Serrate	SERR
Service	SERV
Service Fuel Oil	SFO
Set Screw	SS
Settling	SET.
Sewer	SEW.
Shaft	SFT
Shaft Alley	SA
Shaft Horsepower	SHP
Shaped Charge	SC
Shear Plate	SP
Sheathing	SHTHG
Sheet	SH
Shell	SHL
Shellac	SHL
Shield	SHLD
Shipfitter	SFTR
Shipment	SHPT
Ship Service	SS
Shock Absorber	SH ABS
Shop Order	SO
Shore Connection	SH CON
Short Wave	SW
Shot Blast	SH BL
Shoulder	SHLD
Shower	SH
Shrapnel	SHRAP
Shunt	SH
Shut Off Valve	SOV
Side	S
Siding	SDG
Signal	SIG
Silence	SIL
Similar	SIM
Simplex	SX
Single	S
Single Feeder	SF
Single Groove (Insulators)	SG
Single Groove, Single Petticoat (Insulators)	SGSP
Sink	SK
Sketch	SK
Slate	SL
Slate, Black Enamel	BES
Slate, Black Oil Finish	BOFS
Slate, Dull Black Finish	DBFS
Slate, Marine Finish	MFS
Slate, Natural Black	NBS
Sleeve	SLV
Sleeve Bearing	SB
Slide	SL
Slotted	SLOT.
Slow Release	SR
Small	SM
Small Arms	SA
Smoke	SMK
Smokeless	SMKLS
Socket	SOC
Soft	S
Soil Pipe	SP
Soil Stack	SSK
Solder	SLD
Solenoid	SOL
Soot Blower	SB
Sound	SND
Sounding Tube	ST
South	S
Space	SP
Spare	SP
Speaker	SPKR
Special	SPL
Special Treatment Steel	STS
Specific	SP
Specific Gravity	SP GR
Specific Heat	SP HT
Specification	SPEC
Speed	SP
Spherical	SPHER
Spherical Candle Power	SCP
Spin Stabilized (Rockets)	SS
Spindle	SPDL
Splash Block	SB
Splash Proof	SP
Split Phase	SP PH
Spot Faced	SF
Spring	SPG
Sprinkler	SPR
Squadron	SQUAD.
Square	SQ
Squirrel Cage	SQ CG
Stabilize	STAB
Stainless	STN
Stainless Steel	SST
Stairway	STWY
Stamp	STP
Stanchion	STAN
Standard	STD
Standard Nomenclature List	SNL
Starboard	STBD
Starting	STG
Stateroom	SR
Static Pressure	SP
Station	STA
Stationary	STA
Steam	ST
Steam Working Pressure	ST WP
Steel	STL
Steering	STEER.
Sterilizer	STER
Stiffener	STIFF.
Stirrup	STIR.
Stock	STK
Stone	STN
Storage	STG
Storm Water	ST W
Stowage	STOW.
Straight	STR
Strake	STK
Strand	STRD
Strainer	STR
Street	ST
Stress Anneal	SA
Strip	STR
Structural	STR
Stuffing Box	SB
Subcaliber	SUBCAL
Submerged	SUB
Substation	SUBSTA
Substitute	SUB
Substructure	SUBSTR
Suction	SUCT
Summary	SUM.
Supercharge	S-CHG
Superheater	SUPHTR
Superimposed Current	SC
Superintendent	SUPT
Superquick	SQ
Supersede	SUPSD
Superstructure	SUPERSTR
Supervise	SUPV
Supplement	SUPP
Supr[1],	SUP
Supp. rt	SUP.
Surface	SUR
Survey	SURV
Suspend	SUSP
Swash Bulkhead	SW BHD
Swinging Bracket	SWG BKT
Switch	SW
Switch and Relay Types	
Single Pole Switch	SP SW
Single Pole Single Throw Switch	SPST SW
Single Pole Double Throw Switch	SPDT SW
Double Pole Switch	DP SW
Double Pole Single Throw Switch	DPST SW
Double Pole Double Throw Switch	DPDT SW
Triple Pole Switch	3P SW
Triple Pole Single Throw Switch	3PST SW
Triple Pole Double Throw Switch	3PDT SW
4 Pole Switch	4P SW
4 Pole Single Throw Switch	4PST SW
4 Pole Double Throw Switch	4PDT SW
etc	
Switchboard	SWBD
Switchgear	SWGR
Symbol	SYM
Symmetrical	SYM
Synchronous	SYN
Synchroscope	SYNSCP
Synthetic	SYN
System	SYS

T

Tabulate	TAB.
Tachometer	TACH
Tandem	TDM
Tail Bomb Fuse	TBF
Tangent	TAN.
Tank Destroyer	TD
Taper	TPR
Taper Shank	TS
Target Practice	TP
Target Practice with Tracer	TP-T
Tarpaulin	TARP
Technical	TECH
Technical Bulletin	TB
Technical Manual	TM
Technical Report	TR
Tee	T
Teeth per Inch	TPI
Telegraph	TLG
Telemeter	TLM
Telephone	TEL
Teletypewriter Exchange	TWX
Television	TV
Temperature	TEMP
Temperature Meter	TM
Template	TEMP
Tensile Strength	TS
Tension	TENS.
Terminal	TERM.
Terminal Board	TB
Terra Cotta	TC
Terrazzo	TER
Tertiary	TER
Test Link	TL
Tetrachloride	TET
Thermal Element	TE
That is	IE
Theoretical	THEO
Thermal	THRM
Thermocouple	TC
Thermometer	THERM
Thermostat	THERMO
Thick	THK
Thousand	M
Thousand Circular Mills	MCM
Thousand Cubic Feet	MCF
Thousand Foot Pounds	KIP-FT
Thousand Pound	KIP
Thread*	THD
Threads per Inch	TPI
Throttle	THROT
* See Screw Threads.	
Through	THRU
Ticket	TKT
Tie Line	TL
Timber	TMBR
Time	T
Time and Superquick	TSQ
Time Delay	TD
Time Delay Closing	TDC
Time Delay Opening	TDO
Tinned	TD
Tobin-Bronze	TOB BRZ
Toggle	TGL
Tolerance	TOL
Toll	T
Tongue & Groove	T&G
Tool Steel	TS
Tooth	T
Torpedo	TORP
Torpedo Group	TG
Torpedo Part of Beam	TP
Total	TOT
Total Indicator Reading	TIR
Trace	TR
Tracer	TCR
Trailing Edge	TE
Training	TNG
Transceiver	XCVR
Transfer	TRANS
Transformer	TRANS
Transmission	XMSN
Transmit-Receive	TR
Transmitter	XMTR
Transmitting	XMTG
Transportation	TRANS
Transverse	TRANSV
Transverse Expansion Joint	TEJ
Treated Hard Pressed Fiber Board	THPFB
Trimmer	TRIM.
Trinitrotoluene	TNT
Triode	TRI
Trip Coil	TC
True Air Speed	TAS
Trunk	TRK
Truss	T
Tubing	TUB
Tuned Radio Frequency	TRF
Turbine	TURB
Turbine Drive	TD
Turbine Generator	TURBO GEN
Turnbuckle	TRNBKL
Turret	TUR
Twisted	TW
Typical	TYP

U

Ultimate	ULT
Ultra-High Frequency	UHF
Under Voltage	UV
Under Voltage Device	UVD
Underwater	UNDW
Unit	U
Unit Cooler	UC
Unit Heater	UH
United States Gage	USG
United States Standard	USS
United States Thread*	
Universal	UNIV
Untreated Hard Pressed Fiber Board	UHPFB
Urinal	UR

V

Vacuum	VAC
Vacuum Tube	VT
Valve	V
Valve Box	VB
Vandyke	YD
Vapor Proof	VAP PRF
Variable	VAR
Variable Frequency Oscillator	VFO
Varnish	VARN
Vegetable	VEG
Velocity	V
Vent Pipe	VP
Vent Stack	VS
Ventilate	VENT.
Versed Sine	VERS
Versus	VS
Vertical	VERT
Vertical Ladder	VL
Very-High Frequency	VHF
Very-Low Frequency	VLF
Video-Frequency	VDF
Vibrate	VIB
Viscosity	VISC
Vitreous	VIT
Voice Frequency	VF
Voice Tube	VT
Volt	V
Voltage Detector	VD
Voltage Relay	VR
Voltampere	VA
Voltmeter	VM
Volts per Mil	VPM
Volume	VOL

W

Wall	W
Wardroom	WR
Warehouse	WHSE
Warhead	WARHD
Washer	WASH.
Water	W
Watercloset	WC
Water Cooler	WCR
Water Heater	WH
Water Line	WL
Watertight	WT
Watt	W
Watts per Candle	WPC
Watthour	WHR
Watthour Meter	WHM
Wattmeter	WM
Weather Stripping	WS
Weatherproof	WP
Week	WK
Weight	WT
West	W
Wet Bulb	WB
Wetted Surface	WS
Wheel Base	WB
White Phosphorus	WP
Width	W
Wind	WD
Winding	WDG
Wind Load	WL
Wire	W
Wire, Insulated†	
Wire Way	WW
Wire-Wound	WW
With	W/
With Equipment and Spare Parts	W/E&SP
Without	W/O
Without Equipment and Spare Parts	W/O E&SP

* See Screw Threads.
† See Abbreviations and Letter Symbols for Cable and Magnet Wire.

Wood	WD
Woodruff	WDF
Working Point	WP
Working Pressure	WP
Wrought	WRT
Wrought Iron	WI

X Y Z

Yard	YD
Year	YR
Yield Point	YP
Yield Strength	YS

Abbreviations for Colors

Amber	AMB
Black	BLK
Blue	BLU
Brown	BRN
Green	GRN
Orange	ORN
White	WHT
Yellow	YEL

Abbreviations for Valves

Alarm Check Valve	ACV
Automatic Check Valve	AUTO CV
Back Water Valve	BWV
Butterfly Valve	BTFLY VLV
Gate Valve	GTV
Glove Valve	GLV
Pressure Reducing Valve	PRV
Safety Valve	SV

Abbreviations and Letter Symbols for Cable and Magnet Wire

For convenience in the identification of cable and wire, the following abbreviations and symbols are presented.

6.1 Cable. The identification consists of a letter symbol indicating the insulation used, followed by one or more letter symbols indicative of the kind of finish as follows:

6.1.1 *Insulation*

Asbestos	A
Glyptal Cloth	G
Paper	P
Rubber	R
Silk	S
Varnish	V
Varnished Cambric	VC
Thermo-plastic (Synthetic)	T

6.1.2 *Finish*

Asbestos	A
Braid, of Any Kind	B
Braided Wire Armor	BW
Double Braid	DB
Flat Band Metallic Armor	F
Glass	G
Interlocked Metallic Armor	I
Jute-Asphalted (Non-metallic Armor)	J
Lead Sheath	L
Rubber Sheath	R
Hose Jacket	HJ
Synthetic Thermo-plastic	T
Wire Armor (Round)	W

6.2 Magnet Wire. The basic letter symbols for magnet wire follow. Combination insulations are specified by using the approved letter symbols in the order of applicaiton to the conductor.

6.2.1 *Basic Magnet Wire Letter Symbols*

Bonded	B
Cotton	C
Double	D
Enamel	E
Glass	G
Heavy	H
Cellophane	K
Cellulose Acetate	L
Nylon	N
Paper	P
Rayon	RA
Silk	S
Thermo-plastic (Synthetic)	T
Varnish Treated	V

6.3 Combinations of Basic Symbols. A list of popular combinations of the basic magnet wire letter symbols and their proper symbol indications follows.

6.3.1 *Enameled*

Enamel	E
Heavy Enamel	HE

6.3.2 *Cotton Covered*

Single Cotton	C
Bonded Single Cotton	BC
Single Cotton Varnish	CV
Double Cotton	DC
Bonded Double Cotton	BDC
Double Cotton Varnish	DCV

6.3.3 *Paper and Cotton Covered*

Single Paper Single Cotton	PC
Single Paper Double Cotton	PDC
Double Paper Single Cotton	DPC
Double Paper Double Cotton	DPDC

6.3.4 *Silk and Cotton Covered*

Single Cotton Single Silk	CS
Single Cotton Double Silk	CDS
Double Cotton Single Silk	DCS
Double Cotton Double Silk	DCDS

6.3.5 *Thermo-plastic Insulated*

Single	T
Heavy	HT
Triple	TT
Quadruple	QT

6.3.6 *Glass Insulated*

Single Glass	G
Double Glass	DG
Single Enamel Single Glass	EG
Heavy Enamel Single Glass	HEG

6.3.7 *Cellulose Acetate Covered*

Single Acetate	L
Single Enamel Single Acetate	EL
Single Acetate Single Cotton	LC
Double Acetate	DL

6.3.8 *Cellophane Covered*

Single Cellophane	K
Single Enamel Single Cellophane	EK
Heavy Enamel Single Cellophane	HEK

6.3.9 *Enamel and Cotton Covered*

Enamel Single Cotton	EC
Enamel Bonded Single Cotton	EBC
Enamel Single Cotton Varnish	ECV
Enamel Double Cotton	EDC
Enamel Bonded Double Cotton	EBDC
Enamel Double Cotton Varnish	EDCV
Heavy Enamel Single Cotton	HEC
Heavy Enamel Bonded Single Cotton	HEBC
Heavy Enamel Single Cotton Varnish	HECV
Heavy Enamel Double Cotton	HEDC
Heavy Enamel Bonded Double Cotton	HEBDC
Heavy Enamel Double Cotton Varnish	HEDCV

6.3.10 *Silk Covered*

Single Silk	S
Bonded Single Silk	BS
Single Silk Varnish	SV
Double Silk	DS
Bonded Double Silk	BDS
Double Silk Varnish	DSV
Enamel Single Silk	ES
Enamel Bonded Single Silk	EBS
Enamel Single Silk Varnish	ESV
Enamel Double Silk	EDS
Enamel Bonded Double Silk	EBDS
Enamel Double Silk Varnish	EDSV
Heavy Enamel Single Silk	HES
Heavy Enamel Bonded Single Silk	HEBS
Heavy Enamel Single Silk Varnish	HESV
Heavy Enamel Double Silk	HEDS
Heavy Enamel Bonded Double Silk	HEBDS
Heavy Enamel Double Silk Varnish	HEDSV

6.3.11 *Paper Covered*

Single Paper	P
Single Paper Bonded	BP
Double Paper	DP
Double Paper Bonded	BDP

6.3.12 *Enamel and Paper Covered*

Enamel Single Paper Bonded	EBP
Enamel Double Paper Bonded	EBDP
Heavy Enamel Single Paper Bonded	HEBP
Heavy Enamel Double Paper Bonded	HEBDP

6.4 Colors of Cable and Magnet Wire.

Black	BK
Blue	BL
Brown	BR
Gray	GY
Green	GN
Orange	O or OR
Red	R or RD
Yellow	Y
White	W or WH
Novelty	N
Slate	S

Abbreviations Relating to Screw Threads

Screw-Thread Standards

American National Coarse Thread	NC
American National Fine Thread	NF
American National Extra Fine Thread	NEF
American National Special Pitch, etc, Thread	NS
American National Pitch Thread	8N, 12N, or 16N
American National Acme Thread	NA
American National Taper Pipe Thread	NPT
American National Straight Pipe Thread in Pipe Couplings	NPSC
American National Straight Pipe Threads for Dry Seal Pressure Tight Joint	NPSF
American National Taper Pipe Threads for Dry Seal Pressure Tight Joints	NPTF
American National Straight Pipe Threads for Mechanical Joints	NPSM
American National Straight Pipe Threads for Locknuts and Locknut Pipe Threads	NPSL
American National Straight Pipe Threads for Hose Couplings and Nipples	NPSH
American National Taper Pipe Threads for Railing Fixtures	NPTR
American Truncated Whitworth Coarse Thread	TWC
American Truncated Whitworth Fine Thread	TWF
American Truncated Whitworth Special Thread	TWS
Unified National Coarse Thread	UNC
Unified National Fine Thread	UNF
Unified National Special Thread	UNS

List of Chemical Symbols

Actinium	Ac
Aluminum	Al
Americium	Am
Antimony (stibium)	Sb
Argon	A
Arsenic	As
Astatine	At
Barium	Ba
Berkelium	Bk
Beryllium (glucinum)	Be
Bismuth	Bi
Boron	B
Bromine	Br
Cadmium	Cd
Caesium	Cs
Calcium	Ca
Californium	Cf
Carbon	C
Cerium	Ce
Chlorine	Cl
Chromium	Cr
Cobalt	Co
Columbium (niobium)	Cb
Copper	Cu
Curium	Cm
Dysprosium	Dy
Erbium	Er
Europium	Eu
Fluorine	F
Francium	Fr
Gadolinium	Gd
Gallium	Ga
Germanium	Ge
Gold (aurum)	Au
Hafnium	Hf
Helium	He
Holmium	Ho
Hydrogen	H
Illinium	Il
Indium	In
Iodine	I
Ionium	Io
Iridium	Ir
Iron (Ferrum)	Fe
Krypton	Kr
Lanthanum	La
Lead (plumbum)	Pb
Lithium	Li
Lutecium	Lu
Magnesium	Mg
Manganese	Mn
Masurium	Ma
Mercury (hydrargyrum)	Hg
Molybdenum	Mo
Neodymium	Nd
Neon	Ne
Neptunium	Np
Nickel	Ni
Niobium	Nb
Nitrogen	N
Osmium	Os
Oxygen	O
Palladium	Pd
Phosphorus	P
Platinum	Pt
Plutonium	Pu
Polonium	Po
Potassium (kalium)	K
Praseodymium	Pr
Proactinium	Pa
Promethium	Pm
Radium	Ra
Radon (niton)	Rn
Rhenium	Re
Rhodium	Rh
Rubidium	Rb
Ruthenium	Ru
Samarium	Sm
Scandium	Sc
Selenium	Se
Silicon	Si
Silver (argentum)	Ag
Sodium (natrium)	Na
Strontium	Sr
Sulfur	S
Tantalum	Ta
Technetium	Tc
Tellurium	Te
Terbium	Tb
Thallium	Tl
Thorium	Th
Thulium	Tm
Tin (stannum)	Sn
Titanium	Ti
Tungsten (wolframium)	W
Uranium	U
Vanadium	V
Xenon	Xe
Ytterbium	Yb
Yttrium	Yt
Zinc	Zn
Zirconium	Zr

INDEX